1995

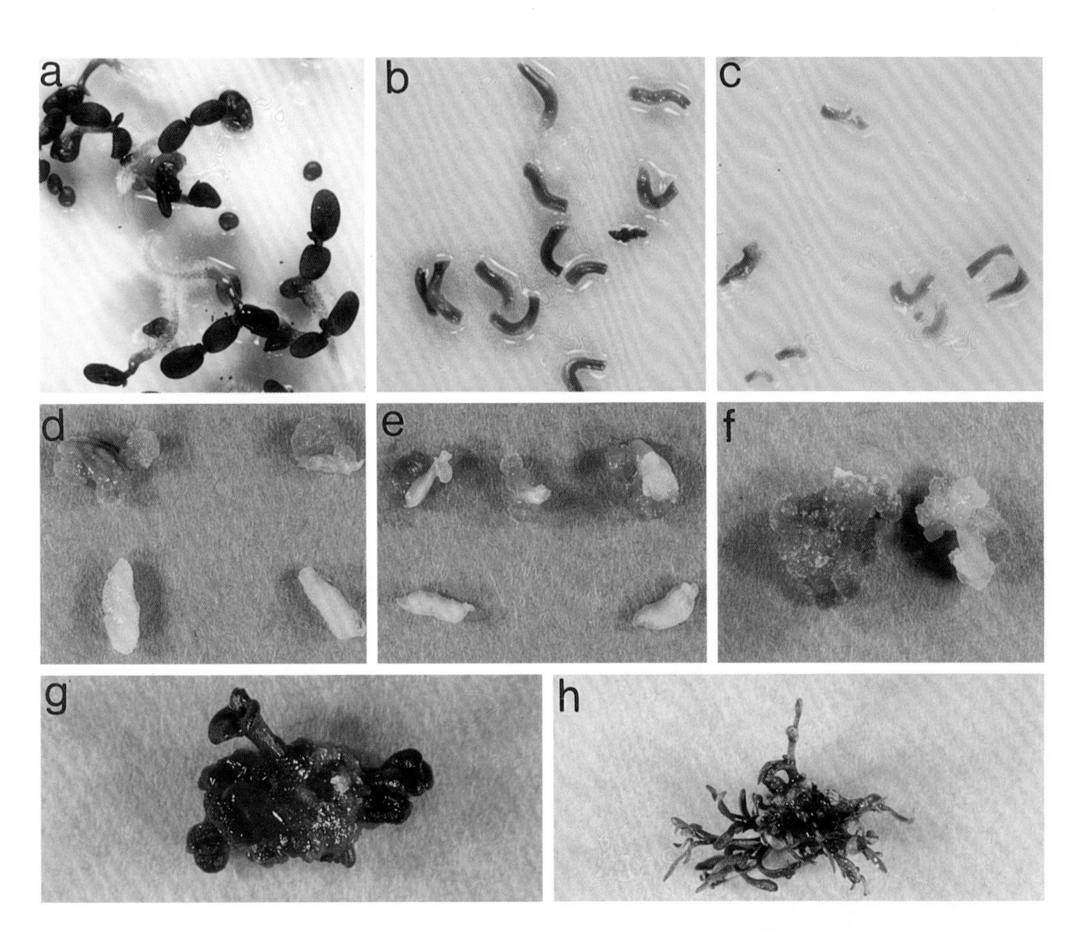

COLOR PLATE 33 Characteristic stages during selection of transgenic calli and regeneration of transgenic *Lotus japonicus* plants. (a) *Lotus japonicus* seedlings germinated for 7 days. (b) Hypocotyl pieces from 7-day-old seedlings on *Agrobacterium*-soaked filter paper. (c) Sliced hypocotyls on cocultivation plates. (d) Green hygromycin-resistant calli on hypocotyl explants. Control explants shown below. (e) Green G418-resistant calli on hypocotyl explants. Control explants shown below. (f) Calli just before transfer-to-shoot induction medium. (g) Emerging shoot structures after 3 weeks on shoot induction medium. The callus piece shown was removed from the edge of a larger callus. (h) Shoots after 2 weeks on shoot elongation medium. The callus piece shown was removed from edge of a larger callus. (See "Transgenic Plants: Agrobacterium-Mediated Transformation of the Diploid Legume *Lotus japonicus*" by Kurt Handberg, Jiri Stiller, Thomas Thykjaer, and Jens Stougaard.)

CELL BIOLOGY

A LABORATORY HANDBOOK

VOLUME 3

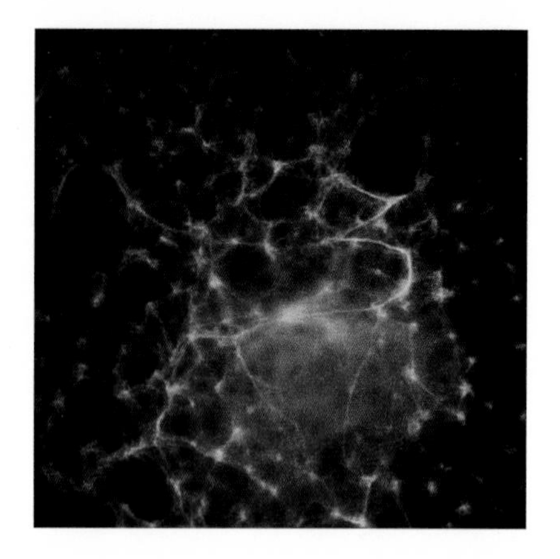

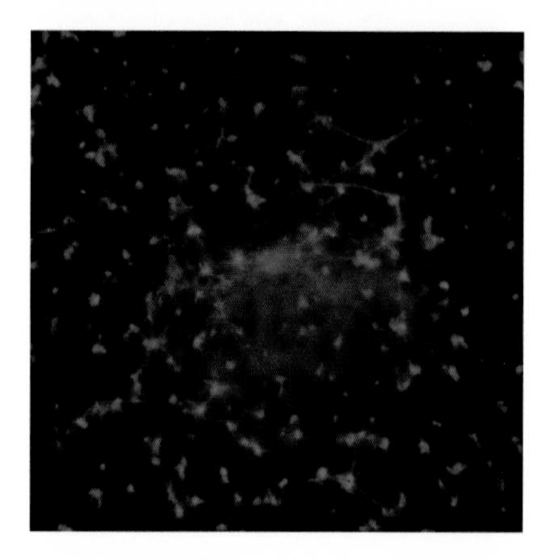

ACADEMIC PRESS

San Diego New York Boston
London Sydney Tokyo Toronto

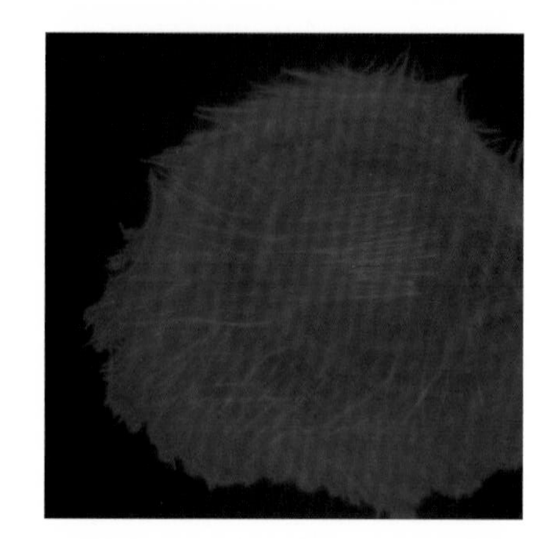

CELL BIOLOGY

A LABORATORY HANDBOOK

Edited by

JULIO E. CELIS

Danish Centre for Human Genome Research
Aarhus, Denmark

VOLUME 3

Cover Photograph for Volume 3: Human skin fibroblasts stained with Coumarin-labeled phalloidin. Courtesy of J. V. Small.

This book is printed on acid-free paper. 

Academic Press, Inc.
A Division of Harcourt Brace & Company
525 B Street, Suite 1900, San Diego, California 92101-4495

United Kingdom Edition published by
Academic Press Limited
24-28 Oval Road, London NW1 7DX

Library of Congress Cataloging-in-Publication Data

Celis, J. E. (Julio E.)
Cell biology / Julio E. Celis.
p. cm.
Includes indexes.
ISBN 0-12-164714-5 (set). -- ISBN 0-12-164715-3 (v. 1). -- ISBN 0-12-164716-1 (v. 2). -- ISBN 0-12-164717-X (v. 3)
1. Cytology-Laboratory Manuals. I. Title.
QH583.2.C45 1994
574.87' 078--dc20 94-27690
CIP

PRINTED IN THE UNITED STATES OF AMERICA
94 95 96 97 98 99 DO 9 8 7 6 5 4 3 2 1

CONTENTS OF VOLUME 3

PART 11
TRANSFER OF MACROMOLECULES AND SMALL MOLECULES

PART 12 CLONING OF EMBRYOS, TRANSGENICS, AND GENE TARGETING

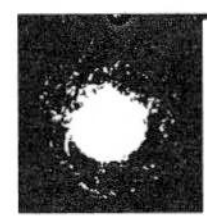

PART 13
CELL-FREE EXTRACTS, PERMEABILIZED CELL SYSTEMS, AND EXPRESSION SYSTEMS

PART 14
PROTEINS

CONTENTS OF OTHER VOLUMES

VOLUME 1

PART 1: TISSUE CULTURE AND ASSOCIATED TECHNIQUES

Section A: General Techniques

Section B: Primary Cultures from Embryonic Tissues

Section C: Cultures of Specific Cell Types

Epithelial Cells

Section E: Model Systems to Study Differentiation

Section F: Immortalization of Cells

Section G: Cell Cycle Analysis

VOLUME 2

PART 4: MICROSCOPY TECHNIQUES

Section A: Light Microscopy

Section B: Fluorescence Microscopy

Section C: Video Microscopy

Section D: Confocal Microscopy

Section E: Electron Microscopy

CONTRIBUTORS TO VOLUME 3

Numbers in parentheses indicate the pages on which the authors' contributions begin. Affiliations listed are current.

RUEDI AEBERSOLD (369), The Biomedical Research Center, University of British Columbia, Vancouver, British Columbia, Canada V6T 1Z3

GUDRUN AHNERT-HILGER (77), Medizinische Klinik und Poliklinik, Gastroenterologie, Universitätsklinikum Steglitz, Freie Universität Berlin 1, D-12203 Berlin, Germany

MICHAEL ALBIN (405), Applied Biosystems Division of The Perkin-Elmer Corporation, Foster City, California 94404

GEERT ANGENON (67, 72), Laboratorium voor Genetica, Universiteit Gent, B-9000 Gent, Belgium

WILHELM ANSORGE (22, 37), Biochemical Instrumentation Program, European Molecular Biology Laboratory, D-69117 Heidelberg, Germany

MICHAEL ARAND (276), Institute of Toxicology, University of Mainz, D-55131 Mainz, Germany

SHOSHANA BAR-NUN (323), Department of Biochemistry, Tel-Aviv University, Ramat-Aviv, Tel-Aviv 69978, Israel

BODIL BASSE (222, 272), Institute of Medical Biochemistry, and Danish Centre for Human Genome Research, Aarhus University, DK-8000 Aarhus C, Denmark

MARY C. BECKERLE (301), Department of Biology, University of Utah, Salt Lake City, Utah 84112

DAVID BELENKY (332), Department of Membrane Research and Biophysics, The Weizmann Institute of Science, Rehovot 76100, Israel

GUOJUN BU (193, 199), Edward Mallinckrodt Departments of Pediatrics and Molecular Biology, and Pharmacology, Washington University School of Medicine, St Louis, Missouri 63110

ARIANA CELIS (222), Institute of Medical Biochemistry and Danish Centre for Human Genome Research, Aarhus University, DK-8000 Aarhus C, Denmark

JULIO E. CELIS (207, 222, 272, 309, 313, 339), Institute of Medical Biochemistry and Danish Centre for Human Genome Research, Aarhus University, DK-8000 Aarhus C, Denmark

RATNA CHAKRABARTI (44), Department of Pediatrics, Division of Neonatology, Health Science Center, University of Florida, College of Medicine, Gainesville, Florida 32610

TERESA CHRISTIANSON (264), COGNIS, Inc., Santa Rosa, California 95407

MARK S. F. CLARKE (30), Department of Cellular Biology and Anatomy, Medical College of Georgia, Augusta, Georgia 30912

PHILIPPE COLLAS (99), Biology Department, Amherst College, Amherst, Massachusetts 01002

AARON W. CRAWFORD (301), Department of Biology, University of Utah, Salt Lake City, Utah 84112

G. JOSEPH CREED (281), Laboratory of Biochemical Genetics, National Institute of Mental Health, NIMH, Neuroscience Center at Saint Elizabeths, Washington, D.C. 20032

MICHAEL P. DAVEY (380), Oregon Health Sciences University, and Department of Veteran Affairs Medical Center, Portland, Oregon 97207

RICHARD W. DAVIES (471), Amersham International PLC, Little Chalfont, Buckinghamshire HP7 9NA, United Kingdom

KURT DEJGAARD (339), Institute of Medical Biochemistry and Danish Centre for Human Genome Research, Aarhus University, DK-8000 Aarhus C, Denmark

WILLY DILLEN (67, 72), Laboratorium voor Genetica, Universiteit Gent, B-9000 Gent, Belgium

CHRISTOPH ECKERSKORN (417), Max-Planck-Institute for Biochemistry, Department of Protein Analysis, D-82152 Martinsried, Germany

THOMAS FRIEDBERG (276), Institute of Toxicology, University of Mainz, D-55131 Mainz, Germany

BARBARA GALAZKIEWICZ (243), Institute of Molecular Biology, Austrian Academy of Sciences, A-5020 Salzburg, Austria

JAMES I. GARRELS (249), Cold Spring Harbor Laboratory, Cold Springs Harbor, New York 11724

JONATHAN M. GERSHONI (323), Department of Cell Research and Immunology, Tel-Aviv University, Ramat-Aviv, Tel-Aviv 69978, Israel

BETH L. GILLECE-CASTRO (389), Genentech, Inc., South San Francisco, California 94080

MARIO GIMONA (243), Institute of Molecular Biology, Austrian Academy of Sciences, A-5020 Salzburg, Austria

JON W. GORDON (106), Departments of Geriatrics and Adult Development and Obs/Gyn & Reproductive Science, Mount Sinai School of Medicine, New York, New York 10029

ANGELIKA GÖRG (231), Chair of Food Technology, Technical University of Munich, D-85350 Freising-Weihenstephan, Germany

ADOLF GRAESSMANN (3), Institut für Molekularbiologie und Biochemie der Freien, Universität Berlin, 14195 Berlin, Germany

MONIKA GRAESSMANN (3), Institut für Molekularbiologie und Biochemie der Freien, Universität Berlin, 14195 Berlin, Germany

GREGORY GREGORIADIS (58), Centre for Drug Delivery Research, School of Pharmacy, London WC1N 1AX, United Kingdom

RUDOLF GRIMM (417), Hewlett Packard, D-76337 Waldbroon, Germany

PAVEL S. GROMOV (313), Institute of Medical Biochemistry and Danish Centre for Human Genome Research, Aarhus University, DK-8000 Aarhus C, Denmark

DALE F. GRUBER (451), Departments of Cell Culture Research and Development and Technical Services, GIBCO-BRL, Life Technologies Inc., Grand Island, New York 14072

MARTIN GUTTENBERGER (169), Botanisches Institut, Universität Tübingen, 72076 Tübingen, Germany

KURT HANDBERG (119), Laboratory of Gene Expression, Department of Molecular Biology, University of Aarhus, DK-8000 Aarhus C, Denmark

ROBERT J. HAY (459), Cell Culture Department, American Type Culture Collection, Rockville, Maryland 20852

JAMES B. HAYDEN (380), Oregon Health Sciences University, and Department of Veteran Affairs Medical Center, Portland, Oregon 97207

CURTIS J. HENRICH (83), Cellular Biochemistry Research and Development, Life Technologies, Inc., Gaithersburg, Maryland 20877

STEFAN HERR (37), Biochemical Instrumentation Program, European Molecular Biology Laboratory, D-69117 Heidelberg, Germany

HANS JÜRGEN HOFFMANN (309), Department of Medical Biochemistry, University of Cape Town Medical School, 7925 Observatory, South Africa

LUKAS A. HUBER (317), Department of Biochemistry, University of Geneva, CH-1211 Geneva, Switzerland

TONY HUNTER (422), Molecular Biology and Virology Laboratory, The Salk Institute, La Jolla, California 92186

DAVID W. JAYME (451), Departments of Cell Culture Research and Development and Technical Services, GIBCO-BRL, Life Technologies Inc., Grand Island, New York 14072

JEAN-PIERRE JOST (345), Friedrich Miescher Institut, CH-4002 Basel, Switzerland

JANET E. JOY (281), Laboratory of Biochemical Genetics, National Institute of Mental Health, Neuroscience Center at Saint Elizabeths, Washington, D.C. 20032

YASUFUMI KANEDA (50), Institute for Molecular and Cellular Biology, Osaka University, Suita City, Osaka 565, Japan

LINDA A. KING (148), School of Biological and Molecular Science, Oxford Brookes University, Oxford 0X3 OBP, United Kingdom

JETTE B. LAURIDSEN (222), Institute of Medical Biochemistry and Danish Centre for Human Genome Research, Aarhus University, DK-8000 Aarhus C, Denmark

ALISON M. LAWRIE (148), School of Biological and Molecular Science, Oxford Brookes University, Oxford, OX3 OBP, United Kingdom

ANDRÉ LE BIVIC (185), Biologie de la Differentiation Cellulaire, Faculté des Sciences de Luminy, Marseille, France

HENRIK LEFFERS (155), Institute of Medical Biochemistry and Danish Centre for Human Genome Research, Aarhus University, DK-8000 Aarhus C, Denmark

HALINA LIS (332), Department of Membrane Research and Biophysics, The Weizmann Institute of Science, Rehovot 76100, Israel

FRIEDRICH LOTTSPEICH (417), Max-Planck-Institute for Biochemistry, Department of Protein Analysis, D-82152 Martinsried, Germany

KUNXIN LUO (422), Molecular Biology and Virology Laboratory, The Salk Institute, La Jolla, California 92186

SUSAN G. MANN (148), School of Biological and Molecular Science, Oxford Brookes University, Oxford OX3 OBP, United Kingdom

AHMED MANSOURI (112), Department of Molecular Cell Biology, Max-Planck-Institute of Biophysical Chemistry, Am Fassberg, D-37077 Göttingen, Germany

GLENN MATTHEWS (88, 131), Department of Biochemistry, University of Birmingham, Birmingham B15 2TT, United Kingdom

ASHLEY L. McCORMACK (380), Department of Molecular Biotechnology, University of Washington, Seattle, Washington 98195

PAUL L. McNEIL (30), Department of Cellular Biology and Anatomy, Medical College of Georgia, Augusta, Georgia 30912

CARL R. MERRIL (281), Laboratory of Biochemical Genetics, National Institute of Mental Health, Neuroscience Center at Saint Elizabeths, Washington, D.C. 20032

MARKUS NIEDERREITER (243), Institute of Molecular Biology, Austrian Academy of Sciences, A-5020 Salzburg, Austria

HEINZ NIKA (369), The Biomedical Research Center, University of British Columbia, Vancouver, British Columbia, Canada V6T 1Z3

FRANZ OESCH (276), Institute of Toxicology, University of Mainz, D-55131 Mainz, Germany

EYδFINNUR OLSEN (207), Institute of Medical Biochemistry and Danish Centre for Human Genome Research, Aarhus University, DK-8000 Aarhus C, Denmark

CHRISTIAN PAECH (264), Genencon International, South San Francisco, California 94080

SCOTT D. PATTERSON (249), Amgen Inc., Amgen Center, Thousand Oaks, California 91320

RAINER PEPPERKOK (22, 37), Department of Cell Biology, University of Geneva, Sciences III, 205 Geneva, Switzerland

MARCUS E. PETER (317), German Cancer Center for Tumor Immunology Program, D-69009 Heidelberg, Germany

ROBERT D. POSSEE (148), NECR Institute of Virology and Environmental Microbiology, Oxford OX1 3SR, United Kingdom

AARON RABINKOV (332), Department of Membrane Research and Biophysics, The Weizmann Institute of Science, Rehovot 76100, Israel

HANNE H. RASMUSSEN (359), Institute of Medical Biochemistry and Danish Centre for Human Genome Research, Aarhus University, DK-8000 Aarhus C, Denmark

GITTE RATZ (222, 272), Institute of Medical Biochemistry, and Danish Centre for Human Genome Research, Aarhus University, DK-8000 Aarhus C, Denmark

ENRIQUE RODRIGUEZ-BOULAN (185), Department of Cell Biology, Cornell University Medical College, New York, New York 10021

PETER ROEPSTORFF (399), Department of Molecular Biology, Odense University, DK-5230 Odense M, Denmark

MICHAEL J. RUDICK (181), Texas Women's University, Biology Department, Denton, Texas 76204

DANIEL SAFER (218), Department of Cell and Developmental Biology, University of Pennsylvania, Philadelphia, Pennsylvania 19104

RAINER SAFFRICH (22, 37), Biochemical Instrumentation Program, European Molecular Biology Laboratory, D-69117 Heidelberg, Germany

HANS PETER SALUZ (288, 345), Hans-Knöll-Institut für Naturstoff-Forschung, D-07745 Jena, Germany

SHELDON M. SCHUSTER (44), Interdisciplinary Center for Biotechnology Research, University of Florida, College of Medicine, Gainesville, Florida 32610

ALAN L. SCHWARTZ (193, 199), Edward Mallinckrodt Departments of Pediatrics and Molecular Biology, and Pharmacology, Washington University School of Medicine, St Louis, Missouri 63110

BARTHOLOMEW M. SEFTON (422), Molecular Biology and Virology Laboratory, The Salk Institute, La Jolla, California 92186

DEBORAH A. SHACKELFORD (258), Department of Neurosciences, University of California, San Diego, La Jolla, California 92093

NATHAN SHARON (332), Department of Membrane Research and Biophysics, The Weizmann Institute of Science, Rehovot 76100, Israel

JIRI STILLER (119), Laboratory of Gene Expression, Department of Molecular Biology, University of Aarhus, DK-8000 Arhus C, Denmark

JENS STOUGAARD (119), Laboratory of Gene Expression, Department of Molecular Biology, University of Aarhus, DK-8000 Arhus C, Denmark

THOMAS THYKJÆR (119), Laboratory of Gene Expression, Department of Molecular Biology, University of Aarhus, DK-8000 Arhus C, Denmark

MIGUEL TORRES (112), Department of Molecular Cell Biology, Max-Planck-Institute of Biophysical Chemistry, Am Fassberg, D-37077 Göttingen, Germany

JOËL VANDEKERCKHOVE (359), Laboratory of Physiological Chemistry, University Ghent, B-9000 Gent, Belgium

PETER VAN DER GEER (422), Molecular Biology and Virology Laboratory, The Salk Institute, La Jolla, California 92186

MARC VAN MONTAGU (67, 72), Laboratorium voor Genetica, Universiteit Gent, B-9000 Gent, Belgium

KIM VETTENRANTA (193), Edward Mallinckrodt Departments of Pediatrics and Molecular Biology, and Pharmacology, Washington University School of Medicine, St. Louis, Missouri 63110

ANDREW WALLACE (288), IRBM, 00040 Pomezia, Italy

YU-LI WANG (16), Worcester Foundation for Experimental Biology, Shrewsbury, Massachusetts 01545

STEFAN WEIMANN (37), Biochemical Instrumentation Program, European Molecular Biology Laboratory, D-69117 Heidelberg, Germany

MARTIN WENDLAND (140), Department of Biology, University of California at San Diego, La Jolla, California 92093

JOHN E. WIKTOROWICZ (405), Applied Biosystems Division of The Perkin-Elmer Corporation, Foster City, California 94404

JOHN R. YATES, III (380), Department of Molecular Biotechnology, University of Washington, Seattle, Washington 98195

RICHARD Y. YEH (258), Department of Neurosciences, University of California, San Diego, La Jolla, California 92093

JUSTIN A. ZIVIN (258), Department of Neurosciences, University of California, San Diego, La Jolla, California 92093

CHIARA ZURZOLO (185), Dipartimento di Biologia e Patologia Cellulare e Molecolare e CEOS, CNR, II Facoltá di Medicina, Universitá di Napoli, Napoli, Italy

PART 11

TRANSFER OF MACROMOLECULES AND SMALL MOLECULES

Microinjection of RNA and DNA into Somatic Cells

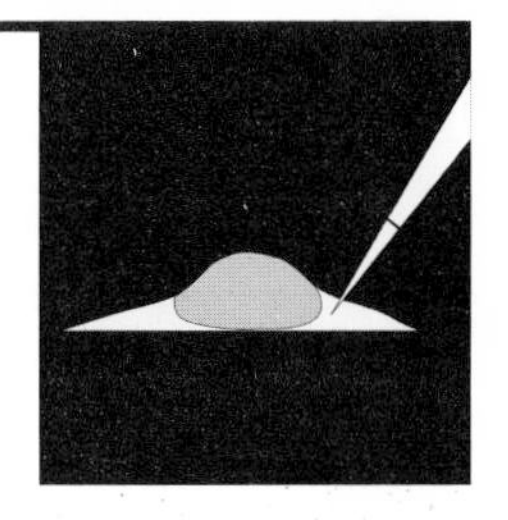

Monika Graessmann and Adolf Graessmann

I. Introduction

The transfer of molecules into eukaryotic cells by microinjection provides an efficient method to study the biological and biochemical activity and the fate of the molecules in their native environment, the living cell (Fig. 1) (see also articles by Yu-Li Wang and by Rainer Pepperkok, Rainer Saffrich, and Wilhelm Ansorge). The microinjection technique, developed in our laboratory (Graessmann, 1968), has almost no cell type restriction; also, suspension culture cells (e.g., lymphocytes, oocytes, eggs, plant protoplasts) are accessible for microinjection. For this, the cells either are held by a capillary or are bound to a substrate by suitable linkers (Graessmann, 1970; Graessmann *et al.*, 1979).

Among the different gene transfer techniques, microinjection is by far the most efficient procedure. Only microinjection allows the transfer of a known number of test molecules either into the cytoplasm or into the nuclei of the recipient cell. Up to 100% of the recipient cells support expression of the transferred material, and stable transformed cell lines can be isolated with a frequency of 20–30%. Biochemical studies can be performed with 50–100 injected cells, and the injected material (e.g., DNA, RNA) can be reisolated and further analyzed by standard techniques (e.g., Southern and Northern blots, electron microscopy) (for review, see Graessmann and Graessmann, 1983; Graessmann *et al.*, 1983; Celis *et al.*, 1986).

II. Materials and Instrumentation

For microinjection experiments, standard or inverted microscopes are used (e.g., Zeiss Axioskop with transmitted light phase contrast and the mechanical micromanipulator from Leitz (see Fig. 1). The capillary puller is homemade (Fig. 2). The glass tubes (1.4-mm outer and 1.2-mm inner diameters) for preparation of the injection capillaries are obtained from either Schott or Clark Electromedical Instruments. Sterile capillaries can be obtained from Eppendorf.

Ambion (ITC Biotechnology GmbH)	$m^7G(5')ppp(5')G$ (Cat. No. 8050)
	RNase inhibitor (Cat. No. 2682)
	T7 and SP6 RNA polymerase (Cat. Nos. 2086 and 2071)
Boehringer-Mannheim	Proteinase K (Cat. No. 745723)
Gibco-BRL	Dulbecco's culture medium (DMEM, Cat. No. 074-01600P)
	Fetal calf serum (Cat. No. 01106290M)

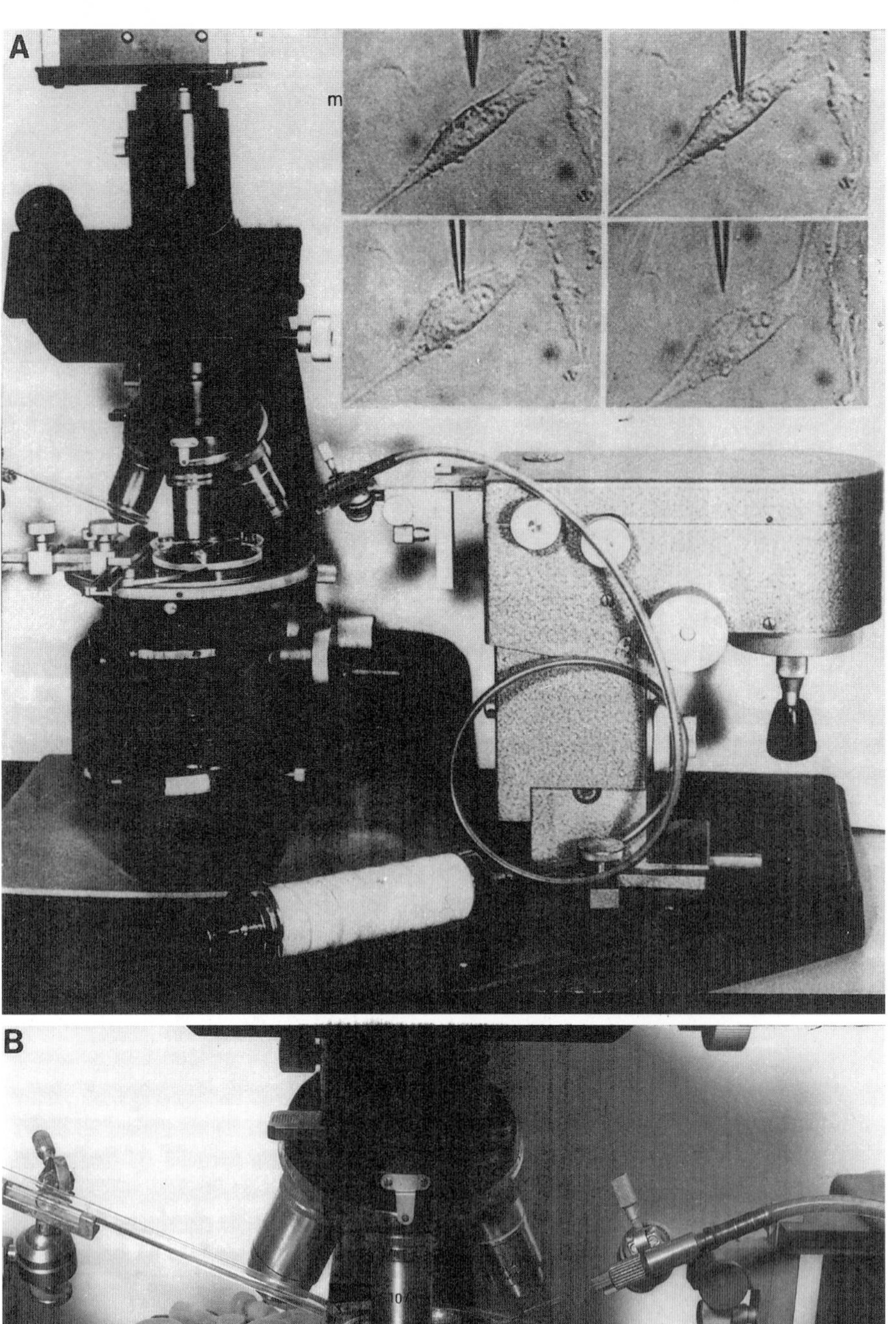

FIGURE 1 (A) Assembly of instruments for microinjection (microscope, manipulator, instrument holder, capillary, and syringe). The insert shows four steps in the injection procedure: capillary above the cell, tip of the capillary inside the cytoplasm of the recipient cell, the cell directly after injection, the capillary again above the cell. (B) The microscope stage with the culture dish.

	CsCl (Cat. No. 540-5507UB)
Merck	CaF_2 (Cat. No. 2840)
	HF (Cat. No. 3380500)
	NaCl (Cat. No. 6404)
	KCl (Cat. No. 4936)
	$MgCl_2 \cdot 6H_2O$ (Cat. No. 5833)
	KH_2PO_4 (Cat. No. 4873)
	$Na_2HPO4 \cdot 2H_2O$ (Cat. No. 6580)
	NaOAc (Cat. No. 6268)
	POPOP (Cat. No. 7249)
	PPO (Cat. No. 2946)
	Ethyl acetate (Cat. No. 9623)
	Toluene (Cat. No. 8325)
	H_2SO_4 (Cat. No. 731)
	HNO_3 (Cat. No. 456)
	HCl (Cat. No. 319)
	Acetic acid (Cat. No. 62)
	Formamide (Cat. No. 9684)
	Formaldehyde (37%, Cat. No. 4003)
	Glycerol (Cat. No. 4094)
	Bromphenol blue (Cat. No. 8122)
	TLC sheet (Cat. No. 5553)
Pharmacia	ATP (Cat. No. 27-1006)
	GTP (Cat. No. 27-2000)
	CTP (Cat. No. 27-12000)
	UTP (Cat. No. 28-0700)
	BSA (RNase/DNase free, Cat. No. 27-8914)
Promega	RQ1-DNase (Cat. No. 6101)
Roth	EDTA-Na_2 (Cat. No. 8043),
	Tris(hydroxymethyl)aminomethane (THAM, Cat. No. 4855)
	Methanol (Cat. No. 4627)
	Ethanol (Cat. No. 9065)
	Trichlormethane (chloroform, Cat. No. 3313)
	Phenol (Cat. No. 0040).
Serva	SDS (Cat. No. 20760)
	Triton X-100 (Cat. No. 37238)
	Guanidine thiocyanate (Cat. No. 24220)
	Herring sperm DNA (Cat. No. 18580)
	Xylene–cyanol (Cat. No. 38505)
Sigma	Acetyl coenzyme A (Cat. No. A-2056)
	DTT (Cat. No. D-9779)
	FITC–dextran solution (Cat. No. FD-150)
	Spermidine (Cat. No. S-2501)
	Mops (Cat. No. M-1254)
	Diethyl pyrocarbonate (DEPC, Cat. No. D-5758)
	X-Omat AR film (Cat. No. 1651454)
	NuncGmbH culture dishes (60 mm, Cat. No. 150288, and 100 mm, Cat. No. 150350)

III. Procedures

A. PREPARATION OF GLASS TUBES

Solution

H_2SO_4/HNO_3 1/2: To make 1 liter, mix carefully 666 ml of concentrated (i.e., 65%) HNO_3 p.a. with 333 ml concentrated (95–97%) H_2SO_4 p.a. Store at room temperature in a dark bottle.

Steps

1. Break glass tubes (Schott) of 1.2-mm inner and 1.4-mm outer diameter into pieces about 20 cm long.
2. Clean tubes by treatment with a mixture of one-third H_2SO_4 and two-thirds concentrated HNO_3 (v/v) for 24 hr.
3. Rinse the tube with tap water for 24 hr.
4. Rinse the tube with double-distilled water and ethanol.
5. Dry the glass tubes at 120°C for 24 hr.
6. Store the glass tubes in a closed container until use.

B. PULLING OF THE CAPILLARY

Steps

1. Before pulling, introduce a constriction (8–15 mm in length and 0.3–0.5 mm in diameter) at the middle of the glass tube, using the small flame of a Bunsen burner. Soften the glass in the flame and pull the ends apart outside of the flame.

2. Clamp the glass tubes into a capillary puller. The diameter and the shape of the tip depend on the heat of the wire and on the force that pulls the glass tubes into two identical capillaries. The diameter at the tip should be about 0.3–0.5 mm (see Fig. 2).

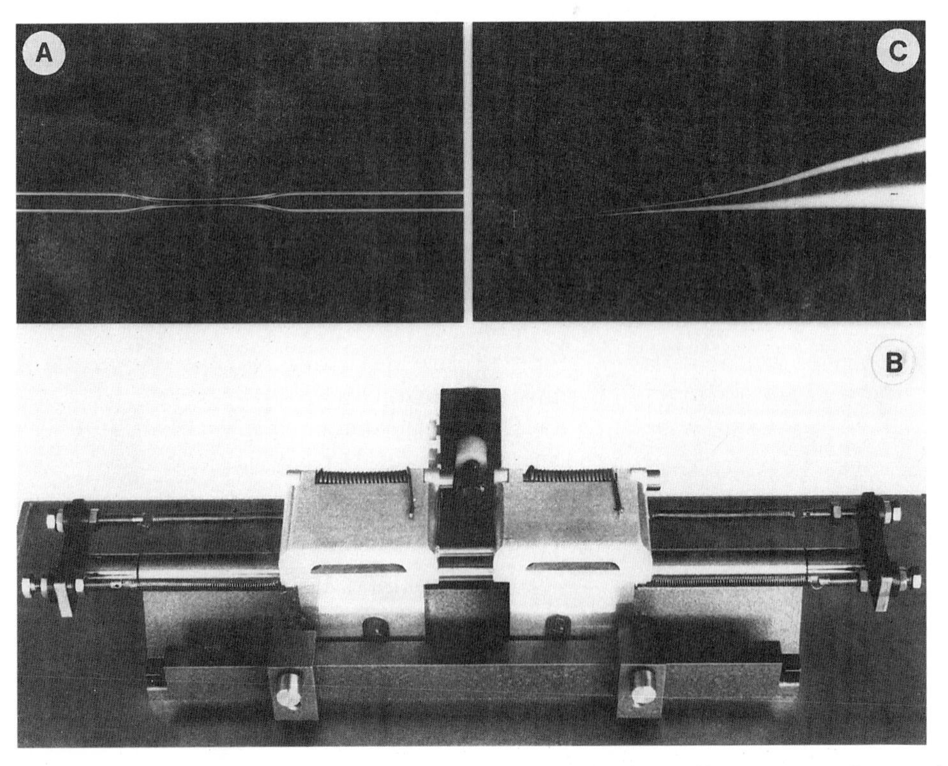

FIGURE 2 Pulling the glass capillaries. (A) Glass tubes before pulling. (B) Partial view of the puller. (C) Capillary tip. Bar = 10 mm.

3. After pulling, store the capillaries upright (tip end up) by inserting them into fitting holes (1.6 mm) pierced into a plastic or metal block without any further treatment until use. To prevent contamination, cover the capillaries with a beaker.

C. SAMPLES

Solution

Injection buffer: 0.01–0.1 M Tris–HCl, pH 7.4. To make 100 ml of 0.1 *M* Tris buffer, dissolve 12.11 g Tris in sterile water, adjust the pH to 7.4 with HCl, and bring the volume to 100 ml. To make 100 ml of 0.01 *M* Tris buffer, take 10 ml of 0.1 *M* buffer and adjust the volume to 100 ml with sterile water.

Steps

1. Dissolve samples in 0.01–0.1 *M* Tris–HCl, pH 7.4, which will be tolerated by most of the cell types.

2. Before injection, centrifuge the samples at 10,000–15,000 rpm (Eppendorf centrifuge) for 10 min. Concentrations up to 1–2 mg DNA or 5–10 mg RNA per milliliter of injection solution can be handled.

D. LOADING OF THE CAPILLARY

Capillaries can be filled either from the tip or from the rear. Rear filling requires glass tubes with an *inner filament* and tip filling requires only glass tubes (*no filament*).

1. Tip Filling

Tip filling has the advantage that it further cleans the capillary. Particles inside the capillary move back with the meniscus. Rear filling washes particles down to the tip, which often causes blocking of the capillary.

Steps

1. Place 2–5 μl of the test solution on a small sheet of Parafilm (2 × 2 cm) located in a sterile culture dish (60 mm).
2. Put a moistened filter paper (60 mm) into the cover part of the dish to prevent evaporation.
3. Place the capillary into the holder of the micromanipulator.
4. Bring the tip of the capillary into focus of the microscope.
5. Place the dish with the sample on the microscope table.
6. Bring the upper surface of the sample drop into focus.
7. Bring the capillary with the help of the manipulator into the sample drop.
8. Load the capillary by negative pressure, exerted by an air-filled glass syringe (50 ml, Fig. 1A).

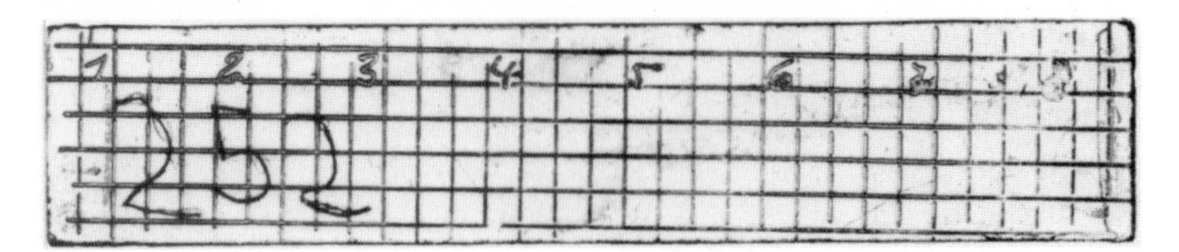

FIGURE 3 Scored and numbered glass slide.

2. Rear Filling

Steps

1. Place a small drop of the test solution at the open end of the capillary; the solution moves down to the tip by capillary attraction. Alternatively, the test solution can be introduced with a second smaller loading capillary.
2. Place the capillary into the holder of the micromanipulator.

E. PREPARATION OF GLASS SLIDES

Steps

1. Coat glass slides (5 × 1 cm) on both sides with a melted mixture of one-third beeswax (beeswax candle) and two-thirds stearine (stearine candle) (w/w) using a cotton plug.
2. Score the beeswax film (squares of 1–4 mm^2) and number the fields with a steel needle (Fig. 3).
3. Etch the glass with a paste made from CaF_2 and 40% HF p.a. for 10–15 min.
4. Split off the wax film by rinsing the slides with cold tap water overnight.
5. Clean the slides as described above for the glass tubes (see Section **A**).

F. CELLS

For biological studies (e.g., autoradiography, morphology, immunofluorescence staining, cell transformation, recombination) cells are grown on either a culture dishes or on glass slides (5 × 1 cm) which have a grid imprinted for better identification of the cells after microinjection (see Fig. 3).

For biochemical studies (e.g., reextraction of injected DNA, RNA) cells are grown on small glass slides (3 × 3 mm). After injection, cells are further cultivated under standard conditions. Suspension culture cells (Fig. 4) are accessible for microinjection after binding to either the culture dish or the glass slides by a suitable linker [e.g., concanavalin A, phytohemagglutinin P, IgG, Fig. 4 (Graessmann *et al.*, 1979)] or by the use of holding needles (Graessmann, 1970).

G. MICROINJECTION

Steps

1. The microscope with phase-contrast equipment (standard or inverted microscope) and a micromanipulator are placed on a vibration-free table. The capillary is fixed to an instrument holder of the manipulator and the tip is

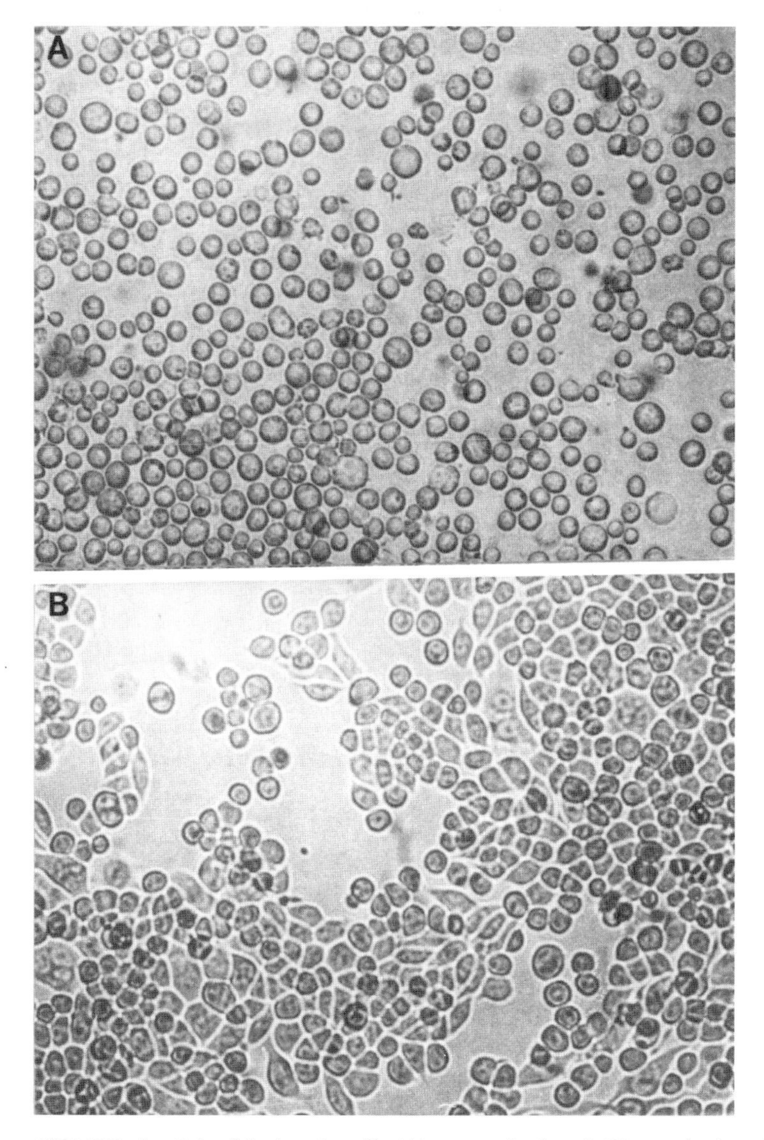

FIGURE 4 Friend leukemia cells (A) unattached and (B) attached to the culture dish.

focused under the microscope. Figure 1 shows the assembled instruments for microinjection.

2. Microinjection is performed at a 160- to 300-fold magnification. Cells grown either on glass slides or on the culture dish are placed on the microscope stage. A gentle stream of CO_2 maintains the pH optimum.

3. Cells are brought into focus and a distinct field is chosen for injection. The capillary is lowered by the manipulator and an individual cell is approached. The cell is injected by further lowering the capillary, and the test material is transferred into the cell by a low pressure exerted with a 50-ml syringe (air-filled) or an automatic injection pump. A small dent is seen at the cell surface when the capillary touches the cell. When the capillary is lowered further, the tip enters into the cell and the dent disappears. Appearance of a white spot indicates that the capillary has penetrated the entire cell and killed the cell. Successful microinjection is marked by slight enlargement of the cell or of the nucleus.

4. After injection, the capillary is brought just above the plane of the cell by turning the vertical knob of the manipulator and moved to the next cell.

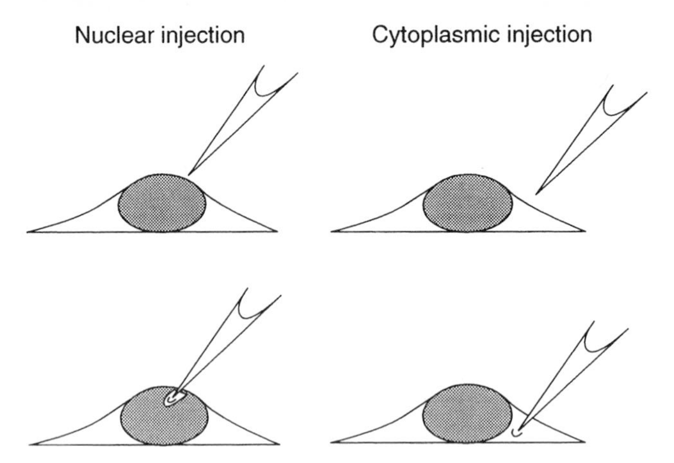

FIGURE 5 Schematic demonstration of intranuclear and cytoplasmic microinjection.

5. About 150–200 cells can be injected within 10 min with some practice. To practice intranuclear and cytoplasmic injections (Fig. 5), a FITC–dextran solution (10 mg/ml injection buffer) can be used to monitor the successful transfer.

H. QUANTIFICATION OF THE INJECTION VOLUME

Steps

1. Microinject 100 cells with radioactive labeled molecules (e.g., [^{32}P]ATP).
2. After injection, lyse cells and count the lysate by liquid scintillation. The volume injected into the nucleus of a mammalian cell is $1–2 \times 10^{-11}$ ml, and up to $1–2 \times 10^{-10}$ ml can be injected into the cytoplasm. A larger injection volume mostly kills the cells.

I. ASSAYS

Immunofluorescence staining and autoradiography are described in detail elsewhere in this book. Grow the cells on slides with numbered squares. This allows identification of the injected cells at any time.

1. CAT Enzyme Activity

Solutions

1. *Phosphate-buffered saline (PBS):* To make 1 liter, solubilize 8 g of NaCl, 0.2 g of KCl, 0.2 g of KH_2PO_4, and 1.15 g $Na_2HPO_4 \cdot 2H_2O$ in distilled water and adjust to 1 liter. The pH is 7.2–7.4. Autoclave the solution and store at 4°C.
2. *250 mM Tris–HCl/5 mM EDTA, pH 7.8:* To make 1 liter, dissolve 30 g Tris and 1.86 g EDTA-Na_2 in distilled water, adjust the pH to 7.8 with HCl, and bring to a total volume of 1 liter. Store at −20°C.
3. *4 mM acetyl coenzyme A:* To make 1 ml dissolve 3.23 mg acetyl coenzyme A in 1 ml distilled water. Store at −20°C. The solution is stable for 1 week.
4. *Chloroform/methanol (95/5):* To make 100 ml, mix 95 ml $CHCl_3$ p.a. with 5 ml CH_3OH p.a.
5. *Liquid scintilation solution:* Dissolve 0.24 g POPOP and 12.2 g PPO in 1.6

liter toluene in a dark bottle. Add to the solution 800 ml Triton X-100. Store at room temperature.

Steps

1. Microinject 100 cells grown on small glass slides (3 × 3 mm) with either DNA or RNA.
2. Grow the cells under standard conditions at 37°C.
3. Wash the cells three times in cold PBS.
4. Transfer the glass slide with cells into an Eppendorf tube which contains 150 μl buffer (250 m*M* Tris–HCl/5 m*M* EDTA, pH 7.8).
5. Break the cells by sonication.
6. Spin for 5 min at 4°C in an Eppendorf centrifuge.
7. Transfer supernatant into a fresh Eppendorf tube.
8. To inactivate endogenous acetylases, incubate for 10 min at 60°C.
9. Spin again for 5 min, and transfer supernatant into a fresh tube.
10. Add 20 μl of 4 m*M* acetyl coenzyme A and 10 μl of 0.1 μCi solution of [^{14}C]chloramphenicol in water.
11. Incubate overnight at 37°C.
12. Add 1 ml ethyl acetate; mix well by vortexing.
13. Centrifuge for 1 min, and transfer the organic upper phase carefully into a fresh Eppendorf tube.
14. Dry sample under vacuum.
15. Resuspend the probe in 20 μl of ethyl acetate.
16. Spot sample on a TLC sheet and place the sheet in a chromatography tank that has been preequilibrated with 100 ml of chloroform/methanol (95/5). Chromatograph until the solvent front is 1 cm from the end of the sheet.
17. Air-dry the plate and expose it to X-ray film in a dark place overnight.
18. Develop the film.
19. To quantify CAT enzyme activity, excise the spots corresponding to acetylated [^{14}C]chloramphenicol from the TLC sheet and count by liquid scintillation.
20. Suspend each spot in 10 ml scintilation solution. Shake the tubes with the probes from time to time during a few hours and then count.

2. DNA Reextraction from Microinjected Cells and Southern Blot Analysis

For a review, see Graessmann *et al.* (1981).

Solutions

1. *Lysis buffer: 10 mM EDTA, pH 7.5, 0.6% SDS.* To make 1 liter, dissolve 3.72 g of EDTA-Na_2 in sterile water, adjust the pH to 7.5 with NaOH, solubilize 6 g SDS, and bring the total volume to 1 liter.

2. *5 M NaCl and 1 M NaCl:* To make 1-liter 5 *M* and 1 *M* NaCl solutions, dissolve respectively 292.2 g and 58.44 g of NaCl in distilled water and adjust the volume to 1 liter.

Steps

1. Grow the cells on small glass slides (3 × 3 mm).
2. Inject 100 cells with DNA.
3. Grow the cells further under standard conditions.
4. After incubation, remove the slides from the culture dish, wash the slide with PBS, and transfer the slide with the cells into an Eppendorf tube filled with 200 μl lysis buffer.
5. After 10 min at room temperature, add 50 μl of 5 *M* NaCl and leave at 4°C for at least 8 hr.
6. Centrifuge for 15 min in an Eppendorf centrifuge.
7. Transfer the supernatant to a fresh tube, add 0.1 vol of 1 *M* NaCl and 3 vol of ethanol, and leave either at −20°C overnight or for 15 min in a dry ice ethanol bath.
8. Pellet the DNA by centrifugation in an Eppendorf centrifuge for 30 min.
9. Dry the pellet and continue with, e.g., Southern blot analysis.

3. Injection of cRNA or mRNA

See Graessmann and Graessmann (1971, 1976, 1982) and Graessmann *et al.* (1991).

a. Preparation of cRNA

Solutions

1. *5× RNA polymerase buffers:* Prepare as described by Ambion. The RNA polymerases T7 and SP6 are from Ambion.

2. *DEPC water:* To make 1 liter, stir 100 μl diethyl pyrocarbonate (DEPC) in 1 liter water for 1 hr. Sterilize the solution for 45 min in the autoclave.

3. *40 mM spermidine:* To make 1 ml, dissolve 10 mg spermidine in DEPC water. Store at −20°C.

4. *XTP mix:* To make 1 ml, dissolve 3 mg from each of the nucleotides ATP, CTP, UTP, and GTP in 250 μl of 0.05 *M* Tris (concentration of each nucleotide is 20 m*M*). Dilute 25 μl of the 20 m*M* GTP solution 1:10 with 0.05 *M* Tris. Mix together the 250-μl volumes of ATP, CTP, and UTP and 250 μl of the 1:10 diluted GTP solution. The 1-ml XTP mixture has final concentrations of 5 m*M* ATP, CTP, and UTP and 0.5 m*M* GTP. Store at −20°C.

5. *40 mM m^7(5′)Gppp(5′)G:* The solution is from Ambion and ready to be used. Store at −20°C.

6. *BSA:* The solution is from Pharmacia and ready to be used. Concentration: 3 mg of BSA per milliliter of 10 m*M* Tris–HCl (pH 8) and 0.2 m*M* EDTA-Na_2. Store at −20°C.

7. *3 M NaOAc, pH 5.2:* To make 100 ml, solubilize 24.6 g of NaOAc in DEPC water, adjust the pH to 5.2 with acetic acid, and bring to total volume of 100 ml.

8. *TE buffer: 10 mM Tris, pH 7.4, 1 mM EDTA-Na_2.* To make 1 liter, dissolve 1.21 g Tris and 0.37 g EDTA-Na_2 in DEPC water, adjust the pH to 7.4 with HCl, and bring the volume to 1 liter.

9. *0.2 M EDTA-Na_2:* To make 10 ml solubilize 0.74 g of EDTA-Na_2 in DEPC water, adjust the pH to 8 with NaOH, and bring the volume to 10 ml.

Steps

1. Clone DNA under control either of the T7 or of the SP6 promoter.
2. Transcribe 1 μg linearized DNA dissolved in TE buffer in a concentration of 1 μg per 10 μl buffer as follow:
3. Add to 10 μl DNA, 10 μl of 5× RNA polymerase buffer, 2.5 μl 40 m*M* spermidine, 5 μl of XTP mix, 0.5 μl of m^7GpppG, 50 U of RNase inhibitor, 2 μl of BSA solution, 10 U of either T7 or SP6 polymerase.
4. Bring the mixture to a total volume of 50 μl with DEPC water.
5. Incubate for 20 min at 37°C.
6. Add 1 μl of 20 m*M* GTP solution and incubate the reaction for 40 min at 37°C.
7. Remove DNA template by further incubation for 10 min with 3 U of RQI DNase.
8. Stop reaction with 5 μl of 0.2 *M* EDTA-Na_2.
9. Treat the mixture twice with phenol–chloroform/isoamyl alcohol (24/1) and once with chloroform/isoamyl alcohol (24/1).
10. Pass the water phase containing RNA through a dry Sephadex G-50 column.
11. Collect cRNA by ethanol precipitation. Add 5 μl of 3 *M* NaOAc, pH 5.2, and 2.5 vol of ethanol.
12. For microinjection experiments dissolve cRNA in a concentration of 1–2 mg/ml in 0.01 *M* Tris–HCl, pH 7.4.

*b. Isolation and purification of m*RNA

Solutions

1. *Lysis buffer:* 4 m*M* guanidine thiocyanate, 20 m*M* sodium acetate (NaOAc), pH 5.2, 0.1 m*M DTT, 0.5% SDS.* To make 100 ml, dissolve 47.2 g guanidine thiocyanate, 0.164 g NaOAc, 1.5 mg DTT, and 0.5 g SDS in DEPC water. Bring the pH to 5.2 with acetic acid and the total volume to 100 ml.

2. *5.7 M CsCl:* To make 100 ml, dissolve 95.6 g CsCl in DEPC water and adjust to 100 ml.

3. *TES buffer: 10 mM Tris–HCl, pH 7.4, 5 mM EDTA, 1% SDS.* To make 100 ml, solubilize 0.12 g Tris, 0.18 g EDTA-Na_2, and 1 g SDS in DEPC water. Adjust the pH to 7.4 with HCl and bring the volume to 100 ml.

Steps

1. Wash the cells growing on the dish (100 mm) two times with PBS.
2. Add 2.5 ml lysis buffer for 5 min at room temperature.
3. Draw the viscous lysate up and down through a 20-gauge needle.
4. Place 1.5 ml of 5.7 *M* CsCl in an autoclaved polyallomer ultracentrifuge tube for the SW 56 rotor.
5. Layer the cell lysate on top of the CsCl cushion.
6. Pellet the RNA through the 5.7 *M* CsCl step gradient by centrifugation at 35,000 rpm in the Beckmann SW 56 rotor for 12–20 hr at 18°C.
7. Remove the supernatant carefully, invert the tube, and pour the remaining liquid off.

8. Resuspend the RNA pellet in 360 μl of Tes and transfer to a clean Eppendorf microcentrifuge tube.
9. For precipitation of total RNA, add 40 μl of 3 *M* NaOAc and 1 ml of ethanol.
10. Purify mRNA by passing total RNA through oligo(dT) spin column.

4. Reextraction of RNA from Microinjected Cells for Northern Blot Analysis

Solutions

1. *2× stock solution:* To make 25 ml, dissolve 605 mg Tris, 925 mg EDTA-Na_2, and 0.25 g SDS in DEPC water, adjust the pH to 7.0 with HCl, and bring the volume to 25 ml.

2. *Proteinase K:* Dissolve 1 mg proteinase K in 100 μl DEPC water. The solution cannot be stored.

3. *tRNA:* Dissolve 10 mg tRNA in 1 ml DEPC water. Store at −20°C.

4. *Lysis buffer:* Prepare immediately before use. Add 250 μl of 2× *stock solution,* 10 μl of *proteinase K,* and 2.5 μl of *tRNA,* and bring the volume to 500 μl with DEPC water.

5. *2.5 M NaOAc, pH 6:* To make 100 ml, solubilize 20.5 g of NaOAc in sterile, DEPC-treated water, adjust pH to 6 with acetic acid, and bring to a total volume of 100 ml.

6. *10× MOPS buffer:* 200 m*M* MOPS, 50 m*M* NaOAc, pH 6.5, 10 m*M* EDTA-Na_2. To make 500 ml, dissolve 20.9 g Mops, 2 g NaOAc, and 1.9 g EDTA-Na_2 in DEPC water. Bring the pH to 6.5 with acetic acid and the total volume to 500 ml.

7. *Denaturation buffer:* Mix 52 μl of formaldehyde (37%) with 150 μl of formamide and 30 μl of 10× Mops buffer. Bring the total volume to 300 μl with DEPC water.

8. *Loading buffer:* To make 1 ml, mix 500 μl glycerol with 2 μl 0.5 *M* EDTA-NA_2, 4 mg bromphenol blue, and 4 mg xylene–cyanol, and adjust the volume to 1 ml with DEPC water. Keep frozen at −20°C.

9. *1% agarose gel in 0.66 M formaldehyde and 1× Mops:* Dissolve 1 g agarose in 85 ml DEPC water by melting in a microwave oven. Bring the temperature of the solution to 60°C in a water bath. Add 10 ml of 10× Mops and 5 ml of deionized formaldehyde (37%).

10. *Prehybridization and hybridization buffer:* To make 100 ml, dissolve 2.3 g of NaCl, 1 g of SDS, and 100 mg of sonicated herring sperm DNA in 100 ml water.

Steps

1. Inject 200 cells (nucleus, cytoplasm) grown on small glass slides and further cultivate the cells under standard conditions.
2. Remove slides with the injected cells from the dish.
3. Wash the slide two times with PBS.
4. Transfer the slide to an Eppendorf tube with 50 μl lysis buffer; add 1 μl (45 U) of RNase inhibitor.
5. Incubate at 37°C for 15 min.

6. Add 6 μl 2.5 *M* NaOAc, pH 6.
7. Treat the mixture twice with phenol–chloroform/isoamyl alcohol (24/1) and twice with chloroform/isoamyl alcohol (24/1).
8. Precipitate RNA with 2 vol ethanol and 0.1 vol of 3 *M* NaOAc pH 5.2.
9. For Northern blot analysis dissolve the RNA sediment in 20 μl denaturation buffer and denature the RNA at 65°C for 15 min.
10. Add 2–3 μl loading buffer.
11. Load the samples on 1% agarose gel in 0.66 *M* formaldehyde and 1× Mops.
12. Run the gel in 1× Mops buffer at 10 V/cm.
13. Transfer the RNA to Hybond-N membrane overnight.
14. Bake the membrane under vacuum for 2 hr at 80°C.
15. Prehybridize the membrane in 0.4 *M* NaCl, 1% SDS, and 100 mg/ml denatured herring sperm DNA at 65°C for 2 hr.
16. Hybridize in the same bag with primer-extended heat-denatured [^{32}P]DNA probe at 65°C overnight.

REFERENCES

Celis, J. E., Graessmann, A., and Loyter, A., eds. (1986) "Microinjection and Organelle Transplantation Techniques." Academic Press, San Diego.

Graessmann, A. (1968) "Mikrochirurgische Zellkerntransplantation bei somatischen Säugetierzellen." Thesis, Freien Universität Berlin.

Graessmann, A. (1970) Mikrochirurgische Zellkerntransplantation bei Säugetierzellen. *Exp. Cell Res.* **60,** 373–382.

Graessmann, A., and Graessmann, M. (1971) Über die Bildung von Melanin in Muskelzellen nach der direkten Übertragung von RNA aus Harding Passey Melanomzellen. *Z. Physiol. Chem.* **352,** 527–532.

Graessmann, A., Graessmann, M., and Mueller, C. (1981) Regulation of SV40 gene expression. *Adv. Cancer Res.* **35,** 111–149.

Graessmann, A., Wolf, H., and Bornkamm, G. (1979) Expression of Epstein–Barr virus genes in different cell types after microinjection of viral DNA. *Proc. Natl. Acad. Sci. USA* **77,** 433–437.

Graessmann, M., and Graessmann, A. (1976) Early simian virus 40 specific RNA contains information for tumor antigen and chromatin replication. *Proc. Natl. Acad. Sci. USA* **73,** 366–370.

Graessmann, M., and Graessmann, A. (1982) Simian virus 40 cRNA is processed into functional mRNA in microinjected monkey cells. *EMBO J.* **1,** 1081–1088.

Graessmann, M., and Graessmann, A. (1983) Microinjection of tissue culture cells. *In* "Methods in Enzymology" (R. Wu, L. Grossman, and K. Moldave, eds.), Vol. 101, pp. 482–492. Academic Press, San Diego.

Graessmann, M., Graessmann, A., and Westphal, H. (1983) SV40 cRNA is spliced following microinjection into monkey cells. *J. Virol.* **48,** 296–299.

Graessmann, M., Michaels, G., Berg, B., Graessmann, A. (1991) Inhibition of SV40 expression by microinjected small antisense RNA and DNA molecules. *Nucleic Acids Res.* **19,** 53–59.

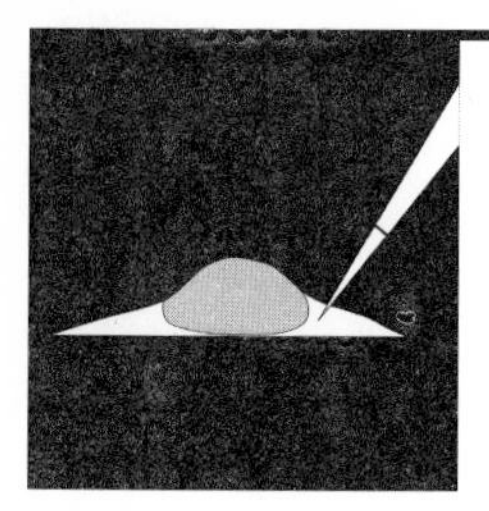

Microinjection of Proteins into Somatic Cells: Needle Microinjection and Scrape Loading

Yu-Li Wang

I. Introduction

Microinjection has been used since the 1920s as a means for delivering foreign molecules into cells. The greatest value of the approach is in allowing direct experimentation on live cells (see also articles by M. Graessmann and A. Graessmann and by Rainer Pepperkok, Rainer Saffrich, and Wilhelm Ansorge). The technique is receiving renewed interest in conjunction with considerable technical improvement and large expansion in the spectrum of probes. In addition, a number of new approaches, such as scrape loading (McNeil, 1989) and electroporation (Glogauer and McCulloch, 1992), have been introduced to complement the direct microinjection approach. To probe different aspects of cells, various types of molecules have been microinjected, including (caged) second messengers, fluorescent probes and indicators, drugs and antibodies, active genes, and antisense nucleic acids. This article focuses on the needle microinjection and scrape loading of protein molecules into cultured somatic cells; however, similar approaches should apply to other types of molecules and cells.

II. Materials and Instrumentation

Collodion bags (Cat. No. 25310 or 25320) and apparatus for vacuum dialysis (Cat. No. 27240) were purchased from Schleicher and Schuell. Centricon filters (Cat. No. 4205 or 4208) were obtained from Amicon. Cells for microinjection were plated in special chamber dishes, with acid-washed No. 2 glass coverslips (Cat. No. 12-543F) as the substrate, as described by McKenna and Wang (1989). In some experiments the medium was covered with a layer of mineral oil (Cat. No. 400-5, Sigma) to minimize evaporation. See McKenna and Wang (1989) for details of culturing cells on the microscope stage.

Microinjection was performed on a Zeiss Axiovert 10 inverted microscope, equipped with a 10× Achrostigmat objective (Cat. No. 44 01 31), a 40× phase-contrast Plan-Neofluar objective (Cat. No. 44 03 51), and 10× eyepieces. Vibration of the table was dampened by installing small tires under the legs. Needles were pulled from Omega-Dot capillary tubing (Cat. No. 30-31-0, Friderick & Haer), using a vertical pipette puller (Model 720, David Kopf). Needles were mounted on a microinstrument collar (Cat. No. 520-145, Leitz) and a micromanipulator (Cat. No. 520-137, Leitz) with a microinstrument holder assembly (Cat. No. 520-142, Leitz). Pressure for microinjection was generated with either an air-filled 10-ml glass

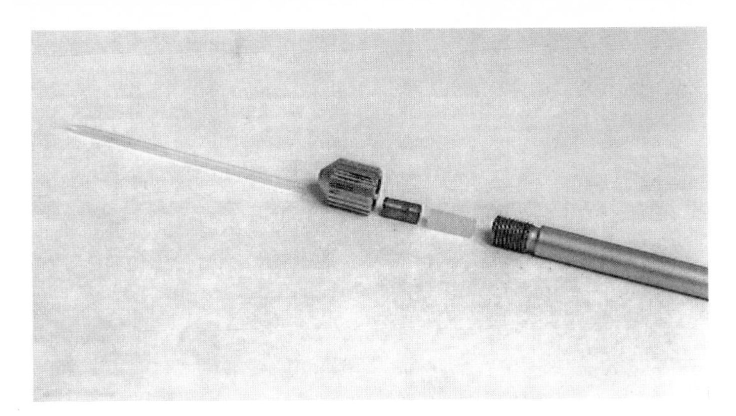

FIGURE 1 Assembly of microneedle and microinstrument collar. The parts from left to right are microneedle, captive nut, brass guide piece, silicon rubber sealing tubing, and metal cylinder. The brass guide piece has one end beveled, which should face toward the sealing tubing. The needle is first passed through the captive nut and the guide piece, and is attached to the silicon rubber tubing. The assembly is then screwed onto the metal cylinder with a gentle tightening pressure.

syringe, coated with a small amount of immersion oil on the inside surface as sealer and lubricant, or with an electronic regulator (custom designed) which maintains a steady air pressure in the range 0.3–1.0 psi. Additional details of the equipment are described in Wang (1992).

A rubber policeman for scrape loading was purchased from Fisher Scientific (Cat. No. 14-105A).

III. Procedures

A. NEEDLE MICROINJECTION

Solutions

1. *Buffer:* Proteins to be microinjected were dialyzed overnight into 2 m*M* Tris–acetate, pH 7.0, or a buffer compatible with both the cell (e.g., low calcium, low buffering capacity, near-neutral pH, limited salt and magnesium, nontoxic) and the protein. Collodion bags were used for the dialysis of small volumes and for the concentration of protein solution by vacuum dialysis. Amicon filters were used for concentration of some proteins. The solution was clarified by centrifugation at 25,000 rpm for 20 min in a Beckman type 42.2 Ti rotor.

2. *Culture medium at 36–37°C.*

Steps

1. Plate cells for 12–48 hr.

2. Scan the dish at a low magnification (e.g., 100×) to choose an area for microinjection. For most experiments, the cell density should be somewhat below confluency to provide adequate space for cells to spread and for maneuvering of microinjection needles.

3. Load protein solution from the back end of the needle with a drawn-out Pasteur pipette. Mount the loaded microneedle on the microinstrument collar (Fig. 1) and the micromanipulator.

4. Apply some pressure to prevent backflow of medium into the needle.

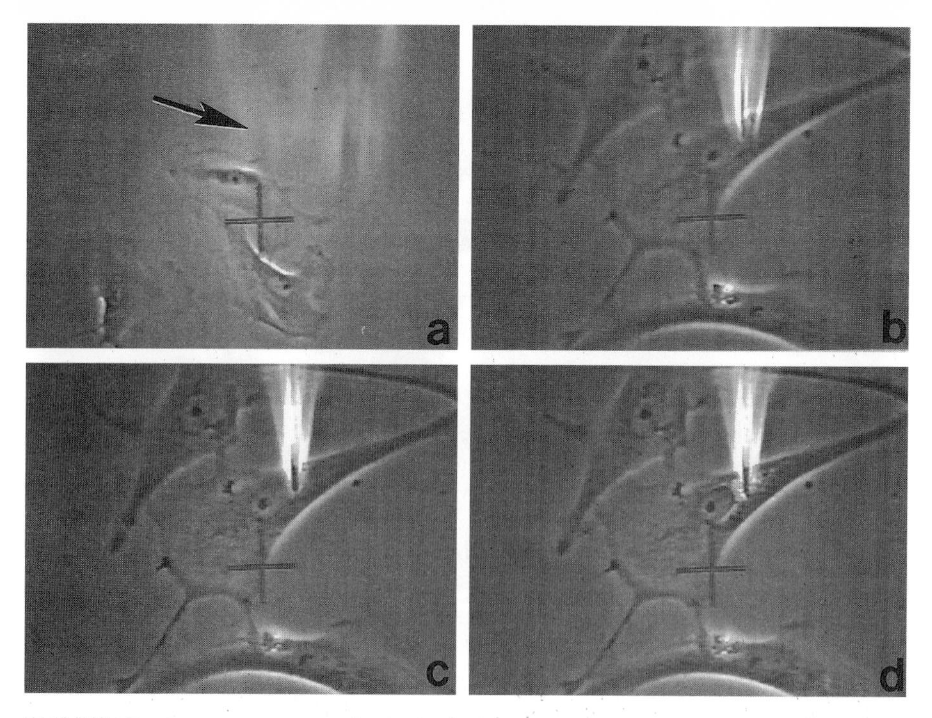

FIGURE 2 Steps in microinjection. (a) Microscope is set at a low power (100×) and is focused on the cell. The needle is at a level higher than the cell and appears as a ghost shadow (arrow). It is carefully brought into the field with a micromanipulator. (b) The magnification is changed to 400×. The needle is positioned above the site of injection and appears slightly out of focus. (c) The tip of the needle is brought into focus and is making a dent on the surface. (d) The delivery of solution starts following a gentle tap at the micromanipulator. The flow induces a local decrease in phase density.

Carefully introduce the needle into the medium. Keep the needle at a level well above cells. The microscope should be focused on cells and the needle should appear as a blurred shadow (Fig. 2a). Bring the needle near the center of the field.

5. Switch to high magnification (e.g., 400×) and focus the microscope on cells. Bring the needle close to focus but still above the level of the cells.

6. Adjust the pressure to about 1/3 psi. The flow of solution can be checked by carefully bringing the needle close to focus and switching to fluorescence optics (if the solution contains a fluorescent marker). Raise the needle back to a higher level.

7. Position a cell to be microinjected directly under the needle (Fig. 2b). Carefully bring the needle to focus, i.e., lower down the needle into the cell (Fig. 2c). Microinjection often starts spontaneously. Otherwise, a gentle tap at the micromanipulator should cause the needle to puncture the cell membrane.

8. The delivery of solution manifests as a change in phase density that spreads out from the needle (Fig. 2d). The volume of injection is controlled by the pressure and by the length of time the needle stays inside the cell. Raise the needle out of the cell to stop the microinjection. Adjust the injection pressure if necessary between cells. An alternative approach is to raise the pressure momentarily after puncture of the membrane, under the control of a timing device (e.g., pressure regulator from Eppendorf).

9. Replace the medium following each hour of injection and at the end of microinjection to correct for any evaporation that may have occurred and to remove materials that spilled into the medium. Alternatively, evaporation can be minimized with an overlay of mineral oil.

B. SCRAPE LOADING

Solutions

1. *Phosphate-buffered saline (PBS):* Contains 137 m*M* NaCl, 2.68 m*M* KCl, 8 m*M* Na_2HPO_4, and 1.47 m*M* KH_2PO_4.

2. *Protein solution in PBS:* The concentration is usually several times higher than that targeted for delivery. The optimal concentration should be determined empirically.

3. *Culture medium at 36–37°C.*

Steps

All steps are performed in a sterile hood.

1. Start with subconfluent cell culture on 35- or 60-mm culture dishes. Cells should adhere well to the dish; otherwise, a shorter plating time may improve the viability of the cells after loading (McNeil, 1989).

2. Rinse the dish three times with PBS. Remove PBS thoroughly by aspiration.

3. Add the protein solution to the dish. The volume should be large enough to distribute over the entire surface after tilting the dish. Two hundred microliters is sufficient for 60-mm dishes.

4. Scrape the entire surface of the dish gently with a sterile rubber policeman. This should be finished within 10–20 sec.

5. Add warm medium to the culture dish and transfer cells into a 15-ml conical centrifuge tube (e.g., Falcon Cat. No. 2099).

6. Spin down cells in a benchtop centrifuge.

7. Remove supernatant and resuspend cells in warm culture medium. Plate cells on fresh culture dishes and culture in an incubator for several hours.

IV. Comments

The presence of a fluorescent marker in the injection solution can greatly facilitate microinjection. It allows examination of flow and easy identification of injected cells. Fluorescent dextran (Sigma or Molecular Probes) at 1–5 mg/ml can be used as an inert marker.

It is critical to obtain an optimal shape of the microneedle by adjusting the temperature and force of the pipette puller. Blunt needles are fragile and cause excessive cell damage; a slender taper traps air bubbles during backloading.

Each needle can be used for more than 50 cells, assuming that the solution for microinjection is reasonably clean. The needle will eventually become clogged by materials inside and from contact with the cytoplasm. High-pressure (e.g., 20 psi) pulses can be used to push out small aggregates; however, it is very difficult to push out any air bubbles due to surface tension. Sometimes it is possible to carefully break the tip, by gently touching the glass, and use at a reduced pressure.

The volume delivered by needle microinjection is usually in the range 1 to 10% cell volume. With some practice the variability can be maintained to within a factor of 2. A number of factors can affect the volume, including the pressure, tip size, accumulation of proteins at the tip, and presence of any air bubbles in the needle.

Without proper landmarks, it can be very difficult to find injected cells once the dish is moved away from the site of injection. Cells can be located by marking the

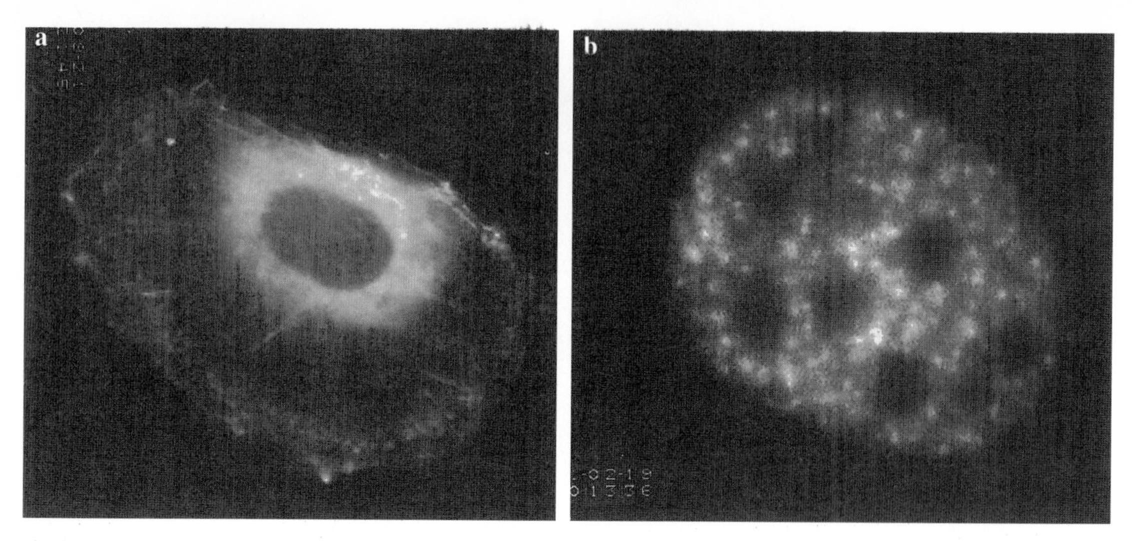

FIGURE 3 Fluorescence images of NRK cells with rhodamine-labeled actin microinjected into the cytoplasm (a) and with rhodamine-labeled human globin pre-messenger RNA microinjected into the nucleus (b). In (a), fluorescent actin becomes incorporated into cytoplasmic structures, with the nucleus appearing as a dark area. In (b), fluorescent pre-mRNA is localized almost exclusively inside the nucleus at numerous discrete sites. Nucleoli appear as dark patches.

coverslip with a diamond pencil and injecting near the mark or by marking the site of injection with a "marker objective."

In some experiments, it may be necessary to recover microinjected cells (e.g., for electrophoresis, polymerase chain reaction). One way to do this is to plate cells on small pieces of coverslips placed inside a culture dish, inject all cells on pieces of coverslips and then remove the pieces with forceps.

Intranuclear microinjections can be achieved in a similar fashion. The needle is first lowered onto the surface above the nucleus, forming a dent on the top cell surface. Injection is started with a gentle tap at the micromanipulator, which causes the needle to penetrate both the plasma membrane and the nuclear envelope. With practice nuclear injections can be achieved with minimal spillage into the cytoplasm. Figure 3 shows an example of cells injected in the nucleus with fluorescent molecules.

V. Pitfalls

Needle Microinjection

1. For well-spread cells, needle microinjection is possible only in the perinuclear phase-dense region. For poorly adherent cells, a second pipette is necessary to hold the cell by suction during microinjection.

2. Physical damage to cells, as during microinjection, induces calcium transients and possibly downstream processes regulated by calcium. Therefore, whenever possible, injected cells should be allowed 1–2 hr for recovery. Controls should be performed to rule out artifacts caused by microinjection.

3. A slight retraction of injected cells is common 5–10 min after microinjection; however the effect should reverse within 30 min.

Scrape Loading

4. Cells must be allowed to recover and respread before microscope observation.

5. Compared with needle microinjection, the amount of delivery varies more extensively among scrape-loaded cells. The yield of injected cells and the extent of cell damage also vary among cell types. Cell damage often manifests as the appearance of large vacuoles.

6. The efficiency of scrape loading varies as a function of molecular weight (McNeil *et al.,* 1984).

7. Some molecules may not be compatible with the balanced salt solution required for scrape loading.

REFERENCES

Glogauer, M., and McCulloch, A. G. (1992) Introduction of large molecules into viable fibroblasts by electroporation: Optimization of loading and identification of labeled cellular compartments. *Exp. Cell Res.* **200,** 227–234.

McKenna, N. M., and Wang, Y.-L. (1989) Culturing cells on the microscope stage. *Methods Cell Biol.* **29,** 195–205.

McNeil, P. L. (1989) Incorporation of macromolecules into living cells. *Methods Cell Biol.* **29,** 153–173.

McNeil, P. L., Murphy, R. F., Lanni, F., and Taylor, D. L. (1984) A method for incorporating macromolecules into adherent cells. *J. Cell Biol.* **98,** 1556–1564.

Wang, Y.-L. (1992) Fluorescence microscopic analysis of cytoskeletal organization and dynamics. *In* "The Cytoskeleton, a Practical Approach" (K. L. Carraway and C. R. C. Carraway, eds.), pp 1–22. IRL Press, Oxford.

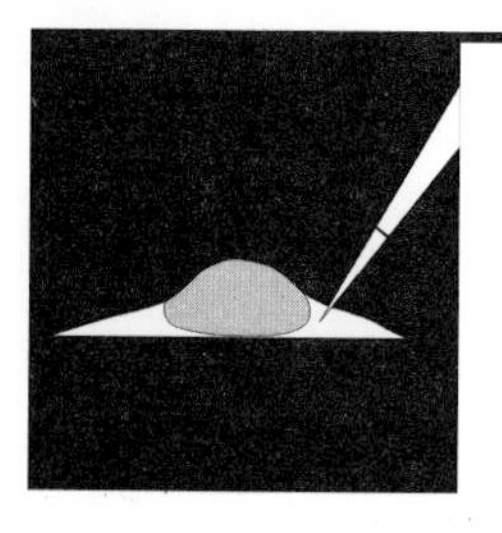

Computer-Automated Capillary Microinjection of Macromolecules into Living Cells

Rainer Pepperkok, Rainer Saffrich, and Wilhelm Ansorge

I. Introduction

Capillary microinjection has proved to be one of the most efficient methods for introducing macromolecules into living cells (Celis, 1984) (see also articles by M. Graessmann and A. Graessmann and by Yu-Li Wang in this volume) The molecules can be transferred at well-defined stages of the cell cycle, and modifications of culture conditions are possible before, during, or after injection. Samples can be delivered either directly into the nucleus or into the cytoplasm. One critical aspect of the technique, the pulling and handling of glass micropipettes (Proctor, 1992), has been significantly facilitated by introduction on the market of micropipette pullers, with built-in computers allowing the highest degree of reproducibility in tip shape and diameter. Improvements with respect to injected sample volumes regulated by a pressure-controlled microinjector were reported (Ansorge, 1982).

Development of a computer-automated microinjection system (AIS) (Ansorge and Pepperkok, 1988) (Fig. 1) that enables injection of more than 1500 cells per hour has considerably simplified the technique. Users usually successfully inject cells after only one training day. Such a system has advantages (Ansorge and Pepperkok, 1988; Pepperkok *et al.*, 1988, 1993a,b) compared with the manual technique: (i) handling and manipulation of the system are easy, (ii) injected cells can be retrieved with high accuracy, (iii) reproducibility of the sample volume delivered to the cells is high, and (iv) biochemical analysis of microinjected cells on a routine basis is possible. Upgrading of the AIS with low-light-level technology for fluorescence microscopy and automated image analysis allows fully automated evaluation of microinjection experiments on an integrated system (Pepperkok *et al.*, 1993a).

II. Materials and Instrumentation

[^{35}S]Methionine and ^{32}P were both obtained from NEN (Du Pont, Cat. No. NEG-009A or NEX-053C, respectively). Purified luciferase (Cat. No. L-5256) is from Sigma. DMEM (Cat. No. 074-02100H), FCS (Cat. No. 011-06290M), trypsin–EDTA (Cat. No. 040-05300H), penicillin–streptomycin (Cat. No. 043-05140H), and L-glutamine (Cat. No. 043-05030H) are obtained from Gibco. Petri dishes (Cat. No. 150350 for 100-mm ϕ, Cat. No. 150288 for 60-mm ϕ, and Cat. No. 153066 for 35-mm ϕ, gamma irradiated) for cell culture are from Nunc. Glass coverslips are from Menzel.

Raw glass capillaries are from Clarke Electromedical Instruments (Cat. No.

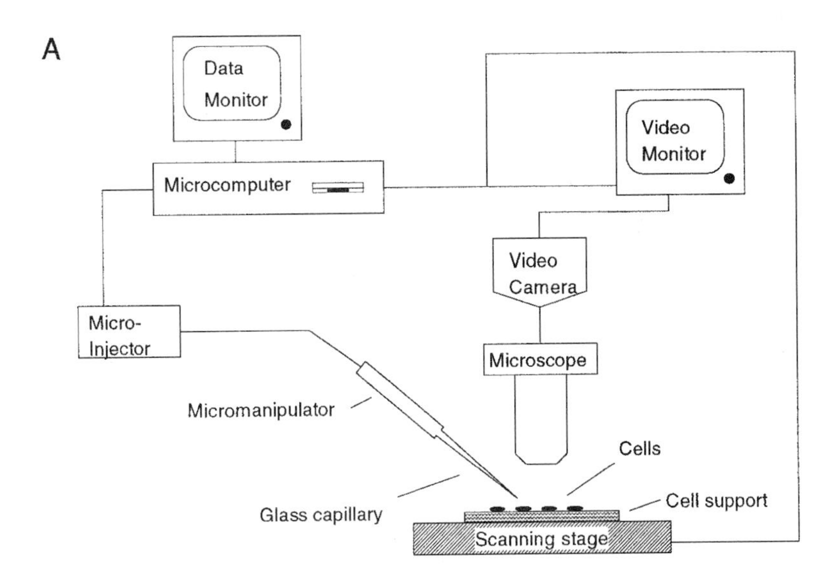

FIGURE 1 (A) Scheme of the setup of the automated capillary microinjection system (AIS). Movements of the microscope scanning stage and the micromanipulator as well as the pressure of the microinjector are controlled by computer. Cells under observation are displayed by a CCD camera on a video monitor. (B) Zeiss automated microinjection system (AIS).

GC120TF-10). The pipette Puller type P-87 is from Sutter Instruments. The microinjector (Model 5242), prepulled and sterile ready-to-use micropipettes (Cat. No. 5242 952.008), and microloaders (Cat. No. 0030 001.222) are from Eppendorf.

The automated injection system (AIS) used was developed at EMBL (Ansorge and Pepperkok, 1988) (see Fig. 1A). The commercial version (see Fig. 1B) is distributed by Zeiss. An inverted microscope (Axiovert 10) with long-distance phase-contrast optics (magnifications: 45×–320×) is used. A CCD video camera displays cells under observation on a monitor. The microscope scanning stage for positioning cells and the micromanipulator moving the micropipette during microinjection are controlled by an IBM-compatible computer. The pressure applied to the micropipette is supplied by an air compressor and is regulated by a microinjector (Eppendorf). All equipment and software can be obtained from Zeiss.

III. Procedures

A. PULLING AND HANDLING OF GLASS MICROPIPETTES

1. Pulling of Micropipettes

Steps

1. Insert raw capillary carefully into the puller without touching the heating filament (square shape). No special treatment of the glass capillaries is required before pulling.

2. Choose the pulling program recommended by the supplier for pulling injection micropipettes.

3. Adjust the value of the current through the heating filament to your individual needs (usually this value should not vary more than 10% from the value recommended by the supplier) and pull the micropipette. The tip diameter of the micropipette decreases with increasing current and vice versa. Capillaries with an outer tip diameter between 0.2 and 1.0 μm are easily available with the puller used. Two micropipettes will be obtained after 20–30 sec. Both can be used for microinjection because they are identical with respect to their physical parameters.

4. Check the shape of the micropipettes under the light microscope with a magnification of 200× or 320× (with the modern and reproducible Sutter Instruments puller this step usually is not required for each capillary).

2. Characterization of Tip Diameter by Bubble Pressure Measurement

The protocol described below allows characterization of the tip diameter by bubble pressure measurement (Mittman *et al.*, 1987). This is a nondestructive method for determining tip size, and micropipettes can still be used for microinjection experiments without any restrictions. This is not the case when micropipettes are characterized by electron microscopy.

Steps

1. Insert the micropipette into the capillary holder of the microinjector (Eppendorf) as for microinjection.

2. Dip the tip into a beaker filled with 100% ethanol (should be filtered through a 0.22-μm syringe filter).

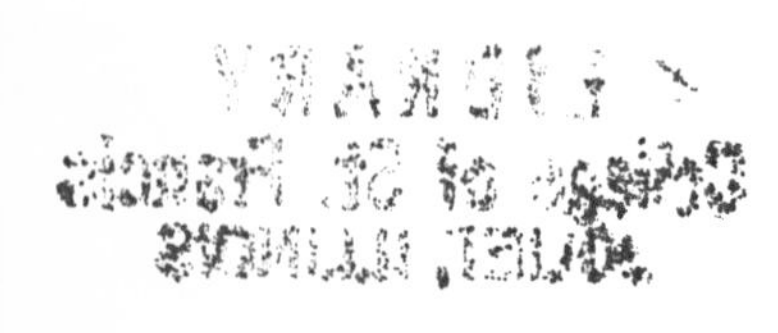

3. Increase the pressure of the microinjector until air bubbles from the micropipette tip appear, indicating that the tip is open. Typical pressure values for good micropipettes, used in our laboratory for nuclear and cytoplasmic injections, are between 2000 and 4000 hPa. Lower values indicate a tip size above 1 μm. For higher pressure values the micropipette is either closed or the risk for clogging during microinjection is rather high.

4. Store the micropipettes in a dust-free and dry environment until use (up to 3 months).

3. Filling Micropipettes with Injection Sample

Steps

1. To avoid micropipette clogging during microinjection, always centrifuge the sample for at least 10 min at 10,000 *g* at 4°C.

2. Deliver the sample through the rear open end of the micropipette down near the tip using a sterile microloader from Eppendorf. Typically loaded volumes are 0.2–1.0 μl.

3. Insert the filled micropipette quickly into the capillary holder of the microinjector and lower it rapidly until the micropipette tip reaches the medium of the culture dish containing cells to be injected.

The speed is important in step 3 because the sample in the micropipette tip may easily dry if it remains too long in the air and micropipette clogging occurs.

B. CENTERING THE MICROPIPETTE IN THE MICROSCOPE FIELD

The following procedure helps to prevent breakage of the micropipette tip during its centering in the microscope field. It is applicable when using the Zeiss automated injection system but can be easily adapted to manual injection. All steps should be performed in the capillary position "Cell" (AIS program menu).

Steps

1. Center the micropipette above the culture dish roughly by eye.

2. Lower the micropipette (using the AIS program menu "Adjust") until it touches the culture medium.

3. Change to the lowest magnification available on the microscope (e.g., 45×).

4. Focus on the cells.

5. Center the micropipette in the field of view in the microscope and lower it carefully, but not all the way, to its focus (breakage of micropipette!).

6. Change to the next higher magnification.

7. Repeat steps 4–6 until you reach the working magnification (320×). Now the cells should be in focus and the micropipette should be centered but not in focus (breakage of micropipette!).

8. Carry out subsequent steps by observing cells and micropipette on the video monitor, *not* in the microscope.

9. Lower the micropipette carefully until the tip comes into focus. Both cells and tip are on the same focal plane.

10. Use the computer mouse to mark the tip position (AIS menu program "Mark Tip").

11. Proceed directly with automated microinjection.

C. AUTOMATED MICROINJECTION

For the following, the micropipette should be centered in the field of view as described in Section B. The pressure applied to the micropipette remains constant during automated injection. It is adjusted at the beginning of the session with the microinjector according to the cell type and injection sample used [see also the Zeiss AIS Operating Instructions (1989)].

Steps

1. Switch the capillary position to "Wait" (AIS program menu).

2. Choose the program menu "Position OK."

3. Choose the program menu "Mark Next."

4. Now mark all the cells to be injected by pointing with the computer mouse to the exact place of injection on the cells displayed on the video monitor. Nuclear injections should be performed in the center of the cell nucleus. Cytoplasmic injections are performed just next to the nucleus (Fig. 2).

5. Choose the program menu "Inject." All the marked cells in the field injected automatically under computer control and their stage coordinates are stored on computer disk.

6. Switch to a neighboring field containing noninjected cells and repeat steps 3 to 5.

D. QUANTITATION OF MICROINJECTED VOLUME

Steps

1. Add purified luciferase (Sigma, final concentration 2 mg/ml) to the solution to be injected in biological experiments.

2. Microinject exact number of cells (50 cells will be enough) with the AIS.

3. Lyse cells and determine luciferase activity of the extract in a luminometer as described (DeWet *et al.*, 1987).

4. Dilute the injection solution containing luciferase (2 mg/ml) in steps of one order of magnitude or less and determine luciferase activity of the dilutions.

5. Calculate the amount of luciferase microinjected into all the cells (e.g., 50 cells) by determining the dilution measured in step 4, which corresponds to the luciferase activity obtained in step 3.

6. Divide the volume calculated in step 5 by the number of injected cells to obtain the average volume injected per cell.

The microinjected volume varies with the pressure applied to the micropipette and the time (controlled by computer) the tip stays inside the cell. Further, the volume depends on the cell type and injection solution used. Typical values are 0.1–0.5 pl for cytoplasmic and 0.01–0.05 pl for nuclear injections.

E. RETRIEVAL OF MICROINJECTED CELLS

Every injected cell can be retrieved by its stage coordinates stored on computer disk during microinjection. For this purpose the glass coverslip on which cells are growing must contain two distinguishable orientation marks (Fig. 3). They are scratched onto the glass coverslips using a diamond pen followed by sterilization in an autoclave oven. The position of these orientation marks must be entered into the computer with the cursor mouse twice, at the beginning of the microinjection session and when the "Find Cells" AIS program menu is used to retrieve injected cells [see also the Zeiss AIS Operating Instructions (1989)].

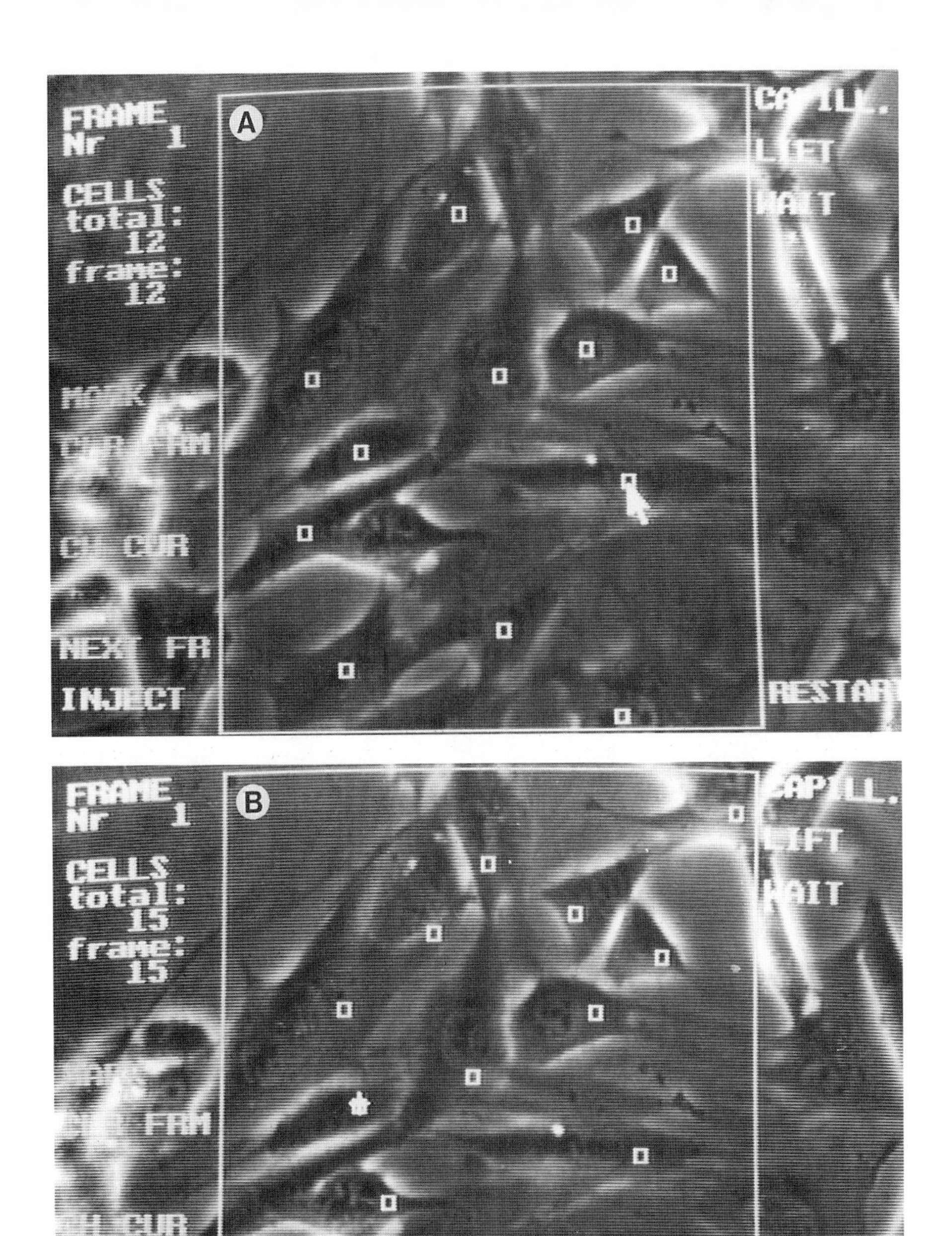

FIGURE 2 Display of cells on the video monitor marked for nuclear (A) or cytoplasmic (B) microinjection.

F. MICROINJECTING THE SAME CELLS TWICE

The method used to retrieve injected cells on glass coverslips is also used to microinject the same cells twice. Therefore, microinjected cells are retrieved as described in Section E and microinjected a second time as described in Section C.

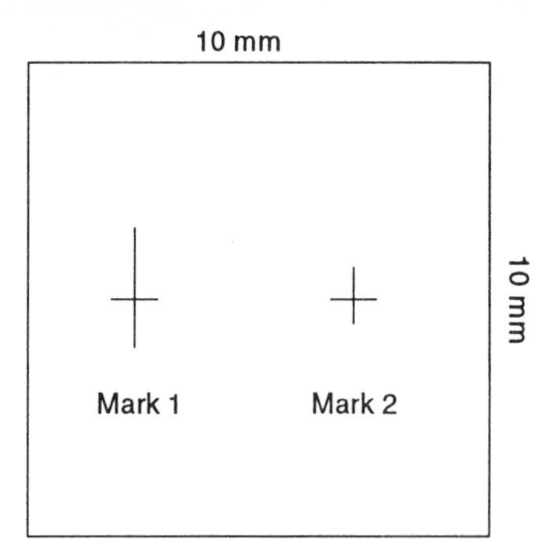

FIGURE 3 Two distinguishable orientation marks are scratched onto glass coverslips as they are used for retrieval of injected cells or microinjection of the same cells twice.

G. BIOCHEMICAL ANALYSIS OF MICROINJECTED CELLS

The speed and efficiency of the automated injection system allow biochemical analysis of microinjected cells (Pepperkok *et al.*, 1993b). Between 500 and 1000 cells that have been labelled with [^{35}S]methionine or ^{32}P are sufficient to analyze labeled proteins by gel electrophoresis. The following protocol is routinely used in our lab for this purpose. It may have to be modified according to the specific requirements of the biological experiments.

Steps

1. Plate 250 cells in 5-μl droplets in the center of a glass coverslip (10 × 10 mm).

2. Place coverslips into a humid chamber and incubate at 37°C until cells have attached to the glass (takes usually 6–8 hr).

3. Transfer coverslips into 35-mm petri dishes containing 2 ml of culture medium and let cells grow for 2 days at 37°C. Usually between 500 and 1000 cells will be in the center of the coverslip after this time.

4. Microinject all cells on the coverslip with the AIS.

5. Incubate cells for 15 min or 2 hr in methionine- or phosphate-free culture medium (labeling medium) to deplete cellular stores.

6. Label with [^{35}S]methionine or ^{32}P in 40 μl labeling medium. Typical concentrations are 1 μCi/μl [^{35}S]methionine and 10 μCi/μl ^{32}P (see also articles by Julio E. Celis, Jette B. Lauridsen, and Bodil Basse and by Scott D. Patterson and James I. Garrels).

7. Wash cells three times with chase medium (complete medium containing normal concentrations of methionine or phosphate).

8. Incubate cells for the appropriate time (depends on particular experiment) with 2 ml chase medium.

9. Lyse cells in 50 μl lysis buffer containing nonradioactively labeled cell lysate at a protein concentration of 1 mg/ml. The presence of these "carrier proteins" in the lysis buffer is extremely important to the success of the experiment (e.g., immunoprecipitation and analysis of specific proteins).

10. Proceed with biochemical analysis of lysed proteins (depends on biochemical experiment).

REFERENCES

Ansorge, W. (1982) Improved system for capillary microinjection into living cells. *Exp. Cell Res.* **140**, 31–37.

Ansorge, W., and Pepperkok, R. (1988) Performance of an automated system for capillary microinjection into living cells. *J. Biochem. Biophys. Methods* **16**, 283–292.

Celis, J. E. (1984) Microinjection of somatic cells with micropipettes: Comparison with other transfer techniques. *Biochem. J.* **223**, 281–291.

DeWet, J. R., Wood, K., DeLuca, M., Helsinki, D., and Subramini, S. (1987) Firefly luciferase gene: Structure and expression in mammalian cells. *Mol. Cell. Biol.* **7**, 725–737.

Mittman, S., Flaming, D. G., Copenhagen, D. R., and Belgum, J. H. (1987) Bubble pressure measurement of micropipette tip outer diameter. *J. Neurosci. Methods* **22**, 161–166.

Pepperkok, R., Herr, S., Lorenz, P., Pyerin, W., and Ansorge, W. (1993a) System for quantitation of gene expression in single cells by computerized micro-imaging: Application to *c-fos* expression after microinjection of anticasein kinase II (CKII) antibody. *Exp. Cell Res.* **204**, 278–285.

Pepperkok, R., Schneider, C., Philipson, L., and Ansorge, W. (1988) Single cell assay with an automated capillary microinjection system. *Exp. Cell Res.* **178**, 369–376.

Pepperkok, R., Scheel, J., Horstman, H., Hauri, H. P., Griffiths, G., and Kreis, T. E. (1993b) β-COP is essential for biosynthetic membrane transport from the endoplasmic reticulum to the Golgi complex *in vivo*. *Cell* **74**, 71–82.

Proctor, G. N. (1992) Microinjection of DNA into mammalian cells in culture: Theory and practise. *Methods Mol. Cell. Biol.* **3**, 209–231.

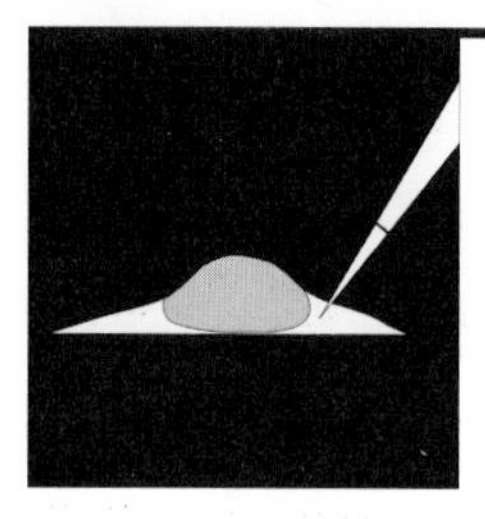

Syringe Loading: A Method for Inserting Macromolecules into Cells in Suspension

Mark S. F. Clarke and Paul L. McNeil

I. Introduction

A common strategy used by the modern cell or molecular biologist is to insert macromolecules (e.g., dyes, proteins and nucleic acids) into the cytoplasm of living mammalian cells to monitor or modify specific intracellular processes (see also other relevant articles in this section). Numerous "cell loading" techniques have been developed that accomplish this, but no one technique is ideal for every application. Electroporation (Knutson and Yee, 1987) and biolistics (Sanford *et al.*, 1987) are two techniques used nearly exclusively for the loading of DNA (e.g., transfection). Other transfection techniques, such as liposome fusion-based methods (Felgner *et al.*, 1987), appear to work well with only a few cell types. Microinjection (Graessmann *et al.*, 1974; Celis, 1978), although the most direct and quantitative method of delivering a wide range of macromolecules to the cytoplasm of different cell types, is time consuming, requires specialized equipment, and is impractical for loading large numbers of cells. Several simple and inexpensive cell loading techniques, based on the use of mechanical force to transiently permeabilize the plasma membrane, achieve loading of adherent cells without the need for expensive or complex apparatus. These techniques, scrape (McNeil *et al.*, 1984), scratch (Swanson and McNeil, 1987), and bead (McNeil and Warder, 1987) loading, have demonstrated the utility of "cell wounding" as a means of gaining entry into the cell cytoplasm, but are not applicable to cells in suspension. We have recently developed a simple, efficient, and gentle mechanically based method of loading cells in suspension, termed *syringe loading* (Clarke and McNeil, 1992). The overall loading efficiency of this technique is increased by the presence of the nonionic surfactant Pluronic F-68, which appears to augment the natural tendency of cells to repair plasma membrane wounds (Clarke and McNeil, 1992). Syringe loading can efficiently introduce into the cell cytoplasm a variety of macromolecules, including dyes, oligonucleotides, and immunoglobulins. Plasmid DNA can also be loaded, although the use of the syringe loading technique for this application remains to be optimized.

II. Materials and Instrumentation

Dulbecco's modified Eagle's medium (×1 concentration, DMEM, Cat. No. 320-1885AG), bovine calf serum (CS, Cat. No. 200-6170AG), penicillin–streptomycin solution (Cat. No. 600-5140AG), Dulbecco's phosphate buffered saline (D-PBS, Cat. No. 310-4040AJ), and trypsin–EDTA solution (Cat. No. 610-5300AG) are obtained ready to use from Gibco-BRL. Pluronic F-68 (Cat. No. P-1300) is purchased from Sigma. Fixable FITC-labeled dextran (FDxLys, Cat. No. D-1820) is obtained from Molecular Probes. Vectashield aqueous mounting medium is purchased from Vector Laboratories.

Tissue culture flasks (T-75, Cat. No. 10-126-41), six-well tissue culture plates (Cat. No. 08-772-1B), sterile polypropylene conical tubes (50-ml capacity, Cat. No. 05-538-55A), sterile polypropylene round-bottom tubes (5-ml capacity, Cat. No. 14-959-10A), and sterile conical-bottom microfuge tubes (1.5-ml capacity, Cat. No. 05-664-63) are obtained from Fisher Scientific. Disposable 1-ml syringes (Cat. No. 309602) and 30-gauge hypodermic needles (Cat. No. 5106) are purchased from Becton-Dickinson. A Hamilton microliter syringe (50-μl capacity, Cat. No. 80501) is obtained from Hamilton Company. Micropipette tips (MC-50) are purchased from West Coast Scientific. The hand-held pipettor (Cat. No. P20) is obtained from Gilson Medical Electronics.

III. Procedures

A. PREPARATION OF TISSUE CULTURED CELLS FOR SYRINGE LOADING

Solutions

1. *Stock FDxLys solution:* Add 200 mg of dry FDxLys powder to 1 ml of serum-free DMEM and vortex periodically over a 30-min period to achieve complete solubilization. Centrifuge this solution at 8000 *g* for 10 min at room temperature to remove any undissolved FDxLys and sterilize, if desired, by ultrafiltration. Stock FDxLys (200 mg/ml) can be stored at 4°C in the dark for up to a month.

2. *Stock Pluronic F-68 solution:* Add 20 g of dry Pluronic F-68 to 100 ml of calcium–magnesium-free phosphate-buffered saline (pH 7.2) and mix until the powder is completely dissolved. Sterilize the solution by steam autoclave. Stock Pluronic solution (20% w/v) can be stored at 4°C for up to a month.

3. *FDxLys loading solution:* Add 50 μl of stock FDxLys solution and 100 μl of stock Pluronic F-68 solution to 850 μl of 5% CS.DMEM to obtain final concentrations of 10 mg/ml FDLys and 2% (w/v) Pluronic F-68. The solution is used immediately.

4. *5% CS.DMEM:* Add 5 ml of sterile penicillin–streptomycin solution and 50 ml of sterile CS to 445 ml of sterile (X1) DMEM solution, to obtain DMEM culture medium containing 5% CS, 100 IU/ml penicillin, and 100 μg/ml streptomycin (5% CS.DMEM). Store at 4°C for up to 21 days.

Steps

1. Grow bovine aortic endothelial cells or NIH 3T3 fibroblasts to confluence in T-75 (75-cm^2) culture flasks using 5% CS.DMEM maintained at 37°C in a 5% CO_2 humidified atmosphere with medium changed every third day.

2. Wash each T-75 culture flask ($\sim 5 \times 10^6$ cells) with three changes of warm (37°C) D-PBS (obtained ready to use) to remove any medium.

3. Detach cells from the culture surface by incubation with 10 ml of warm (37°C) trypsin–EDTA solution (obtained ready to use) for 5 min at 37°C.

4. Inactivate trypsin–EDTA solution by adding 10 ml of 5% CS.DMEM to the suspension.

5. Collect cells by centrifugation in a sterile 50-ml centrifuge tube at 200 *g* (~800 rpm) for 5 min at room temperature.

6. Resuspend the cell pellet in 2 ml of 5% CS.DMEM and determine the cell number by counting in a hemacytometer.

7. Adjust the cell density of the cell suspension to 500,000 cells/ml by the addition of an appropriate amount of 5% CS.DMEM.

8. Dispense samples into sterile round-bottom polypropylene 5-ml tubes (0.2–1 ml) or sterile conical-bottom microfuge tubes (10 or 50 μl).

9. Collect cells by centrifugation at 200 *g* for 5 min at room temperature.

B. SYRINGE LOADING PROTOCOL

1. 0.2- to 1-ml Volumes

Steps

1. Gently resuspend cells at a cell density of 500,000 cells/ml in an appropriate volume (i.e., 0.2–1.0 ml) of FDxLys loading solution.

2. Draw the cell suspension up into a sterile 1-ml syringe through a sterile 30-gauge hypodermic needle by pulling the plunger to the 1-ml level and allowing the barrel of the syringe to fill. Expel the cell suspension using a steady pressure on the plunger. This procedure is defined as two strokes.

3. Repeat the procedure described in step 2 three more times so that the cell suspension has been subjected to eight strokes.

4. Add 4 ml of 5% CS.DMEM to the cell suspension and collect the cells by centrifugation at 200 *g* for 5 min at room temperature.

5. Cells are now loaded and can be gently resuspended in 5% CS.DMEM and replated in the appropriate experimental vessel at the required density.

6. (Optional) Plate an additional sample of the cell suspension at a cell density of 30,000 cells per glass coverslip and culture for 16 hr. Wash the cells with three changes of warm D-PBS and fix with 4% paraformaldehyde for 10 min at room temperature.

7. (Optional) Mount the coverslip in Vectashield aqueous mounting medium and view the cells under fluorescence illumination to qualitatively assess cell loading of FDxLys.

2. 10- to 50-μl Volumes

Ten-microliter volumes are syringe loaded using a MC-50 micropipette tip attached to a Gilson micropipettor. Fifty-microliter volumes are syringe loaded using a Hamilton microsyringe.

Steps

1. Resuspend the cells in microfuge tubes at a cell density of 500,000 cells/ml in an appropriate volume (i.e., 10 or 50 μl) of FDxLys loading solution.

2. Draw the cell suspension up into either a microsyringe or a MC-50 pipette tip and then expel it. This procedure is termed two strokes.

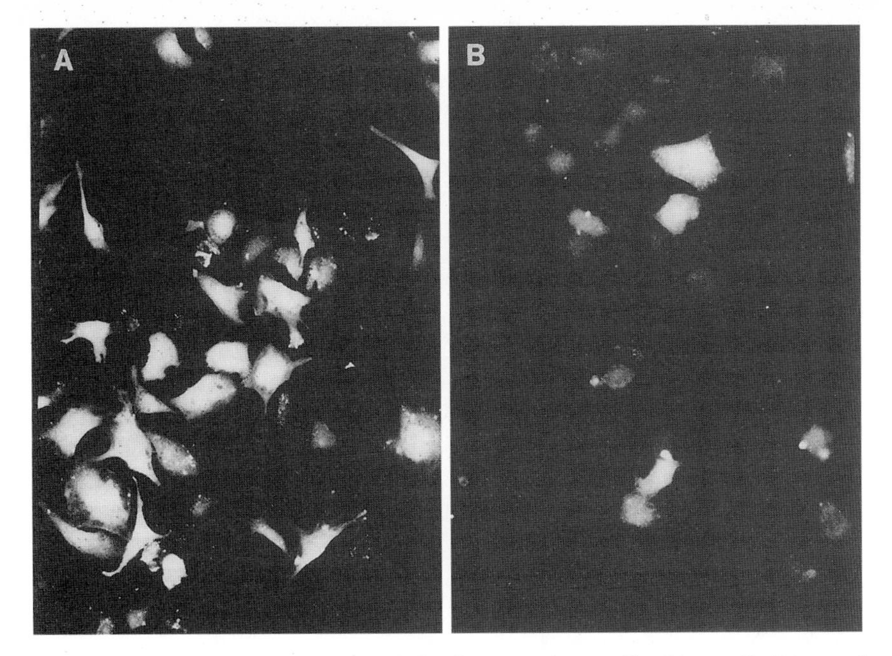

FIGURE 1 Bovine aortic endothelial cells (A) and NIH fibroblast cells (B) cytoplasmically loaded with FDxLys (10 mg/ml) using the manual syringe loading technique (1-ml volume) detailed in the text.

3. Subject the cells to a total of 50 strokes over a period of 1 min and then dilute with 1 ml of 5% CS.DMEM.

4. Collect the cells by centrifugation at 200 *g* for 5 min at room temperature, gently resuspend in 5% CS.DMEM, and replate in an appropriate experimental vessel.

IV. Comments

The method described above is a manual protocol for syringe loading of FDxLys into the cytoplasm of endothelial (Fig. 1A) and fibroblast (Fig. 1B) cells *in vitro* (Clarke and McNeil, 1992). Substitution of other macromolecules (proteins, dyes, or nucleic acids) for FDxLys will result in their loading into the cell cytoplasm by this procedure. Moreover, this technique is not limited to one or two cell types. A variety of other tissue cultured cells have been loaded in this manner, including normal rat kidney epithelial cells, QT6 cells, mouse mammary tumor cells, human angiosarcoma cells, COS-7 cells, PC 12 cells and chick neuronal cells.

The syringe loading technique inflicts shear stress on cells to produce transient disruptions of the cell plasma membranes. As such, the amount of shear stress inflicted is of critical importance: too little results in inefficient loading, too much in cell destruction. Three experimental parameters that determine the degree of shear stress inflicted are (1) the number of syringe strokes, (2) the pressure at which syringing is carried out, and (3) the internal bore size of the hypodermic needle through which the cells are passed.

To achieve reproducible control over the amount of shear stress produced, we have built a mechanical device (Fig. 2A) that eliminates individual operator variability. Using this device, one can clearly demonstrate the relationship between loading efficiency (loading index), number of strokes, and stroke pressure (Fig. 2B). The use of this device to load FDxLys and IgG is illustrated in Fig. 3. We are presently investigating syringe loading as a cell transfection technique (Fig. 3C).

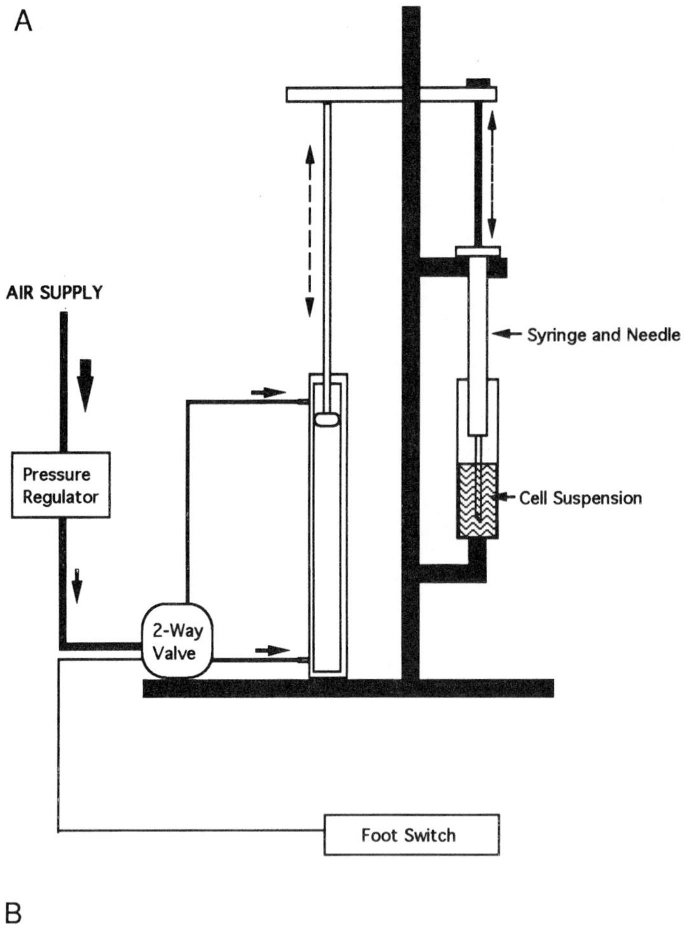

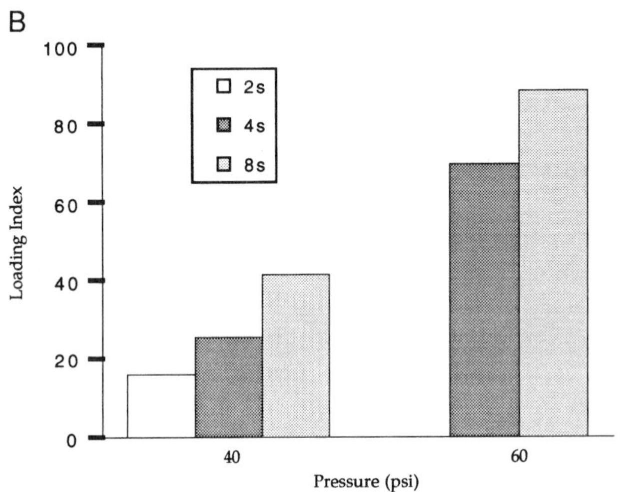

FIGURE 2 (A) Schematic diagram of the automated syringe loader. (B) Relationship between loading efficiency (loading index—*see* Clarke and McNeil, 1992), number of strokes(s), and stroke pressure.

We have previously shown that syringe loading can be carried out with cells suspended in very small volumes (i.e., 5–50 μl), thereby minimizing the required amount of often valuable macromolecule to be loaded (Clarke and McNeil, 1992). The loading obtained with a microsyringe or a hand-held pipettor and micropipette tip, however, is not as efficient as that obtained with the larger 1-ml syringe, possibly due to the lower expulsion pressures achieved when using the Hamilton microsyringe or standard hand-held pipettor.

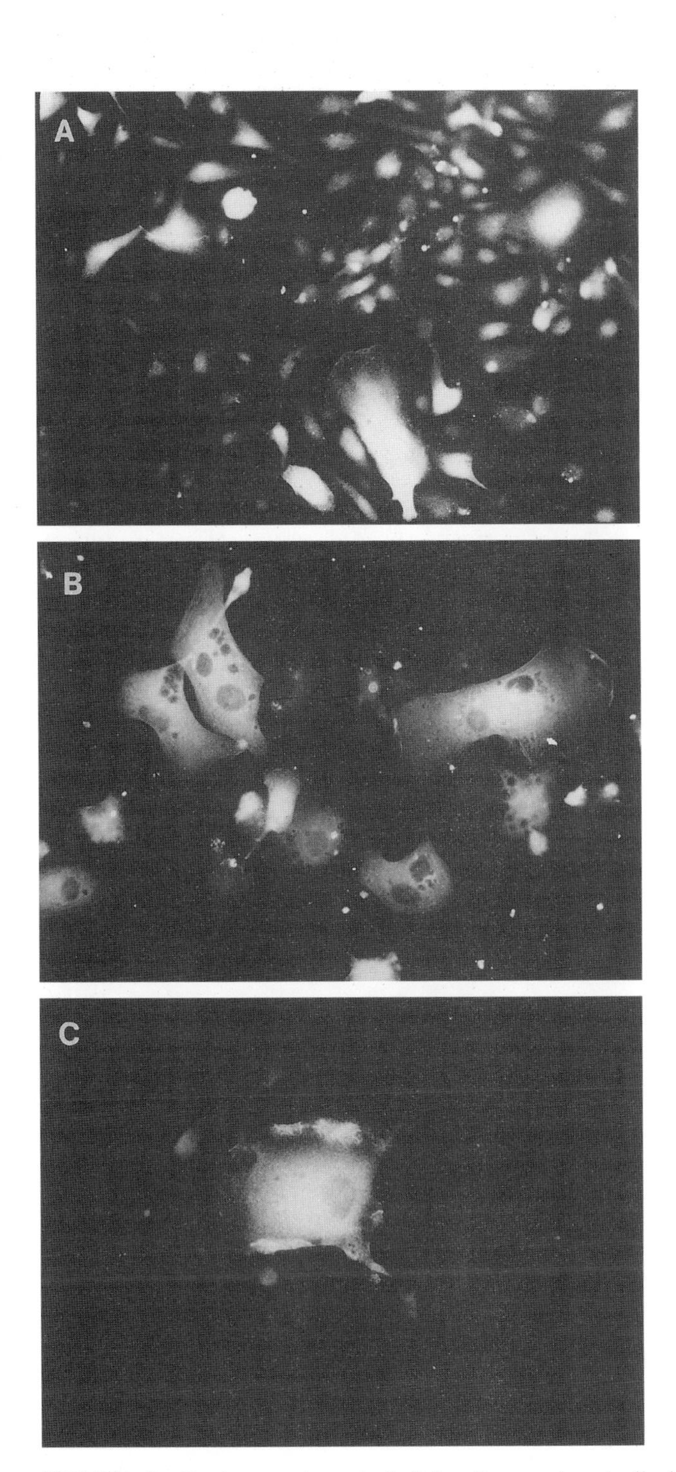

FIGURE 3 Bovine aortic endothelial cells cytoplasmically loaded with (A) FDxLys, (B) rhodamine-conjugated IgG, and (C) plasmid DNA using the automated syringe loader and a loading volume of 1 ml. Cells in (A) were loaded with 10 mg/ml FDxLys using 8 strokes at a pressure of 40 psi. Cells in (B) were loaded with 2 mg/ml rhodamine-conjugated IgG using 12 strokes at a pressure of 50 psi. Cells in (C) were loaded with 200 μg/ml of plasmid DNA (pSVB) using 12 strokes at a pressure of 60 psi, cultured for a further 36 hr, and then immunofluorescently stained with a rabbit polyclonal antibody directed against β-galactosidase.

V. Pitfalls

1. It is very important to maintain the temperature of the cell sample as close to 37°C as possible, before, during, and after syringe loading, as cells do not survive membrane disruptions at room temperature.

2. It is important to watch for excessive pH changes caused by exposure of the bicarbonate-buffered medium to atmospheric air during the procedure as these are potentially harmful to the cells.

REFERENCES

Celis, J. E. (1978) Injection of tRNAs into somatic cells: Search for in vivo systems to assay potential nonsense mutations in somatic cells. *Brookhaven Symp. Biol.* **29,** 178–196.

Clarke, M. S. F., and McNeil, P. L. (1992) Syringe loading introduces macromolecules into living cell cytosol. *J. Cell Sci.* **102,** 533–541.

Felgner, P. L., Gadek, T. R., Holm, M., Roman, R., Chan, H. W., Wenz, M., Northrop, J. P., Ringold, G. M., and Danielsen, M. (1987) Lipofection: A highly efficient, lipid-mediated DNA-transfection procedure. *Proc. Natl. Acad. Sci. USA* **84,** 7413–7417.

Graessmann, A., Graessmann, M., Hoffmann, H., Niebel, J., Brandler, G., and Mueller, N. (1974) Inhibition by interferon of SV40 tumour antigen formation in cells injected with SV40 cRNA transcribed in vitro. *FEBS Lett.* **39,** 249–251.

Knutson, J. C., and Yee, D. (1987) Electroporation: Parameters affecting transfer of DNA into mammalian cells. *Anal. Biochem.* **164,** 44–52.

McNeil, P. L., Murphy, R. F., Lanni, F., and Taylor, D. L. (1984) A method for loading macromolecules into adherent cells. *J. Cell Biol.* **98,** 1556–1564.

McNeil, P. L., and Warder, E. (1987) Glass beads load macromolecules into adherent cells. *J. Cell Sci.* **88,** 669–678.

Sanford, J. C., Klein, T. M., Wolf, E. D., and Allen, N. (1987) Delivery of substances into cells and tissues using a particle bombardment process. *J. Part. Sci. Technol.* **5,** 27–37.

Swanson, J. A., and McNeil, P. L. (1987) Nuclear reassembly excludes large molecules. *Science* **238,** 548–550.

Electroporation of Cells

Stefan Herr, Rainer Pepperkok, Rainer Saffrich, Stefan Wiemann, and Wilhelm Ansorge

I. Introduction

About 10 years ago, a new, easy and versatile technique for the introduction of larger macromolecules into eukaryotic and prokaryotic cells was established (Neumann *et al.*, 1982; Knight, 1981); it is now commonly known as electroporation (Weaver, 1993). It is mainly a physical process, based on the transient permeabilization of cell membranes by pulses of sufficiently high electric fields. The underlying membrane phenomenon, called reversible electrical breakdown (REB) followed by transient pore formation, occurs if the transmembrane potential reaches values of 0.5–1.5 V. Membrane pores are generated and molecules are transported through these pores by diffusion, electrical drift, and electroosmosis. Electroporation seems to be a rather universal process in most natural membranes.

Since its first appearance, the technique has successfully been used in many different applications (Potter, 1988, 1993; Neumann *et al.*, 1989; Chang *et al.*, 1992; Shikegawa and Dower, 1988; Chassy, 1988): transient and stable transfection of bacteria, plant, and mammalian cells with exogenous DNA (electrotransfection); insertion of enzymes, antibodies, biochemical reagents, viruses, and particles into cells; deposition of macromolecules in cell membranes; and electrofusion of whole cells.

As a consequence of all these different applications, a large variety of procedures and protocols exist. To make the most efficient use of the methods, we give general outlines for selection of electroporation conditions and several tested protocols as examples. We concentrate on transfection with DNA because this is the most frequent application.

II. Materials and Instrumentation

Several electroporation devices were developed and are being used (Potter, 1988). In the protocols described here the devices used were the Gene Pulser from Bio-Rad (Cat. No. 165-2977) and a device constructed at EMBL (available on request). Electroporation cuvettes with 0.2-cm and 0.4-cm electrode gaps are from Bio-Rad (Cat. Nos. 165-2088 and 165-2086).

DMEM (Cat. No. 074-02100H), FCS (Cat. No. 011-06290M), trypsin–EDTA (Cat. No. 040-05300H), penicillin–streptomycin (Cat. No. 043-05140H), and L-glutamine (Cat. No. 043-05030H) are obtained from Gibco. Bacto-Peptone (Cat. No. 0118-17-0) and yeast extract (Cat. No. 0127-17-9) are purchased from Difco. All other chemicals are from Merck.

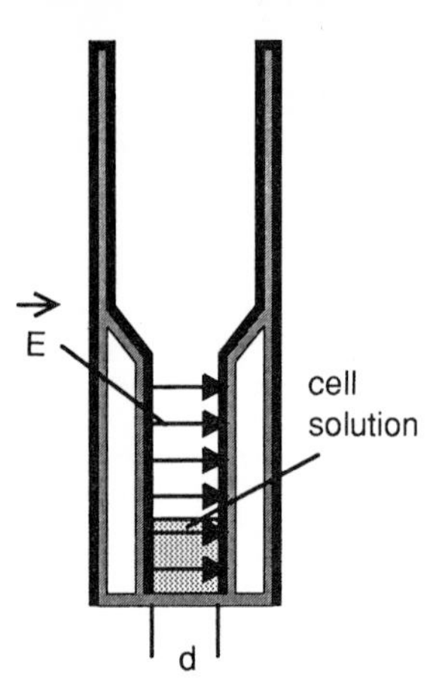

FIGURE 1 Schematic drawing of a typical electroporation cuvette. d, Electrode gap; E, electric field.

Petri dishes (Cat. No. 150350 for 100-mm ϕ and Cat. No. 150288 for 60-mm ϕ, gamma irradiated) for cell culture are from Nunc.

III. Procedures for Electroporation of Eukaryotes and Prokaryotes

A. PARAMETERS AFFECTING EFFICIENCY IN ELECTROPORATION OF MAMMALIAN CELLS

For a given experiment, adjusting the experimental conditions to obtain optimal results is of crucial importance. Important physical parameters are the strength of the applied electric field given by $E = U/d$ and the duration $\tau = R*C$ of the voltage pulses. The voltage U, the electrode distance d of the sample cuvette (Fig. 1), and the capacitance C are controlled by the operator. The resistance R of the electroporation circuit is determined mainly by the conductivity of the solution between electroporation electrodes and, thus, by the biological sample.

Detailed discussion of parameters affecting efficiency in electroporation experiments have been described in detail by Potter (1988, 1993), Neumann *et al.* (1989), Chang *et al.* (1992), Shikegawa and Dower (1988), and Chassy (1988). There are five important parameters to consider in electroporation:

1. *Electrical field (voltage) in the cell chamber:* The voltages used vary from 50 V to several thousand volts. The optimum range depends on the cell type and cell size to be electroporated. If the electrical field is too high, the survival rate of the cells is lowered; if it is too low, efficiency is low.

2. *Duration, form, and number of pulses applied:* The duration of a single electrical pulse is typically varied between a few microseconds and several milliseconds. When low voltages are used usually long pulses are applied, and vice versa, to obtain good results. In most applications the pulse form is exponential (Fig. 2) but square-shaped pulses also have been used successfully (Presse *et al.*, 1988). The number of pulses applied to the cell chamber is usually limited technically to one. More than one pulse (achieved with the EMBL device) may improve transfection efficiency of DNA in mammalian cells. Reports show increased efficiency of electroporation and cell fusion with high-frequency (20–100 kHz) ac pulse trains (Chang, 1989).

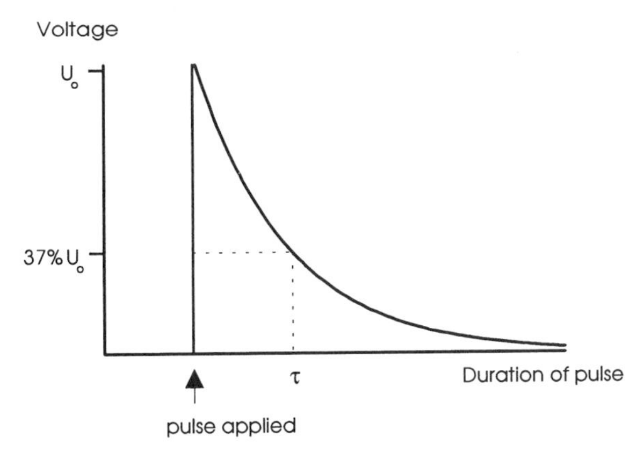

FIGURE 2 Time course of an exponential pulse: the pulse length τ is defined as the time the voltage has decayed to 37% of its initial value.

3. *Concentration of molecules and cells:* Cells are prepared at concentrations of 10^6 to 10^7 per milliliter for mammalian cells and up to 10^{10} to 10^{11} per milliliter for bacterial cells. In our laboratory, typically 40–50 μl of cell solution is used per transfection experiment. DNA concentrations of 5 μg/ml already give good transformation efficiencies. Higher DNA concentrations improve the results and should be used when sufficient amounts of DNA are available. For electroporation of proteins, antibodies and dyes are used at concentrations ranging from 10^{-11} to 10^{-3} *M*.

4. *Culture conditions and electroporation buffer:* Cells are cultured under normal culture conditions. A medium of low ionic strength should be used as buffer solution for electroporation. PBS or HBS is preferred for mammalian cells and pure distilled water or 10% glycerol for bacteria. Successful use of chemical stimulators added to the electroporation buffer has been reported (Satyabhama and Estonia, 1988). Additives increasing cell surface binding of the molecules to be electroporated may be taken into consideration. For the electroporation, cells are kept either on ice or at room temperature. To avoid contamination, sterile working conditions are important for mammalian cells.

5. *Size of molecules to be electroporated:* Successful electroporation of high-molecular-weight DNA (up to 200 kb) has been reported (Belliveau and Travers, 1989). To find suitable electroporation conditions for a given cell type, fluorescently labeled molecules, e.g., FITC–dextran (up to 2,000,000 MW) may be used in electroporation tests.

B. DETERMINATION OF OPTIMAL VOLTAGE FOR ELECTROPORATION

Optimization of parameters for an electroporation experiment is done most easily and rapidly with some test molecules of appropriate size. FITC–dextrans are very convenient for this purpose. They are available in a wide range of molecular weights and are easy to detect and measure.

Solution

PBS (without Ca^{2+} and Mg^{2+}): 8 g NaCl, 0.2 g KCL, 0.2 g KH_2PO_4, 2.16 g $Na_2HPO_4 \cdot 7H_2O$ per liter of double distilled H_2O; adjust to pH 7.3

Steps

1. Prepare cells as described in steps 3 to 8 for, e.g., five electroporation experiments plus one control experiment.

2. Prepare FITC–dextran solution at a concentration of 5 $\mu g/\mu l$ in PBS.

3. Grow cells on 10-cm petri dishes to 70–80% confluence.

4. Remove medium and wash twice with PBS.

5. Add 1 ml of trypsin and incubate until cells detach from the plastic.

6. Add 10 ml of culture medium to stop trypsinization and count cells.

7. Spin down for 10 min at 1000 rpm in a cooled centrifuge at 4°C.

8. Aspirate supernatant and wash cell pellet carefully with cold PBS.

9. Resuspend cell pellet in cold FITC–dextran solution to a final concentration of 10^7 cells/ml.

10. Perform steps 11 to 14 for the five experiments with different voltages in the range 500–1500 V (e.g., 500 V, 750 V, 1000 V, 1250 V, 1500 V). The control sample is not electroporated and only resuspended, as in step 13.

11. Transfer 50 μl of the cell suspension into a precooled cuvette with 0.4-cm electrode distance and apply a single pulse (voltage setting according to step 10, 33 μF with EMBL device, 25 μF with Gene Pulser).

12. Leave transfected cells on ice for 15 min.

13. Resuspend cells in 6-cm plastic dishes containing glass coverslips.

14. Let cells grow for 1 day; fix and stain all cells with Hoechst 33342.

Analysis of the experiments.
Count cells positive for FITC fluorescence in the cytoplasm under a fluorescence microscope in a defined area on the coverslip in relation to all cells in this area. Correct this rate for the number of cells that survived the electroporation using the control experiment. Optimal voltage is determined from a diagram of number of successfully electroporated cells versus voltage. This procedure can also be used to optimize other variables influencing the efficiency of electroporation experiments mentioned above.

C. ELECTROTRANSFECTION OF NIH 3T3 CELLS WITH PSV1 DNA

Highest transfection efficiencies in mammalian cells are usually obtained under electroporation conditions where the cell viability is about 50–70%. Of importance is not only the uptake of DNA into the cells but also the subsequent integration of the DNA into the host genome. Studies show that the topology of the DNA (supercoiled or linear) does not influence the probability of its entering the cell during electroporation, at least not with plasmids (Xie and Tsong, 1993). The fate of the DNA in the cell depends on several factors and determines the resulting transfection efficiencies.

Solution

PBS (without Ca^{2+} and Mg^{2+}): 8 g NaCl, 0.2 g KCL, 0.2 g KH_2PO_4, 2.16 g $Na_2HPO_4 \cdot 7H_2O$ per liter of double-distilled H_2O; adjust to pH 7.3.

Steps

1. Grow cells on 10-cm petri dishes to 70–80% confluence.
2. Remove medium and wash twice with PBS.
3. Add 1 ml of trypsin and incubate until cells detach from the plastic.
4. Add 10 ml of culture medium to stop trypsinization and count cells.
5. Spin down for 10 min at 1000 rpm in a cooled centrifuge at 4°C.
6. Aspirate supernatant and wash cell pellet carefully with cold PBS.
7. Resuspend cell pellet in cold PBS (concentration: 10^7 cells/ml PBS).
8. Add plasmid DNA (final concentration 50 μg/ml) and leave on ice for 5 min.
9. Transfer 50 μl of the suspension into a precooled cuvette with 0.4-cm electrode distance and apply a single pulse (1.1 kV, 33 μF with EMBL device).
10. Leave transfected cells on ice for 15 min.
11. Resuspend cells in 6-cm plastic dishes containing glass coverslips.

Two days after electroporation cells are screened for T-antigen expression by indirect immunofluorescence. Efficiency is expressed as the percentage of T-antigen-positive cells.

D. TRANSFORMATION OF COMPETENT BACTERIA BY ELECTROPORATION

For transformation of bacteria (gram negative and gram positive), electroporation is in many cases the most efficient method. Transformation rates for *Escherichia coli* strains are usually in the range 10^8 to 10^{10} per microgram of plasmid DNA, with optimized parameters for cell preparation and electroporation conditions. Keeping the cells on ice during preparation and throughout the experiment has been shown to increase efficiency.

1. Preparation of Competent Cells

Solutions

1. Tetracycline 5 mg/ml in ethanol.
2. double-distilled H_2O.
3. 10% glycerole (in double distilled H_2O).
4. 2× YT medium: 16 g Bacto-Peptone, 8 g yeast extract, 5 g NaCl in 1 liter double-distilled H_2O.

Steps

1. Take 10 ml of a fresh overnight culture of Xl-1 Blue to inoculate 1 liter of 2× YT medium supplemented with tetracycline (50 μg/ml).
2. Grow bacteria at 37°C; start to measure OD_{660} after 3.5 h. The culture should finish with an OD_{660} of 0.5–1.0.
3. Pour bacteria into four 250-ml Sorvall tubes and leave on ice for 10 min.
4. Spin bacteria down at 4000 g, 4°C, 10 min and decant supernatant.

5. Resuspend pellet in 1 liter ice-cold sterile double-distilled H_2O and spin again at 4000 g, 4°C, 10 min.
6. Repeat steps 4 and 5 twice, once with 500 ml and once with 20 ml ice-cold sterile double-distilled H_2O.
7. Resuspend cells in 2.5 ml ice-cold 10% glycerol, make 40-μl aliquots in Eppendorf tubes, and freeze on dry ice. Store at −70°C for up to 6 months.

2. Transformation

Solution

SOC medium: 2.0% Bacto-Peptone, 0.5% yeast extract, 10.0 m*M* NaCl, 1.0 m*M* $MgCl_2$, 2.5 m*M* KCl, 10.0 m*M* $MgSO_4$, 20.0 m*M* glucose.

Steps

1. Thaw one aliquot of competent cells on ice.

2. The DNA used for the transformation is supercoiled plasmid DNA or cosmid DNA. One microliter of the prepared DNA solution is mixed with the bacteria suspension and incubated on ice for 1 min. The highest transformation efficiency is achieved at a DNA concentration of 250 ng/ml, the highest transformation frequency at 25,000 ng/ml. Usually we use 1 ng of supercoiled plasmid DNA or 50 ng of linear DNA (ligation mix) in 40 μl bacteria suspension.

3. Transfer DNA–bacteria mixture into precooled cuvette with 0.2-cm electrode distance. Make sure that the drop of solution is positioned between the electrodes at the bottom of the cuvette. Apply a single pulse with settings of 12.5 kV/cm, 25 μF, 200 Ω (Gene Pulser, Bio-Rad).

4. Immediately after the pulse add 1 ml cold SOC medium with a pipette to the transformation mixture. Mix and transfer the solution into a 15-ml Falcon tube.

5. Incubate without shaking at 37°C for 1 hr.

6. Plate out on selective agar plates supplemented with the appropriate antibiotic and grow overnight.

3. Results from the Protocol Routinely Used in our Laboratory

Forty microliters of competent Xl-1Blue bacteria are mixed with 1 μl of DNA and electroporated. Calculation of the transformation efficiency gives 10^9 colonies per microgram of supercoiled plasmid DNA. The transformation efficiency with cosmid DNA was much lower, only 3×10^5/μg DNA.

One reason cosmids are transformed less efficiently compared with plasmids is that they are much larger. The cosmid transformed in the experiment was 45 kb, whereas the plasmid was only 5 kb. An order-of-magnitude lower transformation efficiency could already be accounted for by the different molarities of plasmid and cosmid DNA in the solutions. Other reasons are that larger DNAs, in principle, are taken up by bacteria at much lower frequencies; many cosmids contain sequences that cannot establish and replicate in the bacteria strain used; and a host restriction barrier exists. In some cases, the DNA is not clonable in cosmid vectors, and other vectors have to be used.

The advantages of the electrotransformation of bacteria in comparison to other methods are high efficiency (10^8–10^{10} transformants per microgram of supercoiled plasmid DNA); reliable results; speed (competent bacteria are made once, frozen, and kept in the freezer until needed, and the actual transformation takes only seconds); and ease (no elaborate solutions are necessary, compare with Hanahan protocol).

REFERENCES

Belliveau, B. H., and Travers, J. T. (1989) Transformation of *Bacillus cereus* vegetative cells by electroporation. *Appl. Environ. Microbiol.* **55**, 1649–1652.

Chang, D. C. (1989) Cell poration and cell fusion using an oscillating electric field. *Biophys. J.* **56**, 641–652.

Chang, D. C., Chassy, B., Saunders, J. A., and Sowers, A. E. (eds.) (1992) "Handbook of Electroporation and Electrofusion." Academic Press, San Diego.

Chassy, B. M. (1988) Transformation of bacteria by electroporation. *Trends Biotechnol.* **6**, 303–309.

Knight, D. E. (1981) Rendering cells permeable by exposure to high electric fields. *Tech. Cell. Physiol.* **113**, 1–20.

Neumann, E., Schaefer-Ridder, M., Wang, Y., and Hofschneider, P. H. (1982) Gene transfer into mouse myeloma cells by electroporation in high electric fields. *EMBO J.* **7**, 841–845.

Neumann, E., Sowers, A. E., and Jordon, C. A. (eds.) (1989) "Electroporation and Electrofusion in Cell Biology." Plenum, New York.

Potter, H. (1988) Electroporation in biology: Methods, applications and instrumentation. *Anal. Biochem.* **174**, 361–373.

Potter, H. (1993) Application of electroporation in recombinant DNA technology. *In* "Methods in Enzymology" (R. Wu, ed.), Vol. 217, pp. 461–478. Academic Press, San Diego.

Presse, F., Quillet, A., Mir, L., Marchiol-Fournigault, C., Feunteun, J., and Fradelizi, D. (1988) An improved electrotransfection method using square shaped electric impulsion. *Biochem. Biophys. Res. Commun.* **151**, 982–990.

Satyabhama, S., and Estonia, A. L. (1988) Short-term efficient expression of transfected DNA in human hematopoietic cells by electroporation: Definition of parameters and use of chemical stimulators. *DNA* **7**, 203–209.

Shikegawa, K., and Dower, W. J. (1988) Electroporation of eukaryotes and prokaryotes: A general approach to the introduction of macromolecules into cells. *BioTechniques* **6**, 742–751.

Weaver, J. C. (1993) Electroporation: A general phenomenon for manipulating cells and tissue. *J. Cell. Biochem.* **51**, 426–435.

Xie, T., and Tsong, T. Y. (1993) Study of electric field induced DNA transfection. *Biophys. J.* **65**, 1684–1689.

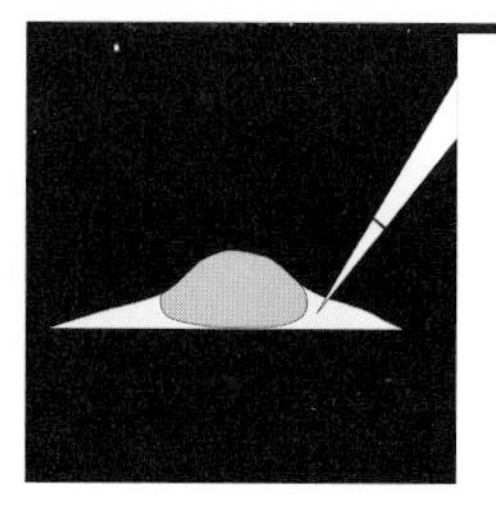

Electroporation of Antibodies into Mammalian Cells

Ratna Chakrabarti and Sheldon M. Schuster

I. Introduction

Electroporation is an efficient technique for the incorporation of macromolecules into mammalian cells (see also article by Stefan Herr, Rainer Pepperkok, Rainer Saffrich, Stefan Weimann, and Wilhelm Ansorge). It has been extensively used for both transient and stable transfection of a wide variety of cell lines (Chu *et al.*, 1987; Toneguzzo *et al.*, 1988; Ohtani *et al.*, 1989). Electroporation has also been found to be very effective in transferring antibodies into mammalian cells (Chakrabarti *et al.*, 1989). Combining the well-established specificity of monoclonal antibody and the potential for obtaining inhibitory antibody even without knowledge of the structure of a target enzyme offers enormous potential. Antibodies have already been proven to be very useful for monitoring functions of proteins in their native environment. For *in vivo* metabolic studies, a sufficient amount of inhibitory antibodies can be incorporated into a large number of both suspension and monolayer cells by electroporation. This opens many new possibilities for the study of metabolic regulation at the level of metabolite flux control, translation, and transcription.

When cells are exposed to a high-voltage electric field for a brief period, a difference in potential across the cell membrane results in the appearance of transient micropores in the membrane (Knight and Scrutton, 1986). This phenomenon allows for the free flow of macromolecules into the cells for a short period, until the membrane integrity is recovered and normal cellular functions are resumed. A potential difference higher than a critical limit for each cell type due to a higher magnitude and length of the electric pulse may lead to irreversible membrane damage and cell death. Optimization of the field strength and duration of the electric pulse for individual cell types is essential to achieve a high-efficiency transfer of the antibodies and a high percentage of cell viability.

Two types of a high-voltage electric pulse can be used for electroporation: square-wave pulse and exponential decay. For a square-wave pulse, the voltage is raised to an amplitude, maintained for a certain length of time, and returned to zero. For exponential decay, a capacitor is charged to a certain voltage and then discharged exponentially. As an exponential pulse is more widely used for electroporation, use of a device that delivers exponential pulses is mentioned in this protocol. Field strength and pulse length are the two major determinants of electroporation efficiency. Field strength can be adjusted by changing the voltage to which the capacitor is charged. Pulse length can be calculated by multiplying capacitance in farads and sample resistance in ohms. Duration of pulse can be adjusted by changing the capacitance or the resistance of the sample.

The resistance of a sample depends largely on the conductivity of the suspension medium. High-ionic-strength media such as phosphate-buffered saline and tissue culture medium offer a lower resistance than Hepes-buffered isotonic sucrose medium and thereby generate a shorter pulse that is less detrimental to cell viability. A medium that resembles the cytosol would facilitate resealing of the pores in the membrane (Michel *et al.*, 1988).

A method will be described that had been successfully used for incorporation of antibodies into a cell line grown in suspension culture (L-51789/D10/Res) and two adherent cell lines: HeLa and a human fibroblast (HT-5).

II. Materials and Instrumentation

Ascites fluid containing monoclonal antibody is collected from hybridoma-injected mice. Ammonium sulfate (Cat. No. A702-500), NaCl (Cat. No. S640-500), KCl (Cat. No. P217-500), sodium phosphate dibasic (Cat. No. S 373-500), potassium phosphate monobasic (Cat. No. P285-500), and sodium bicarbonate (Cat. No. S233) are obtained from Fisher Scientific. Dulbecco's modified Eagle's medium (DMEM) with Hepes (Cat. No. 430-3700EB), Opti-MEM with β-mercaptoethanol (Cat. No. 430-2600EB), antibiotic–antimycotic (Cat. No. 600-5245AE), sodium pyruvate (Cat. No. 320–1360AG), and fetal bovine serum (FBS, Cat. No. 240-6000AG) are purchased from Gibco-BRL. L-Glutamine (Cat. No. G-1517), trypan blue (Cat. No. T-6146), and trypsin–EDTA (Cat. No. T-5775) are from Sigma Chemical Company.

Spectra/pore 3 dialysis tubing (3500 MW cutoff, Cat. No. 132725) is from Spectrum. The Centricon-30 concentrator (Cat. No. 4208) is purchased from Amicon, Inc. Tissue culture flasks (Corning, 75 cm^2, Cat. No. 10-126-41), plastic polystyrene centrifuge tubes (Corning, Cat. No. 05-526A for 15 ml and Cat. No. 05-538-49 for 50 ml), and bottle filters (0.2 μm, Cat. No. 09-740-28E for 150 ml and 09-740-40A) are from Fisher Scientific. Cell-porator Electroporation System I and disposable individually sterilized electroporation chambers (Cat. No. 1600AA) are from Gibco-BRL.

III. Procedures

A. AMMONIUM SULFATE PRECIPITATION OF ASCITES

Solutions

1. *90% Ammonium sulfate:* To make 100 ml, combine 90 ml of saturated $(NH_4)_2SO_4$ and 20 ml of distilled water. Store at 4°C.

2. *Phosphate-buffered saline (PBS):* To make 1 liter, dissolve 8 g of NaCl, 0.2 g of KCl, 1.44 g of Na_2HPO_4, and 0.24 g of KH_2PO_4 to 900 ml of distilled water. Adjust pH to 7.4 with HCl and make up the volume to a liter. Store at 4°C.

Steps

1. Mix 2 ml of ascites and 4 ml of PBS in a centrifuge tube (Nalgene Oak Ridge Fisher Scientific, Cat. No. 05-529C) on ice.

2. Add 6 ml of 90% $(NH_4)_2SO_4$ dropwise and allow it to precipitate for at least 90 min on ice.

3. Centrifuge at 10,000 *g* (10,000 rpm in JA-20 Beckman) for 15 min at 4°C.

4. Decant and discard the supernatant fluid.

5. Resuspend the pellet in 6 ml of PBS.

6. Add 7 ml of 90% $(NH_4)_2SO_4$ dropwise and allow it to precipitate for at least 30 min on ice.

7. Repeat step 3.

8. Decant the supernatant fluid and resuspend the pellet in 2 ml of PBS.

9. Dialyze the suspension in Spectra/pore 3 dialysis tubing against several changes of PBS (2 liters total) at 4°C with constant stirring for 16–18 hr.

10. Remove any precipitate that might appear in the dialyzed antibody solution by centrifugation at 3000 *g* for 5 min at 4°C.

11. Transfer the antibody solution to a concentrator (Centricon-30 with 30,000 molecular weight cutoff).

12. Centrifuge the concentrator in a fixed-angle rotor at 5000 *g* for 30 min at 25°C.

13. Attach the retentate tube to the concentrator. Invert the tube and centrifuge at 3000 *g* for 2 min. Concentrated antibody solution will be collected in the retentate tube. Depending on the protein concentration, a 2-ml sample volume could be concentrated to as low as 25 μl. Store the antibody solution at −20°C in aliquots.

B. SUBCULTURE OF CELLS FOR ELECTROPORATION

Solutions

1. *Glutamine stock solution (100×):* To make 100 ml, dissolve 2.9 g of L-glutamine in 90 ml of DMEM. Filter-sterilize and store at −20°C in aliquots.

2. *0.9% saline:* To make 100 ml, dissolve 900 mg of NaCl in distilled water and make up the volume to 100 ml. Store at room temperature.

3. *Trypan blue stock solution:* To make 100 ml, dissolve 400 mg of trypan blue dye in 0.9% saline. Make up the volume to 100 ml, filter-sterilize, and store at 4°C.

Steps

1. Grow suspension or adherent cells in DMEM containing antibiotic–antimycotic, L-glutamine, and 10% FBS to confluency before the day of electroporation.

2. Wash the adherent cells with sterile PBS and detach them using trypsin–EDTA (5 ml/75-cm² flask) and incubating at 37°C for 10 min or until cells are detached. Hit flasks several times to detach the cells completely.

3. Check the cell viability using trypan blue dye exclusion and count the viable cell number using a hemocytometer.

4. Replate the cells in DMEM/10% FBS in such a way that the cells will grow for two generations and up to 50–70% confluency on the day of electroporation

C. PREPARATION OF CELLS FOR ELECTROPORATION

Steps

1. Trypsinize the monolayer cells using the procedure described earlier.
2. Centrifuge cells at 500 *g* (1500 rpm in Beckman GH 3.8 rotor) for 10 min at 4°C.
3. Aspirate the supernatant fluid without disturbing the pellet.
4. Resuspend cells in 10 ml of Opti-MEM containing antibiotic–antimycotic and 5% FBS.
5. Count cell number using a hemocytometer.
6. Repeat steps 2 and 3.
7. Resuspend cells in Opti-MEM containing 5% FBS at a concentration of 10^7 cells/700 μl. Leave tubes on ice until ready to use.

D. ELECTROPORATION

Steps

Perform all the steps under the tissue culture hood.

1. Thaw an aliquot of antibody solution. Measure the protein concentration using Bio-Rad protein assay reagent (Cat. No. 500-0006, Bio-Rad Laboratories).

2. Transfer aseptically 1–2 mg of antibody into electroporation chambers with lids. The volume of antibody should not exceed 300 μl. If the volume is less than that, make up the volume to 300 μl with Opti-MEM/5% FBS.

3. Transfer 700 μl of cell suspension into the chambers.

4. Invert the chambers several times to mix the cell suspension.

5. Electroporate cells at a brief pulse of 750 V/cm and duration of 0.7–0.9 msec at room temperature. Cell porator settings should be an initial voltage of 300, the resistance switch at low position, and capacitances of 50-μF for suspension cells and 60 μF for adherent cells.

6. Allow the cells to remain in the chamber for 2 min.

7. Gently transfer the contents of the electroporation chamber to a centrifuge tube. Slight foaming of the culture medium may be seen.

8. Add 5 ml of Opti-MEM/10% FBS and mix gently.

9. Centrifuge at 100 *g* (800 rpm in GH 3.8 rotor) for 10 min at room temperature.

10. Aspirate the supernatant and resuspend the pellet in Opti-MEM/10% FBS.

11. Repeat steps 9 and 10 twice.

12. Resuspend the cells in DMEM/10% FBS. Count the number of viable cells using trypan blue.

13. Replate the cells in tissue culture flasks at a density of 1×10^6 cells/5 ml.

14. Culture cells at 37°C in a humidified atmosphere of 10% CO_2 for 24 hr.

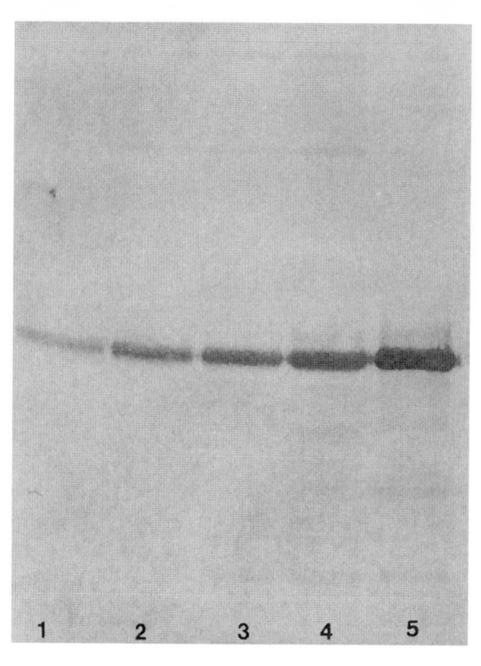

FIGURE 1 Western blot analysis of the electroporated antibody. Extracts from HT-5 cells (5×10^5 cells), electroporated with a monoclonal antibody (Mab) 2B4, were loaded per well at each time point. Lane 5: Mab 2B4 (2 μg), lanes 1–4: cell extracts at 72, 48, 24, and 0 hr, respectively, after electroporation.

IV. Comments

The efficiency of antibody incorporation into the cells electroporated using this method can be determined several ways. The concentration of antibody can be detected by Western blotting of the cell extracts, using an anti-mouse antibody for monoclonal and anti-rabbit antibody for polyclonal antibody (Fig. 1), and quantitated by densitometry. Electroporation efficiency can also be determined by flow cytometry. Fluorescein isothiocyanate (FITC)-labeled antibody can be used for electroporation, and the percentage of fluorescent cells can be determined with a fluorescence-activated cell sorter.

Use of cells at their proper growth phase is critical for electroporation. To achieve a higher percentage of cell viability and a higher efficiency of antibody incorporation, cells at early log phase should be used. When exponentially growing cells are used they resume their normal growth immediately after electroporation (Chakrabarti *et al.*, 1989). The cell concentration is also an important criterion for efficient electroporation. Too many or too few cells can significantly alter the efficiency. A cell suspension volume ranging from 500 μl to 1 ml containing $1-2 \times 10^7$ cells/ml, depending on the cell size, can be used without compromising electroporation efficiency.

The concentration of antibody in the electroporation medium is directly proportional to the amount of antibody transferred into the cells. A balance should be maintained between the concentration of antibody and the number of cells used. For a lower antibody concentration a smaller number of cells should be used. When using this protocol, the structural and functional integrity of the antibody transferred remains intact for 72 hr after electroporation (see Fig. 1).

The electroporation conditions and parameters described here were optimized for a mouse lymphoma cell line (L5178YD10/R) that grows in suspension and two adherent cell lines, HeLa and a human fibroblast (HT-5). Approximately 80–90% cell viability and 85–95% electroporation efficiency were achieved using the above conditions and parameters. Optimum electroporation parameters for any other cell types should be experimentally determined before the actual experiment. Electroporation using a lower voltage (450–800 V/cm) and a longer pulse duration (3–9 msec) may increase the transfer efficiency but at the expense of cell viability. Lower voltage and shorter pulse length (0.7–0.9 msec) were found to be more effective for a higher percentage of cell viability and antibody incorporation.

The choice of electroporation medium and temperature is also important for this technique. A reduced serum-containing medium, Opti-MEM/5%FBS, was found to be most suitable for the cell types chosen for electroporation. Although prechilled cells were used to counteract the local heating by electric pulse, room temperature electroporation was more favorable than 4°C for the rapid recovery of the electroporated cells (Chakrabarti *et al.*, 1989; Chu *et al.*, 1987). At lower temperatures, membrane pores tend to stay open longer (Stopper *et al.*, 1987) which may have impacts on cell survival.

V. Pitfalls

1. A relatively higher concentration of antibody is required for efficient electroporation. When the antibody is limiting, the transfer efficiency also declines significantly.

2. Electroporated cells can be used only for short-term metabolic studies, as the intracellular antibody concentration remained intact only for 72 hr.

3. The electroporation parameters used in this protocol are suitable for transferring antibodies to the cytoplasm but may not be for incorporating antibodies into the nucleus for studies on the functions of nuclear proteins. Optimization of the electrical parameters is essential for such application.

REFERENCES

Chakrabarti, R., Wylie, D. E., and Schuster, S. M. (1989) Transfer of monoclonal antibodies into mammalian cells by electroporation. *J. Biol. Chem.* **264**, 15494–15500.

Chu, G., Hayakawa, H., and Berg, P. (1987) Electroporation for the efficient transfection of mammalian cells with DNA. *Nucleic Acids Res.* **15**, 1311–1326.

Knight, D. E., and Scrutton, M. C. (1986) Gaining access to the cytosol: The technique and some applications of electropermeabilization. *Biochem. J.* **234**, 497–506.

Michel, M. R., Elgizoli, M., Koblet, H., and Kempf, C. (1988) Diffusion loading conditions determines recovery of protein synthesis in electroporated P3X63Ag8 cells. *Experientia* **44**, 199–203.

Ohtani, K., Nakamura, M., Saito, S. Nagata, K., Sugamura, K., and Hinuma, Y. (1989) Electroporation: Application to human lymphoid cell lines for stable introduction of a transactivator gene of human T-cell leukemia virus type I. *Nucleic Acids Res.* **17**, 1589–1604.

Stopper, H., Jones, H., and Zimmerman, U. (1987) Large scale transfection of mouse L-cells by electropermeabilization. *Biochim. Biophys. Acta* **949**, 318–324.

Toneguzzo, F., Keating, A., Glynn, S., and McDonald, K. (1988) Electric field-mediated gene transfer: Characterization of DNA transfer and patterns of integration in lymphoid cells. *Nucleic Acids Res.* **16**, 5515–5532.

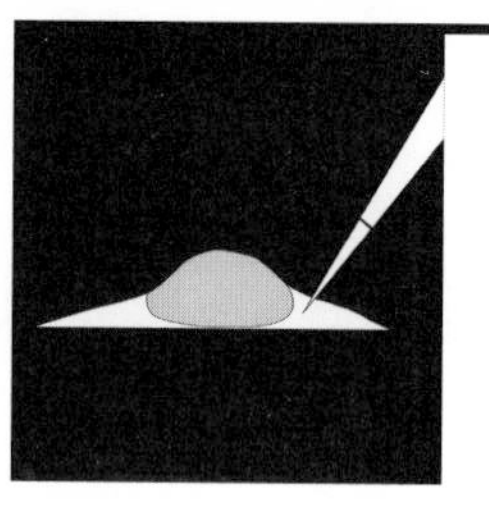

Virus (Sendai Virus Envelopes)-Mediated Gene Transfer

Yasufumi Kaneda

I. Introduction

Several problems are involved in transferring DNA into cells and obtaining efficient expression of genes. Among these problems is the direct introduction of DNA into the cytoplasm without degradation. Although cells generally take up exogenous macromolecules by endocytosis, such endocytosed molecules tend to be degraded in the endosome or lysosome. In this aspect, we focused our efforts on direct introduction of macromolecules into the cytoplasm through cell fusion mediated by Sendai virus [hemagglutinating virus of Japan (HVJ)]. DNA encapsulated in liposomes was successfully introduced into cells by making use of the fusion activity of HVJ (Kaneda *et al.,* 1987). Another problem is efficient delivery of DNA into the nucleus, even in nondividing cells. We found that cointroduction of DNA with nuclear proteins facilitates nuclear migration of the DNA and enhances its expression in animal organs (Kaneda *et al.,* 1989a). A method for delivering DNA with nuclear protein by HVJ-mediated cell fusion (HVJ–liposomes) has been developed (Fig. 1). In this article, I introduce the technique in detail.

II. Materials and Instrumentation

Chromatographically pure bovine brain phosphatidylserine–sodium salt (PS, Cat. No. 83032L, Avanti Polar Lipids Inc., or Cat. No. P-5660, Sigma) and cholesterol (Chol, Cat. No. C-8667, Sigma) were stored at −20°C. Egg yolk phosphatidylcholine (PC, Cat. No. P-2772 Sigma) dissolved in chloroform was divided into 48-mg aliquots into 13-cm-long glass tubes (Pyrex 15, Iwaki Glass Co. Ltd.) and stored at −20°C.

Tetrahydrofuran (TF, Cat. No. 331-25, Nakarai) was divided into 50-ml aliquots in colored glass bottles and stored at −70°C in nitrogen gas. Polypeptone (pancreatic digest of casein, Cat. No. 394-00115), EDTA–3Na (Cat. No. 342-01875), sucrose (Cat. No. 193-07921), K_2HPO_4 (Cat. No. 167-04305), and KH_2PO_4 (Cat. No. 166-04255), and diethyl ether (Cat. No. 055-01135) were obtained from Wako. Trizma base (Cat. No. T-1503) was from Sigma. NaCl (Cat. No. 313-20), KCl (Cat. No. 285-14), and $CaCl_2$ (Cat. No. 06729) were from Nakarai.

Conical tubes (15 ml, Corning 2530, Iwaki Glass, and 50 ml, Falcon 2010, Becton-Dickinson), centrifuge tubes (35 ml, Kurabo Co. Ltd.), and ultracentrifuge tubes (16 PA tube, Cat. No. 332563, Hitachi) were purchased.

For preparing liposomes, glass tubes (24-mm caliber and 12 cm long) were custom-made (Fujiston 24/40, Iwaki Glass Co. Ltd.). The fresh tubes were immersed

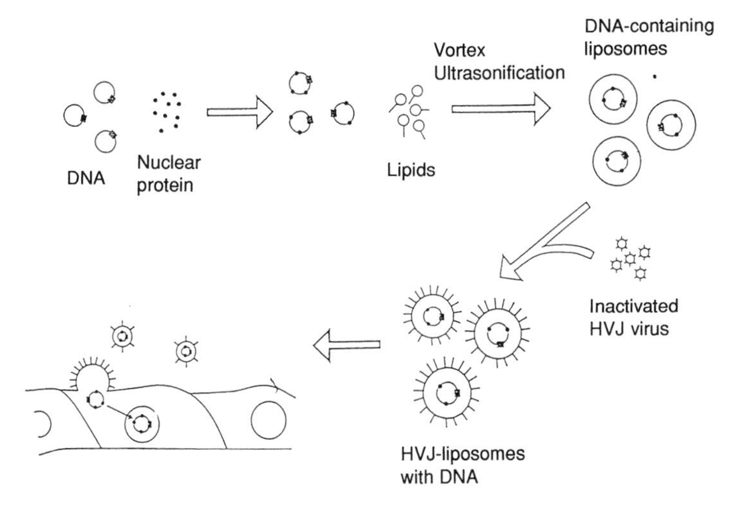

FIGURE 1 Procedure for gene transfer using HVJ–liposomes. DNA and nuclear protein (HMG-1) are enclosed in liposomes by vortexing and sonication, and the liposomes are treated with HVJ (Sendai virus). The resulting HVJ–liposomes deliver the DNA–HMG-1 complex into the cytoplasm, and the complex migrates rapidly into the nucleus.

in saturated KOH–ethanol solution for 24 hr, rinsed with distilled water, and heated at 180°C for 2 hr before use.

A rotary evaporator (Type SR-650, Tokyo Rikakikai Inc.), vacuum pump with pressure gauge (Type Asp-13, Iwaki Glass Co. Ltd.), bath-type sonicator (Ultrasonic Cleaner UT-51N, Sharp Inc.), water bath (Thermominder Jr 80, TAITEC), water bath shaker (Thermominder, TAITEC), photometer (Spectrophotometer DU-68, Beckman Instruments), low-speed centrifuge (05PR-22, Hitachi), centrifuge with JA-20 rotor (J2-HS, Beckman Instruments), and ultracentrifuge with RPS-27 rotor (55P-72, Hitachi) were used. For inactivation of HVJ, an ultraviolet irradiator (a box with two ultraviolet lamps) was fabricated.

III. Procedures

A. PREPARATION OF HVJ IN EGGS

Solutions

1. *Polypeptone solution:* 1% Polypeptone, 0.2% NaCl, pH 7.2. To make 500 ml, solubilize 5 g of polypeptone and 1 g of NaCl in distilled water, adjust pH to 7.2 by adding 1 *M* NaOH, and bring to a total volume of 500 ml with distilled water. Sterilize by autoclaving and store at 4°C.

2. *Balanced salt solution (BSS):* 137 m*M* NaCl, 5.4 m*M* KCl, 10 m*M* Tris–HCl, pH 7.6. Solubilize 8 g of NaCl, 0.4 g of KCl, and 1.21 g of Trizma base in distilled water, adjust pH to 7.6 with 1 *M* HCl, and bring to a total volume of 1 liter with distilled water. Sterilize by autoclaving and store at 4°C.

3. *Seed of HVJ:* Store 100-μl aliquots of the best seed of HVJ (Z strain) in 10% DMSO in liquid nitrogen.

Steps

1. Rapidly thaw the seed and dilute to 1000 times with polypeptone solution. The diluted seed should be kept at 4°C before proceeding to the next step.

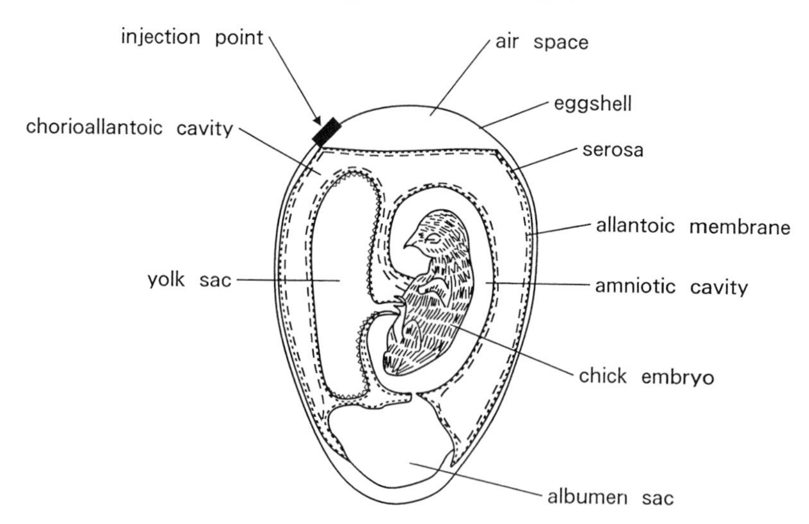

FIGURE 2 Site of injection of HVJ seed is marked on the embryonated chick egg, about 0.5 mm above the chorioallantoic membrane.

2. Observe embryonated eggs under illumination in a dark room, and mark an injection point about 0.5 mm above the chrioallantoic membrane (Fig. 2). Disinfect the eggs with tincture of iodine, and puncture at the point marked.

3. Inject 0.1 ml of the diluted seed into each egg using a 1-ml disposable syringe with a 26-gauge needle. The needle should be inserted vertically so as to stab the chorioallantoic membrane.

4. After inoculation of the seed, cove the puncture site on the egg with melted paraffin. Then, incubate the eggs for 4 days at 35.5°C in sufficient moisture.

5. Chill the eggs at 4°C for more than 6 hr before harvesting the virus.

6. Partially remove the egg shell, and transfer the chorioallantoic fluid to an autoclaved bottle using a 10-ml syringe with an 18-gauge needle. The fluid should be kept at 4°C to avoid freezing. The virus is stable in the fluid for at least 3 months.

Steps 2, 3, and 6 can be carried out at room temperature.

B. PURIFICATION OF HVJ FROM CHORIOALLANTOIC FLUID

Solution

1. *BSS:* Prepare as described above.

Steps

1. Pour 200 ml of the fluid into four 50-ml disposable conical tubes, and rotate at 3000 rpm (1000 *g*) for 10 min at 4°C in a low-speed centrifuge.

2. Then, divide the supernatant between six tubes (Sorvall SS 34), and centrifuge at 15,000 rpm (27,000 *g*) for 30 min at 4°C.

3. Add about 5 ml of BSS to the pellet in one of the tubes, and keep the materials at 4°C overnight.

4. Gently suspend the pellets, collect in two tubes, and centrifuge as described

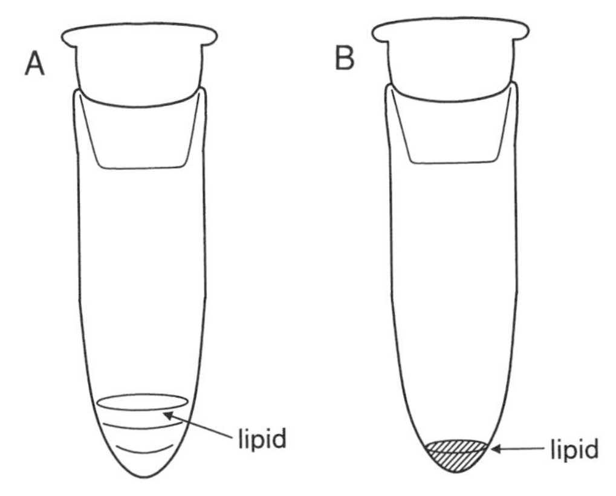

FIGURE 3 Appropriate (A) and inappropriate (B) lipid mixtures for liposome formation.

in step 2. Keep the resultant pellet in each tube at 4°C in 5 ml of BSS for more than 8 hr.

5. Gently suspend the pellets and rotate at 3000 rpm in a low-speed centrifuge.

6. Transfer the supernatant to an aseptic tube, and store at 4°C.

7. Determine virus titer by measuring the absorbance at 540 nm of the 10-times-diluted supernatant using a photometer. An optical density at 540 nm corresponds to 15,000 hemagglutinating units (HAU), which is well correlated with fusion activity. The supernatant prepared as described usually contain 30,000 HAU/ml. An aseptically prepared virus solution maintains the fusion activity for 3 weeks. Note that the virus should never be frozen.

C. PREPARATION OF LIPID MIXTURE

Solution

10 mM potassium phosphate buffer: Solubilize 0.136 g of KH_2PO_4 in 100 ml distilled water and 0.174 g of K_2HPO_4 in 100 ml distilled water. Adjust pH to 6.8 by mixing 51 ml of KH_2PO_4 solution with 49 ml of K_2HPO_4 solution. Sterilize by autoclaving and store at room temperature.

Steps

1. Remove chloroform in PC solution was removed by applying nitrogen gas flow. Dissolve PC (48 mg) again in 1 ml TF. Also dissolve Chol (20 mg) in 1 ml TF. Dissolve PS (10 mg) in 0.1 ml pottasium phosphate buffer–0.9 ml TF.

2. Mix PS, PC, and Chol in a glass tube at a weight ratio of 1:4.8:2, and add 0.9 ml of TF to the mixture.

3. Divide the lipid solution of 0.5 ml into aliquots in seven glass tubes. Each tube contains 10 mg of lipids. Keep the tubes at −20°C in nitrogen gas before evaporation. The lipid solution should be evaporated as soon as possible.

4. Connect the tube to a rotary evaporator. The tube should be immersed in a water bath at the tip. Set the water bath at a temperature of 45°C and the rotator dial of the rotator at 6.

5. Evaporate the organic solvent in a rotary evaporator under vacuum initially set at 400 mm Hg. The lipids usually dry up after about 10 min. Lipids appropriate for liposome preparation are those that adhere to the inside of the tube in a thin layer (Fig. 3a). Those that accumulate at the bottom of the tubes are inappropriate (Fig. 3b).

6. The lipids can be stored, after evaporation, at −20°C in nitrogen gas for 1 week.

D. PREPARATION OF DNA-ENCLOSED LIPOSOMES

Solutions

1. *BSS:* Prepare as described above.

2. *Plasmid DNA:* Purify plasmid DNAs by equilibrium centrifugation in cesium chloride containing ethidium bromide. Dissolve the preparations in 10 m*M* Tris–HCl, pH 8.0, 0.1 m*M* EDTA (final concentration of DNA was 2 mg/ml), and store at −20°C.

3. *HMG-1:* We usually purify nonhistone chromosomal protein, high-mobility group 1 (HMG-1), from calf thymus. Although HMG-1 is a very important material for *in vivo* gene transfer, the procedure for preparing the protein is not described here in detail. Briefly, mince approximately 1 kg of calf thymus and homogenize as described elsewhere (Goodwin *et al.*, 1975). Then, apply the 2% trichloroacetic acid-soluble, acetone-precipitable nuclear extract rich in HMG proteins to a cation-exchange column containing CM-Sephadex C-25 equillibrated with 7.5 m*M* sodium borate buffer (pH 9.0). Fractionate the 0.2 *M* NaCl eluate, and concentrate the fractions enriched in HMG-1 by acetone precipitation. Dissolve the preparation in BSS at a concentration of 1.3 mg/ml, divide into 1-ml aliquots in autoclaved, capped tubes, and store at −70°C. It is not necessary to remove the contaminants of HMG-2 from HMG-1. About 30 mg protein is usually obtained from 1 kg calf thymus. Recombinant rat HMG-1 protein prepared in the baculovirus system was also applicable.

Steps

1. Mix plasmid DNA (200 μg) with 50 μl (65 μg) HMG-1 in a nuclease-free capped tube. Adjust the volume in one tube to 200 μl with BSS. Incubate the mixture in a water bath at 20°C for 1 hr.

2. Add the DNA–HMG-1 solution to a lipid mixture in the glass tube prepared as described above, and agitate intensely by vortexing for 30 sec. Allow the tube to stand in a 37°C water bath for 30 sec. Repeat this vortexing–incubation cycle eight times.

3. Sonicate the glass tube for 3–5 sec in a bath-type sonicator to prepare unilamellar liposomes, and agitate for 30 sec by vortexing. Add 0.3 ml of BSS (0.5 ml in total) to the tube, and incubate the liposome solution at 37°C with shaking (120/min) in a water bath shaker. Leave the tube on ice. With this method, up to 20 kb of plasmid DNA is enclosed at the ratio of 10–30%.

E. PREPARATION OF HVJ–LIPOSOMES

Solutions

1. *BSS:* Prepare as described above.

2. *Sucrose solutions:* To prepare 30% (w/v), 40% (w/v), and 60% (w/v) sucrose solutions, solubilize 150, 200, and 300 g of sucrose in BSS, respectively. Bring to a total volume of 500 ml. Sterilize by autoclaving and store at 4°C.

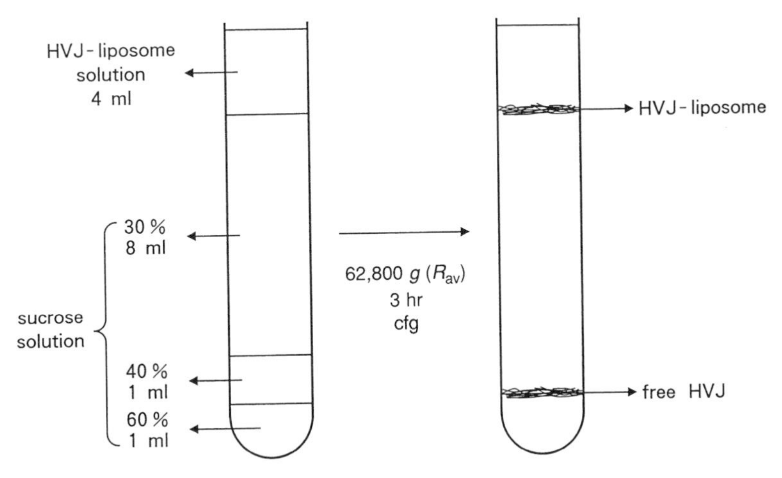

FIGURE 4 Sucrose density gradient is used to separate HVJ–liposomes from free HVJ.

Steps

1. Place 1.5 ml of purified HVJ (30,000 HAU/ml) solution in a petri dish (10 cm in diameter) and inactivate with ultraviolet irradiation (100 ergs/mm^2/sec) for 3 min (Okada and Tadokoro, 1962). Warm the ultraviolet irradiator for at least 5 min before use. Inactivated virus can be kept on ice, but should be used in 1 hr.

2. Add 1 ml of inactivated HVJ (30,000 HAU) to 0.5 ml liposome solution, and chill the mixture on ice for 10 min. Then, add 2.5 ml of cold BSS to HVJ-liposome solution (4 ml in total), and incubate the sample at 37°C for 1 hr with shaking (120/min) in a water bath.

3. During the incubation, construct sucrose density gradients. Pour 1 ml of 60% sucrose solution into an autoclaved ultracentrifuge tube. Then, add 1 ml of 40% sucrose solution, and overlay with 8 ml of 30% sucrose solution.

4. Add 4 ml of HVJ–liposome solution to the sucrose density gradient, and centrifuge for 3 hr at 22,000 rpm (62,800 *g*) at 4°C.

5. After spinning, HVJ–liposomes were visualized in a layer between BSS and 30% sucrose solution, whereas free HVJ sediments between 40% and 60% sucrose solutions (Fig. 4). When liposomes do not form, lipids float in a top layer.

6. Carefully collect HVJ–liposomes. They can be stored for 1 day at 4°C, but should be used for experiments as soon as possible.

F. GENE TRANSFER BY HVJ–LIPOSOMES

1. Transfer of DNA into Cells in Suspension

Solutions

1. *1 M $CaCl_2$:* Solubilize 11.1 g of $CaCl_2$ in 100 ml distilled water, sterilize by autoclaving, and store at 4°C.

2. *BSS with 2 mM $CaCl_2$:* Prepare 500 ml of BSS as described above, sterilize by autoclaving, and add 1 ml of sterilized 1 *M* $CaCl_2$ after the temperature is reduced below 60°C.

Steps

1. Collect suspension cell lines or cells detached from the dishes by trypsinization in a 15-ml conical tube and wash with BSS containing 2 m*M* $CaCl_2$ three times.

2. Count the number of cells; more than 10^6 cells per tube should be used for fusion with HVJ–liposomes.

3. Suspend the cells in 1 ml of HVJ–liposome solution, and add 2 μl of 1 *M* $CaCl_2$ (2 m*M* at the final concentration) to the suspension.

4. Chill the suspension on ice for 5 min, then incubate for 30–60 min with shaking (120/min) in a water bath.

5. After incubation, add fresh medium containing serum to the cell suspension, and centrifuge at 1500 rpm for 5 min in a low-speed centrifuge.

6. Suspend the cells in their culture medium containing serum, and inoculate into appropriate dishes.

2. Transfer of DNA into Cells in Monolayer

Steps

1. Wash monolayers of the cells three times with BSS containing 2 m*M* $CaCl_2$.

2. Add 3 ml of HVJ–liposome solution and 6 μl of 1 *M* $CaCl_2$ (2 m*M* at the final concentration) to the 100-mm petri dish. Incubate the cells first on ice for 5 min and then at 37°C for 30–120 min.

3. Observe the cells in a phase-contrast microscope every 30 min. If the cells seem to be damaged, remove the HVJ–liposome solution, and add fresh complete medium.

3. Gene Transfer *in Vivo* by HVJ–Liposomes

Solution

HVJ–liposomes with 2 mM $CaCl_2$: Add 6 μl of 1 *M* $CaCl_2$ to 3 ml of HVJ–liposomes just before injection.

Steps

1. Chill HVJ–liposome suspension containing 2 m*M* $CaCl_2$ on ice before use.

2. Anesthetize rats (Wistar–Kyoto or Sprague–Dawley, 6–8 weeks old) by ether and subject to abdominal (for liver and kidney) or neck (for carotid artery) surgery.

3. To introduce DNA into rat liver, inject 3 ml of HVJ–liposome solution into the portal vein using a 5-ml syringe with a butterfly-shaped needle (Kaneda *et al.*, 1989a,b) or directly into the liver under the perisplanchnic membrane using a 5-ml syringe with a 27-gauge needle (Kato *et al.*, 1991; Tomita *et al.*, 1992). For gene transfer into rat kidney, inject 1 ml of HVJ–liposome solution into the renal artery (Tomita *et al.*, 1992; Isaka *et al.*, 1993). For gene transfer into rat carotid artery, fill a lumen of a segment of the artery with 0.5 ml HVJ–liposome complex for 20 min at room temperature using a cannula (Morishita *et al.*, 1993b). We succeeded in transferring genes into other organs (mouse testis, mouse skeletal muscle, rat spleen, rat and dog cardiac muscle, etc.) by the same method.

4. After delivery, close the wound. The viability of animals treated with HVJ–liposomes is greater than 80%.

IV. Comments

HVJ–liposomes are applicable for gene transfer to all cells but lymphocytes. Progress in the use of this method has resulted in delivery of antisense oligonucleotides into the nuclei of cells *in vitro* and *in vivo*, where the antisense oligonucleotides are remarkably stable (more than 2 weeks), with long-term suppression of expression of the corresponding gene (Morishita *et al.*, 1993a). In terms of the biological safety of HVJ, although mice suffer from severe pneumonia, the UV-inactivated virus is harmless. The virus is treated with detergent, heat, and UV irradiation.

V. Pitfalls

If HVJ–liposomes do not work, check the following points.

1. Check the fusion activity of HVJ by cell–cell fusion (Okada and Tadokoro, 1962). Do not propagate the virus using harvested chorioallantoic fluid in succession. Make aliquots of the best seed. Do not freeze the purified virus.
2. Sharpen your skill in preparation of the lipid mixture. Use lipids (especially phosphatidylserine–sodium salt) described above. In a good lipid mixture, the inner surface of the glass tube is covered with a film of lipids after evaporation, whereas lipids precipitate to the bottom of the tube in inappropriate mixtures.
3. Cointroduce DNA with HMG-1, especially for gene transfer *in vivo*.

REFERENCES

Goodwin, G. H., Nicolas, R. H., and Johns, E. W. (1975) An improved large scale fractionation of high mobility group non-histone chromatin proteins. *Biochim. Biophys. Acta* **405**, 280–291.

Isaka, Y., Fujiwara, Y., Ueda, N., Kaneda, Y., Kamada, T., and Imai, E. (1993) Glomerulosclerosis induced by *in vivo* transfection with TGF-beta or PDGF gene into rat kidney. *J. Clin. Invest.* **92**, 2597–2601.

Kaneda, Y., Iwai, K., and Uchida, T. (1989a) Increased expression of DNA cointroduced with nuclear protein in adult rat liver. *Science* **243**, 375–379.

Kaneda, Y., Iwai, K., and Uchida, T. (1989b) Introduction and expression of the human insulin gene in adult rat liver. *J. Biol. Chem.* **264**, 12126–12129.

Kaneda, Y., Uchida, T., Kim, J., Ishiura, M., and Okada, Y. (1987) The improved efficient method for introducing macromolecules into cells using HVJ (Sendai virus) liposomes with gangliosides. *Exp. Cell Res.* **173**, p56–69.

Kato, K., Nakanishi, M., Kaneda, Y., Uchida, T., and Okada, Y. (1991) Expression of hepatitis B virus surface antigen in adult rat liver. *J. Biol. Chem.* **266**, 3361–3364.

Morishita, R., Gibbons, G., Ellison, E., Nakajima, M., Zhang, L., Kaneda, Y., Ogihara, T., and Dzau, V. (1993a) Intraluminal molecular delivery of antisense CDC2 kinase and PCNA oligonucleotide prevent restenosis after angioplasty. *Proc. Natl. Acad. Sci. (USA)* **90**, 8474–8478.

Morishita, R., Gibbons, G., Kaneda, Y., Ogihara, T., and Dzau, V. (1993b) Novel and effective gene transfer technique for study of vascular renin angiotensin system. *J. Clin. Invest.* **91**, 2580–2585.

Okada, Y., and Tadokoro, J. (1962) Analysis of giant polynuclear cell formation caused by HVJ virus from Ehrlich's ascites tumor cells. *Exp. Cell Res.* **26**, 98–128.

Tomita, N., Higaki, J., Morishita, R., Kato, K., Kaneda, Y., and Ogihara, T. (1992) Direct in vivo gene introduction into rat kidney. *Biochem. Biophys. Res. Commun.* **186**, 129–134.

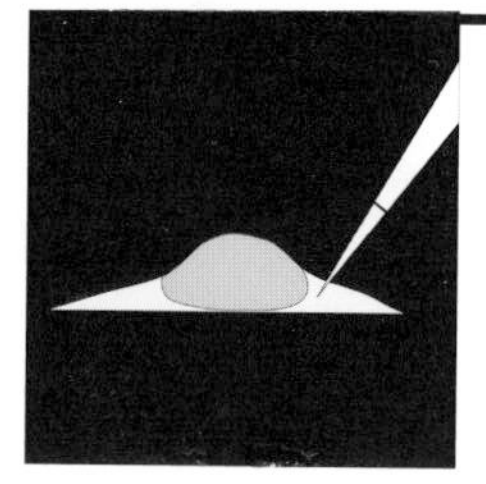

Liposomes in Drug Targeting

Gregory Gregoriadis

I. Introduction

Liposomes are vesicles consisting of one or more concentric bilayers alternating with aqueous compartments (Fig. 1) (Gregoriadis, 1993). Bilayers are usually made up of phospholipids, although other amphiphiles such as nonionic surfactants can also be employed for their construction. Depending on the nature of the amphiphile, bilayers can be in a "fluid" or "rigid" state at ambient temperature, T_a. The former state is achieved with amphiphiles that have a gel–liquid crystalline transition temperature, T_c (the temperature at which the fatty acid chains melt), below the T_a, whereas the latter requires amphiphiles with a T_c above T_a. Because of their ability to incorporate water-soluble and lipid-soluble molecules into their aqueous and lipid phase, respectively, liposomes have been used since 1970 (Gregoriadis and Ryman, 1992) as a means of delivering a great variety of pharmacologically active agents to specific sites in the body in need of pharmacological intervention. In this way, many of the problems associated with direct drug use (e.g., toxicity as a result of indiscriminate drug action, premature drug inactivation or excretion, and inability of drugs to reach the target intracellularly) can be circumvented. Applications in therapeutic and preventive medicine, both in experimental animals and clinically, include antimicrobial and cancer therapy, vaccines, metal detoxification, gene therapy, enzyme or hormone therapy, and blood transfusion (by employing hemoglobin-containing liposomes as a blood surrogate) (Gregoriadis, 1988a, 1993). Recently, two injectable liposome-based products (AmBisome and Amphocyl for the treatment of systemic fungal disease) have been licensed in Europe. Many more products for topical use, mostly cosmetics, have been available since 1986 (Gregoriadis, 1994). Liposomes have been used *in vivo* by every conceivable route, including intravenous, intramuscular, subcutaneous, intrathecal, intratracheal, oral, and topical (skin and a variety of mucosal tissues) routes (Gregoriadis, 1988a).

Much of the work with drug-containing liposomes in the last two decades has dealt with ways to control their fate and behavior and, thus, optimize their pharmacological action (Gregoriadis, 1988a). Such tailoring of liposomes depends on the route of administration (i.e., ultimately the biological milieu interposed between the site of injection and the site of action), the drug they carry, and the intended target. For instance, after intravenous injection liposomes can be destabilized and eventually disintegrated by high-density lipoproteins, with release of entrapped drugs into the circulation. Now this can largely be prevented by the incorporation of cholesterol into the bilayer structure and/or the use of phosphopilids with a T_c above T_a. Moreover, the rate of removal of liposomes from the circulation by the reticuloendothelial system (RES, mostly the fixed macrophages of the liver and spleen) can be

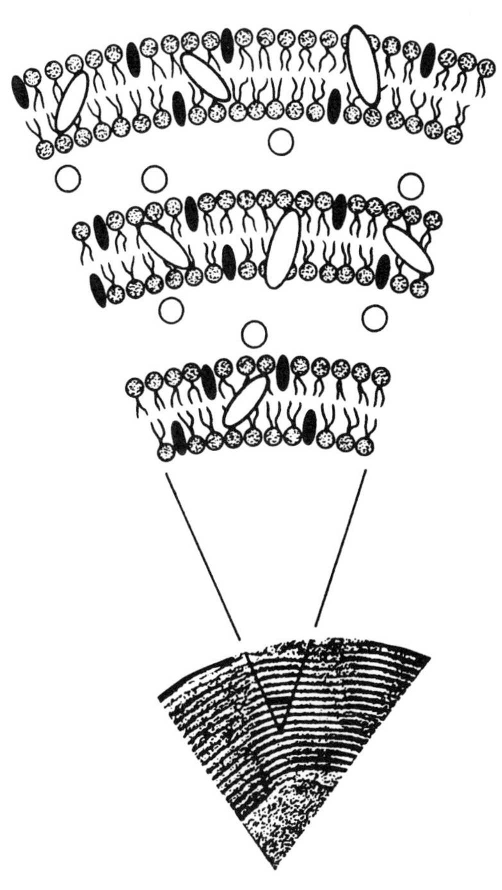

FIGURE 1 A section of an electron micrograph of a negatively stained multilamellar liposome showing lipid bilayers alternating with electron-opaque aqueous channels. Three of these bilayers are enlarged. Polar heads of phospholipids face the water phase and acyl chains form the hydrophobic regions of the leaflet. Open circles denote drugs entrapped in the aqueous channels. Oblong shapes are cholesterol (filled) and membrane-soluble drugs (open) sandwiched between phospholipid molecules. Liposomes can very in size from about 20 nm (small unilamellar vesicles, SUVs) to several micrometers in diameter. The latter can have one (large unilamellar vesicles, LUVs) or more (multilamellar vesicles, MLVs) bilayers. Depending on the methodology and the type of drug, entrapment values can vary from less than 1% to 100% of the drug used. (Reprinted, with permission, from Gregoriadis (1994).)

controlled by adjusting vesicle size and surface charge or surface hydrophilicity (Gregoriadis, 1988b). Slow clearance from the circulation is usually required when liposomes, as such or coated with cell-specific ligands, are to interact with intravascular (or even extravascular) targets that normally do not take up liposomes. Uptake of liposomes by cells *in vivo* is probably entirely endocytic via the lysosomotropic pathway, with cells exhibiting high endocytic activity (e.g., RES) taking up most of the administered dose (Gregoriadis and Ryman, 1972).

Much of the progress in biomedical and other uses of liposomes can be attributed to advances in related technology (Gregoriadis, 1993). This has evolved from the original "classic" method of the 1960s to a variety of sophisticated techniques developed to meet particular needs, for example, large unilamellar vesicles of a diameter greater than 200 nm for cell–vesicle fusion *in vitro* or giant vesicles several micrometers in diameter for the entrapment of live or attenuated microbes (Antimisiaris *et al.*, 1993). Many of these techniques are characterized by a high entrapment yield (i.e., a high drug to lipid mass ratio) and some are amenable to scale up. A few techniques, however, are applicable to all water-soluble drugs, regardless of size, charge, solubility, and other physical characteristics. Indeed, the variety and complexity of techniques for liposome production are now so great that no one laboratory has hands-on experience with all of them. In this article, some of the liposome technology, as developed and applied in my laboratory over the last 10 years, is described. Such technology is characterized by high-yield drug entrapment in vesicles of an average size ranging from about 100 nm to several micrometers under conditions that, generally, preserve the activity of labile drugs (e.g., enzymes, DNA, or live microbes). Specialized techniques, as for instance for the production of liposomes with a high hydrophilic surface (Senior *et al.*, 1991) or the grafting of cell-specific ligands onto the liposomal surface (Gregoriadis, 1988a), are too varied and numerous for inclusion in this article.

II. Materials

Egg phosphatidylcholine (PC), distearoyl phosphatidylcholine (DSPC), phosphatidic acid (PA), and phosphatidyl glycerol (PG) (more than 99% pure) were from Lipid Products Nutfield. All other phospholipids (more than 98% pure), cholesterol, triolein (TO), stearylamine (SA), fluorescein isothiocyanate (FITC), and oil red O were from Sigma Chemical Company. Sepharose CL-4B and polyethylene glycol 6000 were obtained from Pharmacia. All other reagents were of analytical grade.

A. ENTRAPMENT OF LOW-MOLECULAR-WEIGHT SOLUTES AND MACROMOLECULES IN LIPOSOMES OF SUBMICROMETER SIZE BY THE DEHYDRATION–REHYDRATION PROCEDURE

See Kirby and Gregoriadis (1984) and Gregoriadis *et al.* (1987, 1990).

Solutions

1. Dissolve 32 μmole of phospholipid and 32 μmole of cholesterol in about 2–5 ml chloroform. For negatively or positively charged liposomes add 3.2 μmole of PA or SA, respectively. Greater amounts of charged lipids can be added depending on the extent of vesicle surface charge required.

2. Dissolve 10 mg of a water-soluble drug in 2 ml distilled water [or 10 m*M* sodium phosphate buffer, pH 7.2 (PB)] if needed. The nature of buffers with respect to composition, pH, and molarity can be varied as long as this does not interfere with liposome formation or entrapment yield.

Steps

1. Place chloroform solution of lipids in a 50-ml round-bottom spherical Quick-fit flask. Following evaporation of the solvent in a rotary evaporator at 37°C, a thin lipid film forms on the walls of the flask. Flush the film for about 60 sec with oxygen-free nitrogen (N_2) to ensure complete solvent removal and to replace air.

2. Add 2 ml distilled water (H_2O) (add solution 2 instead if step 3 below is not detrimental to the drug) to the flask, if needed, together with a few glass beads, replace stopper, and shake vigorously by hand or mechanically until the lipid film has been transformed into a milky suspension. This process is carried out at T_a (preferably by prewarming H_2O or solution 2 before its placement into a prewarmed flask within a water bath endowed with a shaking facility). The

TABLE I *z*-Average Mean Size (nm) of Microfluidized DRVs[a]

DRVs and medium	Number of cycles				
	1.8	3.5	5.2	7.1	10.6
Washed					
Water	463.5	149.9	115.0	121.9	114.7
PBS	447.4	198.6	168.1	159.5	155.7
Unwashed					
Water	473.9	132.9	116.9	116.6	101.9
PBS	456.3	186.2	186.7	169.8	159.9

[a] Maltose-containing washed or unwashed DRVs (33 μmole PC) were microfluidized in the presence of water or PBS for up to 10.6 cycles, and samples were measured for vesicle size (diameter in nanometers) by dynamic light scattering (photon correlation spectroscopy). Polydispersity indexes ranging from 0.503 to 0.653 (water) and from 0.517 to 0.653 (PBS) were similar to those obtained with some of the lipid compositions of liposomes employed by others.
Reprinted, with permission, from Gregoriadis *et al.* (1990).

emulsion is allowed to stand at T_a for about 1–2 hr. During this period multilamellar liposomes of diverse sizes form.

3. Following removal of glass beads, sonicate the milky suspension at T_a (with frequent intervals of rest) using a titanium probe slightly immersed in the emulsion which is under N_2 (achieved by the continuous delivery of a gentle stream of N_2 through thin plastic tubing). This step is meant to produce a slightly opaque to clear suspension of small unilamellar vesicles (SUVs) about 30–80 nm in diameter. The time required to produce SUVs varies, depending on the amount of lipid used and the diameter of the probe. For the amounts of lipid mentioned above, a clear or slightly opaque suspension is usually obtained within up to four sonication cycles, each lasting 30 sec, with 30-sec rest intervals inbetween, using a 0.75-in.-diameter probe. Sonication is considered successful when adjustment of the settings in the sonicator is such that the suspension is agitated vigorously.

4. Allow the sonicated suspension of SUVs to rest at T_a for about 1–2 hr and then mix with H_2O (or solution 2), rapidly freeze in liquid nitrogen (while the flask is rotated), and freeze-dry overnight under vacuum (<0.1 torr) in a Hetosicc freeze-dryer. If necessary, the suspension can be transferred into an alternative Pyrex container prior to freezing and drying.

5. To the freeze-dried powdery material, add 0.1 ml H_2O (per 32 μmole of phospholipid) prewarmed at T_a and swirl vigorously at T_a. The volume of H_2O added must be kept at a minimum, i.e., enough H_2O to ensure complete dissolution of the powder. Keep the sample at T_a for about 30 min. Repeat the process with 0.1 ml H_2O and, 30 min later at T_a, with 0.8 ml PB supplemented with 0.9% NaCl (PBS) (prewarmed at T_a). Allow the sample to stand for 30 min at T_a.

6. Centrifuge the suspension containing multilamellar liposomes (dehydration–rehydration vesicles, DRVs) with entrapped and nonentrapped drug at 40,000 *g* for 60 min (4°C). Suspend the pellet obtained (drug-containing DRVs) in H_2O (or PBS) and centrifuge again under the same conditions. Repeat the process once again to remove the remaining nonentrapped material. Suspend the final pellet in 2 ml H_2O or PB. When the liposomal suspension is destined for *in vivo* use (e.g., intravenous injection), add NaCl to a final concentration of 0.9%.

7. Monitor the extent of drug entrapment in DRV liposomes by measuring the drug in the suspended pellet and combined supernatants. The easiest way to

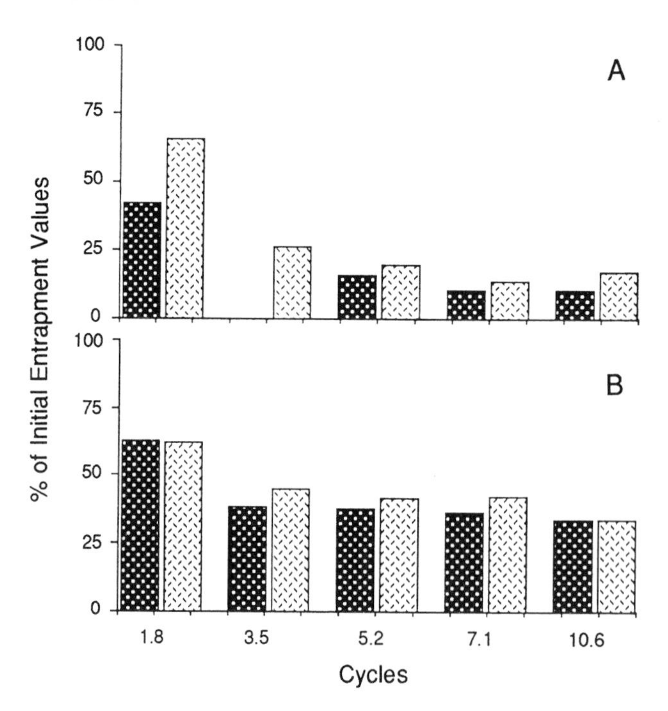

FIGURE 2 The effect of medium during microfluidization on solute retention by DRVs. ^{14}C-labeled, maltose-containing DRVs composed of equimolar PC and cholesterol were microfluidized in the washed (filled bars) and unwashed (shaded bars) forms in the presence of distilled water (A) or PBS (B) for up to 10.6 cycles. The amount of liposomal phospholipid passed through the microfluidizer was 33 μmole. Original entrapment values were 55.2% (PBS) and 54.3% (water) of the material used for entrapment. (Reprinted, with permission, from Gregoriadis *et al.* (1990).)

monitor entrapment is by using a radiolabeled drug. If this is not available, use appropriate quantitative techniques. To determine the drug by such techniques, mix a sample of the liposome suspension with Triton X-100 (up to 5% final concentration) so as to liberate the drug. If, however, Triton X-100 or the solubilized liposomal lipids interfere with the assay of the drug, lipids must be extracted using appropriate techniques. Entrapment values range between about 20 and 80%, depending on the amounts of lipid and drug used.

8. This step and those following are required when drug-containing DRV liposomes are to be converted to smaller vesicles (down to about 100-nm *z*-average mean size) still retaining a considerable proportion of the drug. Dilute the liposomal suspension obtained in step 5 (prior to the separation of entrapped from nonentrapped drug in step 6, unwashed liposomes) to 10 ml with H_2O and pass for a number of full cycles through a Microfluidizer 110 S (Microfluidics). The pressure gauge is set at 60 psi throughout the procedure to give a flow rate of 35 ml/min. The number of cycles used depends on the vesicle size required (Table I). It should, however, be noted that the greater the number of cycles, the smaller the amount of drug retained by the vesicles (Fig. 2). Microfluidization of the sample can also be carried out after removal of nonentrapped drug as in step 6 (washed liposomes), although drug retention in this case is reduced. It appears that the presence of unentrapped drug during microfluidization diminishes solute leakage, perhaps by reducing osmotic rupture of vesicles and/or the initial concentration gradient across the bilayer membranes (Gregoriadis *et al.*, 1990).

9. When the number of cycles required has been completed, the microfluidized sample (about 10 ml) can, if needed, be reduced in volume to about 1–2 ml. To this end, place the sample in dialysis tubing in a flat container and cover the

tubing with polyethylene glycol 6000. Removal of excess H_2O (together with nonentrapped drug) from the tubing is relatively rapid (within 30–60 min) and it is therefore essential that the sample be inspected regularly. When the required volume has been reached, the sample is treated to separate entrapped from the remaining nonentrapped drug. This is carried out either by dialysis against H_2O or by molecular sieve chromatography using a Sepharose CL-4B colum, in which case drug-containing liposomes are eluted at the end of the void volume. The content of drug within liposomes is estimated as in step 7 and is expressed as percentage of drug in the original preparation obtained in step 6. (Because the sample is microfluidized following step 5, i.e., before the estimation of entrapment, it is necessary that a small portion of the sample to be microfluidized be kept aside for estimation of entrapment according to step 6.) Vesicle size measurements are carried out by photon correlation spectroscopy as described elsewhere (Gregoriadis *et al.*, 1990). The minimum vesicle size obtained after 10 cycles of microfluidization is about 100–160 nm (diameter), depending on whether microfluidization is carried out in H_2O or PBS and whether unwashed or washed liposomes are used (see Fig. 2).

B. ENTRAPMENT OF PROTEINS, OTHER MACROMOLECULES, LARGE PARTICLES, OR BACTERIA INTO GIANT LIPOSOMES BY THE DEHYDRATION–REHYDRATION PROCEDURE

See Antimisiaris *et al.* (1993).

Solutions

1. PC or DSPC, cholesterol, PG, and TO (4:4:2:1 molar ratio, 9 μmole total lipid) in 1.0 ml $CHCl_3$.
2. Lipids as in solution 1 dissolved in 0.5 ml diethyl ether.
3. 0.15 *M* sucrose in H_2O.
4. 0.2 M sucrose in H_2O.
5. 5% glucose in H_2O.
6. 0.1 *M* sodium phosphate buffer supplemented with 0.9% NaCl, pH 7 (PBS).
7. Discontinuous sucrose gradient prepared by the use of two solutions, one containing 59.7 g and the other 117.0 g of sucrose per 100 ml H_2O, in swing-out bucket centrifuge tubes (Antimisiaris *et al.*, 1993).

Steps

1. Mix 1 ml of solution 3 with solution 1 by vortexing for 45 sec.

2. Mix the resulting water-in-chloroform emulsion by vortexing for 15 sec with solution 2 and 2.5 ml solution 4.

3. Place the water-in-oil-in-water emulsion formed in a 250-ml conical flask and evaporate the organic solvents by flushing with N_2 at 37°C while the sample is gently agitated in a shaking incubator. This leads to the generation of (sucrose-containing) giant liposomes.

4. Wash the giant liposomes by centrifugation over solution 5 in a benchtop centrifuge at 600 *g* for 5 min. Resuspend the liposomal pellet in 1 ml PBS.

5. Mix the suspended pellet of giant liposomes with 1 ml of a solution of the

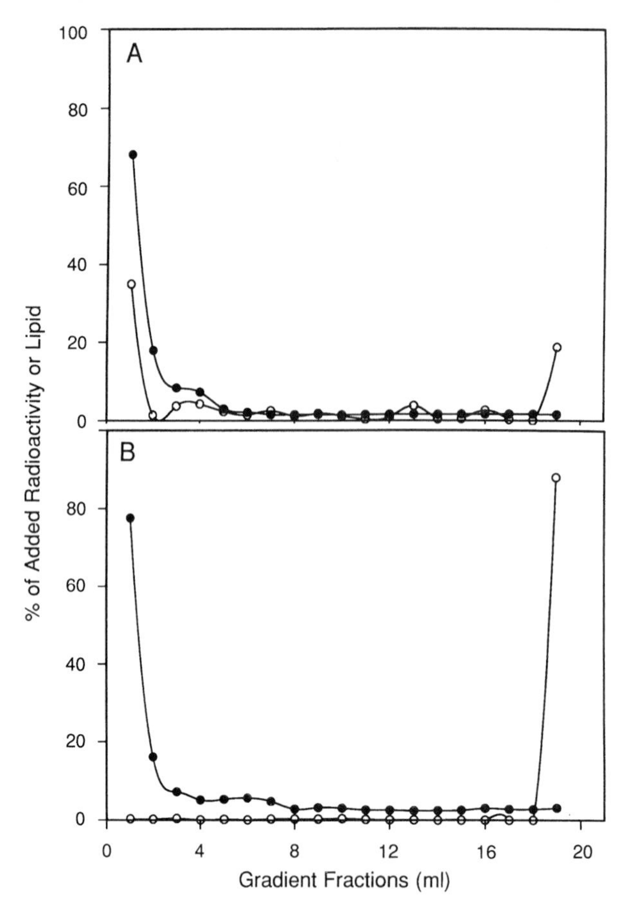

FIGURE 3 Sucrose gradient centrifugation of giant liposomes containing ^{125}I-labeled *B.subtilis*. Separation of liposome-entrapped from nonentrapped *B.subtilis* (A) and of "empty" liposomes from added free *B.subtilis* (B) was carried out by sucrose gradient centrifugation as described. Patterns of ^{125}I radioactivity (○) and lipid (●) shown are typical of PC or DSPC liposomes. Values are expressed as a percentage of the radioactivity or lipid used for fractionation. (Reprinted, with permission, from Antimisiaris *et al.* (1993).)

protein or a suspension of particulate matter [e.g., killed or live *Bacillus subtilis* spores or killed Bacille Calmette–Guérin (BCG) bacteria] and freeze-dry overnight under vacuum (<0.1 torr) in a Hetosicc freeze-dryer.

6. Rehydrate the freeze-dried material, initially by the addition of 0.1 ml H_2O at 20°C (rehydration of liposomes containing the "high-melting" DSPC at T_a does not have a significant effect on percentage entrapment of materials) (Antimisiaris *et al.*, 1993). Vigorously swirl the suspension and allow it to stand for 30 min. Repeat the process after the successive addition of 0.1 ml PBS and of 0.8 ml PBS 30 min later (1-ml total suspension volume).

7. Separate entrapped from nonentrapped macromolecule (e.g., protein) by centrifuging the suspension of the re-formed giant liposomes obtained in step 6 at 600 *g* for 10 min, followed by suspension of the twice-PBS-washed pellet in 1 ml PBS. Estimate entrapment yield by measuring the macromolecule in step 7 of Section A. Typical values for protein (e.g., tetanus toxoid) entrapment are 8–11% of the material used (Antimisiaris *et al.*, 1993). In the case of entrapped particulate matter such as spores or bacteria, separation from nonentrapped material is carried out by sucrose gradient centrifugation as described next.

8. Place the suspension (1 ml) containing entrapped and nonentrapped spores

TABLE II Entrapment of *Bacillus subtilis* and Tetanus Toxoid in Giant Liposomes[a]

	Entrapped material (% of that used)			
	B. subtilis		*Tetanus toxoid*	
Liposomes	*A*	*B*	*A*	*B*
PC, cholesterol, PG, TO	31.6 ± 24.2 (12)	26.7 ± 12.1 (7)	0.0 (4)	8.4 ± 2.6 (4)
DSPC, cholesterol, PG, TO	—	21.3 ± 8.9 (6)	0.0 (4)	11.1 ± 1.9 (4)

[a] ^{125}I-labeled *B. subtilis* and tetanus toxoid were entrapped in giant liposomes as described in column B. Results, based on radioactivity measurements, are expressed as percentages (±SD) of material used for entrapment. In one experiment, entrapment of ^{125}I-labeled BCG in PC giant liposomes was 27.8%. Numbers in parentheses denote numbers of preparations.
Reprinted, with permission, from Antimisiaris *et al.* (1993).

or bacteria on top of the sucrose gradient (solution 7) and centrifuge for 1.5 hr at 90,000 *g* in a Dupont Combi Plus ultracentrifuge using a swing-out bucket. After centrifugation, pipette 1-ml fractions from the top of the gradient and assay for spore or bacteria content. It is convenient to use radiolabeled (e.g., ^{125}I-labeled) spores or bacteria to monitor content. In the case of *B.subtilis* spores or BCG bacteria, these are recovered at the bottom fraction of the gradient when nonentrapped. Entrapped material is recovered mostly in the top seven fractions of the gradient in association with liposomes (Fig. 3).

9. Pool fractions containing the entrapped spores or bacteria and dialyze exhaustively against PBS, until all sucrose has been eliminated. Centrifuge the dialyzed material as in step 4, and resuspend the liposomal pellet in 1 ml PBS for further use. Typical values for *B.subtilis* or BCG entrapment are 21–27% of the material used (Antimisiaris *et al.,* 1993).

III. Comments

The dehydration–rehydration procedures outlined for the entrapment of solutes (e.g., low-molecular-weight drugs, peptides, proteins, DNA, and other macromolecules) or particulates such as spores, bacteria, and viruses are characterized by their mildness and are thus compatible with labile materials. Moreover, it has been shown (Gregoriadis *et al.,* 1987; Antimisiaris *et al.,* 1993) that material-containing liposomal suspension as prepared here can be freeze-dried in the presence of a cryoprotectant (for storage) without significant loss of material from the vesicles on reconstitution with 0.9% NaCl. Although both procedures are simple to use, special care should be taken in rehydration (step 5 in Section IIA and step 6 in Section IIB) of the freeze-dried material. It is important that the water added during the initial rehydration be kept to a minimum volume.

REFERENCES

Antimisiaris, S., Jayasekera, P., and Gregoriadis, G. (1993) Liposomes as vaccine carriers: Incorporation of soluble and particulate antigens in giant vesicles. *J. Immunol. Methods* **166,** 271–280.

Gregoriadis, G. (ed.) (1988a) "Liposomes as Drug Carriers: Recent Trends and Progress." Wiley, Chichester.

Gregoriadis, G. (1988b) Fate of injected liposomes: Observations on entrapped solute retention, vesicle clearance and tissue distribution *in vivo*. *In* "Liposomes as Drug Carriers: Recent Trends and Progress" (G. Gregoriadis, ed.), pp. 3–18. Wiley, Chichester.

Gregoriadis, G. (ed.) (1993) "Liposome Technology," 2nd ed., Vols. I–III. CRC Press, Boca Raton, FL.

Gregoriadis, G. (1994) Liposomes and anti-ageing creams: The facts beneath the face. *Biochemist,* **16,** 8–11.

Gregoriadis, G., da Silva, H., and Florence, A. T. (1990) A procedure for the efficient entrapment of drugs in dehydration–rehydration liposomes (DRV). *Int. J. Pharm.* **65,** 235–242.

Gregoriadis, G., Davies, A., and Davis, D. (1987) Liposomes as immunological adjuvants: Antigen incorporation studies. *Vaccine* **5,** 143–149.

Gregoriadis, G., and Ryman, B. E. (1972) Lysosomal localization of enzyme-containing liposomes injected into rats. *Biochem. J.* **129,** 123–133.

Kirby, C., and Gregoriadis, G. (1984) Dehydration–rehydration vesicles (DRV): A new method for high yield drug entrapment in liposomes. *Biotechnology* **2,** 878–984.

Senior, J., Delgado, C., Fisher, D., Tilcock, C., and Gregoriadis, G. (1991) Influence of surface hydrophilicity of liposomes on their interaction with plasma proteins and clearance from the circulation: Studies with polyethylene glycol-coated vesicles, *Biochim. Biophys. Acta* **1062,** 77–82.

Electroporation-Mediated DNA Transfer to Tobacco Protoplasts for Transient Gene Expression Assays

Geert Angenon, Willy Dillen, and Marc Van Montagu

I. Introduction

Although many plant species can be stably transformed, transient gene expression assays in protoplasts are widely used because of two important advantages. First, gene expression can be measured very shortly after DNA uptake, and second, because most of the introduced plasmid DNA remains extrachromosomal during the period of the assay, gene activity measurements are not biased by position effects, i.e., the influence exerted by DNA sequences surrounding genes that are integrated into chromosomes. Promoter analyses, the identification and characterization of transcriptional and translational regulatory sequences, and the study of induction of gene expression by external stimuli such as hormones, elicitors, and stress conditions, have been carried out with transient gene expression assays. A disadvantage of this type of assay is that expression in isolated protoplasts is not necessarily similar to expression in the intact tissues and organs from which they are derived. Transient assays in intact tissues (see Willy Dillen, Marc Van Montagu, and Geert Angenon, in this volume) could partly circumvent this problem.

The two most often used methods for DNA delivery into protoplasts are electroporation and treatment with polyethylene glycol (Paszkowski *et al.,* 1984). The observation that short electric pulses of high field strength transiently permeabilize cell membranes led to the development of electroporation-mediated gene transfer techniques for mammalian cells (Neumann *et al.,* 1982) and plant cell protoplasts (Fromm *et al.,* 1985). Electroporation is now the preferred technique for direct DNA transfer to plant protoplasts.

Here, we describe the isolation of protoplasts from *Nicotiana tabacum* cv. Petit Havana SR1 (Maliga *et al.,* 1973) and the conditions for electroporation-mediated plasmid DNA delivery to these protoplasts.

II. Materials and Instrumentation

A. CHEMICALS

Sucrose (extra pure, Cat. No. 7653), $CaCl_2 \cdot 2H_2O$ (Cat. No. 2382), Hepes (Cat. No. 10110), and NH_4NO_3 (Cat. No. 1188) were purchased from Merck. DMSO (Cat. No. 12.779.72) and D-(+)-xylose (Cat. No. 14.100.35) were from Janssen Chimica. Gamborg's B5 salts and vitamins (Gamborg *et al.,* 1968, Cat. No. 26-130-22) and Murashige and Skoog salts (Murashige and Skoog, 1962, Cat. No. 26-

330-24) were from Flow Laboratories ICN. α-Naphthaleneacetic acid (NAA, Cat. No. N-0375) and 6-benzylaminopurine (BAP, Cat. No. B-6750) were obtained from Sigma. Cellulase "Onozuka" R-10 (Cat. No. L0012) and macerozyme R-10 (Cat. No. L0021) were obtained from Yakult Honsha. Agar was from Gibco-BRL (Cat. No. 152-00001M) and low-gelling-temperature agarose from FMC Bioproducts (Cat. No. 50102). NaCl was from UCB (Cat. No. 1723).

B. DISPOSABLES

Ten-milliliter pipettes with a wide tip (Falcon 7504), 1-ml pipettes (Falcon 7520), and 9-cm petri dishes (Falcon 1005) were purchased from Becton Dickinson. Ten-milliliter plastic tubes (Cel-cult, Cat. No. 25220) and 5-cm petri dishes (Cat. No. 122) were from Bibby Sterilin. Cuvettes were from Kartell (Cat. No. 1938 PS). Fifty-microliter capillaries were from Hirshmann Labogeräte (Cat. No. 960 0150).

C. INSTRUMENTATION

A capacitor discharge unit, as described by Fromm *et al.* (1985), and 2-mm-thick stainless-steel electrodes with a 6-mm gap and 3 × 9-mm electrode surface area were homemade. The capacitor unit was connected to a regular DC power supply. Filters were assembled from nylon screen (Nytal, 50-μm mesh, PROSEP). A peristaltic pump was obtained from Pharmacia LKB (Cat. No. 2115) and a hemocytometer from Vel (Fuchs–Rosenthal, depth 0.200 mm, Cat. No. 1502030).

III. Procedures

The whole experiment is carried out in a laminar flow hood with sterile materials and solutions.

A. PROTOPLAST ISOLATION

Solutions

1. *MS solid medium:* Dissolve 4.6 g Murashige and Skoog salts and 10 g sucrose in 1 liter of water. Adjust pH to 5.7 with 1 *M* NaOH. Add 8 g agar. Autoclave for 20 min. Distribute over six 1-liter jars.

2. *Washing solution:* B5 salts and vitamins, 0.4 *M* sucrose, pH 5.6. Dissolve 0.39 g B5 powder and 13.7 g sucrose in 100 ml distilled water. Adjust pH to 5.6 with 1 *M* NaOH and filter-sterilize.

3. *Enzyme solution:* Washing solution with 0.5% cellulase R-10 and 0.2% macerozyme R-10. Add 100 mg cellulase and 40 mg macerozyme to 20 ml washing solution. Stir for about 1 hr on a magnetic stirrer and filter-sterilize.

4. *Electroporation buffer (EP):* 0.4 *M* sucrose, 4 m*M* $CaCl_2$, 10 m*M* Hepes, pH 7.2. Dissolve 13.7 g sucrose, 59 mg $CaCl_2 \cdot 2H_2O$, and 238 mg Hepes in 100 ml distilled water. Adjust to pH 7.2 with 1 *M* NaOH and filter-sterilize.

Steps

1. Propagate *Nicotiana tabacum* SR1 plants *in vitro* from stem cuttings on MS solid medium; 6 to 8 weeks after subculture, the plants can be used for

protoplast isolation. For one preparation, use six to eight undamaged leaves. Avoid the very young leaves as well as the ones at the base of the stem.

2. Put the leaves with the upper epidermis down in a 9-cm petri dish containing 20 ml washing solution. Remove the midrib and cut the leaf material in pieces of about 0.25 cm^2 with a new scalpel blade.

3. Leave the pieces in the washing solution for 15 to 60 min.

4. Remove the washing solution completely and add 20 ml of enzyme solution.

5. Incubate the petri dish for 16 hr at 24°C in the dark.

6. Release the protoplasts by gently swirling the petri dish. The solution will be dark green when the digestion is complete. If not, incubate the petri dish for another hour at 24°C on a rotary platform at about 30 rpm.

7. Pass the protoplast suspension through a 50-μm-mesh nylon filter, placed in a 9-cm petri dish. Rinse the petri dish in which the digestion was done with 10 ml washing solution and pass through the filter. Rinse the filter with another 10 ml washing solution. This brings the total volume of the protoplast suspension to 40 ml.

8. Distribute the protoplast suspension over four sterile, disposable plastic tubes and centrifuge for 10 min at 80 *g* in a swinging bucket rotor at room temperature. The protoplasts will float, whereas cell debris will be pelleted.

9. First remove the pellet and then the solution underlying the protoplasts by means of a sterile capillary tube connected to a peristaltic pump. To minimize protoplast loss, perform this step slowly, i.e., at a rate of about 3 ml/min.

10. Immediately add EP buffer to the protoplasts to bring the volume to 10 ml and gently resuspend the protoplasts.

11. Centrifuge as in step 8.

12. Remove the (small) pellet and the underlying solution and transfer the protoplasts to one tube.

13. Take 10 μl of protoplast suspension and dilute 50-fold with EP buffer. Use the diluted suspension to count the number of protoplasts with a hemocytometer. One preparation should yield at least 5×10^6 protoplasts.

14. Dilute the protoplasts with EP buffer to a final concentration of 5 to 7.5×10^6 protoplasts per milliliter.

B. PROTOPLAST ELECTROPORATION

Solutions

1. *0.8% Low-gelling-temperature agarose:* Add 0.4 g of low-gelling-temperature agarose to 50 ml water. Autoclave and keep at approximately 50°C.

2. *3 M NaCl:* Dissolve 175 mg NaCl in 1 ml distilled water and filter-sterilize.

3. *Protoplast culture medium:* B5 medium, 0.4 *M* sucrose, 750 mg/liter $CaCl_2 \cdot 2H_2O$, 250 mg/liter xylose, 250 mg/liter NH_4NO_3, pH 5.6, 0.2 mg/liter BAP, 0.1 mg/liter NAA. To prepare 100 ml, dissolve 0.39 g B5 powder, 13.7 g sucrose, 75 mg $CaCl_2 \cdot 2H_2O$, 25 mg xylose, and 25 mg NH_4NO_3 in 100 ml distilled water, adjust pH, and filter-sterilize. Add 10 μl of a BAP stock solution (2 mg/ml in DMSO) and 5 μl of a NAA stock solution (2 mg/ml in DMSO).

Steps

1. Fill sterile cuvettes with 900 μl 0.8% agarose; allow to solidify. Nonsterile cuvettes should be immersed in ethanol for 1 hr and dried on sterile paper towel.

2. Add sterile 3 *M* NaCl to the protoplast suspension to a final concentration of 150 m*M*.

3. Gently mix the protoplasts to obtain a homogeneous suspension. Immediately transfer 200 μl (1 to 1.5 $\times 10^6$ protoplasts) to each agarose-filled cuvette and put on ice.

4. Add plasmid DNA to each cuvette and mix gently but thoroughly. Incubate on ice for 10 min.

5. Rinse the electrode with ethanol and dip-dry on sterile paper towel. Rinse again with EP buffer and dip-dry once more.

6. Just before the electroporation, tap the cuvette a couple of times to obtain homogeneous distribution of the cells. Insert the electrode in the cuvette and discharge a 200-μF capacitor charged at 200 V (333 V/cm). Place the cuvette back on ice.

7. Repeat steps 5 and 6 for each sample.

8. After the electroporation, incubate the samples for 10 min on ice.

9. Carefully transfer the protoplasts to 5-cm sterile petri dishes containing 5 ml of protoplast culture medium. Seal the dishes with Parafilm and incubate in the dark at 24°C for 40 to 50 hr.

10. Transfer the protoplasts to plastic tubes. Centrifuge the tubes for 10 min at 80 *g* in a swinging bucket rotor at room temperature. Remove the pellet and the solution underlying the protoplasts.

11. Add an extraction buffer, appropriate for the introduced marker gene product, and disrupt the protoplasts by sonication or by quickly pipetting the suspension up and down.

12. Assay expression of the introduced marker gene.

IV. Comments

The amount of plasmid DNA typically added is 5 to 10 μg per cuvette (25 to 50 $\mu g/ml$), although amounts as low as 200 ng still give detectable expression. The DNA should be added as a sterile solution and in a volume of less than 15 μl per cuvette. Therefore, the DNA should be precipitated, washed with 70% ethanol, and redissolved at an appropriate concentration under sterile conditions. When comparing different constructs, plasmids of the same size should be used, because the influence of plasmid size on the efficiency of uptake has not been determined.

The electroporation conditions described here result in an exponentially decaying pulse with a field strength of 333 V/cm and a $1/e$ time constant or pulse length of approximately 50 msec. The capacity and potential required to obtain a similar pulse with other equipment can be deduced from the following formulas:

$$\tau = RC$$

$$R = rd^2W^{-1}$$

$$E = Ud^{-1}$$

where τ = pulse length or $1/e$ time constant; R = resistance; C = capacity; r

= specific resistivity of the electroporation buffer; d = electrode gap; W = solution volume; E = field strength; and U = potential.

Protoplasts of other plant species can be electroporated with similar procedures as described here for tobacco protoplasts. Pulse length and field strength should, however, be optimized for each species and genotype. Optimal DNA uptake usually requires conditions that are lethal for part of the protoplasts. Likewise, the optimal time point at which to measure transient expression has to be determined empirically.

V. Pitfalls

1. Protoplasts are fragile and should be handled with care at all stages. Use pipettes with wide openings to minimize protoplast damage.

2. Protoplasts are very sensitive to ethanol. Do not use hormones or antibiotics dissolved in ethanol and make sure that the ethanol used to rinse the electrode and the cuvettes evaporates completely before there is any contact with protoplasts.

REFERENCES

Fromm, M., Taylor, L. P., and Walbot, V. (1985) Expression of genes transferred into monocot and dicot plant cells by electroporation. *Proc. Natl. Acad. Sci. USA* **82,** 5824–5828.

Gamborg, O. L., Miller, R. A., and Ojima, K. (1968) Nutrient requirements of suspension cultures of soybean root cells. *Exp. Cell Res.* **50,** 151–158.

Maliga, P., Sz.-Breznovits, A., and Márton, L. (1973) Streptomycin-resistant plants from callus culture of haploid tobacco. *Nature New Biol.* **244,** 29–30.

Murashige, T., and Skoog, F. (1962) A revised medium for rapid growth and bio assays with tobacco tissue cultures. *Physiol. Plant.* **15,** 473–497.

Neumann, E., Schaefer-Ridder, M., Wang, Y., and Hofschneider, P. H. (1982) Gene transfer into mouse lyoma cells by electroporation in high electric fields. *EMBO J.* **1,** 841–845.

Paszkowski, J., Shillito, R. D., Saul, M., Mandák, V., Hohn, T., Hohn, B., and Potrykus, I. (1984) Direct gene transfer to plants. *EMBO J.* **3,** 2717–2722.

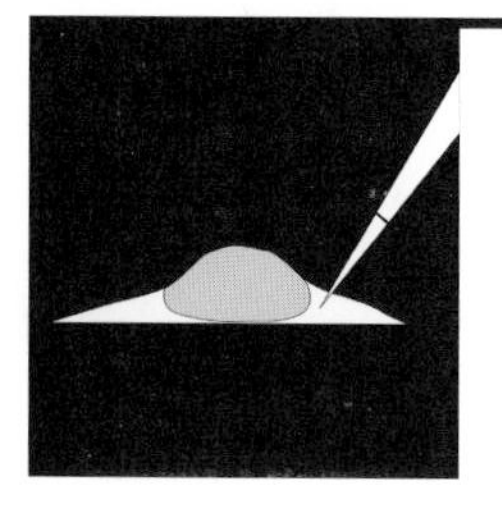

Electroporation-Mediated DNA Delivery to Embryos of Leguminous Species

Willy Dillen, Marc Van Montagu, and Geert Angenon

I. Introduction

Electroporation-mediated DNA delivery to plant protoplasts is a well-established procedure. Recently, it has been shown that also intact cells, both in suspension cultures and as part of organized tissues, can take up DNA through electroporation. The range of species amenable to this novel gene delivery method is rapidly increasing. Transient gene expression has been reported for suspension cultures of *Beta vulgaris* (Lindsey and Jones, 1987); leaf bases of *Oryza sativa, Triticum aestivum, Zea mays,* and *Hordeum vulgare* (Dekeyser *et al.*, 1990); immature embryos of *T. aestivum* and *O. sativa* (Klöti *et al.*, 1993); and immature embryos of *Z. mays* (Songstad *et al.*, 1993). Moreover, stable integration of transgenes has been achieved through electroporation-mediated DNA delivery into enzymatically wounded immature embryos and mechanically wounded type I callus of *Z. mays* (D'Halluin *et al.*, 1992).

Electroporation-mediated gene transfer to intact tissues can be used for a variety of purposes. For example, promoter regulation could be studied by introducing chimeric genes directly into the intact target tissues. From a practical point of view, the technique offers an alternative to the methods currently used to produce transgenic plants.

Here, we describe a protocol for the introduction of DNA into cells of intact embryonic axes of the legume *Phaseolus vulgaris* L. The procedure leads to transient gene expression in hypocotyl and epicotyl tissue and occurs in sectors of variable size and penetration. The protocol yields similar results for all *P. vulgaris* cultivars tested, as well as for other grain legumes such as *Pisum sativum, Vigna unguiculata, Cajanus cajan, Cicer arietinum,* and *Glycine max.*

II. Materials and instrumentation

A. SEED STERILIZATION AND GERMINATION

HDS 10 liquid soap was purchased from Chemical Concentrates RBS, and NaOCl (Cat. No. 7681-52-9) from Janssen Chimica. Murashige and Skoog (MS) salts (Murashige and Skoog, 1962; Cat. No. 26-330-24) were obtained from Flow Laboratories ICN, and MS vitamins (Cat. No. M3900) and 6-benzylaminopurine (BAP, Cat. No. B6750) from Sigma. Sucrose (extra pure, Cat. No. 7653) was obtained from Merck, and bacteriological agar (Cat. No. 152-00001 M) from Gibco-BRL. Culture containers were 350-ml glass jars with polypropylene lids.

B. ELECTROPORATION

1. Chemicals

$CaCl_2 \cdot 2H_2O$ (Cat. No. 2382), Hepes (Cat. No. 10110), and sucrose (extra pure, Cat. No. 7653) were purchased from Merck. Spermidine (Cat. No. S-2626) was obtained from Sigma. NaCl (Cat. No. 1723) was obtained from UCB. Low-gelling-temperature agarose (Cat. No. 50102) was purchased from FMC BioProducts, and D(+)-glucose monohydrate (Cat. No. 5996-10-1) from J. T. Baker.

2. Disposables

Petri dishes (140 mm, Cat. No. 501V) were obtained from Bibby Sterilin, and 0.2-μm filters (Falcon 7107) and replica dishes (Falcon 3047) from Becton Dickinson. Millex-GV 0.22-μm filter units (Cat. No. SLGV 025 BS) were purchased from Millipore, 1-ml syringes from Terumo Medical Europe N.V., and 1-ml cuvettes (Cat. No. 1938 PS) from Kartell.

3. Electroporation Apparatus

Direct-current power supply (a regular power supply used for agarose gel electrophoresis will do), capacitor-discharge unit (for delivery of an exponentially decaying pulse; for circuit, see Fromm *et al.*, 1985), and stainless-steel electrodes (6-mm gap, 3 × 9-mm electrode surface area) were homemade.

III. Procedures

A. SEED STERILIZATION AND GERMINATION

Solution

Germination medium: MS salts and vitamins, 30 g liter^{-1} sucrose, 5 μM BAP, 7 g liter^{-1} agar, pH 5.8. Dissolve 4.6 g MS salts and 30 g sucrose in 1 liter of water. Adjust the pH to 5.8 with 1 M NaOH. Add 7 g agar and autoclave at 121°C for 20 min. Cool to 50 to 60°C and add 113 μl of a 10 mg ml^{-1} BAP stock solution and 1 ml of MS vitamins (1000×). Distribute over 20 culture containers.

Steps

Rinse approximately 50 g seeds in 70% ethanol in a bottle together with a magnetic stirring bar.

2. Pour off ethanol and sterilize in 300 ml 3% NaOCl (+6 drops HDS 10 soap) for 15 min under constant, gentle stirring.

3. Wash five times with sterile water. Place seeds on germination medium (approximately five per jar, hilum side up) and incubate at 22°C under 16 hr light until the root tip starts to emerge from the seed coat. Depending on species and genotype, this stage will be reached after 1 to 7 or more days.

B. ELECTROPORATION

Solutions

1. *MS salts medium:* Dissolve 691 mg MS salts and 4.5 g sucrose in 150 ml water. Adjust pH to 5.8 with 1 *M* NaOH. Autoclave for 20 min at 121°C.

2. *3 M NaCl:* Dissolve 175 mg NaCl in 1 ml of water. Filter-sterilize through a 0.22-μm Millex-GV filter unit using a 1-ml syringe.

3. *200 mM spermidine:* Dissolve 29 mg spermidine in 1 ml of water. Filter-sterilize through a 0.22-μm Millex-GV filter unit using a 1-ml syringe.

4. *MS solid medium:* Dissolve 4.6 g MS salts and 30 g sucrose in 1 liter of water. Adjust pH to 5.8 with 1 *M* NaOH. Add 8 g agar. Autoclave at 121°C for 20 min. Distribute over 20 jars.

5. *Electroporation buffer (EB):* 10% glucose, 4 m*M* $CaCl_2$, 10 m*M* Hepes, 0.2 m*M* spermidine, pH 7.2. To make 100 ml, dissolve 11 g D(+)-glucose monohydrate, 59 mg $CaCl_2 \cdot 2H_2O$, and 238 mg Hepes in 100 ml of water. Adjust the pH to 7.2 with 1 *M* NaOH. Filter-sterilize and add 0.1 ml of a 200 m*M* spermidine stock.

6. *1% Low-gelling-temperature agarose:* Dissolve 1 g low-gelling-temperature agarose in water. Autoclave for 20 min at 121°C.

Steps

1. Remove seed coat and one cotyledon from 20 seeds of uniform size and developmental stage (root tip just emerging from the seed). Collect the explants in a petri dish containing 130 ml MS salts medium.

2. Excise embryos from collected explants; remove primary leaves and transfer to EB in a replica dish (1 ml EB per explant per well).

3. Incubate at room temperature for at least 3 hr. During incubation, melt previously autoclaved 1% low-gelling-temperature agarose and keep in a 45°C water bath. Submerge cuvettes and electrodes in ethanol. After 1 hr, dry the cuvettes on a sterile paper towel and fill with 0.9 ml agarose. After solidification, add 150 μl EB.

4. Wash explants twice with 1 ml EB.

5. Position explants in separate cuvettes. Push the root tip into the agarose, taking care that the tissue to be electroporated is submerged in EB. Add the desired amount of plasmid DNA carrying a reporter gene (a final concentration of 0.1 $\mu g\ \mu l^{-1}$ should give good results).

6. Incubate at room temperature for 1 hr.

7. Add 8.3 μl 3 *M* NaCl to each cuvette.

8. Incubate 10 min on ice.

9. Wash electrodes in EB, drip-dry on a sterile paper towel, and insert electrodes into the cuvette.

10. Discharge the capacitor unit (900 μF charged to 130 V). Between electroporations, wash the electrodes in ethanol and EB. Dip electrodes dry before inserting them into the next cuvette.

11. After delivery of the pulse, incubate on ice for 15 min.

12. Wash the explants in MS salts medium before transferring them to MS solid medium.

13. After 4 days, assay the explants for transient expression of the reporter gene.

IV. Comments

Although any reporter gene could be used to monitor transient expression, the histological localization of β-glucuronidase (GUS) (Jefferson *et al.*, 1987) is particularly suitable in this case. The described electroporation procedure should result in GUS-expressing spots of variable size on hypocotyl, epicotyl, and occasionally meristem tissue. The spots penetrate several cell layers and can cover as much as 50% of the exposed tissue. Due to the vectorial nature of the electroporating field, spots will be observed only in tissues facing the cathode. Diffuse, overall, and uniform staining should be regarded as suspect because endogenous GUS activity can occur in *Phaseolus*. Control treatments (electroporation without DNA) should always be included.

The plasmid DNA should preferentially be linearized (Förster and Neumann, 1989). After phenol extraction, the DNA should be redissolved under sterile conditions.

The electric conditions given in this protocol are the result of optimizations for a particular genotype of *P. vulgaris* (Admires). These conditions permit gene delivery in all *Phaseolus* cultivars tested, as well as in a number of other leguminous species. For optimal results, however, pulse amplitude and pulse length should be optimized for the species and genotype under study.

The developmental stage of the embryos is an important factor determining the transformation efficiency. In general, nongreen or etiolated tissues seem to be more competent to DNA uptake through this procedure than green, hardened tissues.

Under the conditions described in this protocol, the field strength is 217 V cm^{-1} and pulse lengths range between 250 and 300 msec. For chamber designs differing from that presented here, the capacity and potential required to obtain a comparable field strength and pulse length can be deduced from the following formulas:

$$\tau = RC$$

$$R = rd^2W^{-1}$$

$$E = Ud^{-1}$$

where τ = pulse length or $1/e$ time constant, E = field strength, U = potential, d = electrode gap, r = specific resistivity of the electroporation solution, W = solution volume, C = capacity, and R = resistance.

REFERENCES

Dekeyser, R. A., Claes, B., De Rycke, R. M. U., Habets, M. E., Van Montagu, M. C., and Caplan, A. C. (1990) Transient gene expression in intact and organized rice tissues. *Plant Cell* 2, 591–602.

D'Halluin, K., Bonne, E., Bossut, M., De Beuckeleer, M., and Leemans, J. (1992) Transgenic maize plants by tissue electroporation. *Plant Cell* 4, 1495–1505.

Förster, W., and Neumann, E. (1989) Gene transfer by electroporation: A practical guide. *In* "Electroporation and Electrofusion in Cell Biology" (E. Neumann, A. E. Sowers, and C. A. Jordan, eds.), pp. 299–318. Plenum Press, New York.

Fromm, M., Taylor, L. P., and Walbot, V. (1985) Expression of genes transferred into monocot and dicot plant cells by electroporation. *Proc. Natl. Acad. Sci. USA* **82**, 5824–5828.

Jefferson, R. A., Kavanagh, T. A., and Bevan, M. W. (1987) GUS fusions: β-Glucuronidase as a sensitive and versatile gene fusion marker in higher plants. *EMBO J.* **6**, 3901–3907.
Klöti, A., Iglesias, V. A., Wünn, J., Burkhardt, P., Datta, S. K., and Potrykus, I. (1993) Gene transfer by electroporation into intact scutellum cells of wheat embryos. *Plant Cell Rep.* **12**, 671–675.
Lindsey, K., and Jones, M. G. K. (1987) Transient gene expression in electroporated protoplasts and intact cells of sugar beet. *Plant Mol. Biol.* **10**, 43–52.
Murashige, T., and Skoog, F. (1962) A revised medium for rapid growth and bio-assays with tobacco tissue cultures. *Physiol. Plant.* **15**, 473–497.
Songstad, D. D., Halaka, F. G., DeBoer, D. L., Armstrong, C. L., Hinchee, M. A. W., Ford-Santino, C. G., Brown, S. M., Fromm, M. E., and Horsch, R. B. (1993) Transient expression of GUS and anthocyanin constructs in intact maize immature embryos following electroporation. *Plant Cell, Tissue Organ Culture* **33**, 195–201.

Permeabilization by α-Toxin and Streptolysin O

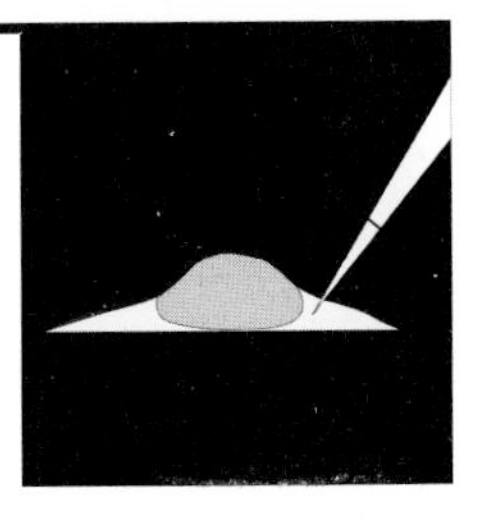

Gudrun Ahnert-Hilger

I. Introduction

Permeabilized cells allow the study of intracellular processes *in situ* under conditions that are believed to be close to the physiological situation in intact cells. Permeabilization by bacterial pore-forming toxins, α-toxin, and streptolysin O (SLO) is now a widely accepted approach in the functional analysis of intracellular organelles. The native forms of the toxins assemble as amphiphilic hexamers into the target lipid bilayers, where they generate small stable transmembrane pores. SLO pores are heterogeneous with a larger diameter (Bhakdi and Tranum-Jensen, 1987; Ahnert-Hilger *et al.*, 1989a,b).

II. Materials

α-Toxin from *Staphylococcus aureus* (strain Wood 46, ATCC 10832, DSM 20491) was kindly provided by U. Weller, Institut für Medizinische Mikrobiologie, Johannes Gutenberg Universität, Mainz, Germany. The toxin can be easily purified from the culture supernatant (Lind *et al.*, 1987; Palmer *et al.*, 1993), lyophilized, and, if necessary, dialyzed against an intracellular buffer (see below). Dissolved α-toxin is stored in aliquots at $-20°C$ for months without loss of biological activity. Streptolysin O (SLO), also kindly supplied by U. Weller, is purified from the culture supernatant of group A β-hemolytic streptococci (U. Weller, K. Bläser, G. Ahnert-Hilger, M. Me ner, and S. Bhakdi, 1994, in preparation) and stored in various buffers at $-20°C$ for months. SLO is active only in the reduced form; thus addition of 1 m*M* dithiothreitol is recommended in the final working dilution.

A commercially available α-toxin preparation from Institut Pasteur has a relatively low titer, but can be concentrated by two successive ammonium sulfate precipitations (55 and 65%) followed by dialysis against an intracellular buffer (see below). SLO may be also obtained from Wellcome Diagnostics. The international units (IU) given by the company refer to its application in the determination of the anti-streptolysin O titer and may not be compared directly with the hemolytic units mentioned above. The material is a rather impure freeze-dried preparation of a partially purified culture filtrate and should be dialyzed against intracellular buffers (see below) before use.

III. Procedures

A. DETERMINATION OF THE BIOLOGICAL ACTIVITY OF BOTH TOXINS USING RABBIT ERYTHROCYTES

Solutions

1. *4% sodium citrate:* To make 100 ml, solubilize 4 g of sodium citrate in distilled water and adjust to a total volume of 100 ml.

2. *Phosphate-buffered saline (PBS):* To make 1 liter, dissolve 6.9 g $NaH_2PO_4 \cdot 2H_2O$ and 7.6 g NaCl in about 600 ml of distilled water, titrate to pH 7.2 with NaOH, and adjust to a total volume of 1 liter. Store at 4°C.

3. *2% SDS:* To make 100 ml, dissolve 2 g of SDS in 100 ml of distilled water.

Steps

1. Mix 9 vol of fresh rabbit blood with 1 vol of 4% sodium citrate.

2. Wash three times with PBS by a 5-min centrifugation at 3000 *g*.

3. Dilute the erythrocyte pellet 1:40 in PBS, which gives an about 2.5% erythrocyte suspension.

4. Mix 5 μl of toxin (diluted in PBS, in the case of SLO in PBS supplemented with 1 m*M* dithiothreitol), 5 μl PBS alone for control, or 5 μl 2% SDS with 50 μl of the 2.5% erythrocyte suspension.

5. Incubate 40 min at 37°C under constant shaking in a water bath.

6. Centrifuge 2 min at 12,000 *g*.

7. Remove 30 μl of the supernatant and dilute with 1 ml of water.

8. Estimate hemoglobin content spectrophotometrically at 412 nm. The reciprocal of the toxin dilution hemolyzing 50% of the erythrocyte suspension at 37°C within 40 min is taken as the hemolytic units per milliliter of undiluted toxin solution (Lind *et al.*, 1987; Ahnert-Hilger *et al.*, 1989b).

B. APPLICATION FOR CELL PERMEABILIZATION

α-Toxin permeabilizes cells for small molecules ($\leq$3 kDa), whereas SLO renders cells permeable for both small and large molecules ($\geq$150 kDa). In this respect SLO resembles digitonin.

An increase in permeability of cells can be quickly checked with membrane-impermeable dyes that stain either various components of the cell body (trypan blue or eosin) or the nucleus (azure A) (Ahnert-Hilger *et al.*, 1985, 1989b). Permeability of α-toxin-treated cells to small molecules is the same as after treatment with SLO or digitonin (Ahnert-Hilger *et al.*, 1985, 1989b). The release of cytoplasmic enzymes such as lactate dehydrogenase (135,000 kDa) can be used to monitor the permeability to proteins after application of SLO (Ahnert-Hilger *et al.*, 1985, 1989b).

The permeability due to α-toxin is restricted to the plasma membrane, for the α-toxin monomers (34 kDa) are too large to pass through the pores generated by the hexamer (Bhakdi and Tranum-Jensen, 1987). Accordingly, proteins are not lost during permeabilization. The large pores generated by SLO oligomers also let proteins pass. To avoid damage to intracellular membranes by SLO monomers, the cells are incubated for a very short time or at 0°C (see below). Under the latter conditions the SLO monomers just bind to the plasma membrane. After washing, pore formation is initiated by warming up the preparation. In contrast to SLO membrane, permeabilization with digitonin is insensitive to temperature and therefore more difficult to control (Ahnert-Hilger *et al.*, 1989a,b).

C. ASSAY FOR EXOCYTOSIS IN PERMEABILIZED BOVINE ADRENAL CHROMAFFIN CELLS AND RAT PHEOCHROMOCYTOMA (PC12) CELLS

Secretion by chromaffin cells has been our specific area of interest. To study the final events during secretion by exocytosis, bovine adrenal chromaffin cells in short-term culture and rat pheochromocytoma (PC12) cells are used. Both cell types take up labeled catecholamines and store them within secretory vesicles from which they can be released on stimulation. The released catecholamines can be detected in the supernatant. After permeabilization of the plasma membrane, release of catecholamines can be triggered by micromolar concentrations of free Ca^{2+} (Ahnert-Hilger *et al.*, 1985, 1989b, 1992).

Most of the studies dealing with exocytosis by permeabilized cells involve an "intracellular medium" containing potassium as a main cation and glutamate as an anion (KG buffer). The free Ca^{2+} concentration under resting conditions as well as during stimulation within the cells is in the micromolar range. Therefore, Ca^{2+} must be carefully controlled in the buffers used. A combination of chelators for divalent cations is suitable to buffer the free Ca^{2+} concentration from 0.1 to 100 μM.

Solutions

Examples of KG buffers used in the analysis of exocytosis from permeabilized chromaffin or PC12 cells follow.

1. *1 M $Mg(CH_3COO)_2$ stock solution:* Dissolve 2.145 g $Mg(CH_3COO)_2 \cdot 4H_2O$ in 10 ml of distilled water.

2. *1 M $CaCl_2$ stock solution:* Dissolve 1.47 g $CaCl_2 \cdot 2H_2O$ in 10 ml of distilled water.

3. *KG buffer I with Mg^{2+}/ATP for permeabilization and incubation before the stimulation:* 150 m*M* K^+-glutamate, 2 m*M* EGTA, 2 m*M* EDTA, 20 m*M* Pipes, 2 m*M* Na^+/ATP, 1 m*M* free Mg^{2+}. For 500 ml, dissolve 13.9 g K^+-glutamate, 0.38 g EGTA (free acid), 0.2 g EDTA (free acid), 3.02 g Pipes (free acid), and 0.61 g Na/ATP in about 300 ml of water, add KOH to a pH of 7.0, and stir at room temperature. Add 2.4 ml of 1 *M* $Mg(CH_3COO)_2$, which gives a final free Mg^{2+} concentration of 1 m*M*, and adjust the pH exactly to 7.0 with KOH. Fill up to 500 ml.

4. *KG buffer II with Mg^{2+}/ATP and Ca^{2+} (15 μM free) for stimulation:* For 100 ml, dissolve one-fifth of the amount of salts for KG buffer I in about 60 ml. Add 370 μl of 1 *M* $Mg(CH_3COO)_2$ and 310 μl of 1 *M* $Ca(Cl)_2$, which gives a final free Mg^{2+} concentration of 1 m*M* and a final free Ca^{2+} concentration of 15 μM. Adjust the pH exactly to 7.0 with KOH. Fill up to 100 ml. In some experiments, i.e., in permeabilized PC12 cells, ATP may be omitted during permeabilization and/or stimulation (Ahnert-Hilger *et al.*, 1985, 1989a,b).

5. *KG buffer III without ATP and Ca^{2+}:* For 500 ml, the procedure is the same except that Na/ATP is omitted. Add 1.55 ml of $Mg(CH_3COO)_2$, which gives a final free Mg^{2+} concentration of 1 m*M*, and adjust the pH exactly to 7.0 with KOH. Fill up to 100 ml.

6. *KG buffer IV without ATP but with Ca^{2+} (15 μM free):* For 100 ml, the procedure is the same as for KG buffer II except that Na/ATP is omitted. Add

190 μl of 1 *M* $Mg(CH_3COO)_2$ and 310 μl of 1 *M* $Ca(Cl)_2$, which gives a final free Mg^{2+} concentration of 1 m*M* and a final free Ca^{2+} concentration of 15 μ*M*. Adjust the pH to 7.0 and fill up to 100 ml.

The free Ca^{2+} and Mg^{2+} concentrations are calculated by a computer program and may be controlled by Ca^{2+}- and Mg^{2+}-specific electrodes (Föhr *et al.*, 1993). Other conditions with respect to chelators, ATP, free Mg^{2+}, or free Ca^{2+} concentrations are also possible but must be calculated by the above-mentioned computer program. Each Ca^{2+} buffer has to be prepared separately. Buffers can be stored at −20°C for months but should be thawed only once mainly because of decomposition of ATP.

D. ASSAY FOR EXOCYTOSIS FROM BOVINE ADRENAL CHROMAFFIN CELLS IN PRIMARY CULTURE

Solutions

1. *Ca^{2+}-free Krebs (KR) buffer:* 140 m*M* NaCl, 4.7 m*M* KCl, 1.2 m*M* KH_2PO_4, 1.2 m*M* $MgSO_4$, 20 m*M* Pipes, 11 m*M* glucose, pH 7.0. For 1 liter, dissolve 8.2 g NaCl, 0.35 g KCl, 0.16 g KH_2PO_4, 0.3 g $MgSO_4 \cdot 7H_2O$, and 4.8 g Hepes (free acid) in 800 ml of distilled water, adjust the pH to 7.0 with NaOH, and fill up to 1 liter. Store in appropriate aliquots at −20°C. Add glucose (0.218 g per 100 ml) before use.

2. *100 mM ascorbic acid:* For 10 ml, dissolve 0.176 g ascorbic acid in distilled water. Store in aliquots at −20°C.

3. *l-[7,8-^{3}H] Noradrenaline ([^{3}H]NE, 15 Ci/mmole):* Catalog No. TRA.584, Amersham Buchler.

4. *DMEM:* Catalog No. 041-01965, Gibco, Germany Life Technologies GmbH.

Steps

Adrenal chromaffin cells grown in 24-multiwell plates

1. To load one 24-multiwell plate, mix 66 μl of 100 m*M* ascorbic acid with 7 μl [^{3}H]NE and 6.6 ml DMEM. For one 100-mm culture dish, mix 100 μl 100 m*M* ascorbic acid with 10 μl [^{3}H]NE and 10 ml of DMEM.

2. Label cells (250 μl/well) with radioactive noradrenaline for 2 hr in the cell incubator.

3. Aspirate the labeling medium and chase cells for 1–2 hr in DMEM.

4. Aspirate DMEM and wash cells with KR buffer four times for 5 min.

5. Wash cells once with 200 μl KG buffer I or III.

6. Aspirate supernatant and add 200 μl of α-toxin or SLO dissolved in KG buffer I or III. Incubate with pore-forming toxins: α-toxin for 20–30 min at 25, 30, or 37°C; SLO for 5 min at 0°C or between 1 and 2 min at 25, 30, or 37°C. About 30 HU/ml α-toxin or SLO, corresponding to 300 HU/10^7 cells, is used.

7. Aspirate solution.

8. Incubate with substances to be tested dissolved in KG buffer I or III from 5 min to 40 min at 25, 30, or 37°C.

9. Aspirate solution.

10. Add 200 μl KG buffer II and incubate for 3–10 min at 25, 30, or 37°C (stimulation).

11. Aspirate solution. Determine released catecholamines in the supernatant by liquid scintillation counting.

12. Add 200 μl/well 0.2% SDS to solubilize the cells and to determine the remaining catecholamines.

PC12 cells

1. Label one 100-mm dish with 10 ml [^{3}H]NE solution for 2 hr in the cell incubator.
2. Aspirate the labeling medium and chase cells for 1–2 hr in DMEM.
3. Aspirate DMEM and wash cells with KR buffer four times for 5 min.
4. Wash cells once with 10 ml KG buffer I or III.
5. Suspend cells in 0.6–0.9 ml KG buffer I or III and divide in 12–18 vials (50 μl each) corresponding to about 2–3 $\times$ 10^5 cells/sample already containing 50 μl of 100 HU/ml α-toxin or SLO corresponding to about 300–500 HU/10^7 cells. Incubate for 20–30 min at 25, 30, or 37°C with α-toxin or 5 min on ice with SLO.
6. Centrifuge each sample at 3000 *g* for 20 sec and remove supernatant.
7. Resuspend pellet in 100 μl of KG buffer I or III containing the substances to be tested and incubate from 5 min to 40 min at 25, 30, or 37°C.
8. Repeat step 6.
9. Resuspend in 100 μl KG buffer II or IV and incubate for 3–10 min at 25, 30, or 37°C (stimulation).
10. Repeat step 6. Determine released catecholamines in the supernatant by liquid scintillation counting.
11. Add 200 μl/tube 0.2% SDS to solubilize the cells and to determine the remaining catecholamines.

Note that stimulation of exocytosis in chromaffin cells requires the presence of Mg^{2+}/ATP.

IV. Comments

The half-maximal free Ca^{2+} concentration necessary to elicit exocytosis varies between 1 and 10 μM depending on the cell preparations, but is always three- to fivefold higher in α-toxin-permeabilized cells; however, the permeability to Ca^{2+} is the same in cells treated with either α-toxin, SLO, or digitonin (see Ahnert-Hilger *et al.*, 1989b). Thus, in the α-toxin-permeabilized preparations an additional buffering of Ca^{2+} by intracellular proteins may be the reason.

Table I gives an example of noradrenaline release from α-toxin- or SLO-permeabilized bovine adrenal chromaffin cells.

TABLE I [^{3}H]Noradrenaline Release (%)

	α-Toxin	SLO
Buffer	2.4 ± 0.3	2.4 ± 0.7
Ca^{2+} 15 μM	21.6 ± 1	17.1 ± 0.7

ACKNOWLEDGMENTS

The author thanks her colleagues in Ulm, M. Gratzl, and in Mainz, S. Bhakdi and U. Weller, who made these studies possible.

REFERENCES

Ahnert-Hilger, G., Bader, M.-F., Bhakdi, S., and Gratzl, M. (1989a) Introduction of macromolecules into bovine adrenal medullary chromaffin cells and rat pheochromocytoma cells (PC12) by permeabilization with streptolysin O: Inhibitory effect of tetanus toxin on catecholamine secretion. *J. Neurochem.* **52**, 1751–1758.

Ahnert-Hilger, G., Bhakdi, S., and Gratzl, M. (1985) Minimal requirements for exocytosis. A study using PC12 cells permeabilized with staphylococcal alphatoxin. *J. Biol. Chem.* **260**, 12730–12734.

Ahnert-Hilger, G., Dayanithi, G., Spicher, K., and Nordmann, J. J. (1992) G-protein mediates inhibition and activation of Ca^{2+}-induced exocytosis from SLO-permeabilized peptidergic nerve endings. *Biosci. Rep.* **12**, 463–469.

Ahnert-Hilger, G., Mach, W., Föhr, K. J., and Gratzl, M. (1989b) Poration by alphatoxin and streptolysin O: An approach to analyze intracellular processes. *Methods Cell Biol.* **31**, 63–90.

Bhakdi, S., and Tranum-Jensen, J. (1987) Damage to mammalian cells by proteins that form transmembrane pores. *Rev. Physiol. Biochem. Pharmacol.* **107**, 147–223.

Föhr, K. J., Warchol, W., and Gratzl, M. (1993) Calculation and control of free divalent cations in solutions used for membrane fusion studies. *In* "Methods in Enzymology" (N. Düzgünes, ed.), Vol. 221, pp. 149–157. Academic Press, San Diego.

Lind, I., Ahnert-Hilger, G., and Gratzl, M. (1987) Purification of α-toxin from *Staphylococcus aureus* and application to cell permeabilization. *Anal. Biochem.* **164**, 84–89.

Palmer, M., Jursch, R., Weller, U., Veleva, A., Hilgert, K., Kehoe, M., and Bhakdi, S. (1993) *Staphylococcus aureus* α-toxin. Production of functionally intact, modifiable protein by introduction of cysteine at positions 69, 130, and 136. *J. Biol. Chem.* **268**, 11963–11967.

Introduction of Small Molecules into Cells Using a Transient Cell Permeabilization System

Curtis J. Henrich

I. Introduction

Introduction of molecules into cells has been an ongoing problem in cell biology (Schulz, 1990; Weisman *et al.*, 1989; see also other articles in this section). A number of methods are currently available for introduction of nucleic acids into cells (Lindau and Gomperts, 1991). Although some of these, including microinjection and electroporation, are also appropriate for small molecules, they tend to require extensive expertise and/or expensive equipment (Knight and Scrutton, 1986; Tsong, 1991). Permeabilization of cells with detergents such as saponin and digitonin has also been commonly used to probe the intracellular environment with small molecules (Koopmann and Jackson, 1990). Unfortunately, detergents cause extensive and irreversible damage, making them unsuitable for experiments requiring intact cells or long time periods. Cell-porating toxins such as α-toxin and streptolysin O maintain membrane structural features but are also irreversible (Bhakdi and Tranum-Jensen, 1991; Menestrina *et al.*, 1990). An alternative approach is the use of a lipid-based transient cell permeabilization system commercially available under the name Trans-Port.

II. Materials and Instrumentation

The Trans-Port Transient Cell Permeabilization Kit, obtained from Gibco-BRL (Cat. No. 3464SA), contains all buffers and permeabilization reagents. Cell lines were obtained from the American Type Culture Collection (ATCC) and were grown in appropriate media (all cell culture materials were from Gibco-BRL).

III. Procedures

A. PERMEABILIZATION OF CELLS IN SUSPENSION

Solutions

The following solutions are supplied with the commercial kit and should be stored at 4°C.

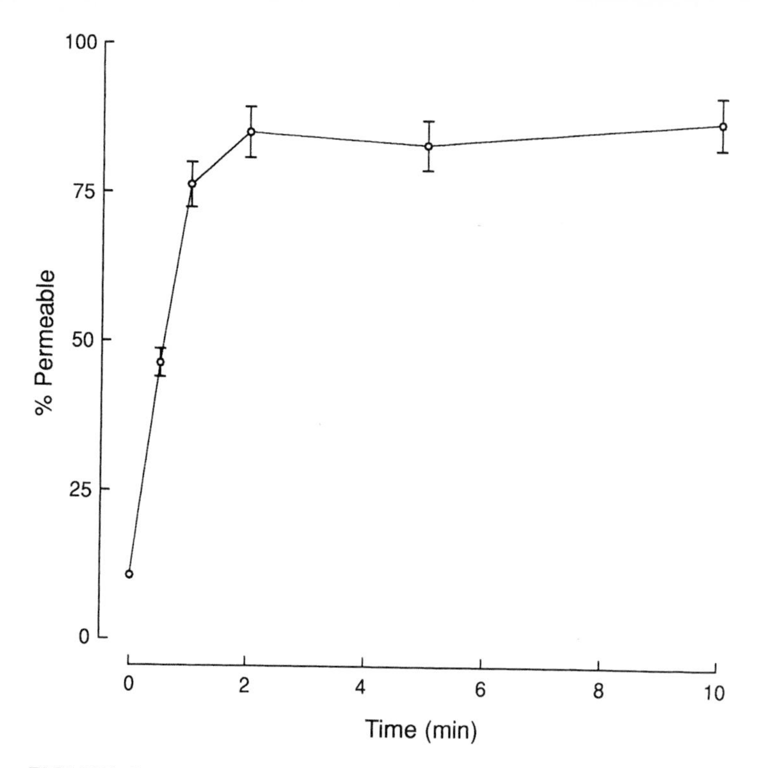

FIGURE 1 *Permeabilization of cells in suspension.* Burkitt lymphoma (Daudi) cells were permeabilized for 0 to 10 min in the presence of trypan blue at 10^6 cells/ml as described in the text. Permeabilization was determined by trypan blue uptake (% blue = % permeable). Error bars represent standard deviations, three independent experiments (>100 cells counted per assay).

1. *Intracellular buffer (ICB):* 10 m*M* Hepes, pH 7.0, 0.14 *M* KCl, 0.01 *M* NaCl, 2.4 m*M* $MgCl_2$.
2. *Trans-Port reagent:* A proprietary lipid mediator of cell permeability, dissolved in ICB.
3. *A protein-containing stop solution for reversal of permeabilization.*
4. *0.5% (w/v) trypan blue in ICB.*

Steps

1. Prepare (trypsinize attached cells, or directly use cells growing in suspension culture) and wash cells by centrifugation and resuspension in Ca^{2+}, Mg^{2+}-free–PBS (CMF–PBS).
2. Resuspend cells in prewarmed (37°C) ICB at 1–2 × 10^6 cells/ml.
3. To 0.25 ml cell suspension, add 25 μl of trypan blue or other test solution in ICB. Trypan blue is recommended in at least one pilot experiment while conditions are being optimized for a particular cell type.
4. *Immediately* add 15 μl Trans-Port reagent and mix gently.
5. Incubate at 37°C for 1–10 min with occasional mixing. Figure 1 shows a typical time course of permeabilization using Burkitt lymphoma cells.
6. Stop by adding of 30 μl Trans-Port stop solution.
7. Recover cells by centrifugation (5 min, 300 *g*) and *gently* resuspend in

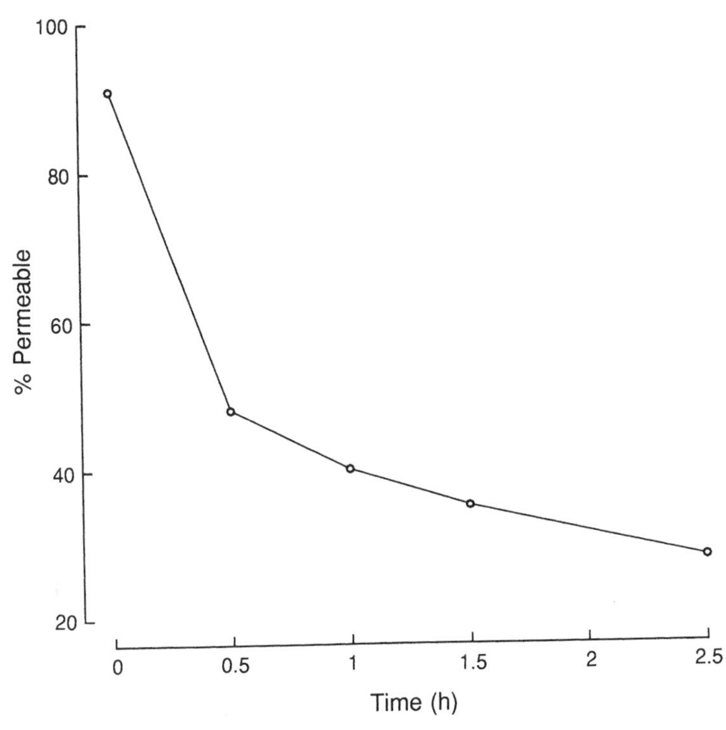

FIGURE 2 *Recovery of membrane integrity after permeabilization.* Burkitt lymphoma cells were permeabilized for 10 min at 10^6 cells/ml, stopped, collected, and resuspended in growth medium as described in the text. At indicated times, cell permeability was determined in aliquots by trypan blue uptake.

culture medium. Membrane integrity is restored over time (see Fig. 2 for an example).

B. PERMEABILIZATION OF ATTACHED CELLS *IN SITU*

Steps

1. Plate cells on 24-well plates at a density (varies with cell type) to achieve about 50% confluency at 1 day.
2. After 24 hr, remove medium and wash cells twice with 0.5 ml CMF–PBS.
3. Add 0.36 ml ICB (at 37°C) per well.
4. Add 30 μl test solution in ICB. Again, a pilot experiment with trypan blue is recommended (although entrance of trypan blue into cells may be more difficult to observe with attached cells).
5. *Immediately* add 10 μl of Trans-Port reagent.
6. Incubate 1–10 min at 37°C. Figure 3 shows a time course of HeLa cell permeabilization.
7. Stop by addition of 40 μl Trans-Port stop solution.
8. Allow cells to recover in medium.

IV. Comments

Cells must be serum free during the permeabilization step. The presence of serum proteins may diminish the effectiveness of the Trans-Port reagent by adsorbing the lipid.

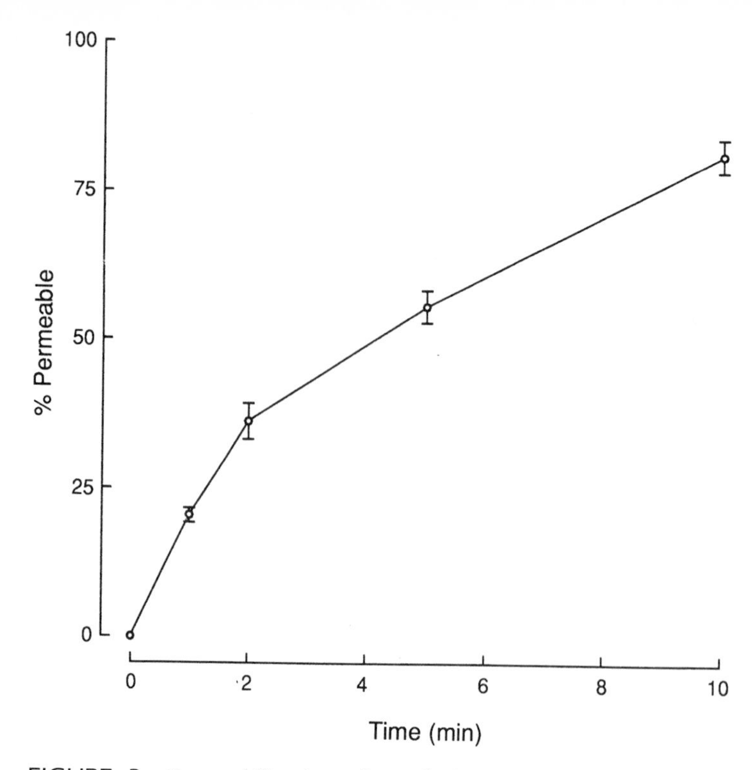

FIGURE 3 *Permeabilization of attached cells.* HeLa cells were permeabilized in 24-well plates for 0 to 10 min in the presence of trypan blue as described in the text. Permeabilization was determined by trypan blue uptake (% blue = % permeable). Error bars represent ranges from duplicate wells (>100 cells counted per well).

The upper size limit for introduction of small molecules into susceptible cells is between 2000 and 6000 based on use of this technique with labeled peptides and small proteins.

Not all cells can be permeabilized by Trans-Port. Table I lists a number of cell types that have been shown to be susceptible (i.e., >75% of cells permeable using the conditions detailed here) and not susceptible (<50%) to Trans-Port.

Applicability of Trans-Port to a specific cell type and small molecule must be tested and optimized.

Because membrane permeability may persist (see Fig. 2), it may be desirable to include small molecules of interest in the recovery medium.

TABLE I Permeabilization of Various Cell Types with Trans-Port

Human	Murine	Other
Susceptibile (>75% permeabilization)		
HeLa	BC3H1	DDT-1 MF2
SiHa	NIE 115	IEC 6
Daudi	32D	
Jurkat	CTB6	
HL-60	7TD1	
Not susceptible (<50% permeabilization)		
WI 38	Swiss 3T3	BHK
	NIH 3T3	COS 7
	401 L	CHO

Examples shown here have been previously published (Henrich, 1990; Karger *et al.*, 1990). This procedure has also been used to introduce ions, nucleotides and analogs (ATP, biotin-14-dATP), fluorescein-labeled peptides, and fluorophores.

V. Pitfalls

1. The Trans-Port reagent inhibits protein kinase C and so care must be taken in applying this procedure where maintenance of protein kinase C activity is necessary. It is important to test the effect of this, or any, cell permeabilizing reagent on cellular criteria of interest such as enzymatic activities.

2. Trans-Port does not work as well on attached cells as on cells in suspension.

3. Cells *must* be healthy. Viability should be greater than 90% at the start of an experiment. We have generally used cells growing in log phase although this is not absolutely necessary.

4. When permeabilizing attached cells, it is often difficult to assess extent of permeabilization using trypan blue.

REFERENCES

Bhakdi, S., and Tranum-Jensen, J. (1991) Alpha toxin of *Streptococcus aureus. Microbiol. Rev.* **55**, 733–751.

Henrich, C. J. (1990) Introduction of small molecules into cells: A transient cell permeabilization kit. *Focus* **12**, 17–19.

Karger, B. D., Sykes-Saloranta, A. G., Shonk, L. A., and Henrich, C. J. (1990) The Trans-Port transient cell permeabilization kit: An update. *Focus* **12**, 110–111.

Knight, D., and Scrutton, M. C. (1986) Gaining access to the cytosol: The technique and some applications of electroporation. *Biochem. J.* **234**, 497–506.

Koopmann, W. R., and Jackson, R. C. (1990) Calcium and guanine-nucleotide-dependent exocytosis in permeabilized mast cells. *Biochem. J.* **265**, 365–373.

Lindau, M., and Gomperts, B. D. (1991) Techniques and concepts in exocytosis: Focus on mast cells. *Biochim. Biophys. Acta* **1071**, 429–471.

Menestrina, G., Bashford, C. L., and Pasternak, C. A. (1990) Pore-forming toxins: Experiments with *S. aureus* α-toxin, *C. perfringens* θ-toxin and *E. coli* haemolysin in lipid bilayers, liposomes and intact cells. *Toxicon* **28**, 477–491.

Schulz, I. (1990) Permeabilizing cells: Some methods and applications for the study of intracellular processes. *In "Methods in Enzymology"* (S. Fleischer and B. Fleischer, eds.), Vol. 192, pp. 280–300. Academic Press, San Diego.

Tsong, T. Y. (1991) Electroporation of cell membranes. *Biophys. J.* **60**, 297–306.

Weisman, G. A., Lustig, K. D., Friedberg, I., and Heppel, L. A. (1989) Permeabilizing mammalian cells to macromolecules. *In "Methods in Enzymology"* (S. Fleischer and B. Fleischer, eds.), Vol. 171, pp. 857–869. Academic Press, San Diego.

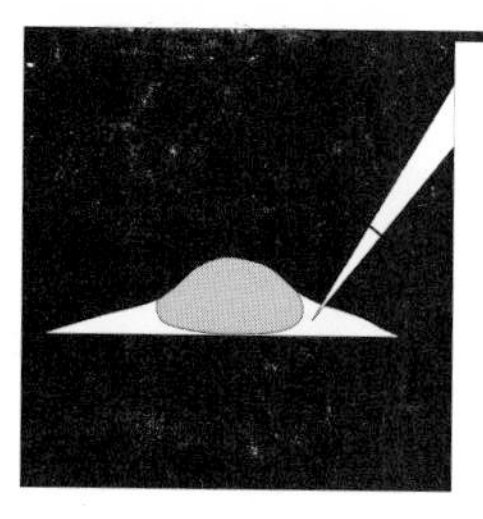

Microinjection of RNAs into *Xenopus* Oocytes

Glenn Matthews

I. Introduction

While translation of mRNA in cell-free systems is a convenient way of generating a primary protein product, expression in living cells is necessary if the full range of post-translational modifications, protein–protein interactions, and final cellular localization of the protein are to be investigated. Although cultured cells can be microinjected with mRNA, the *Xenopus* oocyte is the most robust and easily handled system for such studies.

The fully grown *Xenopus* oocyte is a large (>1-mm-diameter) cell, making manipulation easy, and has a high capacity for translation, synthesizing more than 20 ng of protein per hour. Microinjected mRNAs compete with the endogenous pool and can direct up to 10% of total protein synthesis. Radioactive labeling under routine conditions with [^{35}S]methionine yields a specific activity of around 10^7 dpm/μg protein synthesized, so it is possible to generate on the order of 2×10^4 dpm of product in a single oocyte during a 10-h labeling period.

Despite the presence of a functional secretory pathway, as demonstrated by the appropriate post-translational modification and targeting of many proteins expressed from injected mRNAs (Colman, 1984), the oocyte shows a very low level of endogenous secretion (Zehavi-Wilner and Lane, 1977). Radiolabeled secretory proteins translated from microinjected mRNAs can therefore often be detected directly by electrophoresis and fluorography of samples of media without the need for immunoprecipitation or other purification techniques.

II. Materials and Instrumentation

A. *XENOPUS LAEVIS*

Frogs can be obtained from local commercial suppliers (Blades Biological Ltd) or from the African Reptile Park. Specify large, mature (preferably more than 2 years old) females when ordering.

The maintenance of *Xenopus laevis* is a broad subject and is beyond the scope of this article. Before establishing a new colony it is advisable to consult the relevant animal licensing authority to determine what regulations are in force concerning accommodation and supervision of the animals. This subject is covered in detail by Wu and Gerhart (1991).

B. INJECTION EQUIPMENT

The simplest and most cost-effective injection system is the Drummond Nanoject (Laser Laboratory Systems). This is essentially a motor-driven positive displacement pipette and is available in versions that deliver fixed (46 nl) or variable (4.6–73.6 nl) volumes. The setting of the fixed model can be changed by substituting a chip in the controller, but the flexibility of the variable version is a distinct advantage. The injector can be operated by hand via a control box, but the optional foot switch is worthwhile if more than a small number of oocytes are to be injected in a session.

The injector must be mounted on a micromanipulator. Although many experienced workers use the Singer type, which allows free movement in three planes, a micrometer-driven system such as the Brinkmann MM33 (Laser Laboratory Systems) drives the injection needle into, and out of, the oocyte in a straight line at a preset angle, rather than relying on the manual dexterity of the operator.

Injection needles are prepared from $3\frac{1}{2}$-in. hard glass capillaries (Drummond 3-000-203-G/X) using a Narashige PN-3 horizontal micropipette puller (Narishige International).

C. OTHER EQUIPMENT

A good stereo microscope with a long working distance, ideally equipped with a zoom facility to provide a magnification range of 10× to 40×, and a fiberoptic light source are required for dissection and injection of oocytes. A cooled incubator capable of maintaining a temperature of 21°C is needed for oocyte culture. Microfuge tubes (1.5 ml) with pestles for homogenization of oocytes (Kontes, Cat. No. 749520-0000) are from Hoefer Scientific Instruments Ltd.

D. CHEMICALS

Penicillin–streptomycin (Cat. No. P-0781), gentamicin (Cat. No. G-1397), nystatin (Cat. No. N-1638), 3-aminobenzoic acid ethyl ester (Cat. No. A-5040), and PMSF (Cat. No. P-7626) are from Sigma. Protein A–Sepharose (Cat. No. 17-0708-01) is from Pharmacia Biotech. [^{35}S]Methionine (Cat. No. SJ 204) is from Amersham International. All other reagents are of the best grade available and purchased from major suppliers.

Solutions are prepared using reverse osmosis or double glass-distilled water.

III. Procedures

A. OBTAINING OOCYTES

Solutions

1. *MS-222 (anesthetic solution):* Dissolve 1 g 3-aminobenzoic acid ethyl ester (MS-222) in 1 liter water and use immediately.

2. *High salt stock:* Dissolve 128 g NaCl, 2 g KCl, 5 g $NaHCO_3$, and 89 g Hepes in 800 ml water and adjust the pH to 7.6 using 1 *M* NaOH. Make up to 1 liter and store as 40-ml aliquots at −20°C.

3. *Divalent cation stock:* Dissolve 1.9 g $Ca(NO_3)_2 \cdot 4H_2O$, 2.25 g $CaCl_2 \cdot 6H_2O$, and 5 g $MgSO_4 \cdot 7H_2O$ in 1 liter of water and store as 40-ml aliquots at −20°C.

4. *Antibiotics:* The preparations of antibiotics specified above are supplied as solutions at 1000-fold the working concentration.

5. *Modified Barths' saline (MBS):* 88 m*M* NaCl, 1 m*M* KCl, 2.4 m*M* $NaHCO_3$, 15 m*M* Hepes–NaOH, pH 7.6, 0.3 m*M* $Ca(NO_3)_2$, 0.41 m*M* $CaCl_2$, 0.82 m*M* $MgSO_4$, 10 U/ml penicillin, 10 μg/ml streptomycin, 50 μg/ml gentamicin, 10 U/ml nystatin. To make MBS, mix, in the following order, 900 ml water, 40 ml high salt stock, 40 ml divalent cation stock, 1 ml of each antibiotic stock solution. Make the volume up to 1 liter and use within 2 days. Store at 4°C.

Steps

1. Anesthetize a sexually mature female frog by immersion in 0.1% MS-222 for 30 min to 1 h.
2. Place the frog on its back on a bed of ice and make an incision about 1 cm long in the skin and then the body wall at the side of the abdomen. Avoid the midline, where there is a major blood vessel.
3. Tease a few lobes of the ovary out of the incision, using blunt forceps, snip them off using scissors, and transfer immediately to a petri dish containing MBS.
4. Separately suture the body wall and skin of the frog and return it to shallow water to recover.
5. Wash the tissue in MBS to remove blood and break into small (pea-sized) clumps by tearing it apart with two pairs of watchmakers' forceps.
6. Working under the stereo microscope, hold a small clump of ovary with one pair of watchmakers' forceps and gently pull off individual oocytes using a second pair.
7. Transfer isolated large (≥1-mm-diameter) oocytes to fresh MBS using a Pasteur pipette and store at 15–20°C.

A mature frog contains many tens of thousands of oocytes at various stages of development and only a few hundred would normally be required for most experiments. Occasionally the frog will be killed and the whole ovary removed either because reuse of the animal is forbidden by local animal regulations (as is now the case in the United Kingdom) or because large numbers of oocytes are required. In this case, the frog should be killed by increasing the MS-222 concentration to 2% or by injection of barbiturate, before removal of the ovary.

B. MICROINJECTION

1. Preparation and calibration of injection apparatus

Before attempting a real experiment, it is advisable to become familiar with the apparatus and procedures.

a. Preparing needles

Sterilize capillaries by baking them at 160°C for at least 2 h, in a glass test tube or a small measuring cylinder, capped with aluminum foil.

By use of the Narashige horizontal puller according to the manufacturer's instructions, with all controls set to maximum values, the outside diameter of the resulting needles is reduced from 1 mm to 200–300 μm over about 2 mm of length; it then tapers to 10 μm or so over the next 5–6 mm. Although needles can be produced very rapidly with this apparatus, it is advisable to make a number (10–20) at a session, so they are available immediately during later steps.

The diameter at the tip of the needle should be 20–30 μm; if it is any finer, it will restrict the flow, leading to variability in the amount injected, whereas blunter needles will damage the oocytes. Trim needles back to this point by breaking the tip with a pair of fine forceps. Fill needles from the back with mineral oil, using a 26-gauge spinal needle, and mount onto the injector according to the manufacturer's instructions. Avoid introducing air bubbles during these operations as these will compress and damp the action of the injector. Take care to ensure that all seals are in the correct location and orientation.

Mount the injector to one side of the microscope stage, in a position that allows the full range of movement of the manipulator to be used. The tip of the needle is very fragile, so care should be taken not to bring it into contact with the microscope.

b. Filling the needle

Pipette 1–2 μl of the injection solution onto a piece of sealing film (Parafilm or Nescofilm), lower the tip of the needle into this, and draw the solution up. To avoid taking any air into the system, it is normally necessary to leave some liquid on the film.

c. Calibration

In principle, calibration should be unnecessary when using an automatic system. It is good practice, however, to check that a predictable, reproducible volume is being delivered by the needle and injector. To do this, fill the needle with sterile water and inject it into a 3-μl droplet of mineral oil on a piece of sealing film. Strictly, the diameter of the bubble of water should be measured using a calibrated graticule and the volume determined. Experience has shown, however, that a freely flowing needle will dispense a reproducible (as judged by eye) bubble at every delivery when the device is set to deliver its smallest volume (4.6 nl), whereas needles which are blocked or too narrow deliver variable amounts at this setting. This provides a rapid and simple means of checking a needle during an experiment.

2. Injection

Solution

mRNA: The preparation of mRNA is discussed in Section IV. Whatever the source of the mRNA, the concentration should be in the range 50–1000 μg/ml in sterile water. Before use, clarify RNA solutions by centrifugation in a microfuge for 10 min at 4°C to pellet any suspended matter that would otherwise block the injection needle.

Steps

1. Fill the needle with the mRNA to be injected.
2. Pick up 5–10 oocytes in a shortened Pasteur pipette and transfer them individually, each in a small drop of MBS, onto a microscope slide.
3. Remove most of the medium from the oocytes using a 200-μl pipette and yellow tip.
4. Under the microscope, using forceps, maneuver an oocyte so that the vegetal (unpigmented) pole is facing the needle.
5. Gently drive the needle into the oocyte, until the tip is approximately in the middle of the vegetal half, and inject the mRNA.

6. Withdraw the needle and move to the next oocyte. When all oocytes on a slide have been injected, wash them into a petri dish containing MBS.

C. METABOLIC LABELING OF TRANSLATION PRODUCTS

Although it may not be important for many experiments, in situations where the incubation medium is to be analyzed (e.g., when secretory proteins are translated) cell death can compromise interpretation of data. Dead oocytes can easily be identified by the breakdown of the pigmentation pattern, but it is often difficult to identify this at an early stage. Although some batches are simply refractory to culture, a proportion dying over any period, most death due to injection damage, toxic contaminants in RNA samples, or faulty buffers occurs over the first 12 hr or so. It is therefore best, wherever possible, to incubate injected oocytes overnight before selecting healthy individuals for labeling.

Solutions

1. *Sterile MBS:* Sterilize 50 ml of MBS by passage through a prerinsed 0.22-μm filter and add fresh antibiotics immediately before use.

2. *1 mg/ml BSA:* Dissolve 50 mg bovine serum albumin in 50 ml sterile water. Store unused solution at −20°C.

3. *Labeling medium:* Add [^{35}S]methionine to sterile MBS at 1 mCi/ml. Prepare 6 μl per oocyte to be labeled.

Steps

1. Prepare either 1.5 ml microfuge tubes or 12 × 8 format microtiter plates by filling with 1 mg/ml BSA, standing at room temperature for 1 hr, and then washing repeatedly with sterile water.

2. Wash oocytes in two or three changes of sterile MBS.

3. Transfer five oocytes to each tube or microtiter well, remove medium using a 200-μl pipette, and add 30 μl of labeling medium. Ensure the oocytes are completely submerged.

4. Incubate at 21°C overnight. Microtiter plates should be incubated in a moist chamber, as they are not sealed against evaporation.

5. Collect the medium with a pipette and yellow tip, immediately add fresh unlabeled MBS, and then transfer the oocytes to a petri dish of MBS. Examine the oocytes under the stereo microscope to check that they are healthy. Good oocytes from batches containing dead ones can normally be analyzed for intracellular products, but the medium from these batches should be discarded.

6. Transfer oocytes to 1.5-ml homogenizer tubes and either analyze immediately or freeze by completely draining them of medium and allowing them to stand on dry ice.

D. HOMOGENIZATION AND ANALYSIS

1. Immunoprecipitation of Translation Products

Translation products, particularly secreted proteins in samples of medium, from single mRNAs can often be visualized directly on fluorographs of SDS gels. It is normally necessary, however, to immunoprecipitate from oocyte homogenates to obtain a clear result. A substantial fraction of the protein in an oocyte is yolk and it is normally preferable to remove this from the homogenate before analysis. Yolk platelets are stable in Triton-containing buffers and so can be simply pelleted from the initial homogenate.

Solutions

1. *PMSF:* Prepare 20 ml of a 100 m*M* stock solution in isopropanol and store at 4°C. PMSF is unstable in aqueous solutions and so should be added immediately before use.

2. *Homogenization buffer:* 20 m*M* Tris–HCl, pH 7.6, 0.1 *M* NaCl, 1% Triton X-100. Dissolve 0.24 g Tris base and 0.58 g NaCl in 80 ml water, adjust the pH to 7.6 with HCl, add 10 ml 10% Triton X-100, and make up to 100 ml. Store at −20°C. Immediately before use, add 1% by volume 100 m*M* PMSF.

3. *Immunoprecipitation buffers (NET/NET-Gel):* Prepare NET buffer by dissolving 0.6 g Tris base (50 m*M*) and 0.88 g NaCl (150 m*M*) in 80 ml water, add 200 μl 500 m*M* EDTA (1 m*M*), and adjust the pH to 7.5 with HCl. Add 1 ml 10% Triton X-100 and make up to 100 ml. Store at −20°C. To make NET-Gel, add 25 mg (0.25%) gelatin to 10 ml NET buffer and dissolve by warming to 37°C for 15 min. Allow the mixture to cool and add 100 μl 100 m*M* PMSF. Use immediately.

4. *Protein A–Sepharose:* Swell 350 mg of protein A–Sepharose in 10 ml NET at 4°C for at least 3 hr with gentle agitation. Pellet the beads at 2000 *g* for 5 min at 4°C, decant the supernatant, and add 10 ml 1 *M* Tris–HCl, pH 7.5. Leave at 4°C for 1 hr, then wash twice with NET, estimate the volume of Sepharose (this should be approximately 1 ml), and add 9 vol of NET. Store at 4°C. To use, mix well, remove 100 μl per sample, and wash twice in fresh NET, resuspending in the original volume.

Steps

1. On ice, add homogenization buffer to drained fresh or frozen oocytes at 40 μl per oocyte and homogenize immediately. If a large number of oocytes are to be processed in one tube, it may be easier to add only a fraction of the buffer, break the oocytes, and then add the remainder of the buffer.

2. Pellet the yolk in a microfuge at 13,000 rpm at 4°C for 10 min and transfer the supernatant to a fresh tube. The homogenate can be stored frozen at −20°C at this stage, if required.

3. Add 200 μl oocyte homogenate (5 oocyte equivalents) to 800 μl NET-Gel buffer, then add an appropriate volume of antiserum (usually 1–5 μl of whole serum, depending on the titer). Incubate at 4°C for 3 hr to overnight.

4. Add 100 μl 10% protein A–Sepharose and incubate at 4°C with gentle agitation (e.g., on a rotating wheel) for 1–3 hr.

5. Pellet the Sepharose beads in a microfuge for 30 sec at 4°C and remove the supernatant. The supernatant may now be reanalyzed using a second antibody.

6. Wash the Sepharose beads with at least three washes of 1 ml of NET buffer. Drain the buffer as much as possible after the last wash and add 90 μl SDS sample buffer. Heat to 95°C for 2 min and analyze 20 μl (1 oocyte equivalent) by SDS–PAGE (see article by Julio E. Celis and Eydfinnur Olsen).

2. Membrane Fractionation

Separation of oocyte homogenate into membrane and cytosol fractions before analysis is a relatively simple procedure. It not only can be used to determine the location of cytoplasmic, secretory and integral membrane proteins, but can also provide a degree of concentration and purification that may enable secretory and membrane proteins to be analyzed without the need for immunoprecipitation.

To preserve the integrity of the membranes present, it is particularly important that all solutions and items likely to come into contact with the sample (pipettes, centrifuge tubes, etc.) are completely free of detergents.

Solutions

1. *2× T buffer:* Dissolve 0.375 g KCl (100 m*M*), 0.22 g Mg-acetate·$4H_2O$ (20 m*M*) 0.58 g NaCl (200 m*M*), and 0.24 g Tris base in 40 ml water. Adjust the pH to 7.6 with HCl, make up to 50 ml, and filter-sterilize. Store at −20°C.

2. *40% Sucrose:* Dissolve 20 g sucrose in 50 ml water and filter-sterilize.

3. *T + 10 and T + 20:* Mix 10 ml 2× T buffer with 5 ml water and 5 ml 40% sucrose for T + 10. Mix 10 ml 2× T buffer with 10 ml sucrose for T + 20. Store unused solution at −20°C.

4. *200 mM Sodium carbonate:* Dissolve 2 g anhydrous sodium carbonate in 100 ml water. Check that the pH is 11 and use immediately.

5. *Carbonate sucrose:* Mix 10 ml 40% sucrose with 10 ml 200 m*M* sodium carbonate.

Steps

1. Homogenize 10 oocytes in 0.5 ml T + 10 on ice.

2. Layer the homogenate onto a 1-ml step of T + 20 in a small (1–5 ml) centrifuge tube and centrifuge at 20,000 *g* for 30 min at 4°C in a swing-out rotor. After centrifugation, cytosolic proteins will be in the T + 10 layer, mitochondria at the T + 10/T + 20 interface, and membrane components of the secretory pathway in the pellet, together with yolk platelets and other insoluble matter. The pellet can now be analyzed as a total membrane fraction or further fractionated to separate integral membrane proteins from lumenal secretory proteins, by the following steps.

3. On ice, suspend the membrane pellet in 0.5 ml T + 10, then add 0.5 ml 200 m*M* sodium carbonate.

4. Split the sample into two equal halves and add 50 μl 10% Triton X-100 to one. Incubate both on ice for 30 min.

5. Layer onto a 0.5-ml step of carbonate sucrose and centrifuge at 100,000 *g* for 1 hr at 4°C.

6. Recover 250 μl from the top layer and neutralize by addition of 6 μl concentrated HCl. Discard the carbonate sucrose step and dissolve the pellet in oocyte homogenization buffer.

7. Analyze the fractions directly or by immunoprecipitation. The sample treated with Triton X-100 provides a control to distinguish between membrane-bound and insoluble proteins.

IV. Comments

The methods described here cover only the basic procedures of microinjection, metabolic labeling, and preliminary analysis of translation products. Many further approaches to analysis are possible such as Western blotting, biological/biochemical activity assays, and electrophysiology.

A. MESSENGER RNA

Messenger RNA samples can be from a variety of sources. Commonly they are prepared by either poly(A)+ fractionation of natural RNA, hybrid selection, or *in vitro* transcription. *In vitro* transcription reactions should be designed to incorporate a 5′ cap analog and transcripts should contain a poly(A) tail for efficient translation and stability in the oocyte (Drummond *et al.,* 1985). While transcripts can be tailed enzymatically, the best approach is to clone cDNAs into the vector pSP64T (Krieg and Melton, 1984), where the sequence to be transcribed is flanked by fragments derived from the 5′ and 3′ ends of *Xenopus* β-globin. The 3′ end of this contains a run of 23 A's followed by 30 C's, while sequences at the 5′ end also contribute to enhanced translation (Vize *et al.,* 1991). A simple and reliable protocol for *in vitro* transcription is given by Matthews and Colman (1991). If the yield of an *in vitro* transcription performed by this method is high enough to provide a useful concentration of RNA, the crude transcription mixture can be injected into the oocyte without further purification.

Poly(A)− RNAs are unstable in the oocyte, so labeling of their translation products should be performed immediately after injection.

B. SITE OF INJECTION

Not only do mRNAs move more freely to equilibrate through the cytoplasm if they are injected into the vegetal pole, but this also reduces the chance of injection into the nucleus, which is more likely to be toxic to the oocyte. Although the distribution of mRNA is not important for metabolic labeling studies, some analytical approaches such as electrophysiological measurements will be affected by an uneven distribution of the protein product. In these cases, oocytes should be incubated for 2–3 days before analysis.

C. PROTEIN STABILITY

Most proteins are quite stable in the oocyte but one situation where this may be not the case is where the natural compartment of the protein is not present. Thus nuclear-encoded plant proteins which are localized to the chloroplast or glyoxysome are not detected after mRNA injection into oocytes (Colman, 1984).

Provided that an mRNA is stable, which is normally the case if a 5′ cap and a 3′ poly(A) tail are present, it will continue to direct translation at a more or less constant rate for a number of days. Where the analysis relies on protein activity, prolonged incubation may be advisable as this will lead to increased yields of stable products, although unstable proteins may well reach a steady-state level in just a few hours.

Under the radioactive labeling conditions given here, the rate of ^{35}S uptake increases over the first hour and declines thereafter, so that after 6 hr of labeling, the oocyte is effectively in chase conditions. Clearly, the signal detected from a labeled unstable protein will decrease during a chase.

V. Pitfalls

1. Although mRNAs are normally quite stable in the oocyte, they are prone to degradation during handling. This is normally simple to prevent by baking and autoclaving equipment and buffers that will contact the sample, but some workers experience major problems. Performing a translation reaction in, for example, reticulocyte lysate with a portion of the injection sample provides the simplest check on these effects.

2. Where samples of medium are to be analyzed directly for the presence of secretory proteins, it is particularly important to avoid contamination by bacteria or yeast. These will metabolize radioactive precursors rapidly, leading to a high background signal. Much of the background due to light contamination can be removed by simply pelleting any contaminating cells in a microfuge immediately after harvesting the medium.

REFERENCES

Colman, A. (1984) Translation of eucaryotic mRNA in *Xenopus* oocytes. *In* "Transcription and Translation: A Practical Approach" (B. D. Hames and S. J. Higgins, eds.), pp. 271–300. IRL Press, Oxford.

Drummond, D. R., Armstrong, J., and Colman, A. (1985) The effect of capping and polyadenylation on the stability, movement and translation of synthetic messenger RNAs in *Xenopus* oocytes. *Nucleic Acids Res.* **13**, 7375–7393.

Krieg, P. A., and Melton, D. A. (1984) Functional messenger RNAs are produced by SP6 *in vitro* transcription of cloned cDNAs. *Nucleic Acids Res.* **12**, 7057–7070.

Matthews, G. M., and Colman, A. (1991) A highly efficient, cell-free translation/translocation system prepared from *Xenopus* eggs. *Nucleic Acids Res.* **19**, 6405–6412.

Vize, P., Hemmati-Brivanlou, A., Harland, R. M., and Melton, D. A. (1991) Assays for gene function in developing *Xenopus* embryos. *In* "Methods in Cell Biology" (B. K. Kay and H. B. Peng, eds.), Vol 36, pp. 368–387. Academic Press, San Diego.

Wu, M., and Gerhart, J. (1991) Raising *Xenopus* in the laboratory. *In* "Methods in Cell Biology" (B. K. Kay and H. B. Peng, eds.), Vol. 36, pp. 3–18. Academic Press, San Diego.

Zehavi-Wilner, T., and Lane, C. (1977) Subcellular compartmentation of albumin and globin made in oocytes under the direction of injected messenger RNA. *Cell* **11**, 883–893.

PART 12

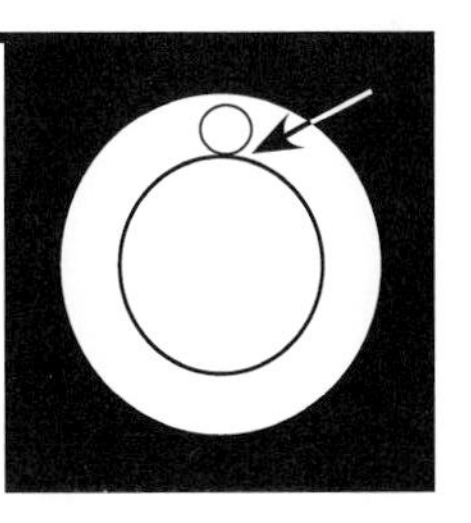

CLONING OF EMBRYOS, TRANSGENICS, AND GENE TARGETING

Cloning Rabbit Embryos by Nuclear Transplantation

Philippe Collas

I. Introduction

The cloning of mammalian embryos is an area of active research around the world. Cloning by nuclear transplantation entails the transfer of each blastomere from an embryo into the cytoplasm of an enucleated, mature oocyte. The transfer per se of the donor blastomere into the recipient oocyte is commonly mediated by electrofusion. After transplantation, the recipient oocyte must be activated to exit meiotic arrest and begin embryo development. Electrical stimulation has, to date, proven to be the most practical and efficient method for activating oocytes. Following fusion and activation, the oocyte initiates a morphological remodeling of the nucleus, including premature chromosome condensation and swelling of the developing pronucleus (Stice and Robl, 1988; Collas and Robl, 1991). Nuclear remodeling is believed to be associated with functional reprogramming of the donor nucleus and results in development to term of nuclear transplant embryos.

Although many offspring have been born, the efficiency of nuclear transplantation remains low. Two critical steps in the procedure have received most attention in the rabbit in particular: (1) Activation of the oocyte has been improved by Collas and Robl (1990) with the use of multiple electrical stimulations. (2) Synchronization of donor blastomeres in G_1 phase of the cell cycle prior to transplantation into enucleated metaphase II oocytes improved development of manipulated embryos to the blastocyst stage (Collas *et al.*, 1992). Although synchronizing donor blastomeres in G_1 improves development *in vitro*, the rate of development to term is still being determined. Therefore, procedures for synchronizing blastomeres in G_1 phase are discussed here. This article presents protocols for the manufacture of micromanipulation pipettes, nuclear transplantation, electrically induced fusion and activation, and culture and transfer of reconstituted rabbit embryos.

II. Materials and Instrumentation

Phosphate-buffered saline (PBS, Cat. No. 310-4287AG; Ca^{2+}-free, Cat. No. 310-4190AG) and Earle's balanced salt solution (EBSS, Cat. No. 310-4010AG) are obtained from Gibco. Fetal calf serum (FCS) is from Hyclone (Cat. No. A-III-L). Bovine testis hyaluronidase (Cat. No. H-3884), trypsin (Cat. No. T-8642), cytochalasin B (Cat. No. C-6762), and mannitol (Cat. No. M4125) are from Sigma.

Instruments for nuclear transplantation are glass capillary tubes (1-mm o.d., Fisher), pipette puller, microforge, pipette grinder, two dissecting microscopes with a 20–80× zoom, inverted microscope with 10, 20, and 40× phase-contrast objec-

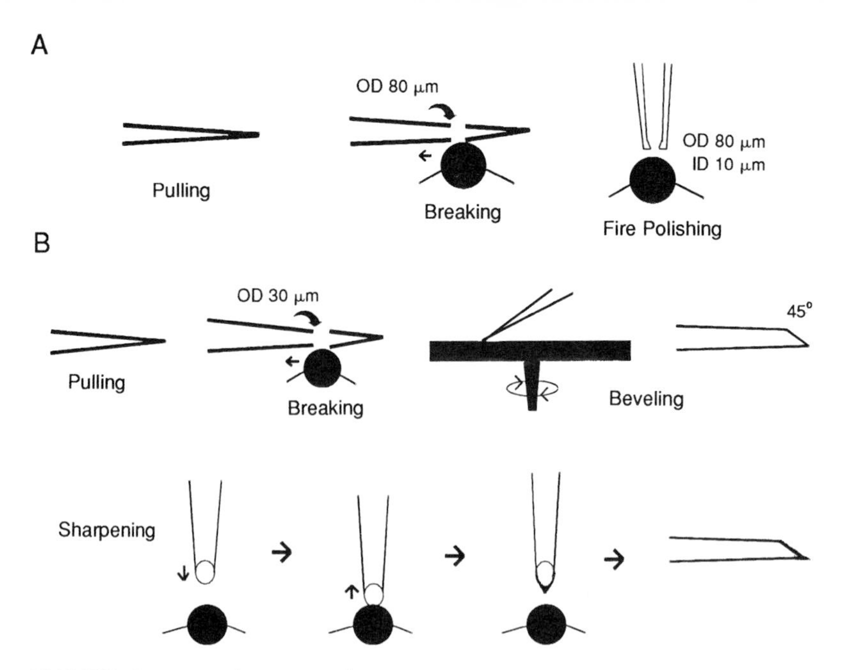

FIGURE 1 Manufacturing of micropipettes for nuclear transplantation. (A) Holding pipette. (B) Enucleation pipette.

tives, two macromanipulators, warming stage, pulse generator (BTX Electro Cell Manipulator 200, BTX, Inc.), and chambers for pulsing embryos (BTX Cat. No. 450).

III. Procedures

A. MANUFACTURING OF MICROPIPETTES

1. Holding Pipette

Pull a glass capillary tube. Secure the pipette horizontally on top of the microforge heating glass bead (Fig. 1A). At an outside diameter (o.d.) of 80 μm (use a micrometric scale) slightly melt the pipette to the glass bead and turn off the heat. Pull the pipette horizontally to break the tip. To fire-polish the tip, secure the tip vertically on top of the bead. Turn on the heat and allow the tip to close off such that the inner diameter is 10 μm.

2. Enucleation Pipette

a. Breaking

Place a capillary tube on the microforge as for the holding pipette. Break the pipette tip at an o.d. of 30 μm (Fig. 1B).

b. Beveling

Lower the pipette onto the grinder such that the tip slightly bends on the stone at an angle of 45°. Grind for 1–2 min. With a 5-ml syringe and a connecting tubing, wash the tip in 0.5 *M* chromic acid and rinse with distilled water.

c. Sharpening

Place the tip vertically above the heating bead, the long side of the bevel facing the operator. Turn on the heat and quickly lower the tip onto the bead. Briefly allow the tip to melt and immediately bring the tip back up. The sharp end created (see Fig. 1B) facilitates penetration of the oocyte zona pellucida for enucleation.

B. RECIPIENT OOCYTE COLLECTION AND PREPARATION

Solution

EBSS/fetal calf serum (EBSS/FCS): One day prior to use, prepare a solution of EBSS with 10% FCS by adding 2 ml FCS to 8 ml EBSS. Filter and allow to equilibrate until use in a tube with a loosened lid at 37°C in a 7% CO_2 incubator.

Steps

1. Recover mature oocytes from the oviducts of superovulated females 14 hr after administration of human chorionic gonadotropin (14 hphCG) with warm equilibrated EBSS/FCS.
2. Digest the cumulus by adding hyaluronidase to 1 mg/ml and remove corona cells by gently pipetting the oocytes with a small-bore pipette.

C. DONOR EMBRYO COLLECTION: BLASTOMERE ISOLATION

Solutions

1. *Trypsin solution:* Trypsin is used to facilitate blastomere separation. To make 10 ml of *stock solution,* dissolve 2.5 g of trypsin into 8 ml Ca^{2+}-free PBS and complete to 10 ml; filter and divided into 310-μl aliquots; store frozen. To make 3 ml of working solution (0.25% trypsin), add 300 μl of trypsin stock to 2.7 ml Ca^{2+}-free PBS.

2. *Acid solution:* Acid is used to digest the zona pellucida of oocytes. Dilute saturated HCl into 25 ml PBS to pH 2.5. Filter and store at 4°C.

Steps

1. Recover embryos at the 32-cell stage from the oviducts 60 hr after mating.
2. Dissolve the zona pellucida in acid solution for 1 min and place embryos in PBS.
3. Remove the mucin coat with two glass needles.
4. Place embryos in 0.25% trypsin for 10 min and isolate blastomeres by pipetting embryos in PBS containing 10% FCS with a 50-μm fire-polished pipette.

D. NUCLEAR TRANSPLANTATION

Solutions

1. *Cytochalasin B:* Cytochalasin B is used to increase the elasticity of the oocyte plasma membrane for enucleation. To make the *stock solution,* add 200 μl

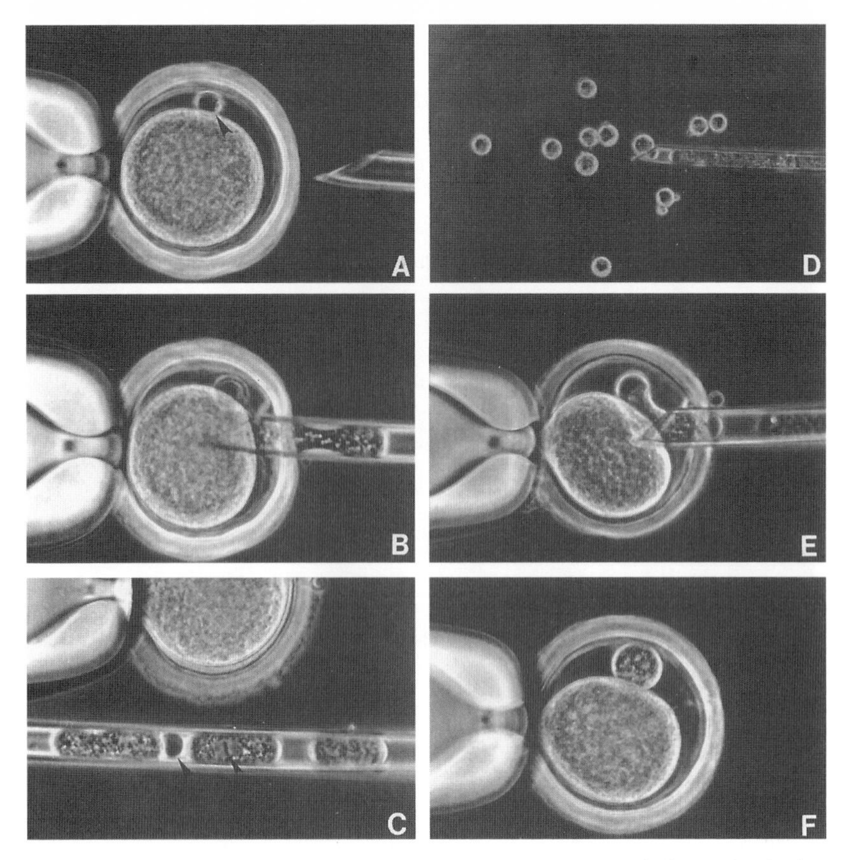

FIGURE 2 Nuclear transplantation. (A) Mature oocyte with first polar body (arrowhead). (B) Aspiration of chromosomes in a membrane-bounded cytoplasmic vesicle. (C) Metaphase II plate (small arrowhead) and first polar body (large arrowhead) in the enucleation pipette. (D) Aspiration of an isolated 32-cell stage blastomere. (E) Insertion of the blastomere into the perivitelline space of the oocyte. (F) Enucleated recipient oocyte and adjacent donor blastomere. 400×, phase contrast.

of 95% ethanol to a 1-mg vial of cytochalasin B; store at −10°C. To make the *working solution* (7.5 μg/ml), add 2 μl of stock solution to 132 μl EBSS/FCS; add 5 μl of this solution to 45-μl drops of equilibrated EBSS/FCS under mineral oil in a 100 × 15-mm plastic petri dish prior to micromanipulation.

2. *Vitreous humor:* The vitreous humor (VH) from the eyes of female rabbits is used as culture medium for nuclear donors and manipulated embryos (Collas and Robl, 1991). Aseptically collect VH by puncturing the eyes of euthanized female rabbits; aspirate 1 to 1.5 ml of VH from each eye with a 3-ml syringe with 18-gauge needle. Immediately centrifuge the fluid at 15,000 *g* for 2 min to pellet cellular debris and filter (0.2 μm) the supernatant in 50- to 100-μl drops immediately overlaid with mineral oil in a 60 × 15-mm plastic petri dish. Incubate dishes at 37°C in a humidified atmosphere of 7% CO_2 in air 12–24 hr prior to culturing embryos.

Steps

Nuclear transplantation is illustrated Fig. 2.

1. At 16 hphCG, place mature oocytes and isolated blastomeres in a 50-μl drop of EBSS/FCS containing 7.5 μg/ml cytochalasin B and overlaid with mineral oil (Collas and Robl, 1990). Wait 15 min before starting enucleation.

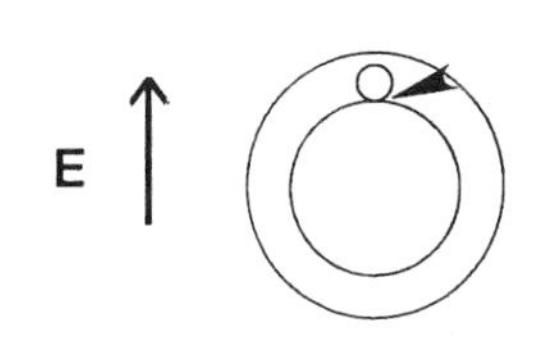

FIGURE 3 Alignment of manipulated embryo prior to blastomere fusion. The blastomere and oocyte plasma membranes to be fused (arrowhead) are oriented parallel to the electrodes, perpendicularly to the electric field *E*.

2. Hold the oocyte firmly with the holding pipette, with the first polar body at 12 o'clock (Fig. 2A). Insert the enucleation pipette at the equator of the oocyte (at 3 o'clock) and draw the first polar body and the membrane-bounded metaphase II chromosomes into the enucleation pipette (Fig. 2B). Enucleation is assessed by visualization of the metaphase plate in the pipette (Fig. 2C).

3. As the pipette is withdrawn, the oocyte plasma membrane pinches off and the cell rounds off rapidly. Aspirate a single blastomere in the same pipette (Fig. 2D) and place it in the perivitelline space against the enucleated oocyte (Figs. 2E,F).

4. Wash and culture manipulated oocytes in VH until fusion and activation.

E. BLASTOMERE FUSION AND OOCYTE ACTIVATION

Solutions

1. *Mannitol:* A 0.30 *M* mannitol solution is used as fusion and activation medium. To make 100 ml of 0.30 *M* mannitol, add 5.49 g mannitol to 80 ml distilled H_2O, stir, and complete to 100 ml. Add 10 μl of a 1 *M* stock solution of $CaCl_2$ and 10 μl of a 1 *M* stock solution of $MgCl_2$. Filter and store at 4°C.

2. *VH:* See Section D.

Steps

Chamber setup

1. Place the BTX 450 fusion chamber in a 100 × 15-mm plastic petri dish and secure it to the bottom with stopcock grease.

2. Cover the chamber with 30 ml of mannitol solution.

3. Secure the petri dish with the fusion chamber to a dissecting microscope, on the warming stage. Allow the mannitol to reach 30°C before pulsing. A second dissecting microscope is useful for handling embryos between pulses.

Embryo pulsing

1. Fusion of the donor blastomere with the recipient oocyte is done at 19 hphCG. Allow embryos to equilibrate for 2 min in a 100-μl drop of mannitol solution.

2. Place and align embryos in the chamber. Alignment consists of orienting embryos such that the membranes to be fused are parallel to the electrodes (Fig. 3). This is done with a glass embryo-handling pipette.

3. Embryos are given 6 direct-current pulses of 2.0 kV/cm (i.e., 100 V with the

BTX 450 chamber) for 60 μsec, each pulse 30 min apart. With proper alignment and oocyte–blastomere contact, 100% of the embryos fuse on the first pulse.

4. Culture embryos in VH between pulses and do not realign fused embryos before subsequent pulses.

F. *IN VITRO* CULTURE OF NUCLEAR TRANSPLANT EMBRYOS

Solutions

See Section D.

Steps

1. After the last pulse, wash and culture embryos in a microdrop of VH containing 7.5 μg/ml cytochalasin B for 1 hr.
2. Wash embryos three times in VH and place 10 embryos per VH drop in a 37°C humidified atmosphere of 7% CO_2 in air.

G. MONITORING NUCLEAR TRANSPLANT EMBRYOS

Embryos can be assessed for fusion as they are placed in culture. If embryos are to be cultured *in vitro,* they can be assessed every 24 hr for activation, lysis, fragmentation, and development. Activated embryos are those showing swelling of the transplanted nucleus. Lysed embryos are those in which the plasma membrane has ruptured and in which the cytoplasm fills the entire zona pellucida. Fragmentation is nonuniform cleavage and often occurs within 3 hr of pulsing. Fragmented embryos contain many unevenly sized anucleate cells. Development to blastocysts can be determined after 4 days of culture.

H. EMBRYO TRANSFER OF MANIPULATED EMBRYOS

Solution

1. *PBS:* Use regular (containing Ca^{2+}) PBS as described above.

Steps

1. Synchronize recipient does by mating to a vasectomized male 12 hr after the time of hCG injection of the oocyte donors.

2. After 18 hr of culture, assess cleavage to the two- to four-cell stage.

3. Transfer embryos to the oviducts of recipient females. With a fire-polished pipette, transfer five to eight embryos in 10 μl PBS to each oviduct, through the infundibulum.

IV. Comments

The procedure described allows a rate of development of nuclear transplant embryos to blastocysts of approximately 50%, and to term, of 10% (21% of embryos transferred). Current studies are investigating the use of G_1–early S phase blastomeres transplanted into enucleated metaphase II oocytes to improve development to term of nuclear transplant embryos (C. Long and J. M. Robl, personal communication).

V. Pitfalls

1. For successful VH preparation and embryo culture, maintain the interval between VH collection and culture dish setup as short as possible (<10 min).

2. Times indicated (in hphCG) are based on ovulation of the oocyte donors approximately 12 hr after hCG administration. Because highest rates of enucleation and fusion occur in recently ovulated oocytes, the times indicated may have to be modulated depending on the time of ovulation after hCG injection. The interval between hCG and ovulation is subject to seasonal variation and breed differences.

REFERENCES

Collas, P., Balise, J. J., and Robl, J. M. (1992) Influence of cell cycle stage of the donor nucleus on development of nuclear transplant rabbit embryos. *Biol. Reprod.* **46**, 492–500.

Collas, P., and Robl, J. M. (1990) Factors affecting the efficiency of nuclear transplantation in the rabbit embryo. *Biol. Reprod.* **43**, 877–884.

Collas, P., and Robl, J. M. (1991) Relationship between nuclear remodeling and development in nuclear transplant rabbit embryos. *Biol. Reprod.* **45**, 455–465.

Stice, S. L., and Robl, J. M. (1988) Nuclear reprogramming in nuclear transplant rabbit embryos. *Biol. Reprod.* **39**, 756–764.

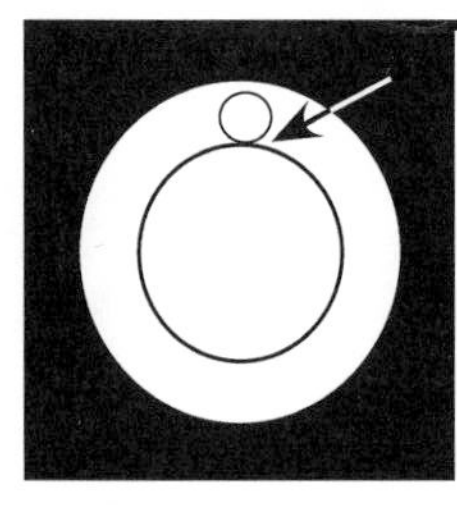

Production of Transgenic Mice by Pronuclear Microinjection

Jon W. Gordon

I. Introduction

The technique for introducing genetic material into the mouse germline by pronuclear microinjection was first developed by Gordon *et al.* (1980). These animals, subsequently called *transgenic* (Gordon and Ruddle, 1981) to indicate the presence of foreign DNA within their genomes, frequently express the donor genes highly efficiently (Brinster *et al.*, 1981), with the tissue distribution of expression determined primarily by *cis*-acting promoter enhancer elements within or in the immediate vicinity of the genes themselves (Brinster *et al.*, 1981; reviewed by Palmiter and Brinster, 1986, Gordon, 1989). This technique has proven extremely important for basic investigations of gene regulation, creation of animal models of human disease (e.g., Stacey *et al.*, 1988, and genetic engineering of livestock (Hammer *et al.*, 1985; Gordon *et al.*, 1987). This technique has also been described in extensive detail in several other publications (Gordon and Ruddle, 1983).

II. Materials and Instrumentation

The following reagents are required for production of transgenic mice. All stock numbers denote compounds from Sigma, unless otherwise indicated: NaCl (S-9888), KCl (P-4504), KH_2PO_4 (P-5379), $MgSO_4 \cdot 7H_2O$ (M-1880), 60% sodium lactate syrup, (L-1375), penicillin G (PEN-NA), streptomycin (S-6501), bovine serum albumin, fraction V (A-8022), Hepes (H-3375), $CaCl_2$ (C-3881), sodium pyruvate (P-5280), hyaluronidase (H-3506), mineral oil (M-3516), propylene glycol (P-5280) NaOH (S-5881), concentrated HCl (Fisher A144-500), 100% ethanol (any supplier), Na pentobarbital, 60 mg/ml (Fort Dodge 1206-1E), pregnant mares' serum (G4877), human chorionic gonadotropin (CG-10), Fluorinert (3M, FC-77).

Other materials needed include 35-mm tissue culture dishes (Falcon, Cat. No. 3001); 100-mm bacterial culture plates (Falcon, Cat. No. 1029); 10-ml pipette (Falcon, Cat. No. 7551); 5-ml pipette (Falcon, Cat. No. 7543); 15-ml sterile concical centrifuge tube (Falcon, Cat. No. 2097); 50-ml sterile conical centrifuge tube (Baxter, Cat. No. C3920-50); 0.22-μm filters, syringe mounted (USA Scientific, Cat. No. F192); sterile filter apparatus (100 ml: Nalgene, Cat. No. 120-0020, 250 ml: Cat. No. 116-0020, 500 ml: Cat. No. 450-0020); 9-in. Pasteur pipette (Kimble, Cat. No. 72050); depression slides (Fisher, Cat. No. 12-565A), surgical needles with cutting edge (Anchor, Cat. No. 1834-9); 4-O silk (Ethicon, Cat. No. A-303); surgical iris scissors (Stroz, Cat. No. E-3404); No. 5 Dumont watchmaker's forceps (Fullam, Cat. No. 14040); hemostat (Fisher, Cat. No. SCM 1004); microcapillary tubing for

DNA injection (Cat. No. 1211L Omega Dot, Glass Co. of America); microcapillar tubing for making holding pipettes (Mertex, 100 × 0.5 mm i.d.); spinal needle for filling barrel of microcapillary tubing (Popper & Sons Quinke Babcock 26 gauge); polyethylene tubing for connecting syringe to microneedle (Intramedic PE60, PE90, PE160, PE190); plastic tubing adapter with luer lock for PE tubing (Clay Adams, Cat. No. A-1026, Size B fits PE60 and PE90, Size C fits PE160 and PE190); vertical or horizontal pipette puller (e.g., David Kopf No. 700C); microforge (e.g., DeFonbrune MF-1); mechanical microinjector (e.g., Narishige M5-A); micromanipulation apparatus with phase-contrast optics; two micromanipulators; dissecting microscope (e.g., Leitz or Narishige). When one micromanipulation device is chosen over another, the choice may dictate the use of supplies that are especially compatible with the equipment available. A CO_2 incubator is obtained from a suitable supplier.

III. Procedures

A. PREPARATION OF CULTURE MEDIA AND RELATED REAGENTS

See Gordon and Ruddle (1983) and Quinn *et al.* (1982).

Solutions

To make stocks A–D, weigh solids into a clean flask or appropriate-sized, disposable, conical centrifuge tube and add appropriate quantity of distilled H_2O (18 MΩ). If Na lactate syrup is weighed (stock A), use a small weighing boat and decant contents into flask, then rinse boat two or three times with distilled H_2O and decant rinse into flask. For stock E, weigh out Hepes and add phenol red. Add 50 ml

Compound	Amount
1. *10× Stock solution A for M16 and M2 culture media, 100 ml (storage time: 3 months)*	
NaCl	5.534 g
KCl	0.356 g
KH_2PO_4	0.162 g
$MgSO_4 \cdot 7H_2O$	0.293 g
Na lactate, 60% syrup	4.439 g *or* 2.610 ml
Glucose	1.000 g
Penicillin	0.060 g
Streptomycin	0.050 g
2. *OX Stock solution B for M16 and M2 culture media, 100 ml (storage time: 2 weeks)*	
$NaHCO_3$	2.101 g
Phenol red, 0.5% solution	1.00 ml
3. *100× Stock solution C for M16 and M2 culture media, 50 ml (storage time: 2 weeks)*	
Na pyruvate	0.180 g
4. *100× Stock solution D for M16 and M2 culture media, 10 ml (storage time: 3 months)*	
$CaCl_2 \cdot 2H_2O$	0.252 g
5. *10× Stock solution E for M2 culture medium, 100 ml (storage time: 3 months)*	
Hepes solid	5.958 g
Phenol red, 0.5% solution	0.010 g

distilled H_2O, then adjust pH to 7.4 with 5 *N* NaOH. Add distilled H_2O to 100 ml. Sterile-filter each stock into a sterile, disposable, conical centrifuge tube of appropriate size.

6. *M16 Medium (500 ml) from concentrated stocks:* Combine 50 ml stock A, 50 ml stock B, 5 ml stock C, and 5 ml stock D. Rinse all pipettes, etc., thoroughly into final flask. Add H_2O to 500 ml. Add 2 g BSA (fraction V); dissolve without excessive frothing. Sterile-filter into 50-ml sterile, disposable, conical centrifuge tubes.

7. *M2 medium (100 ml) from concentrated stocks:* Combine 10.0 ml stock A, 1.6 ml stock B, 1.0 ml stock C, 1.0 ml stock D, 8.4 ml stock E, and 78.0 ml H_2O. Make up as for M16, but recheck pH prior to sterile filtration, and adjust pH to 7.3–7.4 with concentrated NaOH if needed.

8. *M16 supplemented with hyaluronidase to remove cumulus cells:* Add hyaluronidase to a final concentration of 1–2 mg/ml to M2 or M16. Filter-sterilize before use.

9. *Sodium pentobarbital anesthesia for surgery:* Mix 100% EtOH (10 ml), propylene glycol (20 ml), and water (70 ml) to produce 100 ml of diluent. Add Na pentobarbital stock solution (60 mg/ml) to a final concentration of 6 mg/ml. Administer to mice at 60 mg/kg, or 0.1 ml/10 g body weight.

B. PREPARATION OF HOLDING PIPETTES FOR MICROMANIPULATION

Steps

1. Heat microcapillary tubing in a microburner and pull by hand to yield a shaft about 150 μm in outer diameter with a length of about 3 cm.

2. Place the pulled tubing on the microforge and break the shaft cleanly such that the shards of class are protruding from the cylindrical end of the shaft.

3. Fire-polish the aperture such that the diameter of the lumen is reduced to about 20–30 μm.

4. Bend the shaft to 90° in the microburner, and bend the portion of the tubing that has not been heated 90° in the opposite direction, about 2 cm distant from the point at which the shaft was pulled.

5. About 2 cm further away from the tapered shaft, break the tubing with a diamond pen and fire-polish the end to yield an "S-shaped" holding pipet. When used, the pipette shaft will extend, parallel to the floor of the culture dish, into the microdrop for manipulation (Gordon and Ruddle, 1983). The tubing will then extend vertically up and over the edge of the tissue culture dish, and attach to the instrument collar of the manipulator.

C. PREPARATION OF MICRONEEDLES

Step

Pull microneedles from appropriate microcapillary tubing and use directly without further processing.

D. MICROMANIPULATOR SETUP

Steps

1. The micromanipulation microscope should be equipped with interference optics and should be inverted. 4× and 32× objectives, with 10× eyepieces, are recommended.

2. The instrument collar for the holding pipette should be connected via tubing to a microinjection device. The instrument collar for the microneedle may be connected to a 10-cc syringe.

E. RECOVERY AND MICROINJECTION OF EMBRYOS

Steps

1. Superovulate 10 immature female mice (5–6 weeks old) with 2.5 IU of pregnant mares' serum between 12 noon and 1 PM.

2. Forty-eight hours later administer 5 IU of human chorionic gonadotropin between 12 noon and 4 PM, and place female mice with fertile males to mate. At this time place 15 mature, randomly cycling females with vasectomized males to generate pseudopregnant recipients.

3. The morning after mating, check the immature and mature females for vaginal plugs indicative of mating. Retain those that have mated.

4. Between noon and 2 PM the same day, prepare five 35-mm tissue culture dishes, each with 2 ml of M16 medium, a depression slide with about 300 μl M16 containing hyaluronidase, and a 100-mm culture dish for micromanipulation containing a drop of M2 medium covered with mineral oil. This drop should be rectangular with dimensions of about 1 × 4 cm. The M16 and hyaluronidase are placed in the incubator for equilibration, and the M2 microdrop can be placed directly on the microscope equipped for micromanipulation.

5. Between 1 and 2 PM, sacrifice the donor females and remove the oviducts, with ovaries and a small portion of the uterus still attached, to one of the dishes of M16. On the dissecting microscope, identify the distended portion of each oviduct and tear it open to release zygotes and associated cumulus cells. All oviducts are done in the depression slide containing the hyaluronidase.

6. Place the depression slide in the incubator for 5 min. During this incubation, pull a microinjection needle on the pipette puller, and place the base in DNA solution for filling. After the tip is filled, fill the shaft behind the DNA with Fluorinert using a spinal needle.

7. Wash the denuded zygotes several times in M16 medium, and select those with visible pronuclei and/or second polar bodies. Place these together in the M2 microdrop at one end of the drop.

8. Attach the holding pipette and microneedle to the instrument collars and lower them into the microdrop at the opposite end from the zygotes. Brush the microneedle tip against the holding pipette to break it slightly. This will help establish flow of DNA. Raise the microtools off the floor of the dish, and move the microscope stage to bring the zygotes into the field of vision. Lower the holding pipette and use suction to grasp one of the zygotes. Under high power, release and regrasp the zygote until a pronucleus is positioned for microinjection. Lower the microneedle until the tip is in the same focal plane as the pronuclear membrane. Insert the microneedle under the zona pellucida and apply forward

pressure. If the microneedle aperture is open, the perivitelline space will swell slightly.

9. Insert the microneedle into the pronucleus and allow the flow of DNA to cause swelling of the pronucleus. Microinjection should not be considered successful unless this swelling is seen. After microinjection, immediately remove the microneedle from the zygote.

10. Raise the microtools off the floor of the dish, and move the stage so as to carry the microinjected zygote, still attached to the holding pipette, to the opposite end of the microdrop. Release the zygote by applying positive pressure on the holding pipette. Allow the microinjected zygote to drift down to the floor of the dish, then move the stage so as to repeat the process on the next embryo. When all embryos are microinjected, remove them to a dish of M16 for about 1 hr of culture.

F. EMBRYO IMPLANTATION

Steps

1. Load the surgical transfer pipette with medium, an air bubble marker, more medium, and then 10–30 embryos.

2. Approach the ovary through a dorsal incision about 1 cm lateral to the midline, 1–2 cm below the costal margin. The ostium lies immediately adjacent to the ovary and the opening is always oriented toward the tail of the animal.

3. Open the ovarian bursa, avoiding trauma to large blood vessels. Identify the opening of the ostium and insert the surgical transfer pipette. To ensure successful embryo transfer, the pipette should be advanced beyond the point of bursal attachment. Embryos are then expelled until the air bubble marker enters the oviductal lumen. Repeat this procedure on the opposite side if sufficient numbers of embryos are available.

4. Close the wound with a single suture through both the peritoneum and skin. Pups born 19–21 days after transfer are then reared to weaning age and evaluated by polymerase chain reaction or Southern blotting for integration of the transgene.

G. SURGICAL VASECTOMY OF MALES TO GENERATE PSEUDOPREGNANT RECIPIENT FEMALES

Steps

1. Make a ventral midline incision about 1 cm in length above the position of the preputial gland, which is situated under the skin and which can be appreciated as a bulging of the skin in the lower abdomen.

2. Squeeze the scrotal sac to force the testes to the incision, and expose both testes by grasping the associated fat pads with the forceps. Identify the vas deferens and isolate it by blunt dissection.

3. Secure a large loop of the vas deferens in the jaws of a hemostat, crush it, and tear it away.

4. Close the animal with a single suture through both the skin and peritoneum. After about 1 week the animals can be used as breeders.

IV. Comments

Human chorionic gonadotrophin is now considered an anabolic steroid and, as such, requires a license for ordering as a controlled substance in the United States. Although the M16 and M2 culture media are listed as being stable for only 2 weeks, we have found they can be used for at least 2 months without diminution of success in transgenic mouse production. The reason for this is that embryos are maintained in these media for only a short time.

REFERENCES

Brinster, R. L., Chen, H. Y., Trumbauer, M. E., Senear, A. W., Warren, R., and Palmiter, R. D. (1981) Somatic expression of herpes thymidine kinase in mice following injection of a fusion gene into eggs. *Cell* **27**, 223–231.

Gordon, J. W. (1989) Transgenic animals. *Int. Rev. Cytol.* **115**, 171–230.

Gordon, J. W., and Ruddle, F. H. (1981) Integration and stable germ line transmission of genes injected into mouse pronuclei. *Science* **214**, 1244–1246.

Gordon, J. W., and Ruddle, F. H. (1983) Gene transfer into mouse embryos. Production of transgenic mice by pronuclear injection. *In* "Methods in Enzymology" (R. Wu, L. Grossman, and K. Moldave, eds.), Vol. 101, pp. 411–433. Academic Press, San Diego.

Gordon, K., Lee, E., Vitale, J., Smith, A., Westphal, H., and Henninghausen, L. (1987) Production of human tissue plasminogen activator in transgenic mouse milk. *Biotechnology* **5**, 1183–1187.

Gordon, J. W., Scangos, G. A., Plotkin, D. J., Barbosa, J. A., and Ruddle, F. H. (1980) Genetic transformation of mouse embryos by microinjection of purified DNA. *Proc. Natl. Acad. Sci. USA* **77**, 7380–7384.

Hammer, R. E., Pursel, V. G., Rexsroad, C. E., Jr., Wall, R. J., Bolt, D. J., Ebert, K. M., Palmiter, R. D., and Brinster, R. L. (1985) Production of transgenic rabbits, sheep and pigs by microinjection. *Nature* **315**, 680–683.

Palmiter, R. D., and Brinster, R. L. (1986) Germ-line transformation of mice. *Annu. Rev. Genet.* **20**, 465–499.

Quinn, P., Barros, C., and Whittingham, D. G. (1982) Preservation of hamster oocytes to assay the fertilizing capacity of human spermatozoa. *J. Reprod. Fertil.* **66**, 161–168.

Stacey, A., Bateman, J., Choi, T., Mascara, T., Cole, W., and Jaenisch, R. (1988) Perinatal lethal osteogenesis imperfecta in transgenic mice bearing an engineered mutant pro-α1(I) collagen gene. *Nature* **332**, 131–136.

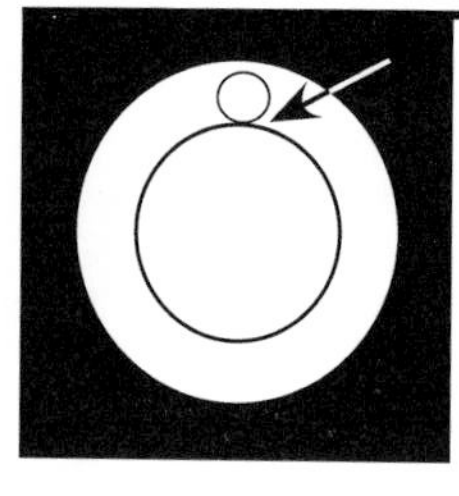

Gene Targeting by Homologous Recombination in Embryonic Stem Cells

Miguel Torres and Ahmed Mansouri

I. Introduction

Embryonic stem (ES) cells are undifferentiated totipotent cells (see Martin Evans in volume 1). They derive from the inner cell mass of a mouse blastocyst and can be perpetuated in culture (Robertson, 1987). Chimeric embryos can be generated by injecting ES cells into blastocysts or by aggregating them with morulae. Adult mice develop normally from these embryos and ES cells contribute to all tissues, including the germline (Robertson, 1986; Gossler *et al.*, 1986). These unique characteristics allow the introduction of foreign DNA, the screening for rare integration events in ES cells, as well as ultimately the generation of ES cell-derived mouse strains. This strategy has been successfully employed for gene targeting by homologous recombination, which has become a powerful tool in study of gene function. By this procedure designed mutations are introduced into particular genes, and mouse lines carrying the mutated allele are generated (Capecchi, 1989).

II. Materials and Instrumentation

Dulbecco's modified Eagle's medium (DMEM, 4.5 g glucose/liter, Cat. No. 041-01965H), nonessential amino acids (Cat. No. 043-01140H), sodium pyruvate (Cat. No. 043-01360H), fetal calf serum (Cat. No. 011-06290M), geneticin (G418, Cat. No. 066-1811), and leukemia inhibitory factor (LIF, Cat. No. 6203275SA or SB) are purchased from Gibco-BRL. EDTA (Cat. No. 4040), NaCl (Cat. No. 0278), KCl (Cat. No. 0509), KH_2PO_4 (Cat. No. 4008), $Na_2HPO_4 \cdot 2H_2O$ (Cat. No. 0326), Trizma base (Cat. No. 1414), and D-glucose (Cat. No. 0114) are purchased from J. T. Baker. Gelatin (Cat. No. G-1890), DMSO (Cat. No. D-8414), mitomycin C (Cat. No. M-0503), SDS (Cat. No. L-4509), and phenol red (Cat. No. P-5530) are purchased from Sigma. Trypsin (Cat. No. L2103) is purchased from Biochrom KG. Proteinase K (Cat. No. 1092766) is purchased from Boehringer-Mannheim. Gene Pulser and electroporation cuvettes (0.4 cm and 0.8-ml volume) are purchased from Bio-Rad Laboratories GmbH. Thirteen- to fifteen-day pregnant mice, sterile scissors and forceps, 50-ml sterilized glass beads (3 mm in diameter), stirring bar in 500-ml Erlenmeyer flask, and 14.5-cm tissue culture dishes are obtained from local suppliers.

III. Procedures

A. PREPARATION OF EMBRYONIC FIBROBLASTS

Solutions

1. *Phosphate-buffered saline (PBS):* To make 1 liter, add 8.0 g of NaCl, 0.2 g of KCl, 1.15 g of $Na_2HPO_4 \cdot 2H_2O$, and 0.2 g of KH_2PO_4 to distilled water, adjust pH to 7.2, and bring to a total volume of 1 liter. Sterilize by autoclaving and store at room temperature.

2. *Trypsin/EDTA:* To make 1 liter, add 8.0 g NaCl, 0.40 g KCl, 0.10 g $Na_2HPO_4 \cdot 2H_2O$, 1.0 g glucose, 3.0 g Trizma base, 0.01 g phenol red, and 2.50 g trypsin (Difco 1:250) to distilled water, adjust pH to 7.6, and bring to a total volume of 1 liter. Filter sterilize and store in aliquots at −20°C. This stock is diluted 1:4 in saline/EDTA for use as 0.05% trypsin/EDTA solution. Store at −20°C in aliquots of 5–10 ml.

3. *Saline/EDTA for dilution of trypsin:* To make 1 liter, add 0.2 g EDTA (disodium salt), 8.0 g NaCl, 0.2 g KCl, 1.15 g $Na_2HPO_4 \cdot 2H_2O$, and 0.2 g KH_2PO_4 to distilled water. Check pH (7.2) and bring to a total volume of 1 liter. Filter-sterilize or autoclave. Store at room temperature.

4. *Gelatin:* To make 1 liter, add 1 g gelatin to 1 liter of distilled water and autoclave. Mix after autoclaving, and store at room temperature.

5. *Mitomycin C:* Resuspend 2 mg of mitomycin C in 2 ml of PBS and filter-sterilize. Keep in the dark at 4°C and use within a week.

6. *Medium for embryonic fibroblasts:* DMEM + 10% (v/v) FCS. To make 1 liter add 100 ml of FCS (the serum is always heat-inactivated at 56°C for 30 min before use for all media) to 900 ml of DMEM. Store at 4°C.

7. *Freezing medium for fibroblasts and ES cells:* To make 10 ml of freezing medium, add 1 ml DMSO (cell culture grade) and 1 ml FCS to 8 ml of ES cell medium. After adding freezing medium, the cells are kept for 1 hr at −20°C and transferred to −70°C overnight before storage in liquid nitrogen.

Steps

1. Dissect ten 13- to 15-day embryos (we normally use NMRI or Balb/c mice) in PBS. Discard head, liver, and internal organs. Wash carcasses several times in PBS to remove blood.
2. Transfer carcasses to 5 ml of trypsin/EDTA and mince in small pieces.
3. Using a wide pipette, transfer the dissected embryo pieces to the Erlenmeyer flask containing the glass beads and add 50 ml of trypsin.
4. Incubate for 30 min at 37°C with gentle agitation on a magnet stirrer.
5. Using a pipette, remove from the flask the cell suspension and transfer to sterile 50-ml tube. Leave the cell clumps in the flask.
6. Add 50 ml trypsin/EDTA to the remaining cell clumps in the flask and repeat step 4.
7. Spin down the cell suspension from step 5 at 1000 rpm for 10 min, and resuspend pellet in embryonic fibroblast medium.
8. Remove the second cell suspension from the flask and treat as in step 7.
9. Pool cells from steps 7 and 8 and plate on 14.5-cm tissue culture dishes (about two embryos per dish).

10. Change medium after 24 hr.
11. Once confluent (after 2 days) freeze cells by making five vials from each plate.
12. For routine culture, thaw one vial on 8.5-cm plate. When confluent, passage the plate on 4 × 8.5-cm plates, which are again passaged (when confluent) on 4 × 14.5-cm plates. Treat the confluent 14.5-cm plates for 2.5 hr with mitomycin C to inactivate the fibroblasts.

B. INACTIVATION OF THE FIBROBLASTS

1. Prepare inactivation medium by adding 100 μl of mitomycin C solution to 10 ml culture medium (calculate 10 ml of medium for each 14.5-cm plate).
2. Change medium to inactivation medium and return plates to incubator for 2.5 hr.
3. Stop inactivation by washing the cells twice with 10 ml of PBS; add 20 ml of fresh medium to each plate.
4. Trypsinize cells and seed on gelatinized plates at a density of 8×10^4 cells/ cm^2.
5. To gelatinize the plates cover the surface with 0.1% gelatin for 15 min or longer at room temperature; remove before using.

C. ROUTINE CULTURE OF EMBRYONIC STEM CELLS

ES cells should be cultured on a feeder layer of inactivated embryonic fibroblasts (Robertson, 1987). Embryonic fibroblasts should be used within a week after inactivation. The ES cells should be split every second day (see below). It is important that the ES cells be trypsinized to obtain a single cell suspension to avoid differentiation. Totipotency in ES cells tends to be lost with passage number; it is therefore advisable to subclone the cells each 20 passages to recover the full potentiality.

Solutions

1. *ES cell medium:* DMEM (4.5 g/liter glucose), 10^{-4} *M* β-mercaptoethanol, 2 m*M* glutamine, 1% stock solution of nonessential amino acids: 1 m*M* sodium pyruvate, 15% (v/v) FCS (tested batches), 1000 U/ml LIF. To make 500 ml, add 5 ml of glutamine, 5 ml of nonessential amino acids, 5 ml of sodium pyruvate, 5 $\times 10^5$ units of LIF, and 0.5 ml of β-mercaptoethanol to DMEM. Adjust to 500 ml with DMEM and add 89 ml of FCS. Store at 4°C.

2. *β-Mercaptoethanol stock:* To make 20 ml, add 140 μl of β-mercaptoethanol (14 *M*) to 20 ml of PBS, mix well, and filter-sterilize. Store in 1-ml stocks at −20°C. When thawed, store at 4°C in the dark and use within 1 week.

Steps

1. Day 0: Wash the confluent ES cells with PBS.
2. Add trypsin/EDTA (2 ml for an 8.5-cm culture dish; 1 ml for 6-cm and 0.5 ml to 3.5-cm culture dishes). Return to incubator for 5 min.
3. Pipette the cells up and down to obtain a single-cell suspension using a plugged Pasteur pipette.

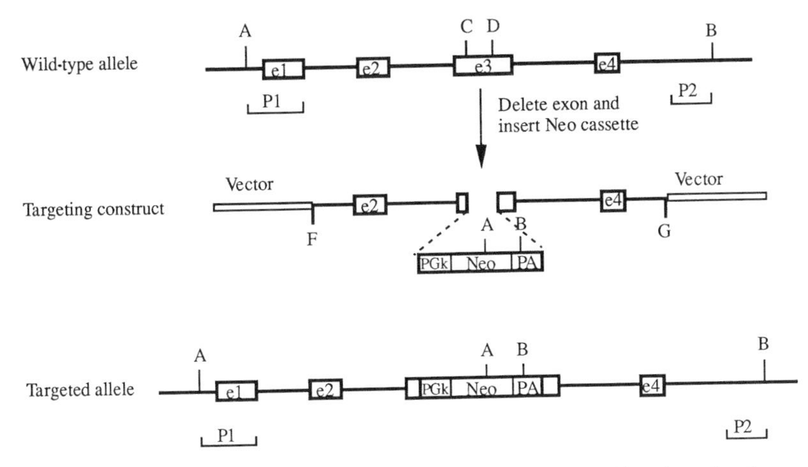

FIGURE 1 Targeting strategy (Soriano *et al.*, 1991). PGk, phosphoglycerate kinase promoter; *Neo*, neomycin; P1 and P2, external probes for screening. Linearize the targeting construct in the vector or at F or G. A, B, C, F, and G are restriction enzyme sites.

4. Add excess medium to stop trypsinization and mix well.
5. Spin down the cells at 1000 rpm for 5 min.
6. Remove the supernatant and resuspend the cells in new ES cell medium.
7. Split the cells 1/5 to 1/8 (depending on the growth rate, which can vary between serum batches and particular cell lines) on newly inactivated feeder plates.
8. Day 1: Change medium.
9. Day 2: Split cells on new feeder as on day 0.

D. TARGETING CONSTRUCT

The targeting construct consists of a genomic fragment, from which exonic regions coding for essential parts of the gene have been removed and substituted by a neomycin cassette (Fig. 1). Expression of the *Neo* gene will confer resistance to the drug G418. This will be used to select for ES cell clones with stable integrations of the construct. Two factors have been shown to affect targeting efficiency: the size of the genomic fragment included in the construct (Deng and Capecchi, 1992) and the origin of the DNA (Riele *et al.*, 1992). Good targeting efficiencies are often obtained with constructs including more than 10 kb of homology. The length of DNA on each side of the *Neo* cassette should not be less than 1.5 kb. Increased targeting efficiencies have been observed when using isogenic DNA isolated from a 129Sv genomic library, the mouse line from which most ES cell lines are derived. The construct should be linearized and introduced into ES cells by electroporation. The DNA for electroporation can be prepared by CsCl centrifugation or by using a Quiagen column. The targeting construct should be linearized within the vector or outside the domain of homology (see Fig. 1) by the appropriate restriction enzyme. The DNA is treated once with phenol/chloroform, precipitated, and resuspended in TE at 0.5 $\mu g/\mu l$. Check DNA on agarose gel before electroporation.

The targeting frequency is variable depending on each particular locus. For some loci the basic targeting strategy described here gives an acceptable targeting frequency. However, for some loci the frequency may be too low to identify the homologous recombinants without enriching strategies. These strategies are designed to select against random integrations and recommended when the targeting efficiency is low. We recommend to use the negative selection marker Thymidine Kinase (TK) gene as enriching procedure (see Capecchi 1989 for review). The TK gene under the control of an ubiquitous promoter is placed on either extreme of the homologous region in the targeting vector. Selection with Gancyclovir will kill all clones that have retained the TK gene which are random integrations. The usual enrichment factor obtained is about 5 fold.

E. ELECTROPORATION

Solution

G418: Dissolve G418 (Gibco) in PBS at a concentration of 250 mg/ml, filter-sterilize, and store in small aliquots (1 ml) at −20°C. Thaw before use and add to the selection medium. G418 potency varies between batches and should be tested empirically with untransfected ES cells. The appropriate G418 concentration is usually between 200 and 350 μg/ml medium (100–175 μg active G418/ml medium). Ideally, control ES cells should die after 7 days and G418-resistant colonies will form by days 8 to 10 depending on the promoter driving *Neo* expression.

Steps

1. Day 0: Split ES cells on 8.5-cm feeder plate as described in Section C. Inactivate fresh feeder and prepare eight 8.5-cm feeder plates. The culture of the feeder for inactivation should be started 1 week before electroporation. The fibroblasts should be prepared from embryos carrying the *Neo* gene, so that they are resistant to G418.

2. Day 1: Change medium.

3. Day 2: Change medium. Remove medium from the eight 8.5-cm feeder plates and add 6 ml of ES cell medium to each plate.

4. Four hours after changing medium, trypsinize the cells as described in Section C, add ES cell medium to 10 ml, mix well, and spin down for 5 min at 1000 rpm.

5. Aspirate the supernatant and resuspend the cells in 30 ml of PBS. Determine the cell number. It should be around 1.5×10^7 cells.

6. Spin down for 5 min at 1000 rpm.

7. Resuspend approximately 10^7 ES cells in 0.8 ml PBS containing 25 μg/ml linearized DNA. Let suspension stand for 5 min at room temperature.

8. Pipette the cells up and down and transfer 0.8 ml of the suspension to one electroporation cuvette, omitting air bubbles. Electroporate with one pulse of 500 μF and 250 V at room temperature. Let stand for 5 min at room temperature.

9. Using a plugged Pasteur pipette, transfer the cells directly to ES medium (28 ml) and plate the cells on seven 8.5-cm feeder plates. Plate control ES cells (electroporated without DNA) at the same cell density.

10. Twenty-four hours after electroporation change medium to selection medium with G418.

11. Change medium every day.

12. Eight days after selection, check control plate (there should be no ES cells left) and transfection plates for G418-resistant colonies. Large ES cell colonies

(about 1000 cells) can already be picked. Do not let them grow too large because they then differentiate.

F. PICKING CLONES

1. Using a microscope marker make a circle under the clone you want to pick.

2. Prepare a 96-well plate with 100 μl trypsin/EDTA in each well.

3. Under a dissecting microscope (in sterile hood) pick every marked clone individually and transfer to one well in the 96-well plate. We pick the colonies with a fine pulled-out mouth pipette (picking side about 150 μm in diameter). Wash picking pipette five or six times with PBS before proceeding to next clone; 12–24 cell clones can be handled in one step.

4. After the colonies are trypsinized (variable time), transfer the 12–24 clones to a 24-well plate with fresh feeder layer and fresh ES cell medium (1 ml in each well). Mix well and return to incubator; change medium every day.

5. Once the cells are confluent (3–5 days), trypsinize the cells by adding 100 μl of trypsin/EDTA to each well and incubating for 5 min at 37°C.

6. Add 600 μl of ES cell medium to each well to stop trypsinization and mix well. Remove from each well 200 μl and transfer into a corresponding 24-well plate (without feeder but the wells should be gelatinized) preequilibrated with 500 μl of ES medium.

7. When all wells are transferred, add 400 μl of 2× freezing medium to each original well. Mix to homogeneity, cover with a plastic bag and paper, and place in Styrofoam box at −70°C. This is the master plate.

8. Proceed with all clones in this way.

9. The ES cells in the gelatinized plated will be used, when confluent, to prepare genomic DNA for screening.

G. ANALYSIS OF THE PICKED CLONES BY SOUTHERN BLOT

Solutions

1. *Lysis buffer:* 100 m*M* Tris–HCl, pH 8.5, 5 m*M* EDTA, 0.2% SDS, 200 m*M* NaCl, 100 μg/ml proteinase K.
2. *Proteinase K stock solution:* 10 mg/ml H_2O.
3. *TE:* 10 m*M* Tris–HCl, pH 8.0, 1 m*M* EDTA (Laird *et al.*, 1991).

Steps

The isolated clones should be checked individually to distinguish between random integrations and homologous recombination. We recommend genomic Southern analysis for this purpose. Genomic DNA is digested with an enzyme that will generate bands of different sizes from the wild-type and targeted alleles, and is probed with a genomic fragment not included in the targeting construct (see Fig. 1).

1. When the cells in the gelatinized plates are confluent remove medium and add 500 μl of lysis buffer to each well.

2. Leave overnight in the incubator at 37°C.

3. Transfer the DNA solution from each well to an Eppendorf tube and add 500 μl of isopropanol to precipitate DNA.

4. Spin down for 10 min and remove supernatant.

5. Add 500 μl 70% ethanol to wash pellet and spin down for 5 min.

6. Remove ethanol and dry pellet. Resuspend DNA in 50 μl 1/10 TE.

7. Use 15 μl from each sample for screening and digest with the appropriate restriction enzyme. Positive clones will be expanded and rechecked. They can be used now to generate chimeras by blastocyst injection or morula aggregation (Bradley, 1987).

ACKNOWLEDGMENT

We are grateful to Professor Peter Gruss for constant support and encouragement.

REFERENCES

Bradley, A. (1987) Production and analysis of chimeric mice. *In* "Teratocarcinomas and Embryonic Stem Cells, a Practical Approach" (E. J. Robertson, ed.), pp. 113–151. IRL Press Oxford, Washington, DC.

Capecchi, M. R. (1989) The new mouse genetics: Altering the genome by gene targeting. *Trends Genet.* **5**, 70–76.

Deng, C., and Capecchi, M. R. (1992) Reexamination of gene targeting frequency as a function of the extent of homology between the targeting vector and the target locus. *Mol. Cell. Biol.* **12**, 3365–3371.

Gossler, A., Doetschman, T., Korn, R., Serfling, E., and Kemler, R. (1986) Transgenesis by means of blastocyst-derived embryonic stem cell lines. *Proc. Natl. Acad. Sci. USA* **83**, 9065–9069.

Laird, P. L., Zijderveld, A., Linders, K., Rudnicki, M., Jaenisch, R., and Berns, A. (1991) Simplified mammalian DNA isolation procedure. *Nucleic Acids Res.* **19**, 4293.

Riele, H. R., Maandag, E. B., and Berns, A. (1992) Highly efficient gene targeting in embryonic stem cells through homologous recombination with isogenic DNA constructs. *Proc. Natl. Acad. Sci. USA* **89**, 5128–5132.

Robertson, E. J. (1986) Pluripotent stem cell lines as a route into the mouse germline. *Trends Genet.* **2**, 9–13.

Robertson, E. J. (1987) Embryo-derived stem cell lines. *In* "Teratocarcinomas and Embryonic Stem Cells, a Practical Approach" (E. J. Robertson, ed.), pp. 71–112. IRL Press Oxford, Washington, DC.

Soriano, P., Montgomery, C., Geske, R., and Bradley, A. (1991) Targeted disruption of the c-*src* proto-oncogene leads to osteopetrosis in mice. *Cell* **64**, 693–702.

Transgenic Plants: *Agrobacterium*-Mediated Transformation of the Diploid Legume *Lotus japonicus*

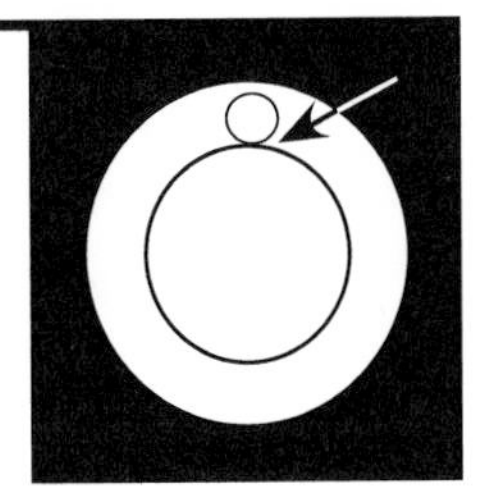

Kurt Handberg, Jiri Stiller, Thomas Thykjær, and Jens Stougaard

I. Introduction

We have previously suggested the diploid *Lotus japonicus* as a "model" plant for the legume plant family (Handberg and Stougaard, 1992). Here we present the current transformation–regeneration procedure for *L. japonicus*, together with biochemical assays for detection of marker gene expression in transgenic tissues and transgenic plants. Protocols for positive selection on hygromycin, kanamycin, and geneticin (G418) are presented and conditions for negative selection using the conditional lethal cytosine deaminase marker gene are outlined (Stougaard, 1993). With the described procedures transgenic plants can be obtained in 4 months and transgenic seeds can be harvested after 6 months.

II. Materials and Instrumentation

Seeds of *L. japonicus* Accession No. B-129 "Gifu" was originally obtained from Professor W. F. Grant, McGill University, Canada. Seeds of the "Gifu" line inbred for eight generations are available on request. Plants are grown in cabinets (18 hr/6 hr day/night cycle, 20°C/18°C day/night temperature, light intensity of 246 μE sec^{-1} m^{-2}, 65% humidity) or in a greenhouse with supplemented daylight, 19°C average temperature, and 70% humidity. A commercial nutrient solution "Hornum" (Cat. No. 33102) containing, in 1 liter of 100× stock, 40 g NH_4NO_3, 30 g KNO_3, 30 g $MgSO_4 \cdot 7H_2O$, 10 g $NaH_2PO_4 \cdot 2H_2O$, 2 g Fe-EDTA (9% Fe), 120 mg $MnSO_4 \cdot H_2O$, 120 mg H_3BO_3, 40 mg $CuSO_4 \cdot 5H_2O$, 40 mg $ZnSO_4 \cdot 7H_2O$, and 8 mg $Na_2MoO_4 \cdot 2H_2O$, is purchased from GiC in a 200× formulation, diluted in tap water, adjusted to pH 6.8, and used for watering. *Lotus japonicus* plants are sensitive to flooding and overwatering. Water plants from below and preferably not directly into the pots. Light brown mature pods are collected and dried at room temperature. Seeds are released from pods using a domestic blender, Krups Type 708A, and collected through a steel mesh (1.5 × 1.5 mm), retaining fragmented pods into a mesh (0.6 × 0.6 mm) retaining seeds, but allowing dust to pass. Seeds are germinated and *in vitro* cultures are grown under a single Philips TLD 30W/33 tube. Tissue culture manipulations are done in vertical-flow benches. Deionized water (Millipore) is used for tissue culture media and solutions. Gamborg B_5 medium for tissue culture (Gamborg, 1970) is purchased from Flow Laboratories (Cat. No. 26-130-22). Vitamin B_5 solution (1000×) (Cat. No. G-1019) and Phytagel-gelrite (Cat. No. P-8169) are from Sigma. Plant containers (Cat. No. 10197) are from Magenta Plast. Universal containers (Cat. No. 364238) are from Gibco-BRL. DC-Alufolien cellulose TLC plates are from Merck (Cat. No. 5552.0001). Antibiotics are purchased from Sigma: kanamycin (Cat. No. K-4378), geneticin (Cat. No. G-9516), hygromycin B (Cat. No. H-8272), cefotaxime (Cat. No. C-7039). Filter paper WH-1 and cellulose phosphate P81 paper are from Whatman. Phytohormones are obtained from Sigma: kinetin (Cat. No. K-0753), 6-benzylaminopurine (BAP, Cat. No. B-9395), α-naphthaleneacetic acid (NAA) (Cat. No. N-0640). 2,4-dichlorophenoxyacetic acid (2,4-D) is from Merck (Cat. No. 820451).

III. Procedures

A. PREPARATION OF MEDIA AND SOLUTIONS FOR GROWTH OF *AGROBACTERIUM*

1. *Solid agar plates:* 0.5% yeast extract, 1% Bacto-tryptone, 0.5% NaCl, 1.4% agar, pH 7.0. For 1 liter, add 5 g of yeast extract, 10 g of Bacto-tryptone, 5 g of NaCl, and 14 g of agar. Adjust pH to 7.0, and autoclave. Stored medium is remelted in a microwave oven and cooled. Antibiotics for selecting appropriate binary T-DNA vectors are added before plates are poured.

2. *YMB liquid growth medium:* For 1 liter, dissolve 2 g mannitol, 0.4 g yeast extract, 0.2 g $MgSO_4 \cdot 7H_2O$, and 0.1 g NaCl, and autoclave. Autoclave a 6.55% $K_2HPO_4 \cdot 3H_2O$, pH 6.8, solution separately; add 10 ml per liter before use.

B. PREPARATION OF SOLUTIONS FOR GROWTH OF SEEDLINGS

1. *Solutions for sterilization and germination of seeds:* 2% hypochlorite and 0.02% Tween 20. For 20 ml, mix 2.7 ml of a 15% sodium hypochlorite solution with autoclaved water in a sterile universal container. Add 4 μl Tween 20, shake gently, and use the same day.

2. *Support material in liquid cultures:* Squares of filter paper, 6 × 6 cm, packaged in aluminum foil and autoclaved.

C. PREPARATION OF SOLUTIONS AND MEDIA FOR COCULTIVATION, SELECTION OF TRANSGENIC CALLI, AND PLANT REGENERATION

1. *Plant hormone stock solutions: Kinetin at 3 mg/ml:* Dissolve 75 mg kinetin in 0.5 ml 6 *M* HCl, add 20 ml water, titrate solution to pH 2.0 with 1 *M* KOH, and add water to 25 ml. *2,4-D at 3 mg/ml:* Dissolve 75 mg 2,4-D in 12 ml 96% ethanol, and add water to 25 ml. *BAP at 1 mg/ml:* Dissolve 25 mg BAP in 0.5 ml 1 *M* NaOH, and add water to 25 ml. *NAA at 0.5 mg/ml:* Dissolve 12.5 mg in 12 ml 96% ethanol and add water to 25 ml. All solutions are filter-sterilized into 5-ml aliquots and stored at −20°C. For use, heat gently in a microwave oven.

2. *Stock solutions of antibiotics: Kanamycin at 100 mg/ml:* Dissolve 3.2 g in 25 ml H_2O; note that most commercial kanamycin preparations have a purity of approximately 80%. *G418 at 50 mg/ml:* Dissolve 1.25 g in 25 ml water. *Hygromycin at 10 mg/ml:* Dilute from commercial stock solution into water. All solutions are filter-sterilized into 5-ml aliquots and stored at −20°C. *Cefotaxime*

at 30 mg/ml for 1 liter of medium: Dissolve 300 mg in 10 ml H_2O, filter-sterilize, and use the same day.

3. *Cocultivation medium:* B_5 medium in 1/10 concentration without sucrose, 5 m*M* MES, pH 5.2, kinetin and 2,4-D at 3 μg/ml. Mix 387 mg readymade B_5 in 1 liter of water, and autoclave. Before use, add 5 ml of a filter-sterilized 1 *M* MES, pH 5.2, stock solution, 1 ml each of kinetin and 2,4-D stock solutions, and 100 μl of B_5 vitamin stock.

4. *Callus medium:* B_5 with 2% sucrose, 0.2% Gelrite, and 2,4-D and kinetin at 3 μg/ml. For 1 liter, add 3.87 g of readymade B_5, 20 g of sucrose, and 2 g of Gelrite, adjust pH to 5.5, and autoclave; this is called L0 medium. Add 1 ml from each stock solution of kinetin, 2,4-D, and B_5 before pouring cooled medium into 9-cm petri dishes.

5. *Shoot induction medium:* B_5 with 2% sucrose, 0.2% Gelrite, 10 m*M* NH_4^+, and BAP at 0.2 μg/ml. Prepare 1 liter L0 as above, add 1.25 ml of filter-sterilized 4 *M* $(NH_4)_2SO_4$ to hot medium, then 200 μl of BAP stock solution and 1 ml of B_5 stock to cooled medium. Pour into plant containers, approximately 100 ml in each.

6. *Shoot growth medium:* B_5 with 2% sucrose, 0.2% Gelrite, 0.2 μg/ml BAP. Prepare 1 liter L0 as above, and add 200 μl of BAP stock solution and 1 ml of B_5 stock. Pour into plant containers.

7. *Shoot elongation medium:* B_5 with 2% sucrose, 0.2% Gelrite. Prepare 1 liter L0 as above, add 1 ml B_5 stock solution, and pour into plant containers.

8. *Root induction medium:* Half-strength B_5 with 1% sucrose, 0.4% Gelrite, 0.5 μg/ml NAA. For 1 liter, add 1.94 g of B_5, 10 g of sucrose, and 4 g of Gelrite, and autoclave; this is called L medium. Before use, add 1 ml of NAA and 0.5 ml B_5 stock solution. Pour into plant containers.

9. *Root elongation medium:* Half-strength B_5 with 1% sucrose, 0.4% Gelrite. Use 1 liter L medium with 0.5 ml B_5 vitamin stock solution and pour into plant containers.

D. TRANSFORMATION–REGENERATION PROCEDURE FOR *LOTUS JAPONICUS*

This protocol is used for transfer of three different gene constructs from *Agrobacterium*. More than 100 independent transgenic calli should be obtained from each line. See also Figs. 1–3 and Color Plate 33.

Steps

1. Surface-sterilize 500 seeds (0.5 g) in 20 ml 2% hypochlorite, 0.02% Tween 20, and shake 20 minutes. If necessary for germination, seeds are first scarified by a short treatment with sand paper.

2. Wash seeds in six shifts of autoclaved water.

3. Place a 0.5-cm-high platform of sterile filter paper in four 9-cm petri dishes; add sterile water until free liquid appears (12–15 ml). Spread aliquot of sterile seeds on top of each wet filter paper; seal petri dishes with Parafilm.

4. Germinate 7 days at 26°C under continuous light.

5. Streak the *Agrobacterium* strains on fresh selective plates. Start on day 5 after start of seeds.

6. Start cocultivation on day 7 after start of seed germination. Scrape 2-day-

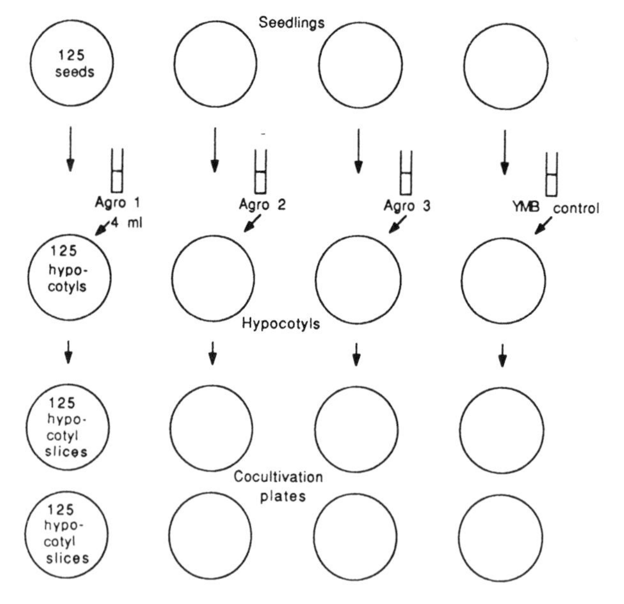

FIGURE 1 Arrangement and starting material for transformation experiment with three different *Agrobacterium*.

old *Agrobacterium* colonies off selective plates with sterile toothpick, and resuspend each strain to a density of approximately 5×10^9 in 5 ml of YMB medium by whirling. Leave bacteria as milky cultures at room temperature while preparing the cocultivation plates.

7. Prepare cocultivation plates by placing 0.5-cm-high platforms of sterile filter paper in eight petri dishes; add cocultivation medium until free liquid appears (12–15 ml).

8. Prepare a new set of four dishes with two layers of sterile filter paper; soak filter papers with 4 ml of *Agrobacterium* YMB suspension or 4 ml of YMB for control plates. Free liquid should appear on surface of filter paper.

9. Using scalpel and forceps, cut seedlings below the shoot primordia and at the stem base. Transfer hypocotyls from one of the germination plates to one of the four *Agrobacterium*- or YMB-soaked filter papers.

10. Cut hypocotyls longitudinally while resting on *Agrobacterium* filters. Use magnifying lamp, hold hypocotyl explants between forceps, and cut with scalpel inbetween. Transfer cut hypocotyl to the cocultivation plates and continue with next hypocotyl.

11. Incubate cocultivation plates for 7 days 21°C, in the dark.

12. To eliminate *Agrobacterium*, transfer explants resting on the top filter paper from the cocultivation plate to callus medium with 300 μg/ml of cefotaxime. Incubate for 7 days 26°C under continuous light.

13. Start selection of transgenic calli by transferring explants, without filter paper, to selective callus medium containing 300 μg/ml cefotaxime. For selection use the following concentrations: kanamycin 100 μg/ml, hygromycin 15 μg/ml, G418 25 μg/ml (Table I). Conditions for subsequent selection and regeneration steps are continuous light, 26°C, except steps 18, 19, 20 which are at 21°C, and 7-day incubation intervals.

14. Continue selection and propagation of transgenic calli on callus medium with cefotaxime 300 μg/ml for 5 weeks. Separate transgenic green calli from

Transformation: Cut hypocotyl explants on *Agrobacterium* soaked filter paper, transfer to cocultivation plate.

7 days

Callus formation: Move top filter paper to callus medium

7 days

Callus formation and selection of transgenic calli: Move individual explants to selective callus medium

5 X 7 days

Shoot induction: Move green calli onto shoot induction medium

3 X 7 days

Shoot growth: Move calli with emerging shoot structures to shoot growth medium

2 X 7 days

Shoot elongation: Move calli with small shoots onto shoot elongation medium

2 X 7 days

Root induction: Cut individual shoots from calli, transfer to root induction medium

7 days

Root elongation: Move shoots to root elongation medium

2 X 7 days

Transfer shoots to pots, move to greenhouse and harvest seeds after two months

FIGURE 2 Flow scheme for transformation and regeneration of *Lotus japonicus*.

explants as soon as possible and propagate in one piece unless clonal material is needed.

15. Start shoot induction by transferring green transgenic calli to shoot induction medium with cefotaxime 300 μg/ml. Shoot structures will develop in the dark green zone appearing at the perimeter of the calli. Keep calli undivided; remove brown and light yellow tissue. Selection is optional.

16. Continue propagation of transgenic calli on shoot induction medium for 3 weeks. Counterselection of *Agrobacterium* with cefotaxime 300 μg/ml is maintained until at least six medium shifts, including step 12, are reached.

17. Transfer calli with emerging shoot structures to shoot growth medium. Continue on shoot growth medium for 2 weeks.

18. For shoot elongation, transfer calli with short shoots onto shoot elongation medium. Continue on shoot elongation medium for 2 weeks at 21°C.

19. Individual shoots, 2–4 cm long, are cut off and moved to root induction medium for 1 week (21° C). If transgenic shoots are selected on G418 or

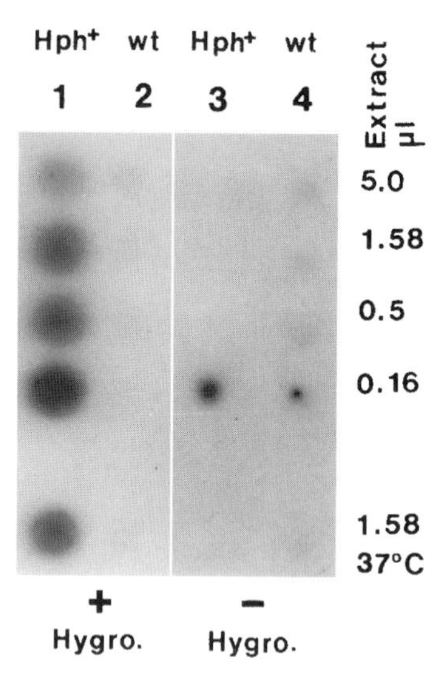

FIGURE 3 Dot-blot assay for determining hygromycin phosphotransferase activity. Lanes 1 and 3 show the activity in transgenic leaves of *Lotus japonicus* plants selected on hygromycin: lane 1 with hygromycin in the assay, lane 3 without hygromycin. Lanes 2 and 4 show the activity in leaves of wild-type control plants with and without hygromycin substrate in the assay. All assays were at 25°C except the last row which was incubated at 37°C.

kanamycin, 50 µg/ml kanamycin can be included in all rooting media as an extra selection.

20. Move shoots to root elongation medium, and incubate for 2 weeks or longer at 21° C.

21. Move shoots with short roots into pots containing peat support; cover with plastic bag.

22. Transfer pots to cabinets or greenhouse, remove plastic bag to harden plant, leave plants to self-pollinate and harvest seeds from mature brown pods after 2 months.

E. NEGATIVE SELECTION USING THE CYTOSINE DEAMINASE MARKER GENE

Step

Slice small calli from step 14 of the transformation procedure. Incubate two slices on callus medium with cefotaxime 300 µg/ml and 5-fluorocytosine 500 µg/ml. Transfer rest of calli to callus or shoot induction medium as required.

TABLE I Summary of Parameters for Transformation and Regeneration of *Lotus japonicus*

	Hygromycin	Kanamycin	Geneticin (G418)
Concentration (µg/ml)	15	100	25
Transformation frequency (% of cocultivated explants)	50–90	2–65	50–90
Time required (weeks)			
For selection of calli	5	9	5
For transfer of shoots to pots	17	25	17
To obtain seeds	26	35	26
Biochemical assay for marker gene expression	+	+	+

F. BIOCHEMICAL ASSAYS FOR DETECTION OF MARKER GENE EXPRESSION IN TRANSGENIC CALLI AND TRANSGENIC PLANTS

1. Hygromycin Phosphotransferase Assay

This assay is modified from that of Sørensen *et al.* (1992).

Solutions

1. *Extraction buffer:* 135 m*M* Tris–HCl, pH 6.8, 20% glycerol, 4 m*M* DTT. For 10 ml, add 2.7 ml 0.5 *M* Tris–HCl, pH 6.8, 2.3 ml glycerol (87%), 6.2 mg DTT.

2. *Reaction buffer:* 67 m*M* Tris, pH 7.1, 42 m*M* $MgCl_2$, 400 m*M* NH_4 Cl. For 500 ml, dissolve 4.04 g Tris, 4.27 g $MgCl_2$, 10.7 g NH_4Cl. Adjust pH to 7.1 using 1 *M* maleic acid.

3. *Assay buffer:* 13.4 m*M* Tris, pH 7.1, 8.4 m*M* $MgCl_2$, 80 m*M* NH_4Cl, 60 μM hygromycin B, 15 μM ATP, 20 μCi[γ-^{32}P]ATP/ml. For 5 ml, add 987 μl of reaction buffer, 10.2 μl 15 mg/ml hygromycin B stock, 7.5 μl of 10 m*M* ATP, 2 μl [γ-^{32}P]ATP (50 μCi/μl).

Steps

1. Homogenize plant material using mortar, pestle, and glass beads. Add 50 μl extraction buffer and transfer to Eppendorf tube; keep on ice. Remember negative control.

2. Centrifuge 10 min 15,000 rpm at room temperature and transfer supernatant to new Eppendorf tube. Determine protein concentration in supernatant.

3. Start assay by transferring 0.5 μl supernatant to Eppendorf tube containing 50 μl assay buffer. Incubate for 1 h at 25°C.

4. Add 150 μl H_2O to assays and load immediately onto a slot-blot manifold fitted with a sandwich of one top layer of nitrocellulose, two layers of P81 cellulose phosphate paper (one piece folded), and a 3MM paper support.

5. Leave samples to run through sandwich for 1 h. Apply vacuum and wash once with 100 μl H_2O.

6. Remove cellulose phosphate P81 paper and wash four times 20 min in H_2O at 65°C. Dry the P81 paper and expose to autoradiography.

2. Aminoglycoside (kanamycin) Phosphotransferase Assay

The aminoglycoside (kanamycin) phosphotransferase activity is determined using the dot assay and extraction buffer B described by McDonnell *et al.* (1987).

3. Cytosine Deaminase Assay

Cytosine deaminase is assayed according to Stougaard (1993).

1. *Extraction buffer:* 200 m*M* Tris–HCl, pH 7.8, 1 m*M* DTT, 1 m*M* EDTA, 0.1% Triton X-100, 0.1% Sarkosyl, 2 m*M* PMSF. For 20 ml, add 4 ml 1 *M* Tris–HCl, pH 7.8, 20 μl 1 *M* DTT, pH 4.8 (stored at −20°C), 40 μl of 0.5 *M* EDTA, pH 8.0, 20 μl Triton X-100, 200 μl 10% Sarkosyl, 500 μl 80 m*M* PMSF in 96% ethanol. Use the same day.

2. *Assay buffer:* 200 m*M* Tris–HCl, pH 7.8, 1 m*M* DTT, 1 m*M* EDTA, 2 m*M* PMSF. For 20 ml, add 4 ml 1 *M* Tris–HCl, pH 7.8, 40 μl 0.5 *M* EDTA, pH 8.0, 500 μl 80 m*M* PMSF in 96% ethanol, 20 μl 1 *M* DTT, pH 4.8 (stored at −20°C). Use the same day.

Steps

1. Homogenize plant material in 10-fold excess (v/w) extraction buffer. Transfer to Eppendorf tube on ice. For quantitation, determine protein concentration. Remember negative control.
2. Transfer 15 μl extract to 15 μl assay buffer in Eppendorf tube.
3. Start assay by adding 0.5 μl [2-^{14}C]cytosine (1.94 μCi/μl) and incubate for 1 hr at 37°C.
4. Spot 5 μl on a DC-Alufolien cellulose TLC plate and blow-dry.
5. Develop TLC plate in *n*-butanol/water 86/14 (v/v) for 7 hr, in fume hood.
6. Blow-dry TLC plate in fume hood, cover plate with Saran wrap, and autoradiograph.
7. For quantitation, cut out spot with [2-^{14}C]uracil and count in liquid scintillation.

IV. Comments

Using the transformation–regeneration protocol described above, transgenic *Lotus japonicus* plants can be obtained after selection for two different resistance genes expressing hygromycin phosphotransferase and neomycin phosphotransferase. Selection for hygromycin and geneticin resistance is very effective and up to 90% of the hypocotyl explants cocultivated with *Agrobacterium* give rise to one or more transgenic calli. Transgenic calli are easily distinguished from the explants and moved to regeneration media. Rooted transformed plants in pots are available after 4 months. Kanamycin is less toxic and the selection less clean. Longer time is required to discern and separate transgenic calli from explant tissue. The transformation frequency is therefore also more variable, typically from 2 to 65% of explants, and rooted transformed plants in pots are typically obtained after 5 months. The transformation frequencies seem not to be influenced by the genetic background of the *Agrobacterium* or the type of binary vectors (Handberg and Stougaard, 1992; Stougaard, 1993). Both nopaline and octopine strains have been used with a number of different binary vectors.

V. Pitfalls

1. The amount of Gelrite is adjusted to give soft plant tissue culture media, and in our hands, media can be stored and remelted once before use. A slightly different autoclave cycle may, however, produce very sloppy media that will not set. Increase Gelrite concentration or use agar noble instead.

2. Smearing of calli with media will increase browning of tissue; always transfer calli gently by placing "on top" of solid media. Move calli into petri dish lid for cutting, removal of brown tissue, and other manipulations. In our hands, the optimal interval for callus transfer is 7 days.

3. For transformation use freshly grown *Agrobacterium* from selective plates.

4. Seeds contaminated with fungal spores are washed 2 min in 96% ethanol prior to hypochlorite treatment and germinated at lower density to minimize loss.

5. The hygromycin phosphotransferase assay has background activity. Include negative control of wild-type plants and assays without hygromycin substrate in tests.

REFERENCES

Gamborg, O. L. (1970) The effects of amino acids and ammonium on the growth of plant cells in suspension culture. *Plant. Physiol.* **45,** 372–375.

Handberg, K., and Stougaard, J. (1992) *Lotus japonicus,* an autogamous diploid legume species for classical and molecular genetics. *Plant J.* **2,** 487–496.

McDonnell, R. E., Clark, R. D., Smith, W. A., and Hinchee, M. A. (1987) A simplified method for the detection of neomycin phosphotransferase II activity in transformed plant tissues. *Plant Mol. Biol. Rep.* **5,** 380–386.

Sørensen, M. S., Duch, M., Paludan, K., Jørgensen, P., and Pedersen, F. S. (1992) Measurement of hygromycin B phosphotransferase activity in crude mammalian cell extracts by a simple dot-blot assay. *Gene* **112,** 257–260.

Stougaard, J. (1993) Substrate-dependent negative selection in plants using a bacterial cytosine deaminase gene. *Plant J.* **3,** 755–761.

PART 13

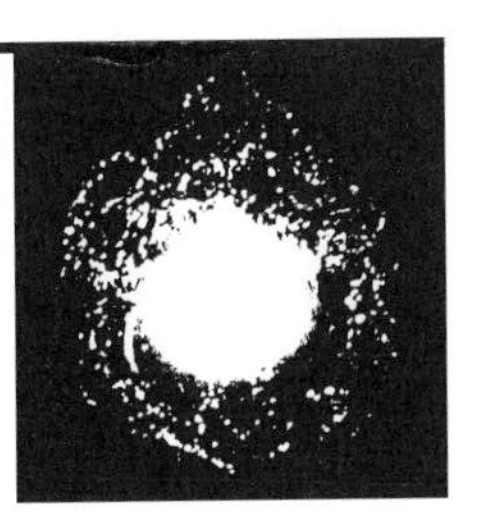

CELL-FREE EXTRACTS, PERMEABILIZED CELL SYSTEMS, AND EXPRESSION SYSTEMS

Preparation and Use of Translocating Cell-Free Translation Extracts from *Xenopus* Eggs

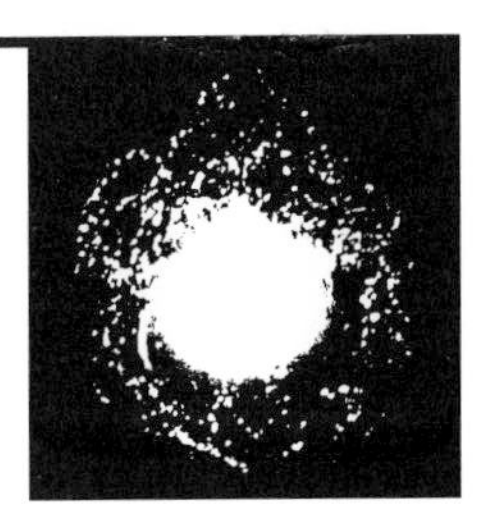

Glenn Matthews

I. Introduction

Extracts prepared by the centrifugal lysis of *Xenopus* eggs were originally developed for the study of chromatin assembly and cell cycling, but have since been used for a variety of other purposes. These extracts have a high capacity for translation, which can be easily rendered mRNA dependent, and the relatively gentle approach to lysis results in the preservation of functional endoplasmic reticulum-derived microsomes. The translocation and primary posttranslational modification of secretory and membrane proteins are, therefore, inherent properties of the extract and these occur at high efficiency and fidelity in all cases so far examined. In addition to signal sequence cleavage, N-glycosylation, and assembly of multimers, two modifications associated with the *cis*-Golgi, O-linked glycosylation and mannose-6-phosphorylation, also occur, albeit at reduced efficiency, indicating that some transport to compartments beyond the endoplasmic reticulum may be supported by the extract.

The procedure for preparing the extract, which is adapted from the protocol developed by Murray and Kirschner (1989), is relatively straightforward and requires no specialized apparatus. A single batch of eggs yields approximately 2 ml of extract, which can be frozen and stored for many months to provide more than 200 individual translation reactions.

II. Materials and Instrumentation

The maintenance of *Xenopus laevis* stocks is covered in detail by Wu and Gerhart (1991).

Hepes (Cat. No. 737 151), aprotinin (Cat. No. 981 532), RNase A (Cat. No. 109 169), RNase inhibitor (Cat. No. 799 025), calf liver tRNA (Cat. No. 647 225), dithiothreitol (Cat. No. 197 777), and creatine phosphate (Cat. No. 127 574) are from Boehringer-Mannheim. Rabbit reticulocyte lysate (Cat. No. 530-8111SA) is from BRL. Chorionic gonadotropin (Cat. No. C-1063), cytochalasin B (Cat. No. C-6762), spermidine (Cat. No. S-0266), PMSF (Cat. No. 7626), and other general chemicals are from Sigma. ^{35}S-labeled methionine (Cat. No. SJ 204) is from Amersham International. Triton X-100 is a 10% solution (Surfact-Amps X-100, Cat. No. 28314) from Pierce and Warriner Ltd. Serum gonadotropin (Folligon) is from Intervet. All solutions should be made using autoclaved, reverse-osmosis or double-glass-distilled water.

A Beckman TL100 benchtop ultracentrifuge equipped with a TLS 55 rotor provides an ideal combination for the preparation of a single batch of extract. It is likely that many centrifuge/rotor combinations would be suitable, the only requirements being a suitable tube size, a swing-out rotor, and a rapid rate of acceleration. Extracts have even been successfully prepared using an Eppendorf microfuge but the fixed-angle rotor leads to a reduction in yield.

A refrigerated benchtop centrifuge equipped with a swing-out rotor capable of accommodating the same tubes as used for the high-speed spin, a cooled water bath at 10°C, and either a water bath or incubator at 21°C are required.

Although not absolutely essential, preparation of the extract is more reliable when performed in a cold (4°C) room and steps such as RNase treatment are more readily controlled.

Care should be taken to avoid the presence of residual detergents on beakers, measuring cylinders, etc., as this will compromise the extract. All centrifuge tubes, pipette tips, and other materials likely to come into contact with the extract after lysis should be autoclaved to inactivate ribonuclease activity.

III. Procedures

A. OBTAINING *XENOPUS* EGGS

Note that the administration of hormones by injection into live frogs normally requires an animal license.

Solutions

1. *Salt water:* Dissolve NaCl in water at 6.4 g per liter (110 m*M*). The water used need not be highly purified but should not be tap water which often contains high levels of chlorine. Frogs are normally maintained in water that has been dechlorinated by storage for a few days and this should be suitable.

2. *Folligon and chorionic gonadotropin:* These should be reconstituted according to the manufacturers' instructions.

Steps

1. Prime large adult female *Xenopus laevis* 3 to 5 days in advance by injection of 50–100 IU of Folligon into the dorsal lymph sac.

2. The evening before preparing an extract, induce ovulation by injecting 750 IU of chorionic gonadotropin into the dorsal lymph sac.

3. Keep frogs overnight individually in plastic boxes measuring approximately 20 × 30 cm, in 1.5 liters of salt water, to prevent activation of the eggs laid.

4. Collect the eggs using a 25-ml disposable plastic pipette with the tip removed to give an orifice of approximately 3 mm. It is easiest to remove the frog temporarily and raise one end of the tank for a few minutes, whereupon the eggs settle in the low end. They can then be aspirated and collected in a 250-ml glass beaker.

5. After collection, remove any obvious contaminants (shed skin, feces, etc.), together with any eggs that are obviously necrotic. These are easily identified by the loss of the normal pigmentation pattern. Bad eggs will often lyse and therefore be removed, during removal of the jelly coat, so a small percentage can be tolerated, but some frogs lay large numbers or strings of eggs in a contiguous jelly coat and such batches should be discarded.

A single large female will normally yield approximately 50 ml of loosely packed eggs, which is enough to make a single batch of extract. It is best to make extracts from individual frogs, where egg yields allow this, but it is sometimes necessary to pool the eggs from two or more frogs.

B. REMOVAL OF JELLY COATS

Solutions

1. *2% Cysteine/110 mM NaCl:* Dissolve 3.2 g NaCl and 10 g cysteine hydrochloride in 450 ml water and adjust the pH to 7.7 with 10 *M* NaOH. Make up to 500 ml, and use within 1–2 hr.

2. *Extract buffer (XB):* 100 m*M* KCl, 0.1 m*M* $CaCl_2$, 1 m*M* $MgCl_2$, 50 m*M* sucrose, 10 m*M* Hepes, pH 7.7. Prepare a 20× salt stock by dissolving 149 g KCl, 0.29 g $CaCl_2 \cdot 2H_2O$, and 4.1 g $MgCl_2 \cdot 6H_2O$ in 1 liter water; dispense into 50-ml portions and store at −20°C. Prepare 1.5 *M* sucrose by dissolving 513.5 g in 1 liter and freezing 40-ml portions at −20°C. Prepare 1 *M* Hepes by dissolving 47.7 g in 200 ml water and freezing 10-ml portions at −20°C. To prepare XB, blend 50 ml of 20× salts with 33 ml of 1.5 *M* sucrose and 10 ml of 1 *M* Hepes in 800 ml of water, adjust the pH to 7.7 with 10 *M* KOH, and make up to 1 liter. If the water used to make this has been precooled by storing at 4°C overnight, less time on ice is required to cool the solution to working temperature. The unused portion of the 1.5 *M* sucrose should be kept on ice for use in the freezing step described later.

Steps

1. Transfer eggs to 2% cysteine with two washes and swirl gently every 30 sec or so.
2. After a few minutes, removal of the jelly coats can be observed as the eggs pack closely together when allowed to settle.
3. Terminate the process by washing four or five times with ice-cold XB.

The loss of the jelly coat reduces the volume of 50 ml of eggs to 8–10 ml.

C. PREPARATION OF THE EXTRACT

Solutions

1. *10 mg/ml Cytochalasin B:* Dissolve the contents of a 1-mg vial of cytochalasin B by adding 100 μl DMSO and vortexing briefly. Store at 4°C. Note that DMSO is frozen at 4°C, so it is necessary to melt the solution at room temperature before use.

2. *10 mg/ml Aprotinin:* Dissolve in water and store in 50-μl aliquots at −20°C.

Steps

This procedure should ideally be performed on ice, in a cold room. If this is not possible, the extract should at least be kept on ice at all stages.

1. Gently pipette the dejellied eggs, using a Pasteur pipette with the end removed to give a diameter of at least 2 mm, into polyallomer TLS 55 tubes.

After allowing them to settle for a minute or so, remove surplus buffer and top the tubes up with any remaining eggs. If the number of eggs available is limited, it is better to reduce the number of tubes used than to only partly fill a rotor-full of tubes as it is easier to collect fractions from full tubes.

2. Centrifuge at 500 *g* for 1 min at 4°C. This should pack the eggs without causing extensive lysis.

3. Remove as much of the buffer as possible using a 200-μl pipette and yellow tip; then load the tubes into a precooled TLS 55 rotor and centrifuge at 15,000 rpm for 15 min at 4°C.

4. Recover the "cytoplasm," a turbid, straw-colored fraction, which occupies about 40% of the volume, by inserting a Pasteur pipette through the lipid pellicle. Pool the material into thick-walled polycarbonate TLS 55 tubes.

5. Estimate the volume recovered, add 5 μl of cytochalasin B per milliliter of cytoplasm, and mix gently by pipetting with a Pasteur pipette. Then recentrifuge at 15,000 rpm for a further 15 min at 4°C.

6. Recover the cytoplasm as described in step 4. Although the cytoplasm now occupies most of the volume of the tube, it is important to recover it carefully as the viscous pellet should be avoided.

7. Add 1 μl of aprotinin per milliliter of product and hold on ice for RNase treatment. Use for translation immediately or freeze as described below.

D. mRNA-DEPENDENT EXTRACTS

Ribonuclease treatment should be performed immediately after preparation of the extract.

Solutions

1. *RNase A:* Dissolve RNase A in water at 1 mg/ml, heat to 80°C for 10 min, then allow to cool at room temperature. Store in 5-μl aliquots at −20°C.
2. *Calf liver tRNA:* Dissolve at 5 mg/ml and store in 50-μl aliquots at −20°C.

Steps

Titration of ribonuclease stocks

Each new stock of ribonuclease must be titrated for activity in the extract. This means that only a proportion of the first extract prepared will be of use in future experiments, but experience has shown that ribonuclease sensitivity is consistent between batches, so a single titrated stock can be used for many subsequent extracts.

1. Divide the extract into six equal portions and treat each with a different level of RNase A from a twofold dilution series to give a range of final concentrations of 2–0.12 μg/ml, according to the protocol given below.
2. Assemble two translation reactions from each concentration point, adding a well-translated eukaryotic mRNA to one.
3. Freeze the remainder of the material, as described below, for future use.
4. Analyze translation products by SDS–PAGE (see article by Julio E. Celis and Eydfinnur Olsen) and/or TCA precipitation and select the level of RNase that leads to the best signal over background for future preparations.

Ribonuclease treatment

1. On ice, dispense 1 μl of a 200-fold concentrated, titered stock of RNase A into each of a series of 0.6-ml microfuge tubes. Add 200 μl of extract to each tube, mixing gently but thoroughly by pipetting. Incubate at 10°C for 15 min.
2. Return the tubes to ice and add 1 μl of 200 m*M* DTT and then 100 units (2 μl) of RNase inhibitor to each. Mix by pipetting and incubate at 10°C for a further 10 min.
3. Add 2 μl of 10 mg/ml tRNA to each tube and mix well.

The extract should now be used directly or frozen for storage.

E. FREEZING

Steps

1. Add 0.15 vol of 1.5 *M* sucrose, mix thoroughly, and dispense aliquots of 50–100 μl into 0.6-ml microfuge tubes, on ice.
2. Freeze in liquid nitrogen, then store either at −70°C or under liquid nitrogen.

F. TRANSLATION REACTIONS

Solutions

1. *500 mM Creatine phosphate:* Dissolve the contents of a 1-g vial in 3 ml of water and store as 50-μl aliquots at −20°C. Aliquots can be thawed and refrozen a number of times.
2. *100 mM Spermidine:* Dissolve in water at 14.5 mg/ml and store at −20°C.

Steps

1. Thaw frozen extract at room temperature until it is mostly liquid, then place on ice.

2. To 100 μl of extract, add 10 μl of reticulocyte lysate, 2 μl 500 m*M* creatine phosphate, 1 μl 100 m*M* spermidine, and 100 μCi [^{35}S]methionine, and mix well.

3. Dispense into tubes containing appropriate amounts of mRNA. The volume of each reaction should be in the range 5–50 μl, containing a final concentration of 10–100 μg/ml mRNA, depending on the nature of the experiment and the translational activity of the mRNA being used. A small reaction should always be performed in the absence of added mRNA to verify the absence of background translation in the aliquot of extract used.

4. Incubate for 1 hr at 21°C.

5. If highly radioactive mRNA has been used, treat with 10 μg/ml RNase A for 15 min at 21°C.

6. Stop the reaction by freezing or analyze immediately.

G. ANALYSIS OF TRANSLATION PRODUCTS

1. SDS–PAGE

Solution

1% Triton X-100, 1 mM PMSF: Prepare a 100 m*M* stock of PMSF by dissolving 174 mg in 10 ml of isopropanol and store this at 4°C. (PMSF has a short half-life in aqueous solution, so the stock should not be diluted until immediately before use.) Add 10 μl 100 m*M* PMSF and 100 μl of 10% Triton X-100 to 890 μl of water, mix, and use immediately.

Step

On ice, add 4 vol of 1% Triton X-100 and 1 m*M* PMSF, mix, then add an equal volume of twofold concentrated SDS–PAGE sample buffer. The sample can now be analyzed immediately or stored at −20°C.

The extract contains around 50 mg/ml protein and so care should be taken not to overload gels. No more than 1 μl of whole extract should be loaded per 5 × 0.75-mm track of a minigel.

2. Recovery of the Membrane Fraction

Where more material must be analyzed or poor translocation is experienced, a crude membrane fraction can be easily prepared. The membranes contain approximately 20% of the protein content of the extract, so this increases the amount of membrane-associated material that can be loaded onto a gel by a factor of 5.

Solution

T + 10 (T buffer + 10% sucrose): Prepare 100 ml by dissolving 0.375 g KCl (50 m*M*), 0.22 g Mg acetate·$4H_2O$ (10 m*M*), 0.58 g NaCl (100 m*M*), 10 g sucrose, and 0.22 g Tris (20 m*M*) in 80 ml of water. Adjust the pH to 7.6 with HCl, make up to 100 ml, and filter-sterilize. Store unused solution at −20°C.

Steps

1. After translation, add 10 vol of T + 10 to each reaction and mix well.
2. Centrifuge in a microfuge at 6500 rpm for 5 min, then 13,000 rpm for 10 min, at 4°C.
3. Remove the supernatant and resuspend the membrane pellet in 1% Triton X-100, 1 m*M* PMSF, then add SDS–PAGE sample buffer before electrophoresis.

3. Protease Protection Analysis

Protease protection provides a convenient means of discriminating between translation products translocated into microsomes, and therefore protected from added protease, and cytoplasmic species, which are degraded.

Solutions

1. *Proteinase K:* Dissolve proteinase K at 20 mg/ml in water and incubate at 37°C for 15 min to digest any contaminating lipases. Store at −20°C in 5-μl

aliquots. Just before use, add 0.4 ml of 10% sucrose to an aliquot of proteinase K and mix well. Transfer half of this to a tube containing 50 μl of 10% Triton X-100 and add a further 50 μl of 10% sucrose to the remainder.

2. *15 mM PMSF in 10% sucrose:* Just before the end of the protease digestion, mix 15 μl 100 m*M* PMSF with 85 μl 10% sucrose. Use immediately and discard any unused material.

Steps

1. Divide a 30-μl translation mixture into three 10-μl portions, on ice.
2. Add 10 μl of 10% sucrose to the first; 200 μg/ml proteinase K in 10% sucrose to the second; and 2% Triton X-100, 200 μg/ml proteinase K in 10% sucrose to the third.
3. Incubate on ice for 1 hr.
4. Add 5 μl of 15 m*M* PMSF in 10% sucrose to each tube and leave on ice for a further 15 min.
5. Analyze by SDS–PAGE (see article by Celis and Olsen).

IV. Comments

A. CONTROLS

Although extracts are stable for a few hours on ice, performance is best assessed by analyzing translation reactions by SDS–PAGE and/or TCA precipitation. It is therefore necessary to prepare extracts "blind." This does not, however, mean that analyzing appropriate control reactions retrospectively is a waste of time as this will help locate problem steps or reagents that can be investigated before repeating the exercise. It is advisable to perform translations using samples of both crude and RNase-treated extract before and after freezing. This will show the difference between extracts that are susceptible to freezing and the failure of the RNase inhibitor to neutralize the added nuclease.

B. ACTIVITY

Under the assay conditions given, extracts that have been neither RNase treated nor frozen should incorporate around 60% of the [^{35}S]methionine added. The pool of methionine is approximately 35 μ*M*, so this equates to roughly 140 μg of protein synthesized per milliliter. On freezing and thawing, approximately half of this activity is retained. Individual synthetic mRNAs direct the translation of up to 15 μg/ml translocated and processed secretory proteins. As mRNA levels are raised (generally beyond 100–200 μg/ml for a well-translated species), the first activity of the system to become saturated is translocation, followed by a reduction in the efficiency of *N*-glycosylation. Translocation without signal sequence cleavage has never been observed.

The kinetics of translation vary depending on the nature of the reaction being performed. In the absence of any additions except [^{35}S]methionine, whole extract (before nuclease treatment) shows approximately linear incorporation over time for a number of hours. When creatine phosphate and reticulocyte lysate are present, the rate of incorporation is enhanced such that a plateau is reached after around 45 min. After nuclease treatment, the rate of reaction is often a function of the activity of the mRNA added. Reactions programmed with *Xenopus* poly(A)+ RNA show kinetics similar to those of the whole extract, while products from individual synthetic mRNAs may continue to accumulate for some hours, even when creatine phosphate and reticulocyte lysate are present.

Although it only stimulates the reaction in a fresh extract, creatine phosphate is essential for activity after frozen storage. Reticulocyte lysate stimulates both fresh and frozen extracts but, alone, will not rescue activity in a frozen extract. An equivalent effect on activity is seen whether whole reticulocyte lysate or an S-100 fraction (which is depleted of ribosomes) is used, indicating that the reticulocyte ribosomes contribute little if anything to translation.

C. mRNAs

As with other *in vitro* systems, different mRNAs exhibit differing translational efficiencies in the *Xenopus* extract. Where comparisons have been possible, relative translational yields in the extract reflect those seen on microinjection into *Xenopus* oocytes. Natural mRNAs normally translate best, while the performance of most synthetic mRNAs is much enhanced when transcribed from the vector pSP64T (Krieg and Melton, 1984), where the cDNA is flanked by sequences from the *Xenopus* β-globin cDNA. A reliable protocol for the synthesis of capped transcripts *in vitro* is given in Matthews and Colman (1991).

D. CHOICE OF RADIOACTIVE AMINO ACIDS

The protocol given here uses [^{35}S]methionine, which is suitable for most routine experiments. Where the protein being translated contains little or no methionine, or to prepare samples for radiosequencing, it may be desirable to use other amino acids. The size of the preexisting pool of amino acids will influence the specific activity of the radiolabeled species used, so lysine, aspartate, threonine, serine, glutamate, glycine, and alanine should be avoided if possible, as these have large pool sizes in the *Xenopus* oocyte which are presumably reflected in the egg and the extract. [^{35}S]Cysteine and tritiated leucine and phenylalanine have been used successfully for translation. A table of amino acid pool sizes for the *Xenopus* oocyte is given in Colman (1984).

As with other *in vitro* translation systems the use of crude extracts of radiolabeled amino acids, such as Translabel, should be avoided, as this will inhibit translation.

V. Pitfalls

Provided that the eggs used are of reasonable quality, preparation of the basic extract gives reliable results. The two points where the extract can be compromised are nuclease treatment and recovery from freezing.

Problems have been experienced with a batch of ribonuclease inhibitor that proved to be less active than claimed by the manufacturer. This can be readily demonstrated by monitoring the survival of radioactive mRNA in a reaction. In a good batch of extract, mRNA is stable over at least 4 hr, whereas residual RNase activity can cause complete degradation within a few minutes. Although RNase inhibitor from many other sources is probably just as good, the Boehringer product is specified here because it is supplied at high concentrations and no such problems have been experienced with it.

Occasionally extracts have been found to be inactivated by freezing and thawing. One possible cause of this may be the failure to remove buffer completely before lysis or it may simply be that the products from some batches of eggs are compromised in some way. The addition of sucrose to 200 m*M* before freezing, recommended by Murray (1991), has been shown to rescue such extracts without affecting the performance of more robust batches. The presence of sucrose in reactions performed using fresh extract, however, reduces translational activity to some extent.

As with other *in vitro* translation systems, care should be taken to avoid bacterial contamination of any solutions used. Not only will this compromise reagents (especially mRNAs), but [^{35}S]methionine is rapidly incorporated into bacterial proteins, leading to high apparent background translation.

REFERENCES

Colman, A. (1984) Translation of eucaryotic mRNA in *Xenopus* oocytes. *In* "Transcription and Translation: A Practical Approach" (B. D. Hames and S. J. Higgins, eds.), pp. 271–300. IRL Press, Oxford.

Krieg, P. A., and Melton, D. A. (1984) Functional messenger RNAs are produced by SP6 *in vitro* transcription of cloned cDNAs. *Nucleic Acids Res.* **12**, 7057–7070.

Matthews, G. M., and Colman, A. (1991) A highly efficient, cell-free translation/translocation system prepared from *Xenopus* eggs. *Nucleic Acids Res.* **19**, 6405–6412.

Murray, A. W. (1991) Cell cycle extracts. *In* "Methods in Cell Biology" (B. K. Kay and H. B. Peng, eds.), Vol. 36, pp. 581–605. Academic Press, San Diego.

Murray, A. W., and Kirschner, M. W. (1989) Cyclin synthesis drives the early embryonic cell cycle. *Nature* **339**, 275–280.

Wu, M., and Gerhart, J. (1991) Raising *Xenopus* in the laboratory. *In* "Methods in Cell Biology" (B. K. Kay and H. B. Peng, eds.), Vol. 36, pp. 3–18. Academic Press, San Diego.

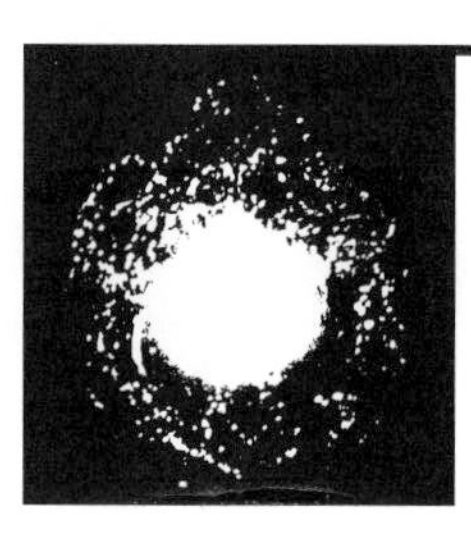

A Permeabilized Cell System to Study Peroxisomal Protein Import

Martin Wendland

I. Introduction

The development of permeabilized cell systems has facilitated the reconstitution and biochemical characterization of a variety of intracellular protein trafficking steps. In this article I describe how coverslip-attached cells are permeabilized with streptolysin O (SLO) and incubated with exogenously added peroxisomal proteins. The protein import into peroxisomes is analyzed by a simple immunofluorescence technique. The procedure is described for CHO cells but it can be used for a variety of mammalian cells. Furthermore, the system can be applied to study the import of proteins into other subcellular organelles.

SLO is a bacterial cytolysin that binds to cholesterol in the plasma membrane and forms pores large enough to allow the exchange of cytosolic components up to 150 kDa or even larger (Ahnert-Hilger *et al.*, 1989; see also Gudrun Ahnert-Hilger, this volume). It has been shown that treatment of cells with SLO results in the specific perforation of the plasma membrane while intracellular membranes remain intact (Miller and Moore, 1991; Wendland and Subramani, 1993a).

The import of proteins into peroxisomes is directed by peroxisomal targeting signals (PTSs) (Subramani, 1992). A carboxy-terminal tripeptide with the sequence SKL (in the one-letter amino acid code) represents a prototype PTS. Crosslinking of a peptide ending in SKL to a carrier protein creates an artificial substrate for the peroxisomal import machinery (Walton *et al.*, 1992).

II. Materials and Instrumentation

CHO wild-type cells are obtained from the American Type Culture Collection. Luciferase from *Photinus pyralis* (Cat. No. L-5256), ATP (Cat. No. A-5394), creatine phosphate (Cat. No. P-6915), and creatine phosphokinase (Cat. No. L-3755) are purchased from Sigma Chemical Company. Human serum albumin (Cat. No. 126658) and Mowiol (Cat. No. 475904) are obtained from Calbiochem-Behring Corporation. SLO (Cat. No. MR16) prepared by Wellcome Diagnostic is purchased from Murex Diagnostics. *m*-Maleimidobenzoyl-*N*-hydroxysuccinimide ester (MBS, Cat. No. 22310) is purchased from Pierce. Pronectin F (Cat. No. PF1001) is obtained from Protein Polymer Technologies, Inc. Rabbit reticulocyte lysate (Cat. No. L4151) is purchased from Promega. Rabbit anti-HSA antibodies (Cat. No. 65-051) are obtained from ICN Biomedicals Inc. Rabbit antiluciferase antibodies are from Dr. S. Subramani (University of California, San Diego). Guinea pig anti-HSA and rabbit antitubulin antibodies are from Dr. S. J. Singer (University of California, San Diego).

Rabbit anticatalase antibodies are from Dr. P. B. Lazarow (Mount Sinai School of Medicine, New York). Rhodamine-conjugated goat anti-rabbit IgG (Cat. No. 111-086-003), rhodamine-conjugated goat anti-guinea pig IgG (Cat. No. 106-086-003), FITC-conjugated goat anti-rabbit IgG (Cat. No. 111-096-003), and FITC-conjugated goat anti-guinea pig IgG (Cat. No. 106-095-003) were purchased from Jackson ImmunoResearch Laboratories. A synthetic peptide with the amino acid sequence NH_2-CRYHLKPLQSKL-COOH is obtained from Multiple Peptide Systems. Centricon-30 microconcentrators (Cat. No. 4208) are from Amicon. All other reagents are purchased from standard sources. Immunofluorescence microscopy is performed on a Zeiss Photoscope II microscope.

III. Procedures

A. COATING OF COVERSLIPS WITH PRONECTIN F

Solution

Pronectin F: Dissolve Pronectin F powder in the diluent supplied by the manufacturer to obtain a 1 mg/ml stock solution and store at room temperature. For immediate use, dilute the stock solution in sterile PBS to 20 μg/ml.

Steps

1. Autoclave coverslips in a glass petri dish.

2. Spot drops of 50–100 μl of diluted Pronectin F solution (20 μg/ml) in tissue culture dishes and invert coverslips over the drops.

3. Leave for 2 hr at room temperature, invert the coverslips (coated side up), and rinse them three times with sterile PBS. The coverslips are now ready for the immediate seeding of cells or can be stored for later use at room temperature for up to 4 months.

B. PREPARATION OF CELLS AND SEEDING ONTO COVERSLIPS

1. Cell Culture

Grow CHO cells in α-MEM containing 10% fetal calf serum (v/v), 200 U/ml penicillin G, and 200 μg/ml streptomycin. Maintain the cultures in a humidified incubator at 37°C with 5% CO_2. For cell passaging use standard trypsinization procedures. It is recommended that cultures never be overgrown.

2. Seeding of Cells onto Coverslips

The seeding of cells should be performed at least 36 hr before the import assay. Place up to 12 coated coverslips, coated side facing up, into a 10-cm tissue dish. Trypsinize cells from a confluent dish and seed at 1×10^6 cells/10-cm dish for permeabilization with 0.2 U/ml SLO and at 3×10^6 cells/10-cm dish for permeabilization with 2.0 U/ml. Avoid cell clumping because it impairs the permeabilization with SLO. Two hours before the import assay the medium should be changed.

Solutions

1. *Transport buffer:* To make 1 liter, dissolve 4.76 g of Hepes (20 m*M*), 10.79 g of potassium acetate (110 m*M*), 0.41 g sodium acetate (5 m*M*), 0.43 g of magnesium acetate (2 m*M*), and 0.38 g of EGTA (1 m*M*) in 800 ml distilled water, adjust pH to 7.3 with 10 *N* potassium hydroxide, and bring the total volume to 1000 ml. Autoclave and store at room temperature. Before use, add DTT to 2 m*M* (0.308 g/liter).

2. *Streptolysin O stock solution:* Vials containing 40 U of SLO as lyophilized powder are supplied by the manufacturer. Dissolve the powder of one vial in 10 ml of distilled water to obtain a 4 U/ml stock solution. Aliquot and store at −70°C. Stock solutions should not be freeze–thawed more than twice. For immediate use, dilute SLO stock in transport buffer/DTT to 0.2 or 2.0 U/ml or any other desired dilution.

Two differing cell permeabilization procedures are described, allowing the study of peroxisomal protein import when it is either independent (0.2 U/ml SLO) or dependent (2.0 U/ml SLO) on externally added cytosol.

1. Permeabilization with 0.2 U/ml SLO

Steps

1. The cells should be at subconfluent density. Dilute the SLO stock solution in transport buffer/DTT to 0.2 U/ml; prepare 40 μl per coverslip. Two minutes before permeabilization prewarm the diluted SLO solution to 30°C.

2. Before treatment with SLO the culture medium has to be rinsed off the cells. A major problem encountered is the loss of cells during the multiple wash steps required throughout the assay. It has been found that careful dip washing of the coverslips allows the highest cell recoveries. Fill three beakers with 50–100 ml of transport buffer (room temperature) and, with the use of forceps, carefully dip the coverslips sequentially into beakers 1–3. Subsequently remove excess fluid by blotting the edge of each coverslip on Kimwipe tissue but do not dry completely. Invert coverslips cell side down over SLO drops (see step 3).

3. The permeabilization and subsequent incubation with transport mix are carried out in a humidified floating box. A household plastic box with a lid works well for this purpose. Insert paper towels on box bottom, soak with water, and place a layer of Parafilm on top. Preincubate the chamber in a water bath at 30°C. Spot drops of 40 μl of diluted SLO solution on top of the Parafilm and invert coverslips cell side down over SLO drops.

4. Incubate for 5–10 min at 30°C. Dip-wash coverslips as before and blot off excess fluid. The cells are now permeabilized and ready for the import assay. By this time have the transport mix spotted onto Parafilm (see Section D, step 1).

2. Permeabilization with 2.0 U/ml SLO

Steps

1. Cells should be at confluent density, ideally forming a contiguous monolayer. However, formation of cell layers is detrimental.

2. The permeabilization procedure is the same as described above, only that

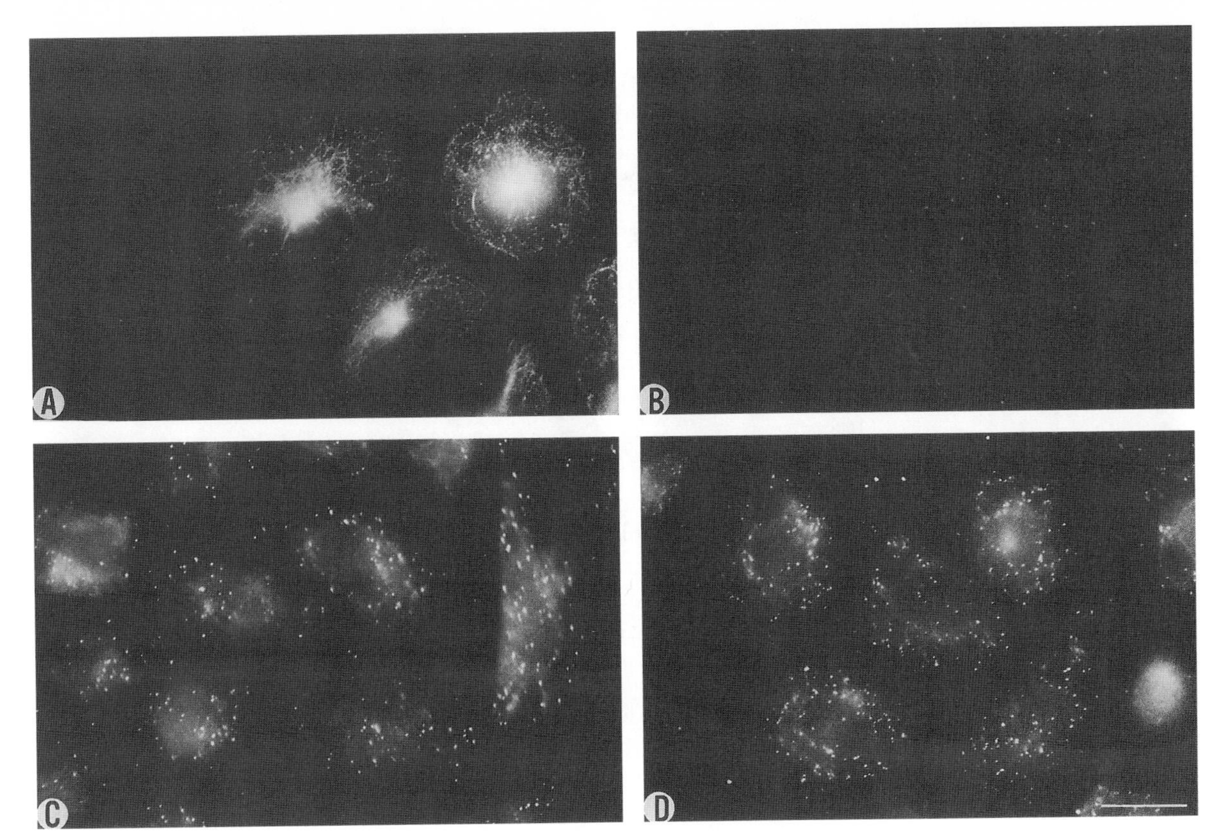

FIGURE 1 Permeabilization of CHO cells with SLO and reconstitution of peroxisomal protein import. Cells were treated with (A) or without (B) 0.2 U/ml SLO, fixed, and incubated with antitubulin antibodies followed by rhodamine-coupled secondary antibodies. Cells permeabilized with 0.2 U/ml SLO were incubated for 45 min at 37°C with HSA–SKL (C) or luciferase (D), and the localization of the exogenously added substrates was analyzed by immunofluorescence. Bar = 20 μm. Reprinted from the *Journal of Cell Biology*, 1993, Vol. 120, pp. 675–685, by copyright permission of the Rockefeller University Press.

the cells are permeabilized with 2.0 U/ml SLO and the incubation with SLO is extended to 10 min.

3. After incubation with SLO, wash the coverslips and incubate them in 1 ml of cold transport buffer for 15 min to ensure the leakage of endogenous cytosol.

4. Dip-wash the coverslips and blot off excess fluid. The coverslips are now ready for incubation with transport mix.

Note that the described conditions were developed for a specific preparation (lot) of SLO and that there may be variations in the use of different cell lines. I recommend starting with a serial dilution of SLO and assaying SLO-treated cells for perforation of the plasma membrane and leakage of endogenous cytosol. The permeabilization and access to the cell interior can be assayed by incubating SLO- or mock-treated cells with antibodies against the cytoskeleton as is shown in Fig. 1. Leakage of endogenous cytosol can be tested by comparing the lactate dehydrogenase activity (a cytosolic marker enzyme of 135 kDa) of SLO-permeabilized cells with that of nonpermeabilized cells as described by Wendland and Subramani (1993a).

D. IMPORT REACTION

Solutions

1. *ATP-regenerating mix*
   a. *ATP stock (100 mM):* Dissolve 60 mg of ATP in 800 μl of H_2O and add about 150 μl of 1 *N* NaOH to neutralize the pH to 7.0–8.0. Check pH and adjust the volume to 1 ml. Aliquot and store at −20°C or, for long-term storage, at −70°C.
   b. *Creatine phosphate stock (250 mM):* Dissolve 64 mg of creatine phosphate in 1 ml of H_2O to make a 250 m*M* stock. Aliquot and store as described for ATP.
   c. *Creatine phosphokinase stock (1000 U/ml):* Dissolve lyophilized powder of creatine phosphokinase in 50% glycerol/H_2O (v/v) to obtain a stock of 1000 U/ml. Aliquot and store at −20°C in a freeze–thaw cycle-free freezer.
   d. *ATP-regenerating mix:* For use in the import assay, mix 1 vol of ATP stock (100 m*M*) with 2 vol of creatine phosphate stock (250 m*M*) and 2 vol of creatine phosphokinase stock (1000 U/ml). Mix well and add 3 μl of this ATP-regenerating mix to 60 μl final volume of the transport mix (see Section D3).
2. *Reporter molecules for the import into peroxisomes*
   a. *HSA–SKL stock solution:* Coupling of human serum albumin (HSA) with a 12-mer peptide (sequence NH_2-CRYHLKPLQSKL-COOH) is performed by using the bifunctional crosslinker *m*-maleimidobenzoyl-*N*-hydroxysuccinimide ester as described by Harlow and Lane (1988, p. 83). Determine the protein concentration and adjust to 3 μg/μl. For the import assay use 1–2 μl per 60 μl transport mix.
   b. *Luciferase stock solution:* Dissolve the lyophilized luciferase powder in transport buffer to obtain a 1 mg/ml solution. For maximum solubility leave on ice for 30 min with periodic gentle agitation. Remove insoluble material by centrifugation (5 min at 10,000 *g*). Dialyze the supernatant overnight against transport buffer, concentrate in a Centricon tube to 1/10th volume, and determine the protein concentration. The stock solution should contain 5–10 μg/μl protein. For the import assay use 1–2 μl per 60 μl transport mix.
3. *Transport mix:* Prepare at least 60 μl of transport mix per coverslip (18-mm circular) to prevent the cells from drying out during the import reaction.
4. *Transport mix without cytosol:* Mix on ice 56 μl of transport buffer/DTT with 3 μl of ATP-regenerating mix and 1–2 μl of the HSA–SKL stock or 1–2 μl of the luciferase stock. Leave on ice until use.
5. *Transport mix with cytosol:* Mix 30 μl of rabbit reticulocyte lysate with 26 μl of transport buffer/DTT, 3 μl of the ATP-regenerating mix, and 1–2 μl of the HSA–SKL stock or 1–2 μl of the luciferase stock.

Steps

1. A humidified chamber, as described, is prewarmed to 37°C in a water bath. By the time the SLO permeabilization is finished, 60 μl of transport mix should be spotted on the Parafilm.

2. Invert SLO-treated coverslips (cell side down) over transport mix and incubate for 45–60 min at 37°C.

3. After incubation carefully lift coverslips, dip-wash, and incubate for 30 min at room temperature in 1 ml of transport buffer containing 4% formaldehyde to fix the cells.

E. IMMUNOFLUORESCENCE ANALYSIS

Solutions

1. *Antibodies for immunofluorescence analysis:* All antibody dilutions are made in PBS. A serial dilution of the antibodies is recommended to find the optimal dilution. Prepare 30 μl of antibody solution per coverslip. Rabbit anti-HSA antibodies are diluted to 1:1000 and rabbit antiluciferase antibodies to 1:50. FITC-conjugated secondary antibodies are diluted to 1:50 and rhodamine-conjugated secondary antibodies to 1:100. Because of a better signal-to-background ratio, FITC-conjugated secondary antibodies are preferred over rhodamine-conjugated antibodies.

2. *Mowiol:* Mowiol, used as mounting medium, is prepared as described by Harlow and Lane (1988, p. 418) (see also article by Monika Herzog, Annette Draeger, Elisabeth Ehler, and J. Victor Small). Instead of DABCO we use 0.1% *p*-phenylenediamine as antifade compound.

Steps

1. Incubate the coverslips for 5 min in PBS containing 1% Triton X-100. Subsequently dip-wash coverslips.

2. Blot off excess fluid and invert the coverslips cell side down over a drop of primary antibody solution spotted on Parafilm. Incubate for 20–30 min.

3. Dip-wash coverslips, blot off excess fluid, invert over a drop of secondary antibody solution, and incubate as above.

4. Dip-wash coverslips and blot off excess fluid. By then have slides prepared with drops of Mowiol and mount coverslips cell side down onto slides. The slides are now ready for microscopic analysis. Mowiol will harden when left at room temperature overnight (keep in the dark). Subsequently the slides are stored at −20°C and can be kept for a month or longer.

Note that the SLO treatment permeabilizes only cell membranes; the membranes of peroxisomes remain intact as judged by the impermeability to antibodies (Wendland and Subramani, 1993a). To allow access of antibodies to peroxisomal matrix proteins the peroxisomal membrane is permeabilized by treatment with Triton X-100.

F. STEP-BY-STEP PROCEDURE

1. Seed cells on coated coverslips 40–48 hr before the import assay (see Section B2).

2. Rinse coverslips and invert over a drop of SLO solution. Incubate in a humidified chamber for 5–10 min at 30°C (see Section C).

3. Rinse coverslips and invert over a drop of transport mix. Incubate in a humidified chamber for 45–60 min at 37°C (see Section D).

4. Rinse coverslips and incubate for 30 min in transport buffer/4% formaldehyde. Treat coverslips for 5 min with PBS/1% Triton X-100 and subject to immunofluorescence analysis (see Section E).

IV. Comments

When SLO-permeabilized cells are incubated with exogenously added proteins like HSA–SKL or luciferase these substrates are imported into vesicular structures

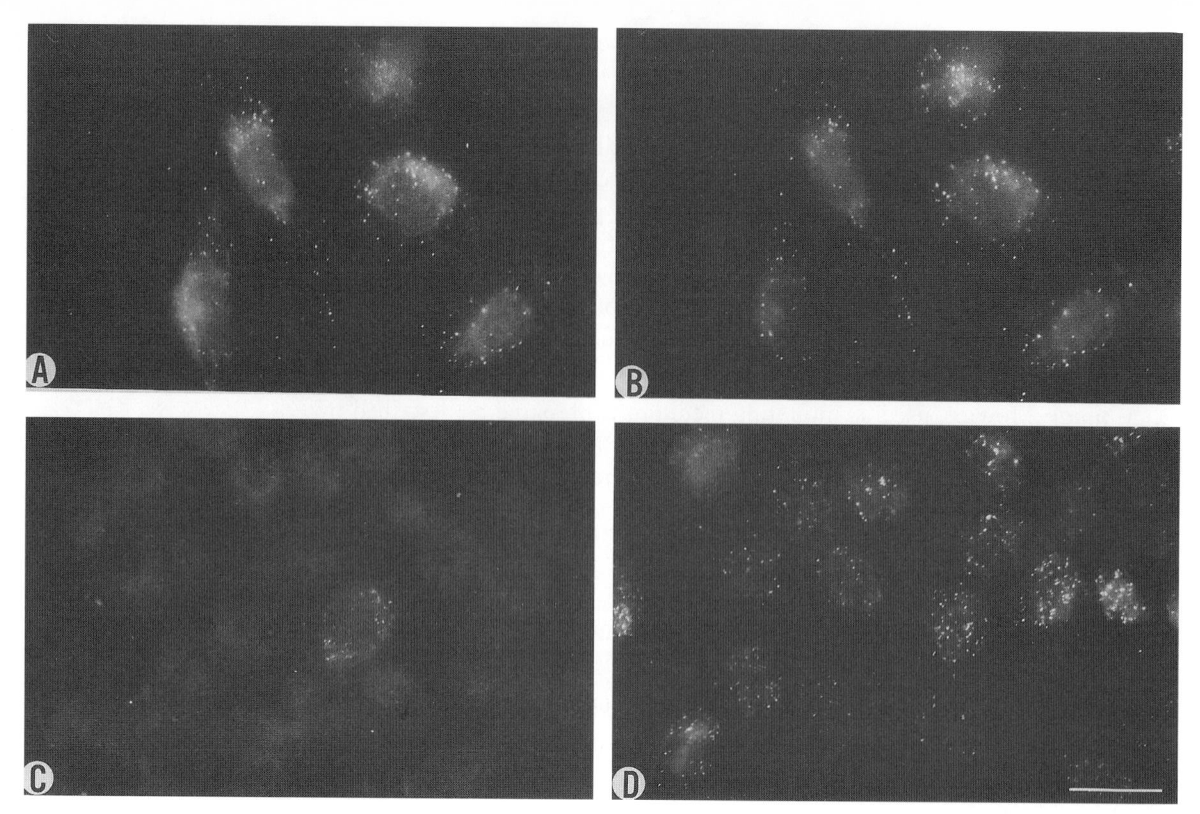

FIGURE 2 Colocalization of imported HSA–SKL with catalase and cytosol dependence of peroxisomal protein import. Cells permeabilized with 0.2 U/ml SLO were incubated with HSA–SKL and processed for double-labeling indirect immunofluorescence. Cells were incubated simultaneously with guinea pig anti-HSA (A) and rabbit anticatalase antibodies (B) followed by species-specific secondary antibodies coupled with FITC (A) and rhodamine (B). Cells were permeabilized with 2.0 U/ml SLO and incubated with HSA–SKL in the absence (C) or presence (D) of external cytosol in the form of rabbit reticulocyte lysate. Bar = 20 μm. Reprinted from the *Journal of Cell Biology*, 1993, Vol. 120, pp. 675–685, by copyright permission of the Rockefeller University Press.

(Figs. 1C, D). These vesicles are identified as peroxisomes by colocalization with the peroxisomal marker protein catalase (Figs. 2A, B). Depletion of endogenous cytosol from SLO-permeabilized cells abolishes the competence to import proteins into peroxisomes, but import is reconstituted by the addition of external cytosol (Figs. 2C, D). Use of the permeabilized cell system has allowed the characterization of several other features of the peroxisomal import event such as signal, energy, time, and temperature dependence (Wendland and Subramani, 1993a). Various factors and compounds can be added to or omitted from the transport mix to study their role in peroxisomal protein import. One important application of the import assay is its use in characterizing cell lines from human patients displaying peroxisomal disorders like Zellweger syndrome. Wendland and Subramani (1993b) have used the assay to characterize several cell lines from patients for cytosolic versus organelle-associated defects.

V. Pitfalls

1. The source and quality of SLO are of critical importance. SLO preparations from certain suppliers did not work reliably.

2. Treatment of cells with SLO, especially with higher SLO concentrations, significantly reduces cell attachment and cells are easily washed off the coverslips. Avoid vigorous washing. Confluent cell densities strengthen cell attachment.

3. When blotting off fluid from coverslips, do not dry coverslips completely.

4. A titration of antibody solution is necessary to find the best signal-to-background ratio. Also, compare the use of FITC- and rhodamine-conjugated secondary antibodies for improvement of signal detection.

REFERENCES

Ahnert-Hilger, G., Mach, W., Fohr, K. J., and Gratzl, M. (1989) Poration by alpha-toxin and streptolysin O: An approach to analyze intracellular processes. *Methods Cell Biol.* **31**, 63–90.

Harlow, E., and Lane, D. (1988) "Antibodies: A Laboratory Manual." Cold Spring Harbor Laboratory, Cold Spring Harbor, NY.

Miller, S. G., and Moore, H.-P. H. (1991) Reconstitution of constitutive secretion using semi-intact cells: Regulation by GTP but not calcium. *J. Cell Biol.* **112**, 39–54.

Subramani, S. (1992) Targeting of proteins into the peroxisomal matrix. *J. Membrane Biol.* **125**, 99–106.

Walton, P. A., Gould, S. J., Feramisco, J. R., and Subramani, S. (1992) Transport of microinjected proteins into peroxisomes of mammalian cells: Inability of Zellweger cell lines to import proteins with the SKL tripeptide peroxisomal targeting signal. *Mol. Cell. Biol.* **12**, 531–541.

Wendland, M., and Subramani, S. (1993a) Cytosol-dependent peroxisomal protein import in a permeabilized cell system. *J. Cell Biol.* **120**, 675–685.

Wendland, M., and Subramani, S. (1993b) Presence of cytoplasmic factors functional in peroxisomal protein import implicates organelle-associated defects in several human peroxisomal disorders. *J. Clin. Invest.* **92**, 2462–2468.

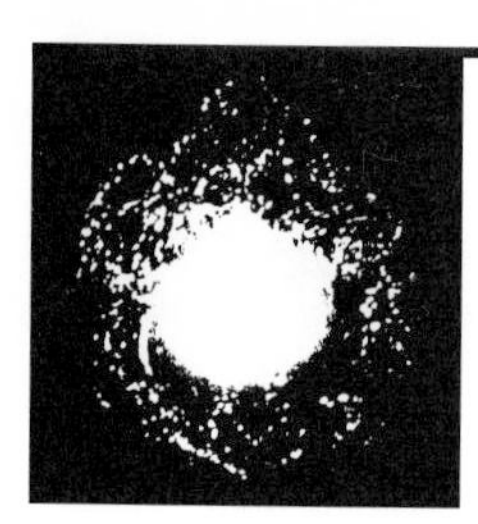

Baculovirus Expression Vector System: Production and Isolation of Recombinant Viruses

Linda A. King, Susan G. Mann, Alison M. Lawrie, and Robert D. Possee

I. Introduction

The baculovirus expression vector system is widely used in many laboratories for the synthesis of a variety of eukaryotic, bacterial, and viral proteins (Atkinson *et al.*, 1990b; Bishop and Possee, 1990; Fraser, 1992; King and Possee, 1992; O'Reilly *et al.*, 1992; Miller, 1993). In most cases, the proteins synthesized in insect cells are biologically active and are similar to their native counterparts. Insect cells have been shown to perform the posttranslational modifications normally associated with eukaryotic cells, although glycosylation is different, being mainly of the high-mannose type. This article describes the basic techniques required to produce and isolate a recombinant baculovirus, using the *Autographa californica* nuclear polyhedrosis virus (AcNPV)–*Spodoptera frugiperda* cell combination, in which foreign genes are expressed under control of the very efficient polyhedrin gene promoter. Further details on insect cell culture, the propagation of baculoviruses *in vitro*, and the analysis of expressed genes in insect cells can be found in the two specialized manuals that are available (King and Possee, 1992; O'Reilly *et al.*, 1992).

II. Materials

TC100 medium and fetal calf serum for insect cell culture can be obtained from a number of suppliers including J. R. Scientific, Gibco Life Technologies, and Sigma. TC100 medium may be purchased as ready-to-use 1× liquid (Cat. No. 13055-025, 500 ml, Gibco) or as a powdered concentrate (Cat. No. T-0907, Sigma; 43000-025, 5 liters, Gibco; Cat. No. 56 941-015, 5 liters, J. R. Scientific) that requires rehydration, adjustment of the pH to 6.2, and sterilization by filtration. Two companies (Clontech and Pharmingen) market baculovirus expression vector kits that provide the basic polyhedrin promoter-based transfer vectors and virus DNA stocks. Some transfer vectors, virus stocks, and cell lines are also available, on request, from Oxford Brookes University. Further details of the availability of virus stocks and transfer vectors can be found in King and Possee (1992). The two most commonly used cell lines, Sf21 and Sf9, are both derived from *Spodoptera frugiperda*, the fall army worm. Sf9 cells may be obtained from the American Type Culture Collection (CRL 1711) and the European Culture Collection (89101605) and both cell lines are available from Pharmingen. Linearized baculovirus DNA for the cotransfections may be purchased (BACPAK6, Clontech; BaculoGold, Pharmingen) or prepared from purified virus DNA as detailed in Section IIIA. Other materials required for the cotransfection and plaque assays are lipofectin (Cat. No. 18292-011, Gibco), X-gal (Cat. No. 15520-034, Gibco); neutral red (Cat. No. N-4638, Sigma, cell culture quality); low-gelling-temperature agarose (e.g., Seaplaque from FMC BioProducts or Sigma type VII agarose, Cat. No. A-4018). Good-quality tissue culture disposables will also be required as follows: 35-mm petri dishes; 25-cm^2 flasks or 60-mm Petri dishes; 75-cm^2 flasks; 10- and 1-ml pipettes; and small polystryrene containers, e.g., 7-ml bijou. You will also require standard equipment for cell culture, including a laminar flow cabinet or class II safety cabinet and a 28°C incubator (without CO_2). The baculovirus work may be performed using standard "Good Microbiological Practices" (King and Possee, 1992), although you should consult your local genetic manipulation safety committee for further advice.

III. Procedures

A. PREPARATION OF LINEARIZED BACULOVIRUS DNA

This procedure is modified from those of Kitts *et al.* (1990), King and Possee (1992), and Kitts and Possee (1993). This section should be omitted if you are starting with DNA that has already been linearized (e.g., commercially obtained BACPAK6 or BaculoGold DNA).

Requirements

1. *Virus DNA:* Purified AcNPV.*lacZ* (also called AcRP23.*lacZ*) DNA can be prepared as described in King and Possee (1992). Use of this virus DNA will yield about 30–40% recombinant virus plaques (Kitts *et al.*, 1990). Use of purified BACPAK6 or BaculoGold DNA will yield virtually 100% recombinant virus plaques (Kitts and Possee, 1993).

2. *Reagents: Bsu*36I (or *Mst*II, *Sau*I) restriction endonuclease (RE) and appropriate 10× concentrated buffer (usually supplied by the manufacturer). Sterile water. Water baths at 37 and 60°C.

Steps

1. Digest 2 μg of purified virus DNA as follows: Combine 2 μg virus DNA, 10 μl 10× RE buffer, 10 units *Bsu*36I RE, and water to 100 μl. Incubate at 37°C for a minimum of 4 hr (can be incubated overnight). Remember to keep the reaction mixture sterile, as the digested DNA will be used to transfect insect cells.

2. To check that the DNA has been digested, remove a sample (100–200 ng) for analysis by electrophoresis in a 0.6% agarose gel. Circular virus DNA remains near the well and linearized DNA migrates into the gel matrix.

3. Heat-inactivate the RE for 10 min at 60°C and then store the linearized virus DNA at 4°C. Do not freeze. You require 100–200 ng DNA for each cotransfection experiment.

B. COTRANSFECTION OF INSECT CELLS TO PRODUCE A RECOMBINANT BACULOVIRUS

This procedure is modified from those of Atkinson *et al.* (1990a) and King and Possee (1992).

Requirements

1. *Insect cells:* For each cotransfection experiment you require one 35-mm petri dish seeded with 1×10^6 Sf21 or Sf9 cells. The cells should be incubated at 28°C for a minimum of 2 hr before the cotransfection is started (can be incubated overnight). Incubate the cells in 2 ml of TC100 growth medium.

2. *Culture media and solutions: TC100 growth medium:* TC100 medium supplemented with 10% FCS and 1% penicillin–streptomycin antibiotics (5000 units/ml stock solution). *Serum-free TC100:* Add antibiotics only, as indicated above. *Lipofectin or similar liposome-mediated transfection reagent.*

3. *Transfer vector and linearized virus DNA:* Linearized baculovirus DNA may be purchased ready-to-use, as previously mentioned, or may be prepared as described in Section A. You require 100–200 ng per cotransfection. You also require 500–1000 ng of purified recombinant transfer vector. It is beyond the scope of this article to provide methods for the introduction of foreign genes into the large variety of baculovirus transfer vectors that are available. Any of the polyhedrin promoter-based transfer vectors may be used in conjunction with the linearized AcNPV DNAs described here. It is important that you have confirmed the correct orientation of the foreign gene coding sequence, with respect to the polyhedrin gene promoter in the transfer vector, before proceeding with a cotransfection experiment. Further information on the selection of transfer vectors and the insertion of foreign genes may be found in King and Possee (1992) or O'Reilly *et al.* (1992).

Steps

It is important to maintain aseptic technique throughout these procedures.

1. Mix together 100–200 ng linearized virus DNA and a 5× excess (by weight) of purified recombinant transfer vector DNA in a sterile, disposable (polystyrene) tube (such as a bijou).

2. Dilute the lipofectin reagent by adding 2 parts of reagent to 1 part of water. Add an equal volume of the diluted reagent to the tube containing the DNA samples, and mix in.

3. Leave at room temperature for 15 min. Meanwhile, prepare the Sf cell monolayers.

4. Remove the growth medium from the dish of Sf cells and wash the cell monolayer twice with about 1 ml of serum-free TC100 medium. Take care not to dislodge the cell monolayer. After washing the cells, add 1 ml of serum-free TC100 medium.

5. Add the lipofectin–DNA complex to the 1 ml of serum-free medium and mix in by swirling the dish gently. Incubate the cells for between 5 and 16 hr at 28°C in an humidified atmosphere (e.g., a sandwich box lined with moist tissue paper).

6. Add 1 ml of TC100 growth medium to the dish of cells and continue the incubation until 48 hr in total has elapsed since the DNA was added to the cells.

7. Harvest the culture medium and store at 4°C. This medium will contain recombinant and parental virus particles that may be separated from one another by plaque assay.

8. If using the AcNPV.*lacZ* (AcRP23.*lacZ*) DNA, you will need to do two or three rounds of plaque assays to ensure that the recombinant virus is not contaminated with parental virus. If using the BACPAK6 or BaculoGold virus

DNA, you will normally only need to perform one round of plaque assay, as long as the dish of cells from which you select recombinant plaques (white phenotype) does not contain any parental plaques (blue phenotype) (see Section C).

C. ISOLATION OF RECOMBINANT VIRUS BY PLAQUE ASSAY

This technique may also be used to titrate recombinant viruses in plaque-forming units (PFU) per milliliter. Further information may be found in King and Possee (1992).

Requirements

1. *Cells and culture medium:* You require approximately 10 × 35-mm dishes of Sf21 (or Sf9) cells when screening for a recombinant virus using the BaculoGold or BACPAK6 viruses and about double this number when using the AcNPV.*lacZ* virus. Dishes should be seeded with healthy, log-phase cells at a density of 1.5×10^6 cells per dish and incubated at 28°C for 2 hr before use, or with 1.0×10^6 cells per dish and incubated overnight at 28°C before use. It is important that the cell monolayer is not too dense (very tiny plaques, or none at all, will form) or too sparse (plaques will have ragged edges and will be hard to define). You will require TC100 growth medium, as described in Section B.

2. *Other solutions and reagents:* 2% (w/v) low-gelling-temperature agarose, sterilized by autoclaving. 0.5% (w/v) Neutral Red in water, sterilized by filtration. Phosphate-buffered saline (PBS), sterilized by autoclaving. 2% (w/v) X-gal in dimethylformamide, stored at −20°C. Water bath at 37°C.

Steps

1. Prepare log (10-fold) dilutions of the harvested cotransfection medium. The dilutions to prepare will depend on the virus DNA used. We suggest plating duplicate samples of neat 10^{-1}, 10^{-2}, and 10^{-3} dilutions for BACPAK6/BaculoGold and at least triplicate samples of 10^{-1} to 10^{-4} dilutions for the AcNPV.*lacZ* virus. A convenient method for preparing the dilutions is to use 50 μl of virus with 450 μl of TC100 growth medium as diluent. Unless using the diluted virus stocks immediately, store on ice.

2. Remove the culture medium from the required number of dishes of Sf cells and replace with 100 μl of the appropriate virus dilutions. Always inoculate at least one dish of cells with TC100 medium, as a control. Add the 100 μl of inoculum gently to the center of the dish.

3. Incubate the cells at room temperature for 1 hr to allow virus adsorption. Meanwhile, prepare the agarose overlay.

4. Mix equal volumes of the 2% agarose solution (at 37°C) and TC100 growth medium (previously warmed to 37°C) together to form the agarose overlay. You will require 2 ml of overlay per 35-mm dish of cells. Keep the solution at 37°C until required, to prevent it from setting.

5. Remove the inoculum from the cell monolayers and discard safely (e.g., into hypochlorite disinfectant or by autoclaving). This step is important as any liquid remaining in the dish will result in poor adhesion of the agarose overlay to the cell monolayer and, consequently, poor plaque formation.

6. Carefully pipette 2 ml of prepared agarose overlay into each dish of cells and allow to set at room temperature. When set, overlay the solidified agarose

with 1 ml of TC100 growth medium (to provide nutrients for virus replication and cell growth).

7. Incubate the cells at 28°C for 3–4 days.

8. Visualize the plaques by staining with neutral red and distinguish recombinant virus (white) and parental virus (blue) plaques by counterstaining with X-gal. We suggest removing the liquid overlay and replacing it with 1 ml of TC100 growth medium containing 15 μl/ml 2% X-Gal for about 3 hr at 28°C. Then add, without removing the X-gal staining medium, a further 1 ml of neutral red stain (dilute the stock stain 1 in 20 with PBS before adding to the cells). Incubate for a further 2 hr at 28°C. Discard the staining medium safely, invert the dishes (with lids on), and allow the plaques to clear for a few hours to overnight. During this period keep the dishes in the dark, as prolonged exposure to light causes the neutral red to precipitate and become very grainy. Plaques will appear as blue or colorless areas in a background of light-pink-stained cells.

9. After identifying putative recombinant virus plaques, the plaques need to be picked into 0.5 ml of TC100 growth medium. This is performed by taking up the plug of agarose in the plaque into a sterile Pasteur pipette and placing it into the TC100 medium (in a bijou). The virus particles are released from the agarose plug by vortexing for a few seconds. The plaque-picked virus stock can be stored at 4°C for several weeks.

10. If you have used the BACPAK6 or BaculoGold virus DNA, and have isolated the putative recombinant plaques from a dish of cells in which no blue plaques were present, the next step is to amplify the virus to test for the presence and expression of the foreign gene. We suggest you test three separate plaque picks. If you have used the AcNPV.*lacZ* virus DNA, you should pick about five plaques and perform a second (or even third) round of plaque purification, on each plaque pick independently, to obtain purified recombinant virus (i.e., the absence of any blue, parental virus plaques). To do this, prepare neat to 10^{-3} dilutions of the plaque-picked virus stock and repeat the plaque assay and staining procedures described above.

D. AMPLIFICATION OF A SMALL STOCK OF RECOMBINANT VIRUS TO TEST FOR THE PRESENCE AND EXPRESSION OF THE FOREIGN GENE

This procedure is modified from that of King and Possee (1992).

Requirements

Insect cells and culture media: You will require a 25-cm^2 flask or 60-mm petri dish seeded with about 1×10^6 Sf21 or Sf9 cells, in 4–5 ml of medium, for each putative recombinant virus to be amplified. You will also require TC100 growth medium, as indicated in Section B, and the plaque-picked virus stocks that have been stored at 4°C.

Steps

1. Remove the medium from the flasks or dishes of cells and inoculate the cell monolayers with 200–250 μl of the plaque-picked virus stock. Pipette the inoculum gently on the cells so as not to dislodge the cell monolayer.

2. Incubate the cells at room temperature for 1 hr to allow virus attachment.

During this time, rock the cell monolayer three or four times to ensure even coverage of the inoculum over the monolayer of cells.

3. Remove the virus inoculum and discard safely. Add 3–4 ml (no more) of fresh TC100 growth medium to the cells and incubate at 28°C until the cells show distinct signs of virus infection (crenated around the edges and rather grainy in appearance; polyhedra will not, of course, be visible as the virus genome is polyhedrin negative). This may take 5–7 days.

4. Harvest the culture medium, which contains your amplified virus, and store at 4°C in the short term (up to 6 months should be possible). It is always wise to store a little (1 ml) of this virus stock at −80°C, where it will keep indefinitely without a reduction in the virus titer.

5. This virus stock will not have a very high titer; it will be in the region of $1–5 \times 10^7$ PFU/ml. If you wish to titer the virus accurately, perform a plaque assay as described in Section C, plating out 10^{-4} to 10^{-6} dilutions and staining only with neutral red. The titer is calculated by counting the number of plaques on a dish, from one particular dilution that gives about 5–30 plaques. This number is multiplied by 10 (only 0.1 ml of inoculum was added to the dish) and by the inverse of the dilution factor. Titers are expressed, therefore, as PFU/ml. There will be sufficient virus, however, to test for the presence and expression of the foreign gene. Further experimental work will almost certainly require you to amplify larger stocks of high-titer virus inoculum. Protocols for these procedures can be found in King and Possee (1992) or O'Reilly *et al.* (1992).

6. Rapidly testing for the presence of the foreign gene, in the putative recombinant virus genome, can be achieved by using 200–250 μl of the amplified virus inoculum to infect a dish of Sf21 cells. After about 18 hr, extract the virus DNA (Possee, 1986; King and Possee, 1992) and analyze by dot-blot, Southern blot, or polymerase chain reaction (PCR) techniques.

7. Testing for the expression of the foreign gene can be achieved by using 200–250 μl of the amplified virus inoculum to infect a 35-mm dish of Sf cells. After 24 or 48 hr, harvest the cells (with or without prior pulse labeling with [^{35}S]methionine, and analyze by SDS–PAGE, immunoprecipitation, or Western blotting, as necessary (see other articles in this volume). Always include controls with noninfected and parental virus-infected cells, so that the identity of the foreign protein can be readily identified against the background of virus-specified and host cell proteins. Further details can be found in King and Possee (1992).

IV. Comments

The protocols described in this article will allow the reader to prepare recombinant baculoviruses for foreign gene expression in insect cells, starting with purified virus DNA and the appropriate recombinant transfer vector.

V. Pitfalls

1. Remember to use aseptic technique throughout, especially when preparing the DNA samples.

2. Only pick plaques for the amplification of recombinant virus if the dish contains no parental virus plaques (blue).

3. If you cannot detect the foreign protein by SDS–PAGE or other more sensitive techniques, check the following: the transfer vector construction; the

synthesis of mRNA; the titer of the virus inoculum (if too low you will not get a good infection, this is characterized by the failure to shut off host cell protein synthesis in virus-infected cells); the actual size of the protein may differ from that expected (in insect cells glycosylated proteins are usually smaller than their native counterparts).

4. Do not freeze the virus DNA or store the virus inoculum at −20°C. Virus DNA must be stored at 4°C and inoculum at 4 or −80°C.

REFERENCES

Atkinson, A. E., Earley, F. G. P., Beadle, D. J., and King, L. A. (1990a) Expression and characterisation of the chick nicotinic acetylcholine receptor α-subunit in insect cells using a baculovirus vector. *Eur. J. Biochem.* **192**, 451–458.

Atkinson, A. E., Weitzman, M. D., Obosi, L. A., Beadle, D. J., and King, L. A. (1990b) Expression of foreign genes in insect cells using baculovirus vectors. *Pestic. Sci.* **28**, 215–224.

Bishop, D. H. L., and Possee, R. D. (1990) Baculovirus expression vectors. *Adv. Gene Technol.* **1**, 55–72.

Fraser, M. J. (1992) The baculovirus-infected insect cell as a eukaryotic gene expression system. *Curr. Top. Microbiol. Immunol.* **158**, 131–172.

King, L. A., and Possee, R. D. (1992) "The Baculovirus Expression System, a Laboratory Guide." *Chapman and Hall,* London.

Kitts, P. A., Ayres, M. D., and Possee, R. D. (1990) Linearisation of baculovirus DNA enhances the recovery of recombinant virus expression vectors. *Nucleic Acids Res.* **18**, 5667–5672.

Kitts, P. A., and Possee, R. D. (1993) A method for producing recombinant baculovirus expression vectors at high frequency. *BioTechniques* **14**, 810–817.

Miller, L. K. (1993) Baculoviruses: High-level expression in insect cells. *Curr. Opin. Genet. Dev.* **3**, 97–101.

O'Reilly, D. R., Miller, L. K., and Luckow, V. A. (1992) "Baculovirus Expression Vectors, a Laboratory Manual." W. H. Freeman, New York.

Possee, R. D. (1986) Cell surface expression of influenza virus haemagglutinin in insect cells using a baculovirus vector. *Virus Res.* **5**, 43–59.

Expression of Recombinant Proteins in the Vaccinia Virus Expression System

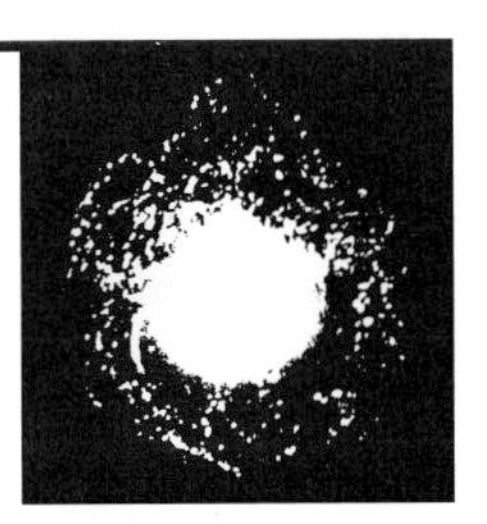

Henrik Leffers

I. Introduction

Expression of cDNAs from vertebrates and other sources is routinely carried out in bacteria or, recently, in insect cells using baculovirus vectors (see also article by Linda A. King, Susan G. Mann, Alison M. Lawrie, and Robert D. Possee). However, the proteins are often nonfunctional due either to problems with the correct folding or to the absence of posttranslational modifications. This can be solved by expressing the cDNAs in vertebrate (human) cells using vaccinia virus vectors that faithfully reproduce posttranslational modifications, including the removal of the start methionine and leader peptides, other posttranslational trimmings, and modifications including glycosylations, palmitoylations, and phosphorylations (Leffers *et al.*, 1994, and references therein). Moreover, a few hours after infection vaccinia virus turns off the synthesis of host cell proteins, enabling the specific labeling of the vaccinia virus-coded proteins with [^{35}S]methionine or [^{35}S]cysteine. These can then be detected by two-dimensional gel electrophoresis followed by autoradiography, whereas the background of cellular proteins can be visualized by silver staining of the same gel (Fig. 1).

Vaccinia virus is a member of the pox virus family of DNA viruses and is composed of a lipoprotein envelope surrounding a core structure containing a linear 200,000-bp double-stranded DNA genome. Vaccinia virus codes for all the enzymes needed to carry out its life cycle in the cytoplasm of the host cells. For recent reviews of vaccinia virus see Moss (1991) and references therein. The insertion of foreign DNA into the virus is accomplished by *in vivo* recombination leading to insertion of the cDNA into the viral thymidine kinase (TK) gene (Panicali and Paoletti, 1982; Mackett *et al.*, 1984). This results in a selectable phenotype, TK$^-$, and recombinant viruses can be rescued from wild-type viruses by selection with 5-bromodeoxyuridine (BrdU). More recently, vectors that allow positive selection for the recombinant viruses have been developed (Falkner and Moss, 1988). These use the *Escherichia coli* xanthine–guanine phosphoribosyltransferase (*gpt*) gene, which makes the recombinants viable in the presence of mycophenolic acid, an inhibitor of purine synthesis (Falkner and Moss, 1988). The most commonly used vectors include the *E. coli gpt* gene under control of the viral intermediate I3 promotor (Vos and Stunnenberg, 1988) and a polylinker region immediately downstream of the viral late 11K promoter (Bertholet *et al.*, 1985; Stunnenberg *et al.*, 1988), flanked by parts of the TK gene. The cassette has been inserted into the pEMBLIII plasmid, resulting in the pGPT-ATA-18 plasmid (Stunnenberg *et al.*, 1988). We have replaced the pEMBLIII polylinker with the larger polylinker from M13-BM 20 (Boehringer-Mannheim), resulting in the pVAC plasmid.

II. Materials and Instrumentation

Mycophenolic acid (Cat. No. M-5255), xanthine (Cat. No. X-2001), hypoxanthine (Cat. No. H-9636), ethidium bromide (Cat. No. E-7637), neutral red (Cat. No. N-4638), Hepes (Cat. No. H-1016), Trizma base (Cat. No. T-1503), EDTA (Cat. No. E-9884), $CaCl_2$ (Cat. No. C-7902), $MgCl_2$ (Cat. No. M-2393), Na_2HPO_4, (Cat. No. S-5011) KCl (Cat. No. P-5405), and NaCl (Cat. No. S-5886) were obtained from Sigma Chemical Company.

Low-melting-point agarose (Sea Plaque GTG, Cat. No. 50112) was from FMC BioProducts.

Modified Eagle's medium lacking methionine (Cat. No. 041-01900H) was from Gibco-BRL. Life Technologies Inc.

Six-well trays (Cat. No. 657160) were from Greiner GMBH.

[^{35}S]Methionine (Cat. No. SJ204) and [^{35}S]cysteine (Cat. No. SJ232) were from Amersham.

All the reagents, materials, and equipment for tissue culture were as described in the article by Julio E. Celis and Ariana Celis in Volume 1.

H_2O was glass distilled three times.

All 37°C incubations are made in a CO_2 incubator with 5–8% CO_2 and 100% humidity.

III. Procedures

A. PREPARATION OF DNA

The plasmid DNA can be prepared by any procedure that results in high-quality supercoiled DNA. The methods for DNA preparation are described in details by Sambrook *et al.* (1989).

Steps

1. Clone the cDNA directionally (if possible) into a vaccinia virus recombination plasmid (e.g., Δ6/gpt, ATA/gpt, or pVAC). Verify the orientation.
2. Purify supercoiled plasmid DNA and dissolve at 1 $\mu g/\mu l$ in sterile H_2O.

B. PREPARATION OF CELLS (AMA)

Solutions

1. *Dulbecco's modified Eagle's medium with 10% fetal calf serum (DMEMS):* Dulbecco's modified Eagle's medium containing 10% (v/v) fetal calf serum, sodium bicarbonate at 0.3% (w/v) final concentration, L-glutamine at 2 m*M* final concentration, and penicillin–streptomycin at final concentrations of 100 U and 100 μg/ml, respectively. To make 500 ml of medium add 50 ml of 10× stock solution of Dulbecco's modified Eagle's medium, 50 ml of fetal calf serum, 20 ml of 7.5% (w/v) sodium bicarbonate, 5 ml of 200 m*M* L-glutamine, and 5 ml of penicillin–streptomycin (penicillin 1000 U/ml, streptomycin 1000 μg/ml), and 370 ml of autoclaved water.

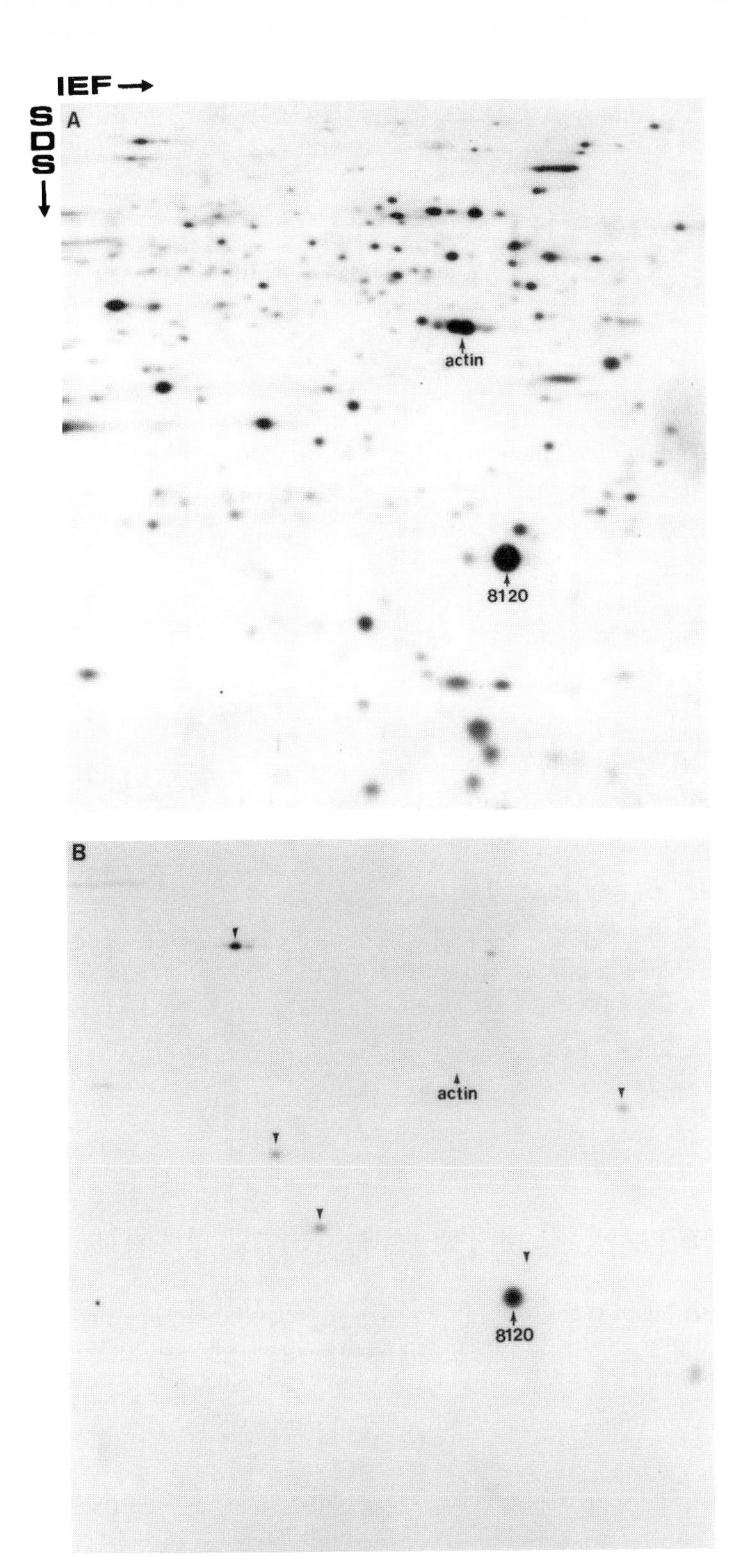

FIGURE 1 Expression of proteins in the vaccinia virus expression system. (A) Silver-stained two-dimensional gel of [^{35}S]methionine-labeled proteins from AMA cells infected with a vaccinia virus expressing IEF SSP 8120 (Rho GDI-related protein). (B) Autoradiograph of the same gel. The silver-stained gel reveals cellular polypeptides, whereas autoradiography detects mainly vaccinia virus-coded proteins, including the protein encoded by the recombined cDNA. By superimposing the autoradiograph with the silver-stained gel, the labeled protein spot coded by the cDNA can be matched to a spot originating from an endogenous protein, detected by silver staining. Five characteristic spots, originating from vaccinia virus endogenous proteins, are indicated with arrowheads in B.

2. *Hanks' balanced salt solution (HBSS):* 10X stock solution: 80 g NaCl, 4 g KCl, 0.6 g $KH_2PO_4 \cdot 2H_2O$, 0.621 g $Na_2HPO_4 \cdot 2H_2O$, H_2O to 1 liter. Sterilize by autoclaving, aliquot, and store at −20°C. Dilute 1:10 with H_2O and sterile-filter to obtain 1× HBSS.

3. *Trypsin stock (2.5%).*

4. *0.25% Trypsin:* Dilute stock trypsin solution (2.5%) 10 times with sterile HBSS. Filter-sterilize (0.20-μm filter) and store in aliquots at −20°C.

Steps

1. Prepare a 100% confluent cell monolayer in a 25-cm^2 culture flask.
2. Trypsinize the 25-cm^2 flask and suspend the cells in 2 ml DMEMS medium. Add 0.5 and 1 ml, respectively, to 45 ml DMEMS; mix by gentle shaking.
3. Transfer 3 ml to each hole of a six-well tray (3.5-cm wells). Incubate for 3–4 days. Use either the "0.5 ml" or the "1 ml" cells, depending on their density. The cells should be 60–70% confluent.

C. RECOMBINATION INTO VACCINIA VIRUS

Solutions

1. *DMEM with 10% fetal calf serum (DMEMS).*
2. *10X HBS:* Dissolve 80 g NaCl, 3.7 g KCl, 1.25 g $Na_2HPO_4 \cdot 2H_2O$, 10 g glucose, and 50 g Hepes in 800 ml H_2O. Adjust pH to 7.05, add H_2O to 1 liter, sterile-filter, and store frozen in aliquots.
3. *250 mM $CaCl_2$:* Dissolve 3.67 g $CaCl_2$ in 100 ml H_2O. Sterile-filter and store at −20°C in aliquots.

Steps

1. Grow cell monolayers to 60–70% confluence in a six-well tray (3.5-cm holes).

2. Infect the cells with "wild-type" vaccinia virus at a titer of about one per cell (about 5 μl per well of a viral stock, prepared as described below) in 0.5 ml DMEMS. Leave at room temperature for 30 min with occasional gentle rocking.

3. Remove the virus-containing medium and add 3 ml DMEMS medium. Incubate for 1–2 hr at 37°C.

4. During the last hour prepare the Ca^{2+}-phosphate DNA precipitate. Ethanol precipitate 5–10 μg DNA, wash with 80% ethanol, and dissolve in 200 μl 2× HBS. Slowly add 200 μl of 250 m*M* $CaCl_2$, mix by whirling the solution. Leave for 30 min at room temperature. Include a control (no plasmid DNA) sample in the Ca^{2+}-phosphate precipitation to check for the selection efficiency.

5. Add the Ca^{2+}-phosphate precipitate to the cells. Leave at room temperature for 30 min with occasional gentle rocking.

6. Add 2 ml DMEM and incubate for 3–4 hr at 37°C.

7. Remove medium and add 3 ml DMEMS. Incubate for 2 days at 37°C.

D. SELECTION FOR RECOMBINANT VIRUS (PRESENCE OF *gpt* GENE)

Solutions

1. *DMEM with 10% fetal calf serum (DMEMS).*

2. *10 mg/ml Mycophenolic acid in 50 mM NaOH:* Dissolve 100 mg mycophenolic acid in 10 ml of 50 m*M* NaOH, sterile-filter, and store in aliquots at −20°C.

3. *10 mg/ml hypoxanthine in 100 mM NaOH:* Dissolve 100 mg hypoxanthine in 10 ml of 100 m*M* NaOH, sterile-filter, and store in aliquots at −20°C.

4. *10 mg/ml xanthine in 50 mM NaOH:* Dissolve 100 mg xanthine in 10 ml of 50 m*M* NaOH, sterile-filter, and store in aliquots at −20°C. The xanthine will precipitate on freezing; it is easily redissolved by vortexing the thawed solution.

5. *Selection medium (S-DMEMS):* 50 ml DMEMS with 125 μl of 10 mg/ml mycophenolic acid in 50 m*M* NaOH; 1250 μl of 10 mg/ml xanthine in 50 m*M* NaOH; 75 μl of 10 mg/ml hypoxanthine in 100 m*M* NaOH.

Steps

1. Harvest the viruses by freezing the lysed cell culture.

2. Thaw the culture and pipette 500 μl of the virus containing freeze–thaw lysate to an Eppendorf tube. Vortex to separate viral aggregates.

3. Remove the medium from the 60–70% confluent cell monolayer grown in a six-well tray. Add the vortexed virus containing freeze–thaw lysate to the cells. Leave at room temperature for 30 min with occasional gentle rocking.

4. Remove the virus-containing medium and add 3 ml of selection medium (S-DMEMS). Incubate for 2–3 days at 37°C.

5. Repeat the selection four to eight times until there is no viral growth in the control (minus plasmid DNA) well. After the last selection, harvest the viruses by freeze–thawing, transfer the virus-containing medium to a tube, and freeze at −80°C. This is the virus stock; it maintains a high titer for several years when kept at −80°C. The titer of the viral stock can be increased by incubating the last selection for an additional 1–2 days, until all the cells are lysed.

If a larger amount of virus is required:

6. Infect a 9-cm 70–80% confluent monolayer of AMA cells with a titer of 0.5–1 virus per cell in 4–5 ml S-DMEMS (if "wild-type" virus, use DMEMS). Leave for 30 min at room temperature.

7. Remove the medium and add 8–10 ml of S-DMEMS (or DMEMS). Incubate for 3–4 days at 37°C.

8. Harvest by freeze–thawing. Split into aliquots and store at −80°C.

E. LABELING OF VIRAL-CODED PROTEINS

Solutions

1. *DMEM with 10% fetal calf serum (DMEMS).*

2. *Methionine- or cysteine-free medium.*

3. *1× HBSS.*

4. *Selection medium (S-DMEMS).*
5. *[^{35}S]Methionine or [^{35}S]cysteine.*
6. *Lysis solution:* 9.8 *M* urea, 2% (w/v) Nonidet P-40, 2% carrier ampholytes (pH 7–9); 100 m*M* DTT. Prepare this solution as described in the article by Julio E. Celis, Gitte Ratz, Bodil Basse, Jette B. Lauridsen, and Ariana Celis in this volume.

Steps

1. Remove the DMEMS medium from a 50–60% confluent cell monolayer. Add 500 μl vortexed viral stock to the cells. Leave at room temperature for 30 min with occasional gentle rocking.
2. Remove the medium and add 3 ml of S-DMEMS. Incubate for 16–24 hr at 37°C.
3. Remove the medium, wash one or two times with 1 ml prewarmed 1× HBSS, and add 0.5 ml methionine (or cysteine)-free medium. Incubate for 1 hr at 37°C.
4. Add 25–100 μCi [^{35}S]methionine (or [^{35}S]cysteine). Incubate for 1 hr at 37°C.
5. Remove the medium and wash two times with 1× HBSS.
6. Lyse the cells by adding 300 μl lysis solution. If the expressed protein is secreted from the cells, aliquots of the medium can be freeze-dried and dissolved in lysis solution.

F. PLAQUE PURIFICATION (OPTIONAL)

Solutions

1. *1× HBSS.*
2. *2× DMEM with 20% fetal calf serum (2× DMEMS).*
3. *1.8% Low-melting-point agarose:* Add 1.8 g low-melting-point agarose to 100 ml H_2O and dissolve by autoclaving.
4. *2× Selection medium (50 ml):* 50 ml of 2× DMEMS with 250 μl of 10 mg/ml mycophenolic acid in 50 m*M* NaOH; 2.5 ml of 10 mg/ml xanthine in 50 m*M* NaOH; 150 μl of 10 mg/ml hypoxanthine in 100 m*M* NaOH.

Steps

1. Prepare 60–70% confluent monolayers on 9-cm petri dishes.

2. Make serial dilutions of freeze–thaw lysate: add 100, 10, and 1 μl lysate to 2-ml aliquots of DMEMS (or 1× HBSS). Vortex vigorously to separate viral aggregates.

3. Add the aliquots to the 9-cm dishes. Incubate for 30 min at room temperature with occasional gently rocking.

4. Autoclave the 1.8% low-melting-point agarose solution. Cool to 37°C in a water bath. Add equal volume of 2× S-DMEMS prewarmed to 37°C.

5. Remove the medium and carefully add 10 ml of the agarose overlay. Allow the agarose to solidify at room temperature. Incubate at 37°C for 2–3 days. The

plaques will appear as small holes in the cell monolayer, but can be difficult to see. They can be visualized by staining the cells with neutral red (see below).

6. Pick a plaque using a sterile Pasteur pipette.

7. Transfer the plaque to 500 μl of S-DMEMS. Vortex vigorously or pipette up and down many times to release the viruses.

8. Transfer the 500 μl to a fresh 60–70% confluent monolayer in a 3.5-cm hole. Leave for 30 min at room temperature with occasional gentle rocking.

9. Remove the medium and add 3 ml S-DMEMS. Incubate for 2–3 days at 37°C. If the cells are not completely lysed, an additional amplification may be necessary.

G. NEUTRAL RED STAINING

Solutions

1. *2× DMEM with 20% fetal calf serum (2× DMEMS):*
2. *1.8% Low-melting-point agarose in H_2O:* Autoclave before use.
3. *0.33% (w/v) Neutral red solution:* 0.33 g Neutral red in 100 ml H_2O. Sterile-filter, and store in aliquots at −20°C.

Steps

1. For each 9-cm plate, prepare 4 ml of 0.9% agarose in DMEMS as described above, add 140 μl 0.33% neutral red solution, and mix carefully.

2. Add the mixture on top of the agarose overlay. Allow the agarose to solidify at room temperature. Continue the incubation for 2–4 hr at 37°C. The cells will be stained and the plaques will become visible as holes in the stained cell layer.

IV. Comments

The progression of the infection can be monitored. After 12–16 hr, the cells adapt a distinct morphology that is easily detectable, and 24–36 hr after infection, the majority of the cells are dead (Fig. 2).

This procedure has been adapted to the AMA cell line but vaccinia virus will infect most cell lines ranging from *Drosophila* Scheider (S3) cells to different human cell lines, but it does so with very different efficiency and the procedures must be adapted to the cell lines used. The virus infects most epithelial cell lines efficiently but grows poorly on fibroblasts. As AMA and most other cell lines are not TK^- cell lines, we only apply the positive selection (for the presence of the *gpt* gene). The procedure for BrdU selection is described in Mackett *et al.* (1985). Also, the intent of this procedure is to link a specific cDNA to a spot on a two-dimensional gel and this does not require plaque purification. If the aim is to do functional studies of a protein it may be advisable to do a plaque purification, as there can be some nonrecombinant viruses left over and the yield of recombinant protein may be increased if they are removed.

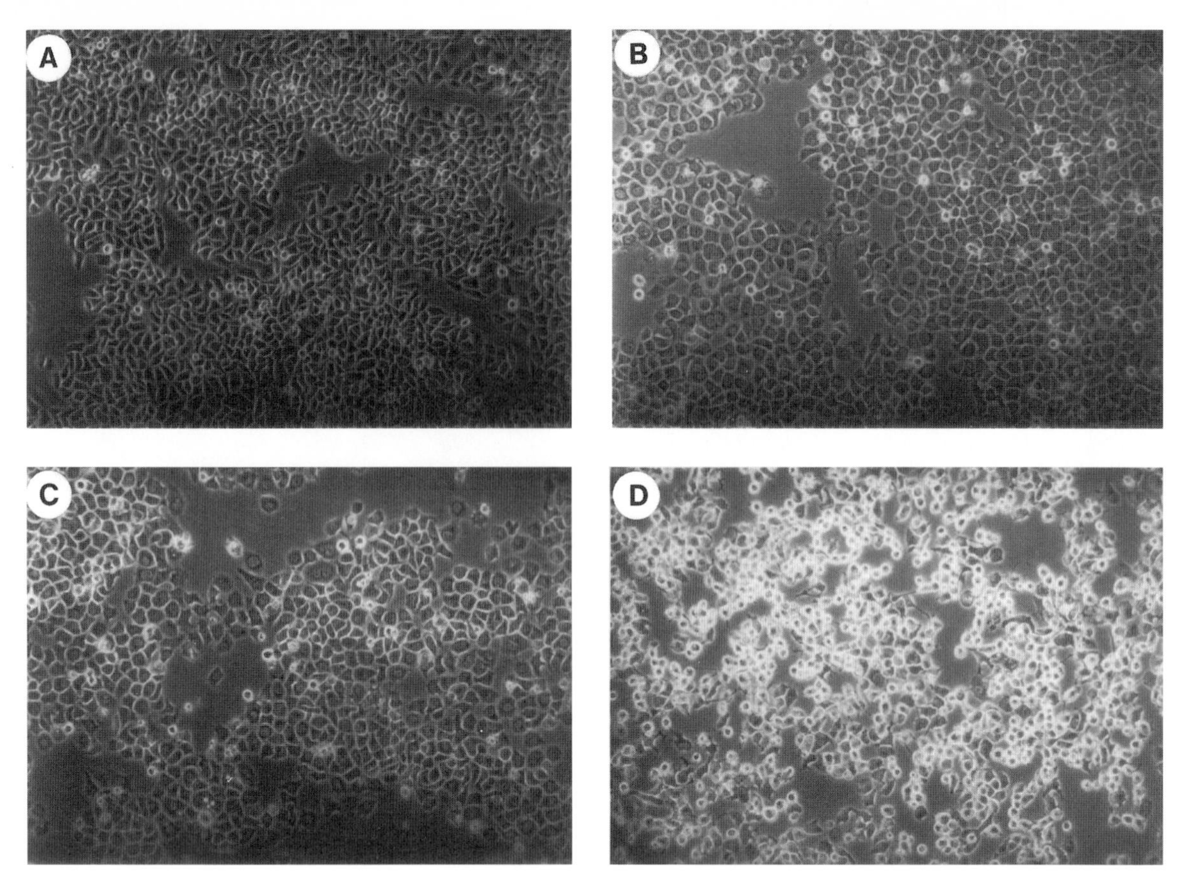

FIGURE 2 Morphology of vaccinia virus-infected AMA cells. (A) Noninfected cells. (B) Twelve hours after infection. (C) Twenty hours. (D) Thirty-six hours. The cells were grown in selection medium (S-DMEMS) and infected with a recombinant virus at a titer of about two viruses per cell.

V. Pitfalls

1. Great care should be taken to ensure that the wild-type vaccinia virus stock is not contaminated with recombinant viruses. Even trace amount of recombinant virus will be rescued during the selections.

2. If there is no viral growth after the selections and, thus, no recombinant virus in the sample, try increasing the amount of plasmid DNA in the transfection to 15–20 μg.

3. The pH in the medium will change as a result of adding the selection drugs in NaOH. This can be readjusted by leaving the medium in the CO_2 incubator with an unscrewed cap for 30–60 min before adding it to the cells.

REFERENCES

Bertholet, C., Drillien, R., and Wittek, R. (1985) One hundred base pairs of 5′ flanking sequence of a vaccinia virus late gene are sufficient to temporally regulate late transcription. *Proc. Natl. Acad. Sci. USA* **82,** 2096–2100.

Falkner, F. G., and Moss, B. (1988) *E. coli* gpt gene provides dominant selection for vaccinia virus open reading frame expression vectors. *J. Virol.* **62,** 1849–1854.

Leffers, H., Honoré, B., Madsen, P., Nielsen, M. S., Hoffmann, H. J., Andersen, A., and

Celis, J. E. (1994) cDNA expression and human 2-D gel protein databases: Towards integrating DNA and protein information. Submitted for publication.

Mackett, M., Smith, G. L., and Moss, B. (1984) General method for production of infectious vaccinia virus recombinants expressing foreign genes. *J. Virol.* **49**, 857–864.

Mackett, M., Smith, G. L., and Moss, B. (1985) The construction and characterization of vaccinia virus recombinants expressing foreign genes. *In* "DNA Cloning," Vol II. "A Practical Approach." (D. M. Glover, ed.). IRL Press, Oxford.

Moss, B. (1991) Vaccinia virus: A tool for research and vaccine development. *Science* **252**, 1662–1667.

Panicali, D., and Paoletti, E. (1982) Construction of poxviruses as cloning vectors: Insertion of the thymidine kinase from herpes simplex virus into the DNA of infectious vaccinia virus. *Proc. Natl. Acad. Sci. USA* **79**, 4927–4931.

Sambrook, J., Fritsch, E. F., and Maniatis, T. (1989) "Molecular Cloning, a Laboratory Manual," 2nd ed. Cold Spring Harbor Laboratory Press, Cold Spring Harbor, NY.

Stunnenberg, H. G., Lange, H., Philipson, L., van Miltenburg, R. T., and van der Vliet, P. C. (1988) High expression of functional adenovirus DNA polymerase and precursor terminal protein using recombinant vaccinia virus. *Nucleic Acids Res.* **16**, 2431–2444.

Vos, J. C., and Stunnenberg, H. G. (1988) Derepression of a novel class of vaccinia virus genes upon DNA replication. *EMBO J.* **7**, 3487–3492.

PART 14

PROTEINS

SECTION A

Protein Determination

Protein Determination

Martin Guttenberger

I. Introduction

Usually, the protein content of tissues or samples is not a major research interest but serves as a reference quantity. As a consequence it is desirable to perform protein determination with the least effort. Nevertheless, care should be taken to obtain correct results, especially when protein-related data (e.g., specific activities of enzyme preparations, yields in protein purification) are calculated. This article focuses on three techniques and outlines the specific pros and cons. With respect to convenience and speed, microplate reader assays are described where appropriate. These assays can be easily read in conventional instruments by employing microcuvettes or by scaling up the volumes (fivefold).

II. Materials and Instrumentation

The following reagents were obtained from the indicated suppliers. All other reagents were of analytical grade [Merck, Darmstadt]:

A. *Lowry assay* (Lowry *et al.,* 1951): Folin–Ciocalteu phenol reagent (Merck).

B. *Bradford assay* (Bradford 1976): Coomassie brilliant blue G-250 (Serva Blue G, Serva). The reagent for this assay is commercially available from Bio-Rad (Cat. No. 500-0006).

C. *Dot-blot assay* (Guttenberger *et al.,* 1991): Ammonium sulfate for biochemical purposes (Merck), benzoxanthene yellow (Hoechst 2495, Calbiochem), cellulose acetate membranes (SM 12000, Sartorius), glycine and SDS (Serva).

Solutions were prepared from bidistilled water. BSA (fraction V, Boehringer-Mannheim) was used as a standard protein. Ninety-six-well, flat-bottomed polystyrene microtiter plates (Greiner, Cat. No. 655101) were used for the photometric tests.

III. Procedures

Samples and standards may be kept at −20°C for a couple of weeks. For longer storage intervals, keep at −80°C.

A. LOWRY ASSAY

See Lowry *et al.* (1951).

Solutions

1. *Reagent A:* 2% (w/v) sodium carbonate (Na_2CO_3) in 0.10 *N* NaOH. To make 1 liter of reagent A (5000 determinations), dissolve 20 g Na_2CO_3 in 1 liter 0.10 *N* NaOH. Keep at room temperature.

2. *Reagent B:* 0.5% $CuSO_4 \cdot 5H_2O$ in 1% sodium or potassium tartrate. To make 20 ml of reagent B, dissolve 0.1 g $CuSO_4 \cdot 5H_2O$ in 20 ml 1% tartrate (0.2 g sodium or potassium tartrate dissolved in 20 ml water). Keep at room temperature.

3. *Reagent C (alkaline copper solution):* Mix 25 ml of reagent A and 0.5 ml of reagent B. Prepare fresh each day.

4. *Reagent D (Folin–Ciocalteu phenol reagent):* Dilute with an equal volume of water just prior to use.

Steps

1. Place 40 μl of sample (protein concentration 0.02–1 mg ml^{-1}) or blank into cavities of a microplate or into appropriate test tubes.
2. Add 200 μl of reagent C and mix. Allow to stand for at least 10 min.
3. Add 20 μl of reagent D and mix immediately. Allow to stand for 30 min or longer.
4. Read the samples in a microplate reader or any other photometer at 750 nm (in the latter case, remember to employ appropriate microcuvettes or larger volumes).

Modifications

1. The sample volume may be raised to 140 μl when samples are low in protein (0.02 mg ml^{-1} or less). In this case employ double-strength reagent C.
2. If samples have been dissolved in 0.5 *M* NaOH (recommended for resolubilization of acid precipitates), omit NaOH from reagent A.

B. BRADFORD ASSAY

See Bradford (1976).

Solutions

1. *Protein reagent stock solution:* 0.05% (w/v) Coomassie brilliant blue G-250, 23.8% (v/v) ethanol, 42.5% (w/v) phosphoric acid. To make 200 ml of stock solution (5000 determinations), dissolve 0.1 g Serva blue G in 50 ml 95% ethanol (denatured ethanol usually works as well), add 100 ml 85% phosphoric acid, and make up to 200 ml by adding water. The stock solution is commercially available (Bio-Rad). Keep at 4°C.

2. *Protein reagent:* The protein reagent is prepared from the stock solution by dilution in water (1:5). It is filtered immediately prior to use.

NOTE

The reagent contains phosphoric acid and ethanol/methanol. Handle with due care (especially when employing a dispenser)!

Steps

1. Place 4 μl of sample (protein concentration 0.1–1 mg ml^{-1}) or blank into cavities of a microplate or into appropriate test tubes.
2. Add 200 μl of protein reagent and mix. Allow to stand for at least 5 min.
3. Read the samples within 1 hr in a microplate reader or any other photometer at 595 nm (in the latter case, remember to employ appropriate microcuvettes or larger volumes).
4. *Microassay:* For diluted samples (less than 0.1 mg ml^{-1}) proceed as follows: Employ 200 μl of sample and add 50 μl of protein reagent stock.

C. DOT-BLOT ASSAY

See Guttenberger *et al.* (1991).

Solutions

1. *Benzoxanthene stock:* To prepare the stock solution add 1 ml of water to 0.5 g of the fluorescent dye (as supplied, weighing not necessary); keep at −20°C.

2. *Destaining solution:* Methanol/acetic acid (90/10, v/v). To make 1 liter of destaining solution, mix 100 ml acetic acid and 900 ml methanol.

3. *Staining solution:* To obtain 100 ml of staining solution, dilute 80 μl benzoxanthene stock in 100 ml destaining solution. Be sure to pour the destaining solution onto the stock solution to prevent the latter from clotting. Staining and destaining solutions are kept in tightly closed screw-cap bottles at 4°C in the dark. They are stable for months and can be used repeatedly.

4. *SDS stock:* To make 30 ml of 10% (w/v) SDS stock solution, dissolve 3 g SDS in approximately 20 ml of water, stir, and make up to 30 ml (allow some time for settling of foam). Keep at room temperature; it is stable for at least 1 year.

5. *Elution buffer:* 0.25 *M* glycine–sulfuric acid buffer (pH 3.6), 0.02% (w/v) SDS. To prepare 1 liter of elution buffer, dissolve 18.8 g glycine in approximately 900 ml water and add 15 ml 0.5 *M* sulfuric acid. Slight deviations from pH 3.6 are tolerable. Add 2 ml SDS stock and make up to 1 liter. Keep at room temperature; it is stable for months.

The following solutions are not needed for the standard protocol.

6. *Washing solution A:* Saturated ammonium sulfate, adjusted to pH 7.0 with Tris. To make 1 liter of washing solution A, stir ammonium sulfate in warm water (do not heat excessively). Let the solution cool to room temperature overnight and titrate to pH 7.0 with a concentrated (approx 2 *M*) solution of Tris (usually approx 1 ml is required). Keep at room temperature. As ammonium sulfate tends to produce lumps in the storage bottle it might be easier to weigh the entire bottle, add some water, remove the resulting slurry, and weigh the empty bottle again. To produce a saturated solution (53.1%, w/v), dissolve 760 g ammonium sulfate in 1 liter water.

7. *Washing solution B:* Methanol/acetic acid/water (50/10/40, v/v). To make 1 liter of washing solution B, mix 100 ml acetic acid and 500 ml methanol, and make up to 1 liter. Keep at 4°C.

8. *Drying solution:* 1-Butanol/methanol/acetic acid (60/30/10, v/v). To make 0.1 liter of drying solution, mix 10 ml acetic acid, 30 ml methanol, and 60 ml butanol. Keep at 4°C; use up to six times.

Steps

The dot-blot assay is a versatile tool; its different modifications enable one to cope with almost every potentially interfering substance. In the following description the steps for all modifications are included.

1. Prepare filter sheets (cellulose acetate membrane). *Handle the sheets with clean forceps and scissors, do not touch!* Cut one corner to aid in orientation during processing of the sheet. Mark the points of sample application (see below). Mount the membrane in such a way that the points of sample application are not supported (otherwise a loss of protein due to absorption through the membrane may be encountered). There are two different ways to achieve these requirements:
   a. For routine assays it is recommended that the sheets be mounted in a special dot-blot apparatus (Fig. 1). The dot areas are marked by piercing the sheets through small holes in the upper part of the device.
   b. For occasional assays the application points are marked by impressing a grid (approx 1-cm edge length) onto the filter surface (use a blunt blade

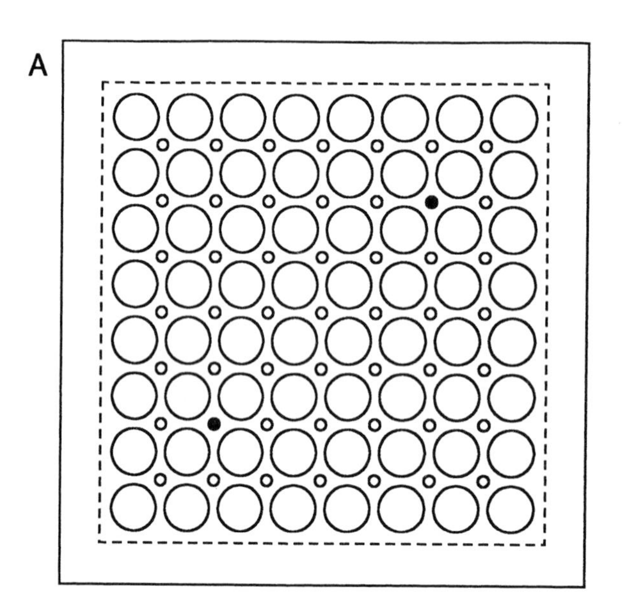

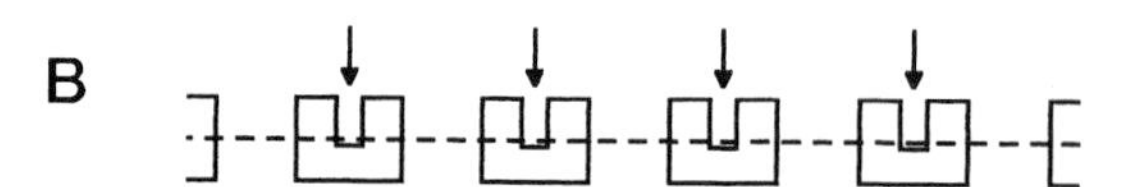

FIGURE 1 Dot-blot apparatus. (a) Top view. (b) Section along the diagonal. The apparatus has not been drawn to scale. Dashed lines indicate the position of the cellulose acetate membrane. The large circles correspond to the application points, the small ones to the holes that are used to pierce the membrane (arrows in Fig. 1b), and the solid small ones to the position of the pins that hold together the apparatus.

and a clean support, preferably a glass plate covering a graph paper). Mount the sheets on a wire grating (preferably made from stainless steel, fixation by means of adhesive tape is recommended).

2. Apply samples (0.01–10 mg ml^{-1}) to the membrane sheets in aliquots of 2 μl (piston pipettes are highly recommended, well-rinsed capillary pipettes may be used instead). Leave to dry for a couple of minutes. Dilute samples may be assayed by applying samples repeatedly.
3. Perform heat fixation. *Note that this step is imperative for samples containing SDS while it might prove deleterious to samples lacking SDS!* Incubate the dot-blot membranes holding the immobilized samples for 10 min at 120°C.
4. Remove interfering substances. *Note that this step is optional! Its use depends on the presence of potentially interfering substances (mainly carrier ampholytes, but also peptides and the buffer Pipes).* Interfering substances are removed prior to protein staining by vigorous shaking in washing solution A (3 × 5 min), followed by gentle agitation in washing solution B (3 × 2 min). From the last washing step the membrane sheets are transferred to the staining solution.
5. Stain and destain. *Take due care in handling the highly volatile methanolic solutions. The toxicity of benzoxanthene is not thoroughly studied!* Staining (10 min) and destaining (5, 5, and 15 min) are performed in closed trays on a laboratory shaker at ambient temperature. For the last destaining bath fresh destaining solution is employed; the first destaining bath is discarded. The incubation times given here represent the minimal time intervals needed. As long as the vessels are closed tightly each of these steps may be delayed according to convenience (in case of the last destaining bath, rinse in fresh destaining solution before proceeding).
6. Dry the stained membrane sheets. To facilitate cutting the dot areas from the sheets, the following drying step is recommended. The membranes are shaken in drying solution for exactly 2 min. Afterward they are mounted between two clamps[1] and left to dry in a fume hood. The sheets may be stored in the dark for later analysis.
7. Elute. Prior to elution the dots are cut from the membrane sheet. Elution (45 min in 2 ml of elution buffer) is performed in glass scintillation vials on a laboratory shaker at ambient temperature (bright illumination should be avoided). Dried sheets have to be rewetted in destaining solution prior to immersion in elution buffer. It is recommended that the destaining solution (25 μl) and the elution buffer be dispensed with appropriate repetitive devices (e.g., Eppendorf Multipette and Brand Dispensette, respectively).
8. Take readings in a fluorometer (e.g., SFM 25, Kontron) at 425 nm (excitation) and 475 nm (emission).

IV. Comments

Standard curves are calculated according to the method of least squares. Appropriate algorithms are provided with scientific calculators and most spreadsheet programs for personal computers. It is better to compute the standard curves employing the single readings instead of means. Be aware of the basic assumptions made in

[1]Test for chemical resistance prior to first use. Be sure to mount the drying membranes between two clamps of sufficient size to prevent distortion by uneven shrinkage (Fig. 2).

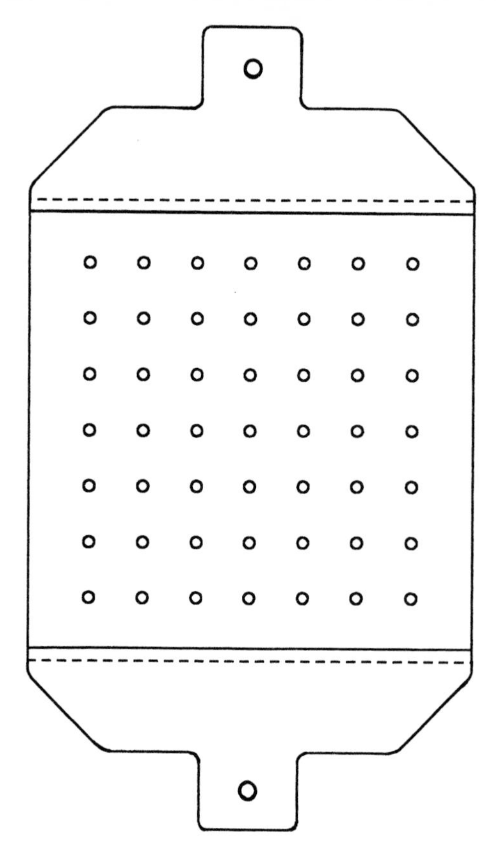

FIGURE 2 Membrane mounted for drying.

regression analysis. For additional reading on the statistics of standard curves compare Sokal and Rohlf (1981).

A. LOWRY ASSAY

Pro: The Lowry assay exhibits the best accuracy with regard to absolute protein concentrations due to the chemical reaction with polypeptides. This contrasts with the other two methods, which, as dye binding assays, exhibit more variation depending on the different reactivity of the given proteins (standards as well as samples).

Con: High sensitivity to potentially interfering substances; least shelf-life of the reagents employed.

Recommendation: Employ where absolute protein contents are of interest.

B. BRADFORD ASSAY

Pro: Assay is widespread because of its ease of performance (only one stable reagent needed, low sensitivity to potentially interfering substances, unsurpassed rapidity), its sensitivity, and its cheapness.

Con: High blank values, not strictly linear, possibly rather high deviations from absolute protein values (depending on the choice of standard protein).

Recommendation: Employ where relative protein contents are sufficient (in most cases like electrophoresis), and where the assay shows no interference by sample constituents.

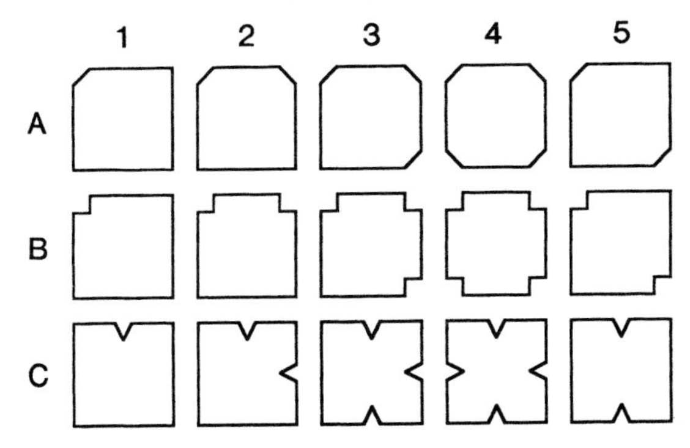

FIGURE 3 Useful incision patterns employed for marking membrane sheets prior to reprobing. Additional patterns may be generated by combination.

C. DOT-BLOT ASSAY

Pro: The dot-blot assay combines high sensitivity, an extended range of linearity (20 ng to 20 μg), and high tolerance to potentially interfering substances. The sample is not used up during assay. Hence, it may be reprobed[2] for immunological tests or detection of glycoproteins (Neuhoff *et al.*, 1981).

Con: More demanding and time consuming than the other assays, rather expensive (chemicals and instrumentation: fluorometer).

Recommendation: Employ where (1) the other assays show interference, especially with complex sample buffers used in one-dimensional[3] and two-dimensional[4] electrophoresis; (2) the amount of sample is limited and/or reprobing of the dotted samples is desirable; or (3) the detection of protein in aliquots from column chromatography or preparative isoelectric focusing on protein purification is needed (spot 2 μl onto membrane, process according to standard protocol, view destained membrane sheets under UV illumination).

V. Pitfalls

1. Solutions containing protein exhibit an altered surface tension. Avoid foaming and pipette slowly and steadily.

2. Extraction or precipitation steps to eliminate interfering substances should be carefully controlled for complete recovery of protein (Lowry *et al.*, 1951). The more demanding dot-blot assay frequently is a good alternative because of a considerable gain of convenience and accuracy with respect to a simplified sample preparation.

3. Omission of known interfering buffer components from just those samples that are intended for protein determination is strongly discouraged as the solubility of proteins might be influenced (carrier ampholytes, e.g., enhance

[2]The sheets containing the single dot areas can be marked conveniently by cutting the edges (Fig. 3, Neuhoff *et al.*, 1979).

[3]Sample buffer according to Laemmli (1970): 62.5 m*M* Tris–HCl (pH 6.8), 2% (w/v) SDS, 10% (v/v) glycerol, 5% (v/v) 2-mercaptoethanol, 0.003% (w/v) bromphenol blue. Range of the assay: 0.04 to 10 mg ml^{-1}, i.e., 80 ng to 20 μg in the test.

[4]Sample (lysis) buffer according to O'Farrell (1975): 9.5 *M* urea, 2% (w/v) Nonidet P-40, 5% (v/v) 2-mercaptoethanol, 2% (w/v) carrier ampholytes. Standards are prepared by stepwise dilution of the BSA stock solution in a modified sample buffer lacking carrier ampholytes. These are added from a doubly concentrated stock solution (4% w/v) in sample buffer. Range of the assay: 0.02 to 8 mg ml^{-1}, i.e., 40 ng to 16 μg in the test.

solubilization of membrane proteins in two-dimensional electrophoresis sample buffer, see Guttenberger *et al.*, 1991, for references).

4. There is some uncertainty as to which assay gives the most reliable results in combination with extracts from plant tissues rich in phenolic substances. The influence of such substances can never be predicted. It is therefore imperative to minimize interaction of these substances and protein in the course of sample preparation. For a more detailed discussion of this problem, see Guttenberger *et al.* (1994).

5. In the case of photometers/fluorometers operating with filters (usually microplate readers) the correct wavelength may not be available. Instead, a similar wavelength may be employed: Lowry assay: 500–800 nm, Bradford assay: 540–620 nm, dot-blot assay: 380–450 nm (excitation), 450–520 nm (emission). In the case of fluorometry allow for a sufficient wavelength interval between excitation and emission (consult the operating instructions of your instrument). Be aware that considerable deviations from the standard wavelengths will be at the expense of sensitivity.

6. In microplates it is important to achieve uniform menisci: Prick air bubbles with a thin wire and mix the plates on a gyratory shaker.

7. Analysis of dilute samples by application of larger sample volumes also increases the amount of potentially interfering substances. Include appropriate controls.

A. LOWRY ASSAY

1. Many reagents commonly used in protein extraction interfere with this assay. The main groups of interfering substances are reductants (e.g., sulfhydryl compounds like mercaptoethanol, reducing sugars like glucose), chelating agents (like EDTA), amine derivatives (many common buffering substances like Tris), and detergents (e.g., Triton, SDS). A detailed list of interfering substances along with remedies and tolerable limits is provided by Petersen (1979).

2. Reagent D is not stable at a basic pH. Immediate mixing after the addition of reagent D is imperative. In microplates the use of a small plastic spatula is convenient for this purpose (change or rinse between samples).

B. BRADFORD ASSAY

1. The commonly used standard protein BSA is highly reactive in this dye binding assay. As a consequence the protein content of the samples is underestimated. This systematic error does not matter in comparative analyses but brings about wrong absolute values. It is recommended that bovine γ-globulin be employed as a standard instead.

2. The standard curves are not strictly linear. Do not extend the range of standard concentrations beyond one order of magnitude or do not calculate standard curves by means of linear regression.

3. Samples containing detergents (1% will interfere) must be diluted (if possible) or precipitated (compare Section V.2.) prior to analysis.

4. The protein–dye complex is insoluble and will precipitate with time (Marshall and Williams, 1992). For highest accuracy take the readings within an interval between 5 and 20 min after addition of the reagent. With crude extracts (e.g., from mycelia of certain fungi) this interval may be considerably shorter, too

short to take meaningful readings. In this case alter the method of sample preparation or use another assay.

5. Plastic- and glassware (especially quartz glass) tends to bind dye. The resulting blue color can be removed by one of the following procedures: (1) Rinse with glassware detergent (avoid strongly alkaline detergents with cuvettes, rinse thoroughly to remove detergent again); (2) rinse with ethanol or methanol; (3) soak in 0.1 *M* HCl (takes several hours).

C. DOT-BLOT ASSAY

1. Generally, it is imperative to prevent the membrane sheets from drying during one of the transfer steps (residual acetic acid will destroy the filter matrix).

2. In case of highly variable results inspection of the stained filters (last destaining bath or dried) under UV illumination may be helpful: Background staining resulting from improper handling of the membranes will be visible (do not use for quantitative analyses).

3. When employing the washing procedure, (1) commercially available ammonium sulfate frequently contains substantial amounts of undefined UV-absorbing and fluorescing substances. These lead to more or less yellowish solutions. To avoid possible interference in fluorometry only colorless solutions should be used. (2) Thorough rinsing in washing solution B is imperative. Ammonium sulfate accumulating in the staining solution will interfere with the assay.

4. Although the dot-blot assay is extremely insensitive to potentially interfering substances it is advisable to include appropriate controls (at least blank buffer and unknown buffer plus standard).

5. In the case of buffers containing detergent plus carrier ampholytes the storage conditions and the number of freeze–thaw cycles may prove important. Use fresh solutions or run appropriate controls.

6. If membrane sheets turn transparent on drying they have not been equilibrated properly in the drying solution (keep in time: 2 min) or the drying solution has been diluted by accumulation of destaining solution (do not reuse the drying solution too often).

REFERENCES

Bradford, M. M. (1976) A rapid and sensitive method for the quantitation of microgram quantities of protein utilizing the principle of protein–dye binding. *Anal. Biochem.* **72**, 248–254.

Guttenberger, M., Neuhoff, V., and Hampp, R. (1991) A dot-blot assay for quantitation of nanogram amounts of protein in the presence of carrier ampholytes and other possibly interfering substances. *Anal. Biochem.* **196**, 99–103.

Guttenberger, M., Schaeffer, C., and Hampp, R. (1994) Kinetic and electrophoretic characterization of NADP dependent dehydrogenases from root tissues of Norway spruce [*Picea abies* (L.) Karst.] employing a rapid one-step extraction procedure. *Trees* **8**, 191–197.

Laemmli, U. K. (1970) Cleavage of structural proteins during the assembly of the head of bacteriophage T4. *Nature* **227**, 680–685.

Lowry, O. H., Rosebrough, N. J., Farr, A. L., and Randall, R. J. (1951) Protein measurement with the Folin phenol reagent. *J. Biol. Chem.* **193**, 265–275.

Marshall, T., and Williams, K. M. (1992) Coomassie blue protein dye-binding assays measure formation of an insoluble protein–dye complex. *Anal. Biochem.* **204**, 107–109.

Neuhoff, V., Ewers, E., and Huether, G. (1981) Spot analysis for glycoprotein determination in the nanogram range. *Hoppe-Seyler's Z. Physiol. Chem.* **362**, 1427–1434.
Neuhoff, V., Philipp, K., Zimmer, H.-G., and Mesecke, S. (1979) A simple, versatile, sensitive and volume-independent method for quantitative protein determination which is independent of other external influences. *Hoppe-Seyler's Z. Physiol. Chem.* **360**, 1657–1670.
O'Farrell, P. H. (1975) High resolution two-dimensional electrophoresis of proteins. *J. Biol. Chem.* **250**, 4007–4021.
Peterson G. L. (1979) Review of the Folin phenol protein quantitation method of Lowry, Rosebrough, Farr, and Randall. *Anal. Biochem.* **100**, 201–220.
Sokal, R. R., and Rohlf, F. J. (1981) "Biometry." Freeman, New York.

SECTION B

Preparation of Tagged Proteins and Others

Controlled Radioiodination of Proteins

Michael J. Rudick

I. Introduction

When carried out under the appropriate conditions, radioiodination of protein molecules allows them to be easily detected in nanogram quantities so that they can be used in tracer amounts, while retaining biological activity (Seevers and Counsell, 1982). Thus, radioiodinated proteins have been used in studies of receptor-mediated endocytosis, radioautographic detection of antigens in Western blots, calibration of antibody titers, radioimmunoassay, and many other applications. Because routinely working with this isotope engenders health considerations (see also article by R. W. Davies), it is important to select an iodination method that minimizes such risk. In this regard the use of iodobeads (polystyrene beads with covalently bound chloramine-T) was first described by Markwell (1982) as a means of iodinating proteins under very mild, controlled conditions. Recently, a simple method was developed for determining the kinetics of protein radioiodination that takes advantage of the properties of iodobeads, so that the optimum degree of labeling for a particular application can be established relatively quickly (Cheng and Rudick, 1991). The method described allows estimation of the time course of radioiodine incorporation into proteins without tedious precipitations and centrifugations.

II. Materials and Instrumentation

All chemicals are at least reagent grade and may be purchased from any convenient source. Carrier-free Na[^{125}I] is obtained from ICN (Cat. No. 63034), but the equivalent radioisotope from any source is acceptable. Iodobeads are purchased from Pierce (Cat. No. 28665 G) and kept at 4°C. Solutions of protein and radioiodine are contained in 5-ml snap-cap polypropylene vials (Bio-Rad, Cat. No. 223-9820) and are transferred from one vial to another using 1.5-ml polypropylene transfer pipettes. These minimize the loss of protein due to adsorption to glass or other surfaces. Nitrocellulose (25 × 25-cm NC sheets with a 045-μm pore size, Cat. No. 00850) is from Schleicher and Schuell. Washed iodobeads are blotted on Whatman No. 540 paper (Cat. No. 1540N321). Prepacked columns for desalting solutions of macromolecules are from Pierce (2- or 5-ml Excellulose gel columns, Cat. No. 20439 G or 20449 G, respectively) or Amersham (NAP 5 column, Cat. No. 17-0853-01). Any available gamma detector can be used to quantitate radioiodine. All operations are carried out at room temperature in a fume hood.

III. Procedure

A. DETERMINATION OF THE TIME COURSE OF RADIOIODINATION

Solutions

1. *Buffer A:* 0.1 *M* sodium phosphate buffer, pH 7.0.
2. *Buffer B:* 0.01 *M* acetate buffer, pH 5.0.
3. *Buffer* C (modified from Towbin *et al.*, 1979): 20% methanol and 10 m*M* Nal in Tris–glycine buffer, pH 8.3. Prepare by titrating 25 m*M* Tris base with 192 m*M* glycine to pH 8.3. Then add Nal to 10 m*M*. Combine 800 ml of this with 200 ml of methanol to make 1 liter of buffer C.

Steps

1. Prepare a set of sequentially numbered pieces (use a No. 2 pencil) of NC whose dimensions allow them to be handled by the available gamma counter, and arrange them in order on a nonabsorbent surface in the fume hood. The number of pieces should equal the number of time points to be taken.
2. Prepare a solution of the protein molecule that is to be radioiodinated by dissolving it (up to 500 μg) in 0.25 ml of buffer B and diluting with 0.5 ml of buffer A, bringing the total volume to 0.75 ml.
3. Wash an iodobead (handle iodobeads with forceps) twice for 30 sec each with 0.5 ml of buffer A and dry by gently blotting on Whatman No. 540 paper.
4. Place the washed bead into 0.25 ml of buffer A containing 1.0 mCi of Na[^{125}I] for 5 min, and then add the protein solution to make a total volume of 1.0 ml.
5. Immediately remove a 5-μl sample (a smaller volume can be taken, depending on the reproducibility of pipetting) from the vial and spot it onto the first piece of NC. At every 30-sec or 1-min interval thereafter, spot a 5-μl sample from the reaction mixture onto an appropriately numbered piece of NC, until a total of 20 min has elapsed.
6. Wash all of the NC pieces together four times in 50 ml (each time) of buffer C with gentle agitation, to remove unincorporated radioiodide.
7. Count the radioactivity on each piece of washed NC. There is still significant activity even with the first sample taken, but this is due to the irreversible binding of oxidized forms of the radioiodide whose quantity in the reaction mixture remains constant throughout the iodination procedure.
8. Subtract the radioactivity of the first NC piece from that of each of the other pieces. The remaining counts represent radioiodine incorporated into protein. Examples of the results of iodination of human growth hormone and pancreatic ribonuclease are presented in Fig. 1.

B. OPTIMAL RADIOIODINATION OF PROTEINS

Once the time course of radioiodination of the specific protein has been determined, the protein molecules can be iodinated to any desired degree by following the prescribed procedure and stopping the reaction at the appropriate time on the established incorporation curve. This is done, as follows.

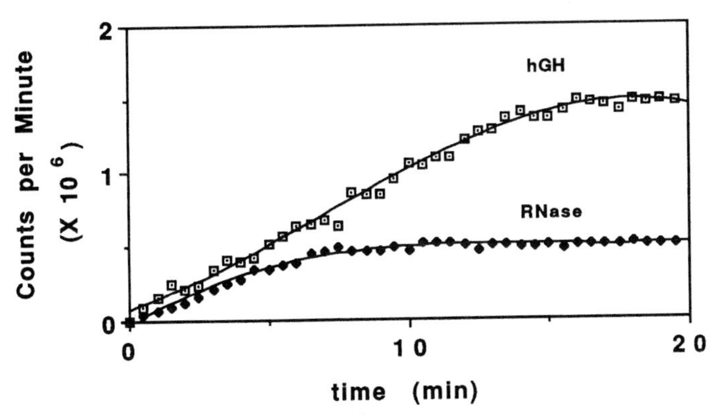

FIGURE 1 Time course of protein radioiodination using the membrane blotting method. Reaction mixtures contained 0.5 mCi of $Na^{125}I$ and 200 μg of either human growth hormone (hGH) or bovine pancreatic ribonuclease (RNase).

Steps

1. Allow the iodination reaction to proceed for the desired time, as determined by the radioiodine incorporation curve. Then remove the entire solution from the iodobead using a transfer pipette and place it into a fresh vial. Oxidation of iodide occurs only in the vicinity of the iodobead to which all of the chloramine-T is attached; thus, simply removing the reaction mixture from the iodobead immediately stops the iodination.

2. Desalt the protein by passage through a small, prepacked gel permeation column. If it will be necessary to concentrate the sample, desalt against water or ammonium bicarbonate buffer.

IV. Comments

Use of the iodobead allows the reaction to be controlled such that it is possible to observe the kinetics of iodine incorporation. This is not possible with the use of free chloramine-T, where the iodination reaction is complete within seconds. In addition, with free chloramine-T, long after iodination is complete the protein molecule is in contact with the oxidizing agent and there is a continuing risk of molecular damage, unless the reactant is quenched with an excess of a strong reducing agent like metabisulfite. This also may have deleterious effects on the protein molecules. The ideal situation is to iodinate the protein molecule to its highest possible specific radioactivity, while retaining those biological properties for which the protein molecule was selected. It is a good idea to first iodinate a sample of the protein molecule to the maximum level and then to determine whether or not it is active in the appropriate assay. If it is not, then a submaximum iodination time can be chosen and the assay performed again, until the desired result is obtained.

V. Pitfalls

1. Care should be taken not to store the iodobeads in the presence of reducing agents, especially volatile ones, such as 2-mercaptethanol. Iodobead activity is readily checked by placing a bead into 1 ml of buffer A containing 1% Nal (or Kl) and observing within a few seconds the development of the brown coating around the bead, which indicates the formation of elemental iodine.

2. It is important not to freeze the solution of radioiodine, as this leads to instability and volatilization. Radioiodine is routinely stored within a lead container and, when in use, is kept behind lead bricks in a fume hood vented to the outside.

REFERENCES

Cheng, H., and Rudick, M. J. (1991) A membrane blotting method for following the time course of protein radioiodination using iodobeads. *Anal. Biochem.* **198**, 191–193.

Markwell, M. A. K. (1982) A new solid-state reagent to iodinate proteins. I. Conditions for the efficient labelling of antiserum. *Anal. Biochem.* **125**, 427–432.

Seevers, R. H., and Counsell, R. E. (1982) Radioiodination techniques for small organic molecules. *Chem. Rev.* **82**, 575–590.

Towbin, H., Staehelin, T., and Gordon, J. (1979) Electrophoretic transfer of proteins from polyacrylamide gels to nitrocellulose sheets: Procedure and some applications. *Proc. Natl. Acad. Sci. USA* **76**, 4350–4354.

Cell Surface Biotinylation Techniques

Chiara Zurzolo, André Le Bivic,
and Enrique Rodriguez-Boulan

I. Introduction

A fundamental property of epithelial cells is the polarized distribution of proteins and lipids in the apical and basolateral domains of the plasma membrane. These two domains are physically separated from each other by the tight junction. Many studies have been done over the last 15 years to understand the mechanisms that lead to the establishment and maintenance of the polarized distribution of proteins and lipids in the plasma membrane of epithelial cells (Rodriguez-Boulan and Nelson, 1989).

A major innovation for the study of epithelial cell polarity was achieved with the introduction of a new culturing system different from the classical methods and which involves the use of a permeable filter chamber. Cell lines used for the study of epithelial cell polarity, such as MDCK (see article by Kai Simons and Hilkka Virta), Caco2, and FRT, can be grown on such a permeable filter support (either nitrocellulose or polycarbonate) and polarize after a few days. The state of polarization can be assessed by measuring the transepithelial resistance of the cells, which gives an indication of the development of a tight monolayer and of the presence of tight junctions (Hanzel *et al.*, 1991).

One of the biggest advantages of this culture system is the accessibility of either the apical or basolateral surface to any reagent that can be added to the medium in contact with either of the two surfaces. This is the basis of the biotinylation techniques that have been developed to selectively label proteins present in the apical or the basolateral domains of the plasma membrane of filter-grown cells.

Confluent filter-grown monolayers can be labeled with the water-soluble cell-impermeable biotin analog sulfo-NHS-biotin, which is incorporated selectively into proteins present on the surface to which it has been added. Detection of biotinylated proteins can then be achieved by blotting with ^{125}I or peroxidase–streptavidin. Furthermore, the cells can be metabolically pulse-labeled and the protein(s) of interest can then be studied using biotinylation, immunoprecipitation, and subsequent streptavidin–agarose precipitation. This technique is very versatile and is applicable to study of diverse aspects of epithelial cell polarity, such as steady-state distribution of specific antigens, or dynamic processes, such as targeting to the surface and transcytosis of transmembrane and glycosylphosphatidylinositol-anchored proteins (GPI-anchored proteins). This article describes a basic protocol for selective cell surface biotinylation plus some modifications of the assay to study protein targeting and endocytosis.

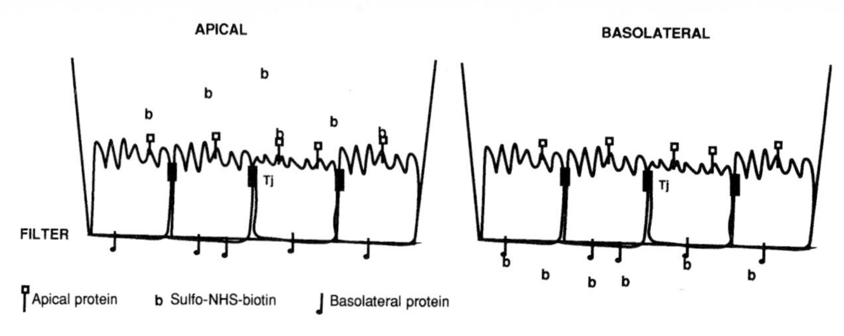

FIGURE 1 Cell surface biotinylation.

II. Materials and Instrumentation

Sulfo-NHS-biotin (sulfosuccinimidobiotin, Cat. No. 21217H), NHS-LC-biotin (sulfosuccinimidyl-6-(biotinamido)-hexanoate, Cat. No. 21335H); NHS-SS-biotin (sulfosuccinimidyl-2-(biotinamido)-ethyl-1,3-dithiopropionate, Cat. No. 21331H), and immunopure-immobilized streptavidin (Cat. No. 20394H) were obtained from Pierce. Protein A–Sepharose CL-4B (Cat. No. 17-0780-01) was purchased from Pharmacia. Glutathione (Cat. No. G-4251) and DMEM (Cat. No. D-5648) were from Sigma. *Staphylococcus aureus* cells (Pansorbin, Cat. No. 507858) were purchased from Calbiochem. The cells were grown on polycarbonate filters (Transwell, Cat. No. 3412) from Costar, and transepithelial resistance was measured with a Millicell apparatus (Millipore).

III. Procedures

A. CELL SURFACE BIOTINYLATION

This procedure is used to determine the distribution of plasma membrane proteins of epithelial cells grown on permeable filters support (Fig. 1) (modified from Sargiacomo *et al.,* 1989).

Solutions

1. *PBS-CM:* Phosphate-buffered saline containing 1 m*M* $MgCl_2$, 0.1 m*M* $CaCl_2$.
2. *Sulfo-NHS-biotin* (or *sulfo-NHS-LC-biotin,* from Pierce): Stock solution (200 mg/ml in DMSO) stored at −20°C is thawed just before use. Dilute to a final concentration of 0.5 mg/ml in PBS-CM and use immediately.
3. *50 mM NH_4Cl or Dulbecco's modified Eagle's medium (DMEM):* To quench the biotin in excess.

Steps

1. For all experiments use confluent monolayers of cells plated at confluency (2×10^6 cells/filter) 4–5 days before. Measure the transepithelial resistance (TER) of each filter before use (different cell lines have different TER values, you should use the monolayer at plateau values of TER).
2. Rinse filters placed on ice with cold PBS-CM, twice.
3. Add fresh solution of sulfo-NHS-biotin (0.5 mg/ml in PBS-CM) to apical or

basolateral chamber. Add PBS-CM to other chamber. Use 0.7 ml apical, 1.5 ml basal. Incubate for 30 min at 4°C, twice (on shaker in cold room).

4. Quench reaction by removing the biotin solution and adding 1 ml 50 m*M* NH_4Cl in PBS (or DMEM) to each chamber. Incubate 10 min at 4°C.

5. Rinse twice with PBS-CM.

6. At this point you can freeze the cells on filters at −80°C or immediately proceed with the extraction of the biotinylated proteins.

B. EXTRACTION OF BIOTINYLATED PROTEINS

Solutions

1. *TBS:* 10 m*M* Tris, pH 7.4, 150 m*M* NaCl, 1 m*M* EDTA.
2. *Triton X-114 stock:* Approximately 10% in TBS. Triton X-114 must be precondensed prior to use.
3. *Lysis buffer:* 1% Triton X-114 in TBS (or any other extraction buffer that is suitable in case of immunoprecipitation of a specific protein).
4. *Reextraction buffer:* 0.06% Triton X-114 in TBS.

Steps

1. To visualize the pattern of biotinylated proteins, excise filters from the chamber with a scalpel and extract them in Eppendorf tubes with 1 ml of ice-cold lysis buffer in the presence of protease inhibitors. Lyse for 1 hr at 4°C (use rotator in cold room). Make sure filters are completely submerged during lysis.

2. Carefully remove filter, trying to leave as much supernatant as possible.

3. Clarify supernatants by centrifugation (14,000 *g* for 2–5 min).

4. Collect supernatants and subject them to phase separation to distinguish hydrophilic "peripheral" membrane proteins from hydrophobic "integral" membrane proteins.

5. Phase separation: Incubate sample at 37°C for 1–3 min, until solution becomes cloudy. Spin in microfuge for 1 min at room temperature. You should see distinct upper and lower phases. The lower phase is the detergent phase and should contain membrane proteins; the upper phase is aqueous and should contain soluble proteins.

6. Discard aqueous phase. Extract detergent phase with 900 μl of reextraction buffer (add more protease inhibitors each time you add more buffer). Repeat phase separation as above, again saving detergent phase. *Note:* If a pellet forms during extraction or after spinning, place sample on ice, so that Triton X-114 goes back into solution. Spin again in microfuge in the cold to pellet insoluble material. Transfer supernatant to new tube and continue with the extractions.

7. Repeat step 6.

8. Precipitate the final detergent phase with 5 vol of acetone (−20°C for 30 min) and resuspend in 60 μl of Laemmli sample buffer. Boil for 2–5 min and run on SDS–PAGE under reducing conditions.

9. After electrophoresis, transfer proteins to nitrocellulose as described by Towbin *et al.* (1979).

10. Alternatively, if you want to look at a specific antigen, after extraction of

the monolayers in a particular lysis buffer you can immunoprecipitate your protein of interest with a specific antibody and proceed with SDS–PAGE. Then follow the same protocol for the detection of the antigen.

C. DETECTION OF BIOTINYLATED PROTEINS WITH ^{125}I-STREPTAVIDIN (I)

Solutions

1. *Blocking buffer:* 1% nonfat dry milk (Carnation) in PBS.
2. *TGG buffer:* 0.2% BSA, 0.5% (v/v) Tween 20, 10% (v/v) glycerol, 1 *M* glucose in PBS.
3. *^{125}I-Streptavidin:* You can iodinate streptavidin yourself or buy it from Amersham.
4. *Washing buffer:* 0.2% BSA, 0.2% Triton X-100 in PBS.

Steps

1. Block the nitrocellulose sheet with 50–100 ml of blocking buffer on slow shaker for 1 hr at room temperature (you can leave it overnight at 4°C).
2. Wash once with TGG buffer.
3. Add 50 ml of TGG containing 0.2% BSA and ^{125}I-streptavidin ($1-2 \times 10^6$ cpm/ml). Leave it for 2 hours on slow shaker at room temperature.
4. Wash with washing buffer 3 × 10 min.
5. Dry the blot and autoradiograph it on Kodak XAR Film.

D. DETECTION OF BIOTINYLATED PROTEINS WITH STREPTAVIDIN (II)

Another way to detect the biotinylated proteins is to metabolically label ([^{35}S]-methionine/cysteine) the cells grown on filters at steady state (e.g., overnight) and then proceed with the biotnylation and extraction (±immunoprecipitation) (Zurzolo and Rodriguez-Boulan, 1993) as described above. The biotinylated proteins are detected, in this case, by precipitation using streptavidin beads as described in the biotin targeting protocol.

E. BIOTIN TARGETING ASSAY

This procedure is used to determine if proteins are delivered directly to the apical or basolateral surface or via a transcytotic pathway through the opposite surface (Fig. 2) (modified from Le Bivic *et al.*, 1990).

Solutions

1. *Starvation medium:* DME without methionine or cysteine.
2. *[^{35}S]Methionine/cysteine:* 1 mCi per six filters.
3. *Chase medium:* DME containing 10× cysteine/methionine.
4. *HCO_3-free DME, 20 mM Hepes, and 0.2% BSA.*

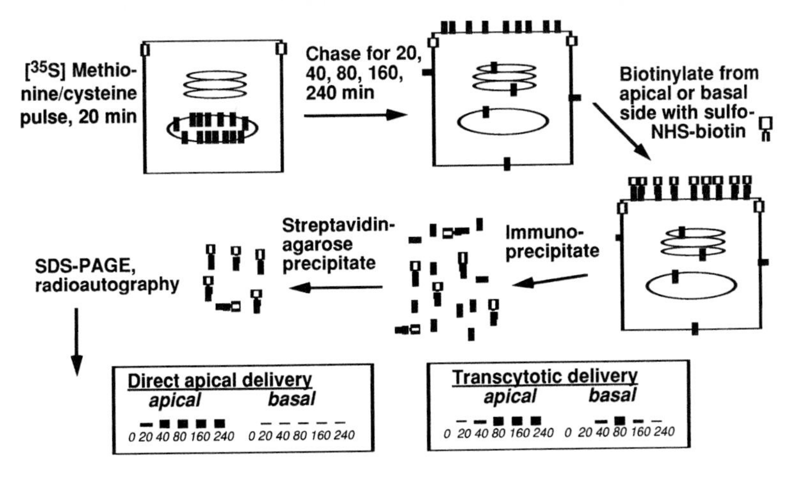

FIGURE 2 Biotin targeting assay.

5. *NHS-biotin (or NHS-LC-biotin or NHS-SS-biotin):* 0.5 mg/ml in PBS-CM plus all the solutions mentioned in the cell surface biotinylation protocol.
6. *Lysis buffer:* 150 m*M* NaCl, 20 m*M* Tris, pH 8.0, 5 m*M* EDTA, 1% Triton X-100, 0.2% BSA, and protease inhibitors.
7. *Staphylococcus A suspension cells:* Pansorbin.
8. *Protein A–Sepharose:* Pharmacia.
9. *Immunopure-immobilized streptavidin on agarose beads:* Pierce, Cat. No. 20394.

Steps

1. Incubate cells on filters for 30 min in DME without cysteine or methionine.

2. Pulse for 20 min in same medium containing [^{35}S]methionine/cysteine (1 mCi per six filters).

3. Wash cells once with DME.

4. Chase for different times in DME containing 10× cysteine/methionine.

5. Store at 4°C in $NaHCO_3$-free DME, 20 m*M* Hepes, 0.2% BSA before biotinylation.

6. Proceed to apical or basolateral biotinylation following the protocol described before. At this point you can store the filters at −20°C or proceed as follows.

7. Excise filters and solubilize cells in 1 ml of lysis buffer for 1 hr at 4°C on rotation.

8. Preclear extracts with 100 μl of Pansorbin for 20 min and centrifuge at 15,000 *g* for 10 min.

9. Proceed with the immunoprecipitation of the protein of interest by using specific antibodies and protein A–Sepharose to bring down the antigen–antibody complex.

10. Block streptavidin beads in lysis buffer, 1–12 hr at 4°C. Use 60 μl of beads per sample in a final volume of 1 ml per sample.

11. To recover immunoprecipitated biotinylated antigens, from the antigen–

antibody complexes bound to protein A–Sepharose beads, boil the beads with 10 μl of 10% SDS for 5 min.

12. Dilute with 500 μl of lysis buffer, and centrifuge immediately at 15,000 *g* for 1 min.

13. Transfer 500 μl of supernatant to a tube containing rinsed streptavidin beads.

14. Add 100 μl of lysis buffer to pellet; mix and spin again.

15. Combine supernatant with the 500 μl obtained in step 13.

16. Incubate overnight at 4°C.

17. Wash beads with the immunoprecipitation buffers and boil in Laemmli sample buffer.

18. Run on SDS–PAGE, dry the gel, and expose for autoradiography.

F. BIOTIN ASSAY FOR ENDOCYTOSIS

This procedure is from Graeve *et al.* (1989).

Solutions

1. *PBS-CM.*
2. *Cleavable biotin reagent:* NHS-SS-biotin.
3. *DME plus 0.2% BSA.*
4. *Reducing solution:* 310 mg glutathione (free acid) dissolved in 17 ml H_2O (50 m*M*). Add 1 ml of 1.5 *M* NaCl, 0.12 ml of 50% NaOH, and 2 ml of serum just before use.
5. *Quenching solution:* 5 mg/ml iodoacetamide in PBS-CM + 1% BSA.

Steps

1. Wash cells on filters four times, 15 min each time with cold PBS-CM.

2. Add NHS-SS-biotin to a final concentration 0.5 mg/ml in cold PBS-CM. Use 1 ml per chamber; to chambers not being labeled add PBS-CM. Incubate for 20 min at 4°C; repeat with fresh NHS-SS-biotin.

3. Wash filters twice with DME/0.2% BSA. Keep two filters on ice (one of these will represent the total amount of proteins at the surface before internalization, the other will be treated with the reducing solution and will represent your control of efficiency of reduction), transfer the other filters to 37°C for various times to allow the biotinylated proteins to be internalized.

4. Stop incubation by transferring filters back to 4°C.

5. Wash twice in PBS-CM + 10% serum.

6. Incubate filters for 20 min in reducing solution. Repeat. (Mock-treat one filter.)

7. After washing, quench free SH groups in 5 mg/ml iodoacetamide in PBS-CM + 1% BSA for 15 min.

8. Lyse cells and immunoprecipitate.

9. Run the samples on SDS–PAGE and autoradiograph.

IV. Comments

The methods described above represent examples of applications of the biotinylation technique; other examples of possible applications are (1) a transcytotic assay using a combination of the targeting and endocytosis protocols (Le Bivic *et al.*, 1989; Zurzolo *et al.*, 1992) and (2) detection of GPI-anchored proteins at the cell surface using a modification of the biotinylation technique that combines specific digestion of the GPI moiety with phospholipase C (PiPLC) and phase separation in Triton X-114 (Lisanti and Rodriguez-Boulan, 1990). Furthermore, another analog of biotin, biotin hydrazide, can be used to label oligosaccharides of surface glycoproteins following periodate oxidation (Lisanti *et al.*, 1989).

V. Pitfalls

1. A recent report suggests that use of a pH 9 buffer to dilute S-NHS-biotin would enhance the efficiency of labeling of surface proteins (Gottardi and Caplan, 1993). In our experience this is not always true and depends on different proteins and cell lines.

2. Always cut first the filters from the plastic holder and then lyse the cells by submerging the filter in lysis buffer. We have shown that cells grow on the inside of the plastic ring supporting the filter; thus, cells that are lysed *in situ* (in the intact Transwell) will be included in the assay and this could lead to erroneus experimental results (Zurzolo and Rodriguez-Boulan, 1993).

3. Sometimes in targeting experiments, intracellular forms, not biotinylated forms, are recovered on streptavidin beads. Using NHS-LC-biotin and keeping SDS to 0.4% (instead of 0.2%) in the incubation medium help reduce this nonspecific binding.

REFERENCES

Gottardi, C., and Caplan, M. (1993) Cell surface biotinylation in the determination of epithelial membrane polarity. *J. Tissue Culture Methods* **14,** 173–180.

Graeve, L., Drickamer, K., and Rodriguez-Boulan, E. (1989) Functional expression of the chicken liver asialoglycoprotein receptor in the basolateral surface of MDCK cells. *J. Cell Biol.* **109,** 2909–2816.

Hanzel, D., Nabi, I. R., Zurzolo, C., Powell, S. K., and Rodriguez-Boulan, E. (1991) New techniques lead to advances in epithelial cell polarity. *Semin. Cell Biol.* **2,** 341–353.

Le Bivic, A., Real, F. X., and Rodriguez-Boulan, E. (1989) Vectorial targeting of apical and basolateral plasma membrane proteins in a human adenocarcinoma epithelial cell line. *Proc. Natl. Acad. Sci. USA* **86,** 9313–9317.

Le Bivic, A., Sambuy, Y., Mostov, K., and Rodriguez-Boulan, E. (1990) Vectorial targeting of an endogenous apical membrane sialoglycoprotein and uvomorulin in MDCK cells. *J. Cell Biol.* **110,** 1533–1539.

Lisanti, M., Le Bivic, A., Sargiacomo, M., and Rodriguez-Boulan, E. (1989) Steady state distribution and biogenesis of endogenous MDCK glycoproteins: Evidence for intracellular sorting and polarized cell surface delivery. *J. Cell Biol.* **109,** 2117–2128.

Lisanti, M., and Rodriguez-Boulan, E. (1990) Glycophospholipid membrane anchoring provides clues to the mechanism of protein sorting in polarized epithelial cells. *Trends Biochem. Sci.* **1990,** 113–118.

Rodriguez-Boulan, E., and Nelson, W. J. (1989) Morphogenesis of the polarized epithelial cell phenotype. *Science* **245,** 718–725.

Sargiacomo, M., Lisanti, M., Graeve, L., Le Bivic, A., and Rodriguez-Boulan, E. (1989) Integral and peripheral protein compositions of the apical and basolateral membrane domains in MDCK cells. *J. Membr. Biol.* **107,** 277–286.

Towbin, H. T., Staehelin, T., and Gordon, J. (1979) Electrophoretic transfer of proteins from polyacrylamide gels to nitrocellulose sheets: Procedures and some applications. *Proc. Natl. Acad. Sci. USA* **76**, 4350–4354.

Zurzolo, C., Le Bivic, A., Quaroni, A., Nitsch, L., and Rodriguez-Boulan, E. (1992) Modulation of transcytotic and direct targeting pathways in a polarized thyroid cell line. *EMBO J.* **11**, 2337–2344.

Zurzolo, C., and Rodriguez-Boulan, E. (1993) Delivery of Na^+, K^+-ATPase in polarized epithelial cells. *Science* **260**, 550–552.

Assays for Cellular Protein Binding and Ligand Internalization

Kim Vettenranta, Guojun Bu, and Alan L. Schwartz

I. Introduction

Studies employing several model systems have established the general characteristics of receptor-mediated endocytosis as well as delineated its pathways and mechanisms of regulation. The experimental procedures described below are designed to allow a basic evaluation of the process of receptor-mediated endocytosis using tissue-type plasminogen activator (tPA) binding and endocytosis as an example (Bu *et al.*, 1992a, b). For details on a comprehensive, quantitative evaluation of receptor-mediated endocytosis, see Goldstein *et al.* (1983) and Owensby *et al.* (1989). For principles and practice in receptor biochemistry and cell biology see Hulme (1990) and Limbird (1986).

II. Materials and Instrumentation

Carrier-free sodium [^{125}I]iodide was purchased from DuPont New England Nuclear Products (Cat. No. NEZ033A). Iodo-gen was purchased from Pierce Chemical Company (Cat. No. 28600). PD-10 columns (Sephadex G-25M) were purchased from Pharmacia (Cat. No. 17-0851-0), cytochrome c from Sigma (Cat. No. C-6913), and D-tyrosine from Sigma (Cat. No. T-3254). Pronase was obtained from Calbiochem (Cat. No. 53702). Rat MH_1C_1 hepatoma cells can be obtained from American Type Culture Collection and grown in Eagle's minimal essential medium with Earle's salts supplemented with 10% fetal calf serum, penicillin (100 U/ml), and streptomycin (100 μg/ml) at 37°C in humidified air containing 5% CO_2. Cell monolayers were used at approximately 90% confluence, and the medium was replaced the day before each experiment.

III. Procedures

A. RADIOLABELING OF THE LIGAND

Reagents

1. *Iodo-gen tubes:* Prepare according to manufacturer's instructions and store under vacuum at room temperature. They can be stored indefinitely.

2. *D-Tyrosine solution (10 mg/ml):* Prepare in water, store at +4°C, and use to quench the iodination reaction.

3. *Cytochrome c solution (20 mg/ml):* Prepare in phosphate-buffered saline, store at +4°C, and use as a void volume marker. Both solutions 2 and 3 should be filtered (0.22 μm) and can be stored at least for 3 months at +4°C.

Steps

1. Perform the iodination at room temperature. While preparing the reagents for iodination equilibrate the PD-10 column with three column volumes of phosphate-buffered saline containing 0.01% (v/v) Tween 80 (PBS/Tween).

2. Make sure that the iodination area is properly shielded and ventilated.

3. Into the Iodo-gen tube add 50 μg of tPA, 0.5 *M* sodium phosphate buffer, pH 7.4, and 1 mCi of ^{125}I in this order, acquiring a final reaction volume of 100–200 μl. Mix with gentle swirling; allow the reaction to proceed 10 min.

4. Transfer the entire reaction mixture into a new tube containing 20 μl of the D-tyrosine solution and mix well by pipetting up and down.

5. Add 20 μl of the cytochrome c solution into the above tube and mix well.

6. Spread the entire mixture as evenly as possible on the top of the PD-10 column and allow it to descend into the column before twice applying 200 μl of PBS/Tween on top of the column. Then, fill up the column with PBS/Tween.

7. Start collecting just before the orange color of cytochrome c appears at the bottom of the column and continue collecting until the color begins to fade.

8. Bring the volume in the tube containing the labeled tPA to 1 ml with PBS/Tween, remove it to a shielded container, and store at +4°C.

9. Assess the amount of incorporated and unincorporated ^{125}I following the gel filtration step by preparing a separate vial with 700 μl of H_2O and 100 μl of bovine serum albumin (10 mg/ml) as carrier protein. Then, add 200 μl of 100% trichloroacetic acid (TCA), to precipitate the protein, and 2 μl of the mixture recovered from the column. Mix well and incubate on ice for 10 min followed by centrifugation (14,000 *g*) at +4°C for 4 min. Count the pellet and supernatant separately. The counts in the supernatant represent unincorporated ^{125}I. The amount of unincorporated should not exceed 2% of the total. The counts in the pellet represent incorporated ^{125}I and can be used to calculate protein specific radioactivity.

10. Dispose of all radioactive waste properly.

B. SATURATION BINDING ASSAY

Quantitative evaluation of unoccupied functional receptors involves determining the amount of ligand–receptor complex formed as a function of both time and concentration of ligand added. The equilibrium dissociation constant (K_d) is given by

$$K_d = \frac{k_{off}}{k_{on}}$$

The procedures described below allow the determination of ligand–receptor parameters for a cell surface receptor.

Solution

Ligand binding buffer: Phosphate-buffered saline supplemented with 0.2 m*M* $CaCl_2$ and 10 m*M* ε-aminocaproic acid.

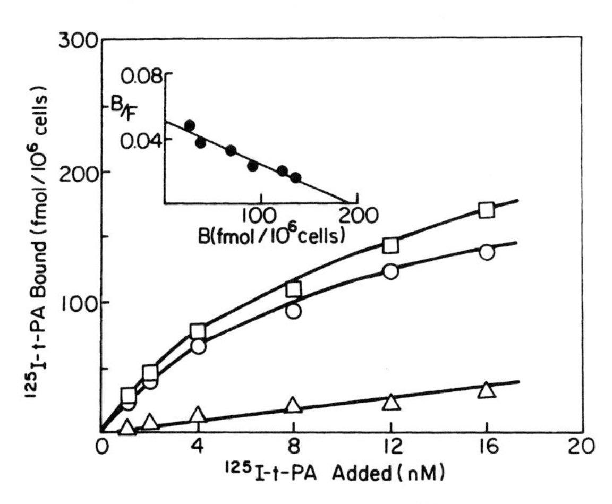

FIGURE 1 Saturation binding of ^{125}I-tPA to MH_1C_1 cells. The cells were incubated with increasing concentrations of ^{125}I-tPA in the absence or presence of excess unlabeled tPA as described in Section B. Total (*squares*) and nonspecific (*triangles*) binding was determined. Specific binding (*circles*) was derived as the difference between total and nonspecific binding. The results represent the means of triplicate determinations. *Inset:* Scatchard plot of specific binding.

Steps

1. Seed MH_1C_1 cells onto 12-well dishes to obtain a final cell density of 0.5–1.0 × 10^6 cells per well 2 days prior to assay. Change the culture medium the day before assay.

2. Cool the plates on ice and remove the culture medium.

3. Wash each well three times, employing swirling with 1 ml of ice-cold binding buffer.

4. Add 500 μl of binding mix containing increasing (up to 48 n*M* final concentration) amounts of ^{125}I-t-PA in binding buffer with or without an excess (500 n*M* final concentration) of unlabeled tPA into each well. The absence of excess unlabeled protein allows the assessment of total binding (specific plus nonspecific), and its presence, the assessment of nonspecific binding. (See Fig. 1 depicting the binding of ^{125}I-tPA plotted against its concentration in the binding mix as well as the respective Scatchard plot allowing the estimation of the equilibrium dissociation constant, K_d, and the maximal concentration of specific binding sites per cell, B_{max}).

5. The binding reaction is carried out at +4°C with gentle swirling of the plates for 90 min.

6. Move the plates back onto ice. Terminate the binding through suction of the binding mix and washing of the monolayers three times, swirling with ice-cold binding buffer.

7. Lyse the cell monolayers with 1 *N* NaOH for 10 min at room temperature.

8. Determine the amount of cell-associated ^{125}I-ligand by gamma scintillation spectrometry of the cell lysate.

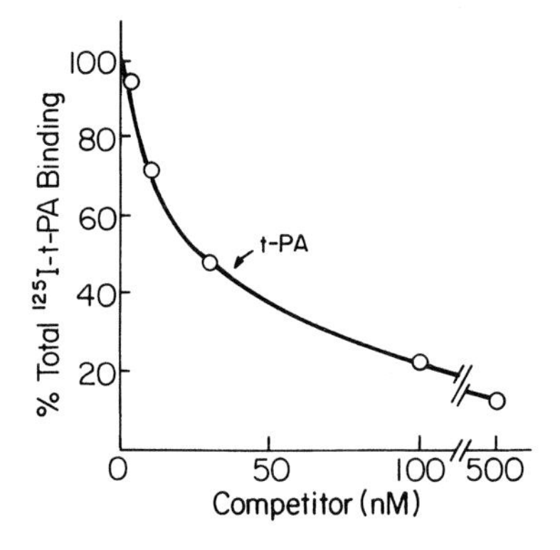

FIGURE 2 Competition binding onto MH_1C_1 cells showing inhibition of ^{125}I-tPA binding by increasing concentrations of unlabeled tPA. One hundred percent binding was determined without competitor protein.

C. LIGAND BINDING COMPETITION ASSAY

Solution

Ligand binding buffer: See Section B.

Steps

1–3. As in Section B.

4. Add 500 μl of binding mix containing a tracer amount (e.g., $\leq$1 n*M* final concentration) ^{125}I-tPA with or without increasing (up to 500 n*M* final concentration) amounts of unlabeled tPA into each well. The absence of unlabeled ligand allows the determination of total binding, and the presence of increasing amounts of unlabeled ligand, its competing effect on the tracer binding. (See Fig. 2 showing the percentage of total ^{125}I-tPA binding plotted against the concentration of unlabeled, competing ligand and allowing the estimation of the apparent K_i).

5–8. As in Section B.

D. LIGAND INTERNALIZATION: SINGLE COHORT KINETICS

Solution

Ligand binding buffer: See Section B.

Steps

1–3. As in Section B except that six-well plates were used.

4. Add 1 ml of binding mix containing ^{125}I-tPA in binding buffer in a final concentration of 5 n*M* into each well to allow binding to the cell surface pool of receptors. The binding is performed in either the absence or the presence of excess (1 μ*M*) unlabeled tPA for the determination of specific versus nonspecific binding.

5, 6. As in Section B.

7. Place the dishes at 37°C and simultaneously add 1 ml of a prewarmed (37°C) solution of unlabeled tPA in binding buffer in a final concentration of 200 n*M* into each well to initiate internalization of the prebound ^{125}I-tPA.

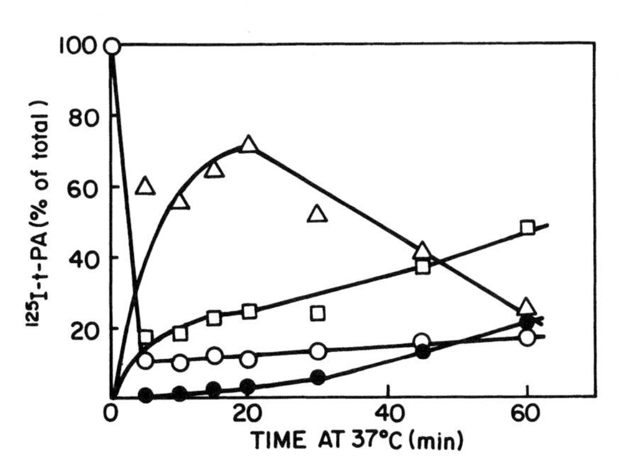

FIGURE 3 Distribution of ^{125}I-tPA during a single cycle of endocytosis in MH_1C_1 cells. Binding of ^{125}I-tPA to cells as well as incubation in the presence of excess unlabeled tPA at +37°C was performed as described in Section D. Changes in the relative amounts of plasma membrane-associated ligand (*open circles*), intracellular ligand (*triangles*), ligand dissociated from receptor (*squares*), and fraction degraded (*filled circles*) are shown. Results represent the specific signals (i.e., the difference in the absence and presence of unlabeled tPA) and means of triplicate determinations.

8. At 0, 5, 10, 15, 15, 20, 30, 45, and 60 min, cool one of the dishes directly on ice and recover the overlying solution.

9. Wash the cell monolayers three times with prechilled binding buffer.

10. Add 1 ml of a mixture containing 0.25% (w/v) Pronase in binding buffer into each well and incubate for 30 min at +4°C. The Pronase treatment results in the digestion of the membrane-associated ligand and allows the determination of cell-associated (i.e., Pronase-resistant) as well as membrane-associated (i.e., Pronase-sensitive) binding. (See Fig. 3 depicting in relative terms the changes in the different ligand pools during a single cycle of internalization.)

11. Remove the cells from each well.

12. Pellet the cells through centrifugation at 14,000 *g* for 5 min at +4°C.

13. Count the cell pellets (cell-associated binding) and the supernatants (membrane-associated binding) separately by gamma scintillation spectrometry.

14. Precipitate the overlying solution recovered in step 9 through the addition of bovine serum albumin up to a final concentration of 10 mg/ml and then 100% TCA up to a final concentration of 20% (v/v), followed by incubation of the mixture on ice for 10 min and centrifugation at 14,000 *g* at +4°C for another 4 min.

15. Count the TCA-soluble fraction (representing extracellular, degraded ligand) and TCA-insoluble fraction (representing extracellular, unbound ligand) separately (see Fig. 3.)

IV. Comments

The experimental procedures described above for ligand binding are designed for the basic evaluation of cell surface receptor K_d and B_{max} and therefore are conducted at +4°C to avoid ligand internalization and degradation. Parameters related to internalization and degradation of ligand via receptors participating in endocytosis are best evaluated at +37°C as described in Section D.

V. Pitfalls

1. Failure to store Iodo-gen tubes under vacuum results in reagent degradation and ineffective iodination.
2. Failure to spread the iodination solution evenly on top of the column results in unnecessary dilution of the labeled peptide.
3. When washing cell monolayers, to avoid detaching the cells pipette the washing solution along the wall of the well instead of directly on the cells.
4. Remove the washing solution promptly to minimize ligand dissociation during the wash.
5. Perform all cell surface studies on ice to avoid ligand internalization at temperatures above +4°C.

REFERENCES

Bu, G., Morton, P. A., and Schwartz, A. L. (1992a) Identification and partial characterization by chemical cross-linking of a binding protein for tissue-type plasminogen activator (t-PA) on rat hepatoma cells. *J. Biol. Chem.* **267**, 15595–15602.

Bu, G., Williams, S., Strickland, D. K., and Schwartz, A. L. (1992b) Low density lipoprotein receptor related protein/alpha2-macroglobulin receptor is an hepatic receptor for tissue-type plasminogen activator. *Proc. Natl. Acad. Sci. USA* **89**, 7427–7431.

Goldstein, J. L., Basu, S. K., and Brown, M. S. (1983) Receptor-mediated endocytosis of low-density lipoprotein in cultured cells. *In* "Methods in Enzymology," (S. Fleischer and B. Fleischer, eds.), Vol. 98, pp. 241–260. Academic Press, New York.

Hulme, E. C. (ed.) (1990) "Receptor Biochemistry: A Practical Approach." IRL Press, Oxford.

Limbird, L. E. (1986) "Cell Surface Receptors: A Short Course on Theory and Methods." Martinus Nijhoff, Boston.

Owensby, D. A., Morton, P. A., and Schwartz, A. L. (1989) Quantitative evaluation of receptor-mediated endocytosis. *In* "Methods in Cell Biology" (A. M. Tartakoff, ed.), Vol. 32, pp. 305–328. Academic Press, New York.

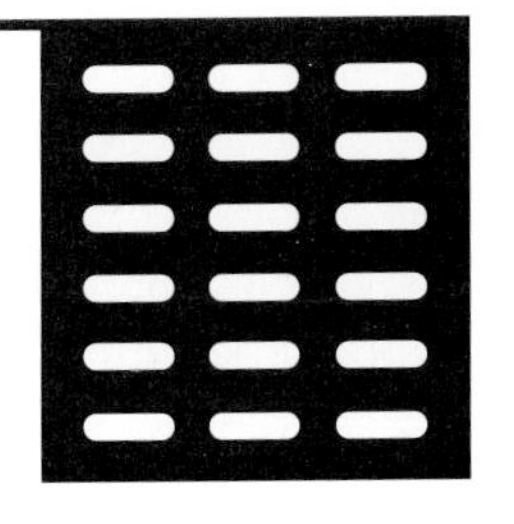

Identification of Cell Surface Binding Proteins via Covalent Crosslinking

Guojun Bu and Alan L. Schwartz

I. Introduction

Covalent crosslinking, also called chemical crosslinking, involves the introduction of covalent bonds via chemical crosslinkers between tightly associated neighboring molecules. It is commonly used as a coupling procedure to conjugate proteins, as well as to identify cell surface binding proteins. Among different types of crosslinkers, *N*-hydroxysuccinimide (NHS) esters (especially the water-soluble sulfo-NHS esters) have been widely used to crosslink ligands and their cell surface binding proteins due to their reactivity at physiological pH and relatively long half-lives in aqueous solution (Staros, 1988). NHS homofunctional crosslinkers react with primary amines of proteins such as the ϵ-amino groups on lysines and available N-terminal amines. Analysis of crosslinked ligand-binding protein complexes via polyacrylamide gel electrophoresis (PAGE) enables one to identify the molecular nature of the specific cell surface ligand-binding proteins.

In choosing a crosslinker for a particular application, several properties must be considered including its size, water solubility, membrane permeability, and thiol cleavability. Table I lists four commonly used crosslinkers along with their important properties. All of these crosslinkers are available from Pierce Chemical Company.

To identify cell surface ligand-binding proteins, two different approaches to crosslinking may be employed. Figure 1 illustrates these two strategies which we have used successfully to identify the tissue-type plasminogen activator (tPA)-binding protein on hepatoma cells (Bu *et al.*, 1992): either radiolabeled tPA crosslinked to unlabeled cells, or unlabeled tPA crosslinked to [^{35}S]methionine metabolically labeled cells. Each of these two approaches is separately described in detail.

II. Materials and Instrumentation

Crosslinker dithiobis(sulfosuccinimidylpropionate) (DTSSP) was obtained from Pierce Chemical Company (Cat. No. 21577 G). [^{35}S]Methionine was purchased from Amersham (specific activity > 1000 Ci/mmole, Cat. No. SJ. 1015). Single-chain recombinant human tPA was from Genentech. Rabbit anti-tPA antibody was generated against recombinant human tPA. Reagents for tPA iodination are described in the article by Kim Vettenranta, Guojun Bu, and Alan L. Schwartz.

III. Procedures

Solutions

1. *PBSc:* Phosphate-buffered saline (PBS) supplemented with 1 m*M* $CaCl_2$, 0.5 m*M* $MgCl_2$. To make 1 liter of the solution, add 100 ml of 10× PBS, 10 ml of

TABLE I

Crosslinker	Size (Å)	Water soluble	Membrane permeable	Thiol cleavable	Application
DSP	12.0	No	Yes	Yes	Laburthe *et al.*, 1984 Park *et al.*, 1986
DTSSP	12.0	Yes	No	Yes	Bu *et al.*, 1992 Lee and Conrad, 1985
DSS	11.4	No	Yes	No	Kull *et al.*, 1985 Wood and O'Dorisio, 1985
BS^3	11.4	Yes	No	No	Staros *et al.*, 1987 D'Souza *et al.*, 1988

[a] DTSSP, dithiobis(sulfosuccinimidylpropionate); DSP, dithiobis(succinimidylpropionate); DSS, disuccinimidyl suberate; BS^3, Bis(sulfosuccinimidyl) suberate.

$CaCl_2$ and $MgCl_2$ stock (100 m*M* $CaCl_2$ and 50 m*M* $MgCl_2$ in water). Bring the final volume to 1 liter with deionized water. Store at 4°C.

2. *Ligand binding buffer:* PBSc with 10 m*M* ϵ-amino-*n*-caproic acid (EACA). To make 1 liter of the solution, see above for PBSc, except add 10 ml of 100× stock of EACA (1 *M* EACA in water) before bringing the final volume to 1 liter. Store at 4°C.

3. *Crosslinking solution:* PBSc containing 0.5 m*M* DTSSP. Prepare the solution freshly just prior to use.

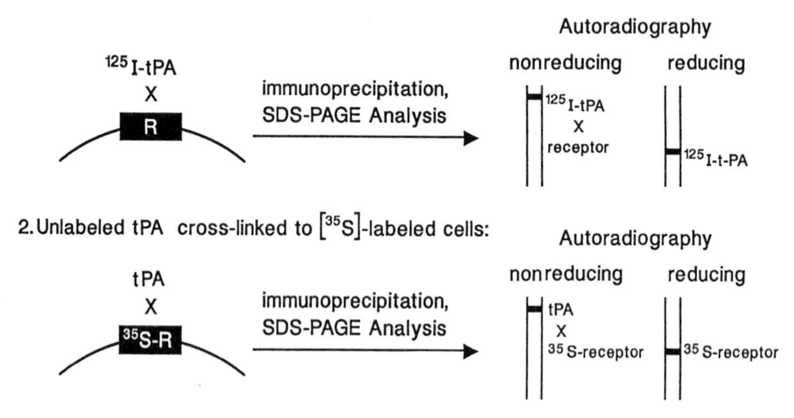

FIGURE 1 **Two strategies of tPA crosslinking to its binding protein with DTSSP.** *Strategy 1. ^{125}I-tPA crosslinked to unlabeled cells:* Binding of ^{125}I-tPA to its cell surface receptor was performed, followed by chemical crosslinking with the thiol-cleavable crosslinker DTSSP. After immunoprecipitation with anti-tPA antibody, the crosslinked complexes were analyzed by SDS–PAGE under both nonreducing and reducing conditions, and the resulting gels were subjected to autoradiography. Under nonreducing conditions, the crosslinked complexes remained associated and their molecular size should be equivalent to the sum of ^{125}I-tPA and its receptor. Under reducing conditions, however, the crosslinked complexes were cleaved to individual molecular. In this case, only radioactive ^{125}I-tPA is observable; the receptor is not because it is not radiolabeled. *Strategy 2. Unlabeled tPA crosslinked to ^{35}S-labeled cells:* Binding of unlabeled tPA to its cell surface receptor was performed, followed by crosslinking, immunoprecipitation, SDS–PAGE analysis, and autoradiography. Under nonreducing conditions, the observed crosslinked complexes shared the same migration with those in *strategy 1,* except the radioactivity in this case came from ^{35}S-labeled receptor. Under reducing conditions, the observed band was the cell surface, ^{35}S-labeled tPA-binding protein.

4. *Tris-buffered saline (TBS):* 50 m*M* Tris–HCl, pH 7.4, 100 m*M* NaCl. Store at 4°C.

5. *Lysis solution:* PBSc containing 1% (v/v) Triton X-100 and 1 m*M* PMSF. Make fresh cold and chill on ice before use.

6. *Immunomix:* PBSc containing 1% (v/v) Triton X-100, 0.5% (w/v) sodium deoxycholate, 1% (w/v) SDS, 0.5% (w/v) bovine serum albumin, 1 m*M* PMSF. Make fresh cold and chilled on ice before use.

7. *Laemmli sample buffer:* 62.5 m*M* Tris–HCl, pH 6.8, 2% (w/v) SDS, 10% (v/v) glycerol.

A. ^{125}I-tPA CROSSLINKED TO UNLABELED CELLS

Steps

1. Plate rat hepatoma MH_1C_1 cells into four 10-cm dishes 2 days before the experiment. Feed the cells 16 hr before use. Cells should be about 80–90% confluent at the time of experiments.

2. Iodinate tPA as described in the article by Vettenranta *et al.*

3. Perform ^{125}I-tPA binding (10 n*M*) to MH_1C_1 cells in the absence (two dishes) and the presence (two dishes) of excess unlabeled tPA (1 μM) at 4°C as described in the article by Vettenranta *et al.*

4. After ligand binding, place dishes on ice. Wash cell monolayers three times with prechilled PBSc. After the last wash, into one dish without and one dish with excess unlabeled tPA, add 4 ml of PBSc without crosslinker as nonspecific crosslinking control, into the other two dishes add 4 ml of freshly prepared crosslinking solution containing 0.5 m*M* DTSSP. Incubate 30 min at 4°C.

5. Place dishes back on ice. Wash cell monolayers two times with prechilled TBS to quench the crosslinking reaction.

6. To solubilize the cells, add 2 ml of lysis solution into each dish. Scrape cells off the dish with cell scraper. Pipette up and down the cell lysates several times to assist cell lysis.

7. Transfer the cell lysates into 12 mm × 10 cm glass tubes. Incubate on ice for 30 min; vortex every 5 min. Sonicate the cell lysates for 10 sec.

8. Aliquot each cell lysate into four microfuge tubes with 0.5 ml per tube. To each tube, add 0.5 ml immunomix. Mix well by vortexing.

9. Add 10 μg rabbit anti-tPA total IgG. The other three tubes from each lysate can be frozen and used later, or they can be used for immunoprecipitation with other antibodies.

10. Rock samples in microfuge tubes at 4°C overnight.

11. Next morning, add 50 μl of protein A–agarose beads into each tube. Rock for additional hour at room temperature.

12. Wash protein A–agarose beads three times with immunomix and three times with PBSc. For each washing step, add 1 ml of washing solution, mix well, spin 20 sec in microcentrifuge, and aspirate supernatant.

13. With PBSc in the last wash, divide each sample into two equal parts. After washing, add to one bead pellet 50 μl Laemmli sample buffer without β-mercaptoethanol (β-ME), and add to the other sample 50 μl Laemmli sample buffer with β-ME to reduce the crosslinker. Boil for 5 min, and spin for 30 sec.

14. Analyze samples with SDS–PAGE as described in the article by Julio E.

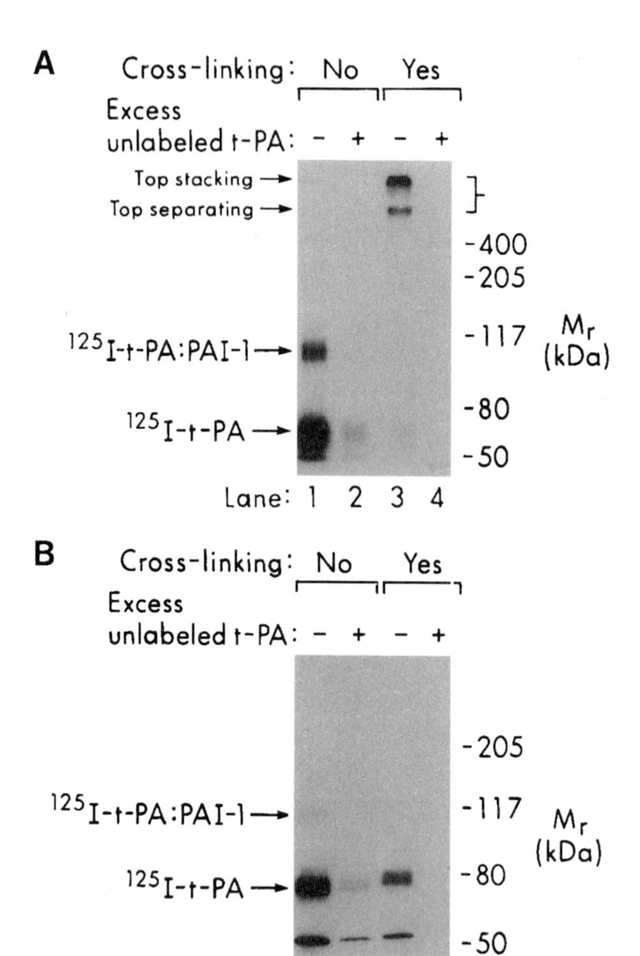

FIGURE 2 **Chemical crosslinking of ^{125}I-tPA to MH_1C_1 cells.** Binding of ^{125}I-tPA was performed in the absence and the presence of excess unlabeled tPA (1 μM). After 1.5 hr at 4°C, cells either were lysed directly without crosslinking or were lysed after the ligand has been crosslinked to its binding protein with 0.5 m*M* DTSSP. Cell lysates without or with crosslinking were then immunoprecipitated with anti-tPA antibody and analyzed by SDS–PAGE (6% acrylamide) under nonreducing (*A*) or reducing (*B*) conditions. The region of crosslinked material is marked with a *bracket*. The positions of ^{125}I-tPA and ^{125}I-tPA complexed with plasminogen activator inhibitor (PAI-1) are indicated.

Celis and Eyδfinnur Olsen. Dry gels and perform autoradiography. Results are shown in Fig. 2.

B. UNLABELED tPA CROSSLINKED TO ^{35}S-LABELED CELLS

Steps

1. As in Section **A**, *step 1*, except only two dishes of MH_1C_1 cells are required.

2. Wash cell monolayers with prewarmed, serum-free Earle's minimum essential medium lacking L-methionine and containing 2 mM L-glutamine. Incubate the cell monolayers with the same methionine-free medium twice, 15 min each time.

3. Initiate metabolic labeling by adding the above methionine-free medium

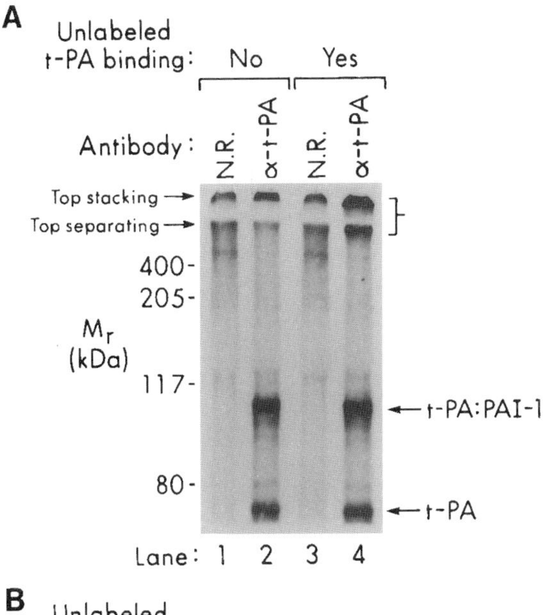

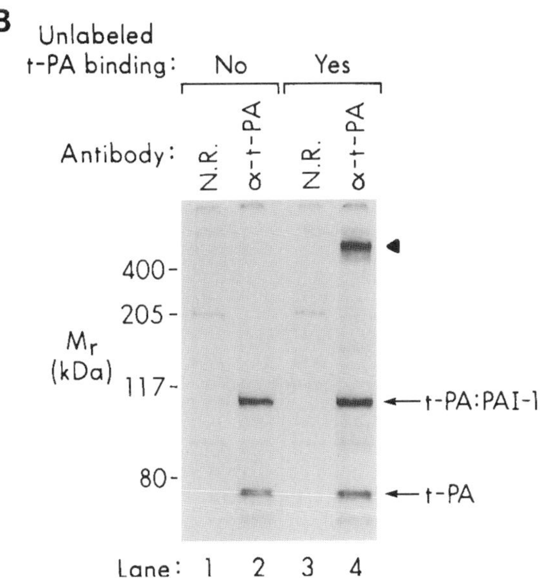

FIGURE 3 **Chemical crosslinking of tPA to [^{35}S]methionine-labeled MH_1C_1 cells.** MH_1C_1 cells were metabolically labeled with [^{35}S]methionine (200 μCi/ml). Following incubation for 5 hr at 37°C, cell monolayers were incubated in the binding buffer at 4°C without or with unlabeled tPA (10 nM). After 1.5 hr of incubation, cells were crosslinked with 0.5 mM DTSSP. Cell lysates without or with unlabeled tPA binding were immunoprecipitated with either normal rabbit serum (N.R., *lanes 1* and *3*) or anti-tPA antibody (α-tPA, *lanes 2* and *4*) and analyzed by SDS–PAGE under nonreducing (*A*) or reducing (*B*) conditions. The positions of tPA and tPA:PAI-1 complexes are indicated. The region of crosslinked material in the nonreducing gel is marked with a *bracket,* and the position of the tPA-binding protein in the reducing gel is indicated by an *arrowhead.*

supplemented with [^{35}S]methionine (200 μCi/ml). Incubate for 5 hr at 37°C in a cell incubator.

4. Wash cell monolayers with prechilled tPA binding buffer. Add to one dish just the binding buffer without ligand, and to the other dish, binding buffer containing unlabeled tPA (10 nM). Incubate for 90 min at 4°C.

5. Proceed with crosslinking for both dishes as described in Section **A,** *steps 4*

through 14, except cell lysates from each dish are immunoprecipitated either with normal rabbit serum as nonspecific control or with anti-tPA antibody. The results are shown in Fig. 3.

IV. Comments

Selection of an appropriate crosslinker is critical to the success of identifying cell surface receptors. Often, one should try several crosslinkers with different properties (see Table I). The ligand concentration for crosslinking should be just at subsaturation. Lower ligand concentrations will yield a weaker signal, and higher ligand concentrations will yield higher nonspecific background.

V. Pitfalls

1. Keep crosslinker desiccated.
2. Dissolve the crosslinker just prior to use. Do not reuse leftover, dissolved crosslinker that is more than half an hour old.
3. Do not oversonicate the cell lysates as this may shear some large receptor proteins.
4. Always include proper controls to make sure any crosslinked bands are specific for the analyzed ligand.

REFERENCES

Bu, G., Morton, P. A., and Schwartz, A. L. (1992) Identification and partial characterization by chemical cross-linking of a binding protein for tissue-type plasminogen activator (t-PA) on rat hepatoma cells. *J. Biol. Chem.* **267,** 15595–15602.

D'Souza, S. E., Ginsberg, M. H., Lam, S. C.-T., and Plow, E. F. (1988) Chemical crosslinking of arginyl–glycyl–aspartic acid peptides to an adhesion receptor on platelets. *J. Biol. Chem.* **263,** 3943–3951.

Kull, F. C., Jr., Jacobs, S., and Cuatrecasas, P. (1985) Cellular receptor for ^{125}I-labeled tumor necrosis factor: Specific binding, affinity labeling, and relationship to sensitivity. *Proc. Natl. Acad. Sci. USA* **82,** 5756–5760.

Laburthe, M., Breant, B., and Rouyer-Fessard, C. (1984) Molecular identification of receptors for vasoactive intestinal peptide in rat intestinal epithelium by covalent crosslinking. *Eur. J. Biochem.* **139,** 181–187.

Lee, W. T., and Conrad, D. H. (1985) The murine lymphocyte receptor for IgE III. Use of chemical cross-linking reagents to further characterize the B lymphocyte Fc_ϵ receptor. *J. Immunol.* **134,** 518–525.

Park, L. S., Friend, D., Gillis, S., and Urdal, D. L. (1986) Characterization of the cell surface receptor for a multi-lineage colony-stimulating factor (CSF-2α). *J. Biol. Chem.* **261,** 205–210.

Staros, J. V. (1988) Membrane-impermeant cross-linking reagents: Probes of the structure and dynamics of membrane proteins. *Acc. Chem. Res.* **21,** 435–441.

Staros, J. V., Lee, W. T., and Conrad, D. H. (1987) Membrane-impermeant cross-linking reagents: Application to the study of the cell surface receptor for IgE. *In "Methods in Enzymology"* (G. De Sabato, ed.), Vol. 150, pp. 503–512. Academic Press, San Diego.

Wood, C. L., and O'Dorisio, M. S. (1985) Covalent cross-linking of vasoactive intestinal polypeptide to its receptor on intact human lymphoblasts. *J. Biol. Chem.* **260,** 1243–1247.

SECTION C

Gel Electrophoresis

One-Dimensional Sodium Dodecyl Sulfate–Polyacrylamide Gel Electrophoresis

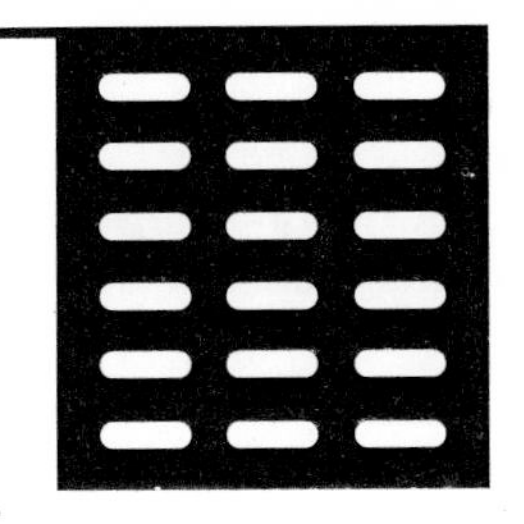

Julio E. Celis and Ey∂finnur Olsen

I. Introduction

Sodium dodecyl sulfate (SDS)–polyacrylamide gel electrophoresis has become one of the most used techniques for resolving and determining the apparent molecular mass of protein subunits. The SDS solubilizes insoluble proteins, making possible the analysis of otherwise insoluble mixtures. Here we describe the discontinuous gel system of Laemmli (1970) as well as a high-gel-density urea procedure for the separation of low-molecular-weight proteins (Schägger and von Jagow, 1987).

II. Materials and Instrumentation

Acrylamide (Cat. No. 161-0100), *N,N'*-methylenebisacrylamide (Cat. No. 161-0201), *N,N,N',N'*-tetramethylenediamine (TEMED, Cat. No. 161-0800), and ammonium persulfate (Cat. No. 161-0700) were from Bio-Rad. Glycine (Cat. No. G-7126), Tris–HCl (Cat. No. T-3253), Trizma base (Cat. No. T-1503), DL-dithiothreitol (DTT, Cat. No. D-0632), and bromphenol blue (Cat. No. B-6131) were from Sigma. Urea (Cat. No. 821519) was from Schwartz/Mann Biotech, and Nonidet P-40 (NP-40, Cat. No. 56009) was from BDH. SDS (Cat. No. 20763), N-tris(hydroxymethyl)methylglycine (Tricine, Cat. No. 37195), and Serva blue G (Cat. No. 35050) were purchased from Serva. Acrylamide (Cat. No. 10674) from Serva has also been used with essentially the same results. Glycerol (Cat. No. 4094), 2-mercaptoethanol (Cat. No. 15433), and Coomassie brilliant blue (R-250, Cat. No. 12553) were from Merck.

The gel dryer (Model 583) was obtained from Bio-Rad, the vacuum device (HETOSUC SUQ/3) from Heto, and the shaker (Red Rotor PR70) from Hoefer. The power supplies (EPS 500/400) were from Pharmacia-Biotech. The electrophoresis chambers were homemade, and the gel drying frames (Cat. No. 5030) and cellophane sheets (Cat. No. 5190) were purchased from Kem-En-Tec. Thin foils (clean TNP 0.25 mm) to cover gels while drying were obtained from Hestbeck.

III. Procedures

A. SDS–POLYACRYLAMIDE GEL ELECTROPHORESIS ACCORDING TO LAEMMLI

Solutions

1. *Acrylamide–bisacrylamide mixture:* 30% acrylamide, 0.8% bisacrylamide. To make 500 ml, add 150 g of acrylamide and 4.0 g of *N,N'*-methylenebis-

acrylamide. After dissolving, complete to 500 ml with distilled water. Store at 4°C.

NOTE

Acrylamide is toxic.

2. *Separating gel buffer (stock solution):* To make 1 liter of 1.5 *M* Tris–HCl, pH 8.8, add 181.7 g of Trizma base, dissolve in distilled water, and titrate with HCl. Complete to 1 liter with distilled water. Store at 4°C.

3. *Stacking gel buffer:* To make 1 liter of 1 *M* Tris–HCl, pH 6.8, add 121.1 g of Trizma base, dissolve in distilled water, and titrate with HCl. Complete to 1 liter with distilled water. Store at 4°C.

4. *10% SDS:* To make 1 liter, add 100 g of SDS and complete to 1 liter with distilled water. Store at room temperature.

5. *10% Ammonium persulfate (APS):* To make 10 ml, add 1 g of ammonium persulfate and complete to 10 ml with distilled water. This solution should be prepared just before use.

6. *N,N,N',N'-Tetramethylenediamine (TEMED):* Store at 4°C.

7. *Electrode buffer:* To make 1 liter of a 5× solution, add 30.3 g of Trizma base, 144 g of glycine, and add 50 ml of 10% SDS solution. Complete to 1 liter with distilled water. Store at room temperature.

8. *Sample buffer:* To make 50 ml, add 0.493 g Tris–HCl, 1 g SDS, 5.75 ml glycerol (87% solution), 2.5 ml 2-mercaptoethanol, and 0.5 ml of a 0.1% bromphenol blue stock solution. Dissolve in distilled water and titrate to pH 6.8 with HCl. Complete to 50 ml with distilled water. Store at room temperature.

Steps

1. Store clean glass plates in dust-free boxes (Fig. 1A, a). One of the plates is 16.5 cm wide and 20 cm high and has a notch 2 cm deep and 13 cm wide. Cover the edges of the plate with vaseline. Place 1.5-mm-thick polystyrene spacers (Fig. 1A, b) at the edges of the plate and cover with vaseline (Fig. 1B). When using a commercial apparatus follow the manufacturer's instructions for assembling the glass plates.

2. Assemble the rectangular glass plate 16.5 cm wide and 20 cm high together with the notched plate and the spacers. Make sure that the vertical spacers are in contact with the horizontal one at the bottom (Fig. 1B). Hold the assembled plates together with the aid of fold-back clamps (Fig. 1C). Mark a line 3 cm from the top of the notched plate.

3. Prepare the acrylamide solutions according to the values given in Table I.

4. Mix the solutions in a filter flask containing a magnetic bar. Stir and add APS and TEMED. Degas using a vacuum pump.

5. Pour the solution into the assembled plates and overlay with distilled water. Leave the gel solutions to polymerize for approximately 1 hr.

6. Remove the excess liquid and dry the top of the gel with a strip of Whatmann 3MM paper.

7. Prepare the 5% acrylamide solution for the stacking gel as described in Table II.

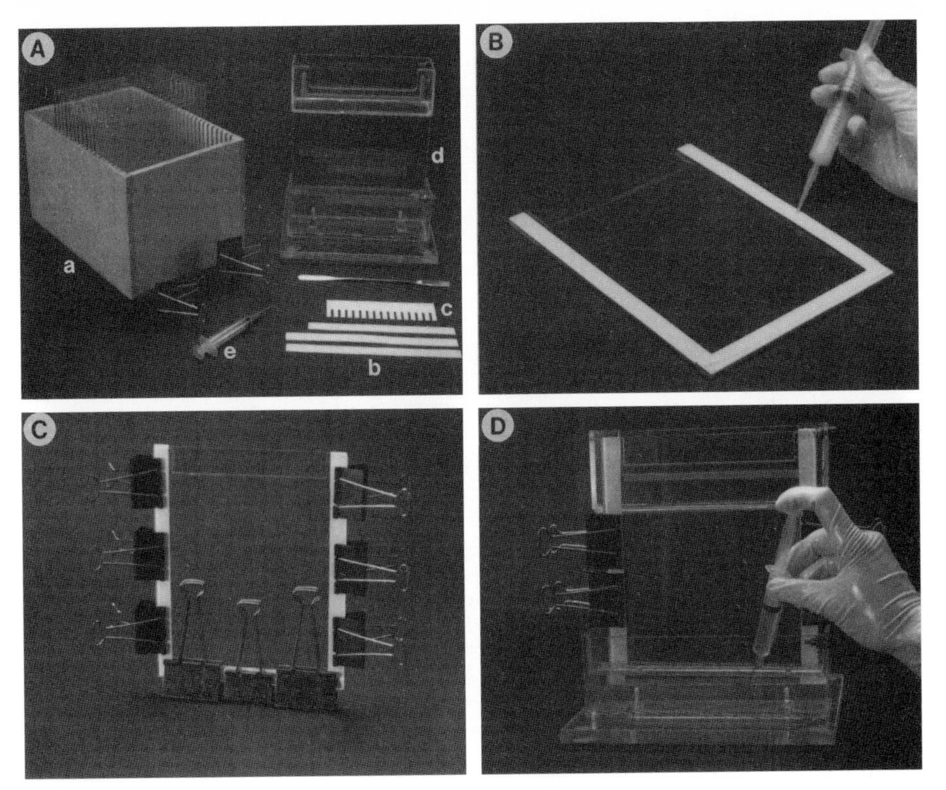

FIGURE 1 Material and equipment needed for one-dimensional electrophoresis. (A) Chamber, glass plates, spacers, and accessories needed to prepare gels. (B) Placing vaseline on top of the spacers. (C) Fold-back clamps to hold the glass plates. (D) Removing air bubbles from the bottom of the gel.

8. Mix the solutions in a filter flask containing a magnetic bar. Stir and add the APS and TEMED just before degassing.

9. Add the stacking gel solution after degassing and insert a polystyrene comb (Fig. 1A, c). Overlay the edges with distilled water. Leave the gel solutions to polymerize for approximately 1 hr.

10. When the gel has polymerized, remove the comb and clean the top of the gel with a strip of Whatman 3MM paper. Remove the clamps as well as the horizontal spacer at the bottom with the aid of a spatula. Clean the space between the two glass plates using a thin spatula covered with tissue paper.

11. Clamp the gel plates to the homemade electrophoresis chambers (Fig. 1A, d), which have been prefilled with 1× electrode buffer. Fill the upper chamber until the slots are submerged 0.5–1.0 cm. Remove air bubbles trapped at the bottom of the gel with electrode buffer using a syringe joined to a bent needle (Figs. 1A, e, and 1D). Apply the samples into the bottom of the wells using a micropipette fitted with a long narrow tip. Samples should be resuspended in sample buffer and heated for 5 min at 95°C prior to application.

12. Connect the electrodes to the power supply. Run the gels at 3 mA per gel at room temperature until the tracking dye has reached 1 cm from the bottom. At the end of the run, turn off the power supply, remove the plates, and disassemble them with the aid of a spatula. Remove the stacking gel with the aid of a scalpel and process for fluorography (see article by Julio E. Celis, Gitte Ratz, Bodil Basse, Jette B. Lauridsen, and Ariana Celis), silver staining (see article by Carl R. Merril, Janet E. Joy, and G. Joseph Creed), or Coomassie brilliant blue staining (see

TABLE I

	1 separating gel	2 separating gels	4 separating gels	6 separating gels
	15%	15%	15%	15%
30%, 0.8% mixture (ml)	17.5	35	70	105
1.5 *M* Tris–HCl, pH 8.8 (ml)	8.7	17.4	34.8	52.2
Water (ml)	8.3	16.6	33.2	49.8
10% SDS (ml)	0.35	0.7	1.4	2.1
10% APS (μl)	87.5	175	350	525
TEMED (μl)	8.8	17.6	35.2	52.8
Total volume	35	70	140	210
	12%	12%	12%	12%
30%, 0.8% mixture (ml)	14	28	56	84
1.5 *M* Tris–HCl, pH 8.8 (ml)	8.7	17.4	34.8	52.2
Water (ml)	11.8	23.6	47.2	70.8
10% SDS (ml)	0.35	0.7	1.4	2.1
10% APS (μl)	87.5	175	350	525
TEMED (μl)	8.8	17.6	35.2	52.8
Total volume	35	70	140	210
	10%	10%	10%	10%
30%, 0.8% mixture (ml)	11.7	23.3	46.7	70
1.5 *M* Tris–HCl, pH 8.8 (ml)	8.7	17.4	34.8	52.2
Water (ml)	14.1	28.2	56.3	84.5
10% SDS (ml)	0.35	0.7	1.4	2.1
10% APS (μl)	87.5	175	350	525
TEMED (μl)	8.8	17.6	35.2	52.8
Total volume	35	70	140	210
	7.5%	7.5%	7.5%	7.5%
30%, 0.8% mixture (ml)	8.8	17.5	35	52.5
1.5 *M* Tris–HCl, pH 8.8 (ml)	8.7	17.4	34.8	52.2
Water (ml)	17	34	68	102
10% SDS (ml)	0.35	0.7	1.4	2.1
10% APS (μl)	87.5	175	350	525
TEMED (μl)	8.8	17.6	35.2	52.8
Total volume	35	70	140	210
	5%	5%	5%	5%
30%, 0.8% mixture (ml)	5.8	11.7	23.3	35
1.5 *M* Tris–HCl, pH 8.8 (ml)	8.7	17.4	34.8	52.2
Water (ml)	19.9	39.6	79.6	119.4
10% SDS (ml)	0.35	0.7	1.4	2.1
10% APS (μl)	175	350	700	1050
TEMED (μl)	17.5	35	70	105
Total volume	35	70	140	210

Section C below). Gels can be used directly for blotting (see article by Julio E. Celis, Jette B. Lauridsen, and Bodil Basse).

13. Gradient gels can be prepared in any combination of acrylamide concentrations using a gradient maker and standard recipes.

TABLE II

	1 stacking gel	2 stacking gels	4 stacking gels	6 stacking gels
	3%	3%	3%	3%
30%, 0.8% mixture (ml)	1	2	4	6
1.0 *M* Tris–HCl, pH 8.8 (ml)	1.3	2.6	5.2	7.8
Water (ml)	7.6	15.1	30.3	45.4
10% SDS (ml)	0.1	0.2	0.4	0.6
10% APS (μl)	75	150	300	450
TEMED (μl)	7.5	15	30	45
Total volume	10	20	40	60

B. SDS–POLYACRYLAMIDE GEL ELECTROPHORESIS TO SEPARATE LOW-MOLECULAR-WEIGHT PROTEINS

This procedure is performed according to Schägger and von Jagow (1987). The composition of the gels is defined by the letters T and C, as described by Schägger and von Jagow (1987).

Solutions

1. *Acrylamide–bisacrylamide mixture:* 49.5% T, 6% C. To make 500 ml, add 232.5 g of acrylamide and 15.0 g of bisacrylamide. After dissolving, complete to 500 ml and store at 4°C.

2. *Acrylamide–bisacrylamide mixture:* 49.5% T, 3% C. To make 0.5 liter add 240 g of acrylamide and 7.5 g of bisacrylamide. After dissolving, complete to 500 ml and store at 4°C.

3. *Anode buffer:* 0.2 *M* Tris base, pH 8.9. To make 5 liters of the solution, add 121.1 g of Tris base. After dissolving in distilled water, adjust pH to 8.9 with HCl, and complete to 5 liters. Store at room temperature.

4. *Cathode buffer:* 0.1 *M* Tris base, 0.1 *M* Tricine, 0.1% (w/v) SDS, pH 8.25. To make 5 liters of the solution, add 60.6 g of Tris base, 89.6 g of Tricine, and 5.0 g of SDS. After dissolving, complete to 5 liters (adjustment of pH is not required). Store at room temperature.

5. *Gel buffer:* 3.0 *M* Tris base, 0.3% (w/v) SDS, pH 8.45. To make 1 liter of the solution add 363.3 g of Tris base and 3.0 g of SDS. After dissolving, adjust pH to 8.45 with HCl and complete to 1 liter. Store at room temperature.

6. *10% APS:* As in solution 5 of Section A.

7. *N,N,N',N'-Tetramethylenediamine (TEMED):* Store at 4°C.

8. *Glycerol:* 87% solution.

9. *Sample application buffer:* 4% SDS (w/v), 12% glycerol (w/v), 50 m*M* Tris base, 2% mercaptoethanol (v/v), 0.01% Serva blue G (w/v), pH 6.8. To make 50 ml, add 2 g of SDS, 6.9 ml of glycerol (87% concentration), 0.302 g of Tris base, 1 ml of 2-mercaptoethanol, and 500 μl of a 1% stock solution of Serva blue G, and adjust pH to 6.8 with HCl.

Steps

1, 2. See Section A, steps 1 and 2. Mark an additional line 5.5 cm from the top of the notched plate.

TABLE III

		1 separating gel	2 separating gels	4 separating gels	6 separating gels
		16.5% T, 6% C	16.5% T, 6% C	16.5% T, 6% C	16.5% T, 6% C
A	49.5% T, 6% C solution (ml)	11.7	23.4	46.8	70.2
	Gel buffer (ml)	11.7	23.4	46.8	70.2
	Water (ml)	1	2	4	6
	Urea (g)	12.6	25.2	50.4	75.6
	10% APS (μl)	175	350	700	1050
	TEMED (μl)	17.5	35	70	105
	Total volume (ml)	35	70	140	210
		16.5% T, 6% C	16.5% T, 6% C	16.5% T, 6% C	16.5% T, 6% C
B	49.5% T, 6% C solution (ml)	11.7	23.4	46.8	70.2
	Gel buffer (ml)	11.7	23.4	46.8	70.2
	Glycerol (ml)	4.4	8.8	17.6	26.4
	Water (ml)	7	14	28	42
	10% APS (μl)	175	350	700	1050
	TEMED (μl)	17.5	35	70	105
	Total volume (ml)	35	70	140	210
		16.5% T, 3% C	16.5% T, 3% C	16.5% T, 3% C	16.5% T, 3% C
C	49.5% T, 3% C solution (ml)	11.7	23.4	46.8	70.2
	Gel buffer (ml)	11.7	23.4	46.8	70.2
	Glycerol (ml)	4.4	8.8	17.6	26.4
	Water (ml)	7	14	28	42
	10% APS (μl)	175	350	700	1050
	TEMED (μl)	17.5	35	70	105
	Total volume (ml)	35	70	140	210
		10% T, 3% C	10% T, 3% C	10% T, 3% C	10% T, 3% C
D	49.5% T, 3% C solution (ml)	7.1	14.2	28.4	42.6
	Gel buffer (ml)	11.7	23.4	46.8	70.2
	Glycerol (ml)	4.4	8.8	17.6	26.4
	Water (ml)	11.6	23.2	46.4	69.6
	10% APS (μl)	175	350	700	1050
	TEMED (μl)	17.5	35	70	105
	Total volume (ml)	35	70	140	210

3. Prepare the acrylamide solutions according to the values given in Table III: 16.5% T, 6% C separating gels with 6 *M* urea (Table IIIA); 16.5% T, 6% C separating gels (Table IIIB); 16.5% T, 3% C separating gels (Table IIIC); and 10% T, 3% C separating gels (Table IIID).

4. Add APS and TEMED to the appropriate separating gel solution just before pouring into the assembled glass plates. Fill to the mark 5.5 cm from the top or up to the mark 2.5 cm from the top, if separation of proteins between 1 and 5 kDa is of minor importance.

5. Immediately add the "spacer" gel solution up to the mark, 2.5 cm from the top, and overlay with distilled water. Leave the gel solutions to polymerize together for approximately 15 min.

6. To make 10% T, 3% C "spacer" gels mix the solutions listed in Table IV.

7. Add APS and TEMED to the stacking gel solution just before pouring on top of the separating gel.

TABLE IV

	1 "spacer" gel 10% T, 3% C	2 "spacer" gels 10% T, 3% C	4 "spacer" gels 10% T, 3% C	6 "spacer" gels 10% T, 3% C
49.5% T, 3% C solution (ml)	1.8	3.5	7.1	10.6
Gel buffer (ml)	2.9	5.9	11.7	17.58
Glycerol (ml)	0	0	0	0
Water (ml)	4	8	16	24
10% APS (μl)	43.8	87.6	175.2	262.8
TEMED (μl)	4.4	8.8	17.6	26.4
Total volume (ml)	8.7	17.5	35	52.5

8. Remove the excess liquid and dry the top of the gel with a piece of Whatmann 3MM paper. Add the stacking gel solution and insert a polystyrene comb into the assembled plates. Leave the gel solutions to polymerize for approximately 1 hr.

9. To make 4% T, 3% C stacking gels mix the solutions listed in Table V.

10. When the gel has polymerized, remove the comb and the clamps as well as the horizontal spacer at the bottom with the aid of a spatula. Clean the space between the two glass plates using a thin spatula covered with tissue paper.

11. Clamp the gel plates to the homemade electrophoresis chambers, and fill the upper chamber with cathode buffer and the bottom one with anode buffer. Remove air bubbles at the bottom of the gel with anode buffer using a syringe joined to a bent needle.

12. Connect the electrodes. Run the gels at 20 mA/100 V per gel overnight (until the tracking dye has reached 1 cm from the bottom). At the end of the run, disassemble the plates and remove the stacking gel with the aid of a scalpel. Process the separation gel for fluorography (see article by Julio E. Celis, Gitte Ratz, Bodil Basse, Jette B. Lauridsen, and Ariana Celis), silver staining (see article by Carl R. Merril, Janet Joy, and G. Joseph Creed) or Coomassie brilliant blue staining (see Section C). Gels can be used directly for blotting (see article by Julio E. Celis, Jette B. Lauridsen, and Bodil Basse).

C. STAINING OF GELS WITH COOMASSIE BRILLIANT BLUE

Solutions

1. *Coomassie brilliant blue R-250:* To make 1 liter, weigh 1 g of Coomassie brilliant blue R-250 and add 500 ml of methanol and 100 ml of acetic acid. Filter and complete to 1 liter with distilled water. Keep at room temperature in a hood.

TABLE V

	1 stacking gel 4% T, 3% C	2 stacking gels 4% T, 3% C	4 stacking gels 4% T, 3% C	6 stacking gels 4% T, 3% C
49.5% T, 3% C solution (ml)	1	2	4	6
Gel buffer (ml)	3.1	6.2	12.4	18.6
Glycerol (ml)	0	0	0	0
Water (ml)	8.3	16.6	33.2	49.8
10% APS (μl)	125	250	500	750
TEMED (μl)	12.5	25	50	75
Total volume (ml)	12.5	25	50	75

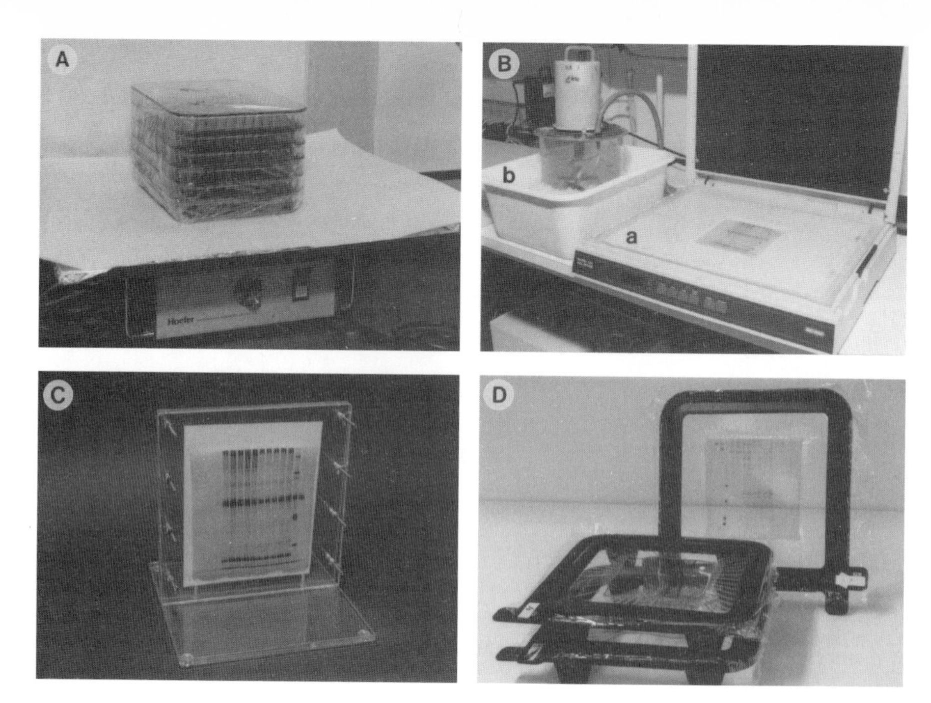

FIGURE 2 (A) Gels being stained with Coomassie brilliant blue. (B) Drying gels. (C) Flattening gels between two plates of acrylic. (D) Drying gels between cellophane sheets.

2. *Destaining solution:* To make 1 liter, add 350 ml of methanol and 50 ml of acetic acid. Complete to 1 liter with distilled water. Keep at room temperature in a hood.

Steps

1. Place gel in a rectangular pie dish and add the Coomassie brilliant blue solution. Cover with Saran wrap and shake for 8 hr in a hood (Fig. 2A).
2. Destain with several changes of the destainer solution.

D. DRYING GELS

1. Drying under Vacuum

Steps

1. Place gel on a piece of wet 3MM Whatman paper slightly larger than the gel placed on a Bio-Rad gel dryer (Fig. 2B, a).
2. Add a few drops of distilled water on top of the gel and cover with a thin plastic foil. Rub the surface of the plastic foil to eliminate bubbles.
3. Cover the sandwich with the gel dryer plastic and connect the dryer to a vacuum source (Fig. 2B, b).
4. Dry for 2 hr at 80°C.
5. Open the plastic cover slowly and recover the gel. Turn off the vacuum source and the dryer.
6. To straighten the gels place between two plates of acrylic as shown in Fig. 2C.

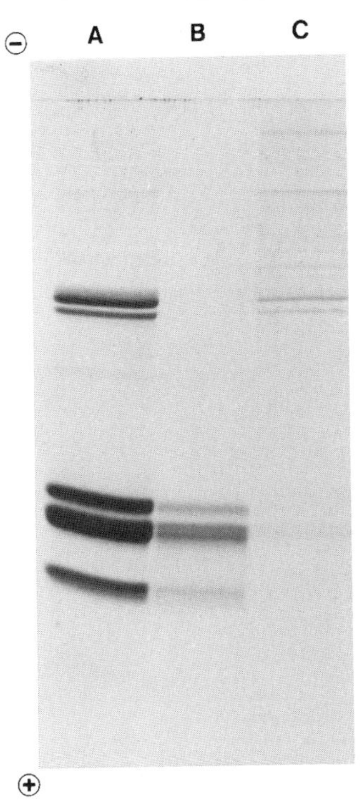

FIGURE 3 One-dimensional gel electrophoresis (Laemmli's, 15% acrylamide) of histone (A, B) and nonhistone (C) proteins.

2. Drying Gels between Two Pieces of Cellophane

Solution

3% glycerol in fluorography fixer.

Steps

1. Equilibrate the gel and two sheets of cellophane in 3% glycerol in fluorography fixer (see article by Julio E. Celis, Gitte Ratz, Bodil Basse, Jette B. Lauridsen, and Ariana Celis). Shake for at least 3 hr at room temperature.

2. Place the upper part of the frame upside down on the table. Cover the frame with one sheet of saturated cellophane and place the gel on top of the cellophane. Gently squeeze out air trapped between the gel and the cellophane sheet.

3. Cover the gel with a second sheet of wet cellophane and snap the two parts of the frame together (Fig. 2D). This is done by turning the lower part of the frame upside down and pressing it onto the upper part on the table. Note that the handles of the frames must be positioned in the same corner.

4. The gel is dried in front of an air jet (2 hr) or by standing overnight at room temperature in a hood. Hot air from a heating fan may damage the frames. Use cool air only.

5. Several frames can be stacked on top of each other when drying multiple gels (Fig. 2D).

IV. Comments

Using the procedures described in protocol Sections IIIA and IIIB, it is possible to resolve proteins having apparent molecular weights between 1 and 1000 kDa.

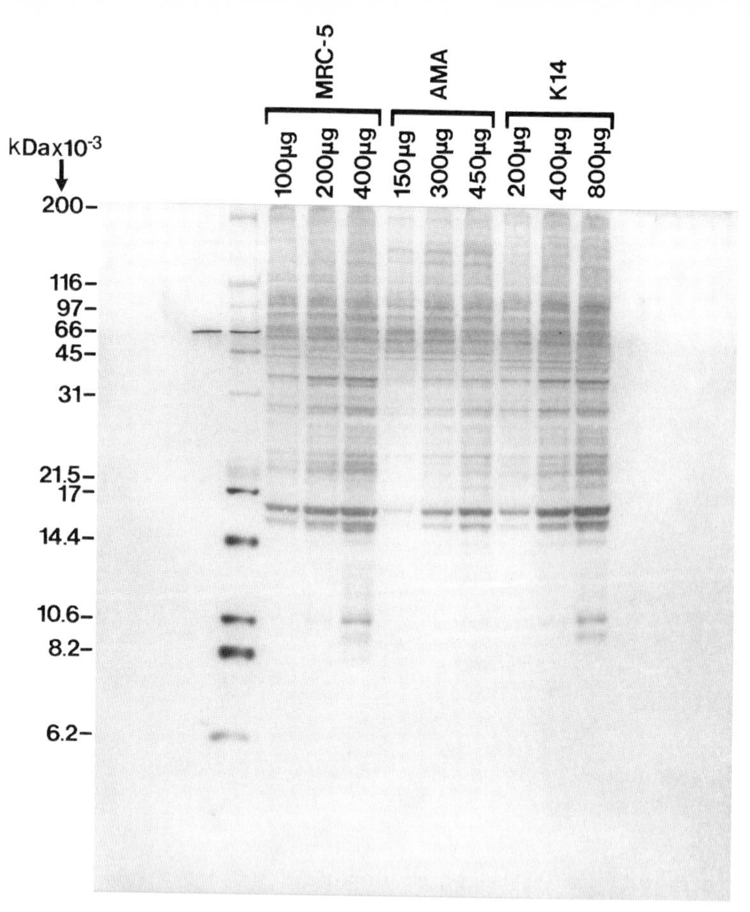

FIGURE 4 One-dimensional gel electrophoresis (Schägger and von Jagow, 1987; 16.5% T, 6% C separating gel, 2.5-cm "spacer" gel, and Tricine in the cathode buffer). From the left, the lanes were loaded with human albumin, molecular weight markers, MRC-5 (SV40-transformed human embryonal lung fibroblasts), AMA (transformed human amnion cells), and K14 (SV40-transformed human keratinocytes), amounts as indicated. Proteins were visualized by silver staining.

Figure 3 shows one-dimensional gels of histones (Figs. 3A and B) and nonhistone proteins (Fig. 3C) run in a 15% acrylamide Laemmli gel and stained with Coomassie brilliant blue. Representative silver-stained gels of 16.5% T, 6% of proteins from three different cell types are shown in Fig. 4. Serva blue G migrates as a broad band in front of the smallest proteins in the gels as described here. This is not always the case for the commonly used bromophenol blue.

V. Pitfalls

1. Use sterile, disposable pipettes to dispense solutions.
2. Make sure that all glassware is washed properly. Rinse with glass-distilled water before drying.
3. If the gels do not polymerize, check the TEMED and APS solutions. APS should be made fresh.
4. If the gels polymerize too fast, the concentration of the TEMED is most likely too high.
5. If the gels do not polymerize at the edges near the spacers, add less vaseline.

6. If the protein bands streak, lower the concentration of sample. Alternatively, dilute the sample with additional sample buffer.
7. If part of the bands does not move equally down the gel it is most likely due to air bubbles trapped between the plates at the bottom of the gel.
8. The pH of the gel buffer should be checked carefully. Preferably titrate and then leave overnight before retitrating again.
9. Remember to heat the samples at 95°C for 5 min prior to application.

REFERENCES

Laemmli, U. K. (1970) Cleavage of structural proteins during the assembly of the head of bacteriophage T4. *Nature* **227**, 680–685.

Schägger, H., and von Jagow, G. (1987) Tricine–sodium dodecyl sulfate–polyacrylamide gel electrophoresis for the separation of proteins in the range from 1 to 100 kDa. *Anal. Biochem.* **166**, 368–379.

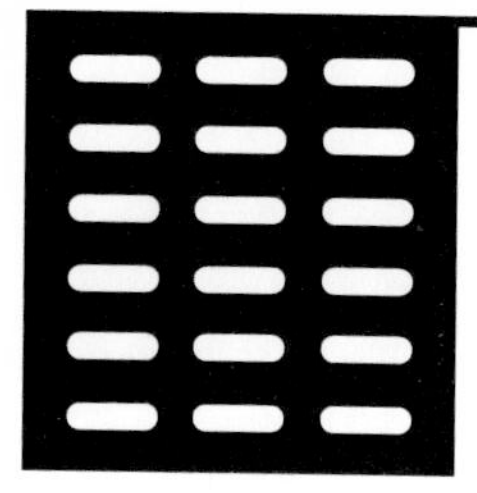

Nondenaturing Polyacrylamide Gel Electrophoresis (NPAGE) as a Method for Studying Protein Interactions

Daniel Safer

I. Introduction

Polyacrylamide gel electrophoresis was first performed under nondenaturing conditions, for the analysis of water-soluble serum proteins (Ornstein, 1964); electrophoresis in the presence of sodium dodecyl sulfate, however, soon became the most widely used electrophoretic technique for protein analysis both because of its applicability to a broader range of protein samples and because it directly gives an empirical measure of molecular weight (Weber and Osborn, 1969). NPAGE nonetheless remains a useful method for studying interactions between proteins and for characterizing multicomponent complexes. The system described here was developed for studying the formation of stable complexes between actin and actin-sequestering proteins (Safer, 1989); other recent applications of NPAGE have included studying the aggregation state of newly synthesized tubulin (Zabala and Cowan, 1992) and the formation of chaperone protein complexes (Langer *et al.,* 1992).

II. Materials and Instrumentation

NPAGE as described here has been performed in the "minigel" (8 × 10 cm) format using both homemade and commercial apparatus (Fig. 1) and an inexpensive voltage-regulated power supply, at 4–6°C. The commercial apparatus was from Hoefer (electrophoresis instrument, Model SE-250, and casting chamber, Model SE-275, Hoefer Scientific Instruments). Reagents are from Sigma: acrylamide (Cat. No. A-9099), *N,N'*-methylenebisacrylamide (Cat. No. M-2022), Bicine (Cat. No. B-3876), triethanolamine (Cat. No. T-1377), ATP (Cat. No. A-2383), EGTA (Cat. No. E-4378), *N,N,N',N'*-tetramethylethylenediamine (TEMED, Cat. No. T-9281), ammonium persulfate (APS, Cat. No. A-3678), and bromphenol blue (Cat. No. B-7021). Acrylamide and *N,N'*-methylenebisacrylamide from other suppliers have also been used, both as dry reagents and as preformulated solutions.

III. Procedure

Solutions

1. *Acrylamide solution:* 40% (w/v) acrylamide and 1.05% (w/v) *N,N'*-methylenebisacrylamide. To make 100 ml of the solution, add 40 g of acrylamide

Cell Biology: A Laboratory Handbook

FIGURE 1 Commercial (left) and homemade (right) gel casting and electrophoresis chambers.

and 1.05 g of bisacrylamide to 60 ml distilled water; after dissolving, adjust to 100 ml and store at 4°C.

2. *Buffer stock:* 1 *M* Bicine, 0.8 *M* triethanolamine. Triethanolamine is a very viscous liquid and is best measured by weight. To make 500 ml of the solution, weight 59.68 g of triethanolamine into a beaker and add 300 ml distilled water and 81.6 g Bicine; after dissolving, adjust the volume to 500 ml and store at room temperature.

3. *ATP stock:* The formula weight of ATP may vary from batch to batch, depending on the degree of hydration and the actual salt form. To make 25 ml of the 0.2 *M* stock solution, weigh out 5 mmole of ATP (about 3 g, depending on the actual formula weight), suspend in 20 ml distilled water, and adjust the pH with 1 *M* NaOH; the ATP will dissolve as the pH rises. Note that the buffer capacity drops rapidly above pH 6, and further addition of NaOH should be made cautiously. When the material is fully dissolved at pH 7, adjust the volume to 25 ml, freeze in aliquots, and store at −20°C.

4. *EGTA stock:* To make 100 ml of a 0.5 *M* stock solution, suspend 19.02 g EGTA in 75 ml distilled water and adjust the pH slowly with concentrated (at least 5 *M*) NaOH. The pH will rise rapidly with each addition, then drop as more EGTA goes into solution. The buffer capacity of EGTA drops precipitously above pH 6, and further adjustment should be made cautiously with 1 *M* NaOH, to a pH of 7.0–7.5. When the material is dissolved and neutralized, adjust the volume to 100 ml and store at 4°C.

5. *APS:* A 10% (w/w) solution of APS is prepared fresh each day by adding 0.9 ml distilled water to 100 mg APS.

6. *Bromphenol blue tracking dye:* To prepare a 0.05% solution, dissolve 5 mg of bromphenol blue in 10 ml of 50% glycerol and store at 4°C.

Steps

1. The "sandwich" of plates and spacers can be sealed by any standard method, such as sealing the edges with 1% agarose or enclosing it in a casting chamber. Thirty-three milliliters of gel solution is sufficient to cast four, 8 × 10-cm minigels, 0.75 mm thick, using the Hoefer SE-275 casting chamber. To make four gels, use 6.2 ml of acrylamide solution, 1.65 ml of buffer stock, 33 μl of 0.2 *M* ATP, 33 μl of 0.5 *M* EGTA, 24.75 ml of distilled water, 17 μl of TEMED, and 330 μl of 10% APS. The solutions are mixed and the gel is poured at room temperature. Pour the mix into the plate sandwiches, tap to remove air bubbles, and insert the combs. Polymerization should take 10–20 min; if polymerization is very slow or incomplete, it may be necessary to increase the amount of APS used.

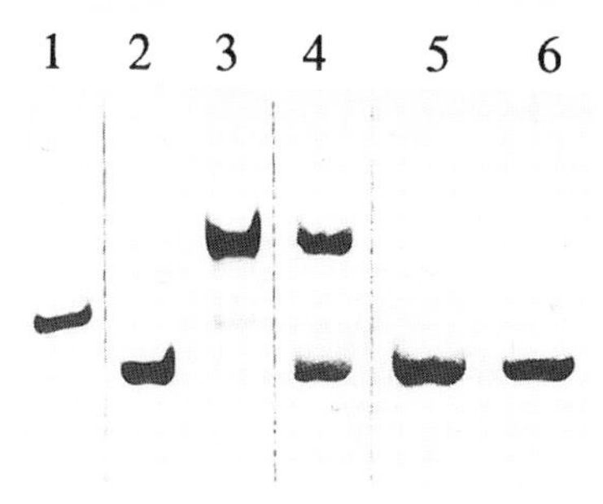

FIGURE 2 Nondenaturing PAGE. Lane 1, actin; lane 2, actin–thymosin β_4 complex; lane 3, actin–actin-depolymerizing factor complex; lane 4, chick embryo fibroblast lysate; lane 5, human platelet lysate; lane 6, chick embryo brain lysate. Lanes 1–3 were stained with Coomassie brilliant blue; lanes 4–6 were probed by immunoblotting with an antiactin antibody. Chick actin-depolymerizing factor was generously provided by Dr. James Bamburg.

2. The volume of electrode buffer required varies with different gel apparatus. Make twice the volume required to fill the apparatus, so that the buffer can be poured off and replaced following the prerun (see step 3). To make 500 ml, use 25 ml of buffer stock, 500 μl of 0.2 *M* ATP, 500 μl of 0.5 *M* EGTA, and 474 ml of distilled water at 4°C. Check the pH: it should be 8.2–8.3 at 4°C, and may be adjusted, if necessary, with 1 *N* HCl.

3. Prerun the gels for 1 hr at 140 V in the cold to remove residual catalyst, initiator, and acrylamide monomer, which can react with proteins. Discard the electrode buffer and replace with fresh buffer; then load the samples.

4. Pure actin should be loaded in the G-form. For other samples, a wide range of buffer compositions is allowable; e.g., cell lysates in physiological buffers, or fractions collected from chromatographic separations in low- or high-salt nondenaturing buffers, can be used directly. Samples should contain 5–10% glycerol to facilitate loading, and should be kept on ice until loaded. Bromphenol blue tracking dye can either be added to the samples (1 μl bromphenol blue solution per 10 μl of sample) or loaded separately in other wells; some proteins appear to bind bromphenol blue, and this might influence their migration.

5. After loading the samples, run the gels at 140 V in a cold room or refrigerator at 4–6°C; it takes 1.5–2 hr to run the dye to the bottom.

6. When the run is complete, the gels can be stained with Coomassie brilliant blue, processed for fluorography, or transferred to a membrane for immunoblotting (Fig. 2).

IV. Comments

This protocol was devised for investigating the interaction of actin with actin-sequestering proteins. In general, complexes having dissociation constants below 1 μM are stable enough for detection. The formation and stability of some actin-containing complexes is calcium dependent, and for some purposes we have prepared gels and electrode buffer containing 0.5 m*M* $CaCl_2$ instead of EGTA; other ions or effectors could similarly be incorporated into the gel and electrode buffer to investigate their effect on the stability of complexes. ATP is required to prevent actin from denaturing, and may not be necessary for studying other protein systems. Small variations in the pH of the electrode buffer cause major changes in the relative mobilities of different actin-containing complexes; in applying this procedure to other protein systems, it may be necessary to experiment with the pH to obtain the desired separations. The presence of nonionic detergent (1% Triton X-100, or Nonidet P-40, or 0.01% saponin) in the samples, or of 0.1% Triton X-100 in the gel itself, has no effect on the mobilities of water-soluble proteins and may be useful in extending this procedure to membrane proteins.

We have also used NPAGE as the first dimension of a two-dimensional separation, to identify the components of multicomponent complexes and determine their stoichiometry (Safer, 1989).

V. Pitfalls

The mobilities of proteins and protein complexes are affected both by the composition of the electrode buffer (concentration, pH, and presence or absence of divalent cations) and by the composition of the sample. Precise formulation of the electrode buffer is essential to obtain reproducible separations. While satisfactory separations can be obtained even with fairly high (up to 0.4 *M*) salt concentrations in the sample, high salt concentrations in a sample can significantly reduce the mobilities of proteins in that lane. Thus, where small differences in mobility are important, the concentrations of salt and buffer should be identical in all samples.

REFERENCES

Langer, T., Pfeifer, G., Martin, J., Baumeister, W., and Hartl, F.-U. (1992) Chaperonin-mediated protein folding: GroES binds to one end of the GroEL cylinder, which accommodates the protein substrate within its central cavity. *EMBO J.* **11,** 4757–4765.

Ornstein, L. (1964) Disc electrophoresis. I. Background and theory. *Ann. N.Y. Acad. Sci.* **121,** 321–349.

Safer, D. (1989) An electrophoretic procedure for detecting proteins that bind actin monomers. *Anal. Biochem.* **178,** 32–37.

Weber, K., and Osborn, M. (1969) The reliability of molecular weight determinations by dodecyl sulfate–polyacrylamide gel electrophoresis. *J. Biol. Chem.* **244,** 4406–4412.

Zabala, J. C., and Cowan, N. J. (1992) Tubulin dimer formation via the release of α- and β-tubulin monomers from multimolecular complexes. *Cell Motil. Cytoskel.* 23, 222–230.

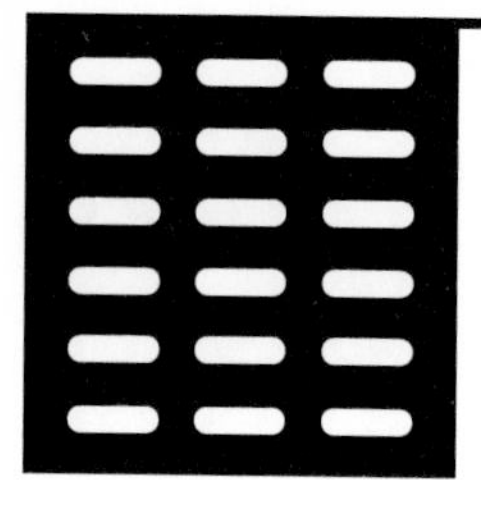

High-Resolution Two-Dimensional Gel Electrophoresis of Proteins: Isoelectric Focusing and Nonequilibrium pH Gradient Electrophoresis (NEPHGE)

Julio E. Celis, Gitte Ratz, Bodil Basse, Jette B. Lauridsen, and Ariana Celis

I. Introduction

High-resolution two-dimensional (2D) gel electrophoresis is today considered the method with the highest resolution for the separation of complex protein mixtures such as those present in eukaryotic cells (O'Farrell, 1975; Klose, 1975; O'Farrell *et al.*, 1977; Anderson and Anderson, 1978; Bravo, 1984; Celis and Bravo, 1984; Celis *et al.*, 1993). The technique, which separates proteins in terms of their isoelectric points and molecular weights, is commonly used to identify new cellular components (cytoskeletal proteins, organelle components, etc.) and to detect alterations in their expression using qualitative and quantitative comparisons (Celis and Bravo, 1984; Celis, 1991; see also articles by Angelika Görg; by Mario Gimona, Barbara Galazkiewicz, and Markus Niederreiter; and by Scott D. Patterson and James I. Garrels).

II. Materials and Instrumentation

Ampholines were obtained from Pharmacia Biotech AB (pH 3.5–10, Cat. No. 80-1125-87; pH 7–9, Cat. No. 80-1125-94; pH 8–9.5, Cat. No. 80-1125-95) and Serva (pH 5–7, Cat. No. 42905). Acrylamide (Cat. No. 161-0100), *N,N'*-methylenebisacrylamide (Cat. No. 161-0201), *N,N,N',N'*-tetramethylenediamine (TEMED, Cat. No. 161-0800), agarose (Cat. No. 162-0100), and ammonium persulfate (Cat. No. 161-0700) were from Bio-Rad. DTT (Cat. No. D-0632), glycine (Cat. No. G-7126), Trizma base (Cat. No. T-1503), and bromphenol blue (Cat. No. B-6131) were purchased from Sigma. Urea (Cat. No. 821519) was obtained from Schwartz–Mann Biotech, Nonidet P-40 (NP40) (Cat. No. 56009) from BDH, and SDS (Cat. No. 20763) from Serva. Acrylamide (Cat. No. 10674) from Serva has also been used for the second dimension with essentially the same results. DMSO (Cat. No. 2950) was from Merck and 2,5-diphenyloxazole (Cat. No. NEF 901) from NEN Du Pont. Filter-Count was from Packard.

First-dimension glass tubes (14 cm in length and 2 mm in inside diameter) were obtained from Bie & Berntsen. Prior to use they were washed with a solution containing 60 ml of alcohol and 40 ml of HCl. The glass tubes should be immersed in this solution for at least 30 min. Afterward they are washed thoroughly with glass-distilled water. Spacers were cut from 1-mm-thick polystyrene plates (Metzoplast SB/

Hk). First- and second-dimension chambers, as well as the rack to hold the first-dimension tubes, were homemade. Rectangular (24 × 19 cm) pie dishes were obtained from Corning (Cat. No. PX 385687), and X-ray films (X-Omat DS, 18 × 24 cm, Cat. No. 508 7838) were from Kodak. The scalpels (Paragon No. 11) were from Paragon, and the long (Cat. No. V2A 1415 LL-10) and short (Cat. No. V2A 1406 LL-7) needles from Acufirm.

The power supplies were from Pharmacia Biotech (EPS 500/400). The orbital shaker (Red Rotor PR70) was from Hoefer and the Microman pipettes (M25 and M50) were purchased from Gilson.

III. Procedures

A. PREPARATION AND RUNNING OF FIRST-DIMENSION GELS (IEF, NEPHGE)

This procedure is modified from those of O'Farrell (1975), O'Farrell *et al.* (1977), and Bravo (1984).

Solutions

1. *Lysis solution:* 9.8 *M* urea, 2% (w/v) NP-40, 2% ampholytes pH 7–9, 100 m*M* DTT. To make 50 ml of the solution, add 29.42 g of urea, 10 ml of a 10% stock solution of NP-40, 1 ml of ampholytes pH 7–9, and 0.771 g of DTT. After dissolving, complete to 50 ml with distilled water. The solution should not be heated. Aliquot in 2-ml portions and keep at −20°C.

2. *Overlay solution:* 8 *M* urea, 1% ampholytes pH 7–9, 5% (w/v) NP-40, 100 m*M* DTT. To make 25 ml of the solution, add 12.012 g of urea, 0.25 ml of ampholytes pH 7–9, 12.5 ml of a 10% stock solution of NP-40, and 0.386 g of DTT. After dissolving, complete to 25 ml with distilled water. The solution should not be heated. Aliquot in 2-ml portions and keep at −20°C.

3. *Equilibration solution:* 0.06 *M* Tris–HCl, pH 6.8, 2% SDS, 100 m*M* DTT, 10% glycerol. To make 250 ml of the solution, add 15 ml of a 1 *M* stock solution of Tris–HCl, pH 6.8, 50 ml of a 10% stock solution of SDS, 3.857 g of DTT, and 28.73 ml of glycerol (87% concentration). After dissolving, complete to 250 ml with distilled water. Store at room temperature.

4. *Acrylamide solution:* 28.38% (w/v) acrylamide (Bio-Rad) and 1.62% (w/v) *N,N'*-methylenebisacrylamide. To make 100 ml of the solution, add 28.38 g of acrylamide and 1.62 g of bisacrylamide. After dissolving, complete to 100 ml with distilled water. Filter if necessary. Store at 4°C and use within 3 to 4 weeks.

5. *NP-40:* 10% (w/v) NP-40 in H_2O. To make 100 ml of the solution, weigh 10 g of NP-40 and complete to 100 ml with distilled water. Store at room temperature.

6. *Agarose solution:* 0.06 *M* Tris–HCl, pH 6.8, 2% SDS, 100 m*M* DTT, 10% glycerol, 1% agarose, 0.002% bromphenol blue. To make 250 ml of the solution, add 15 ml of a 1 *M* stock solution of Tris–HCl, pH 6.8, 50 ml of a 10% stock solution of SDS, 3.857 g of DTT, 28.73 ml of glycerol (87% concentration), 2.5 g of agarose, and 2.5 ml of a 0.2% stock solution of bromphenol blue. Add distilled water and heat carefully in a microwave oven. Complete to 250 ml with distilled water, and aliquot in 20-ml portions while the solution is still warm. Keep at 4°C.

7. *1 M NaOH stock:* Weigh 4 g of NaOH and complete to 100 ml with distilled water. Keep at 4°C for not more than 2 weeks.

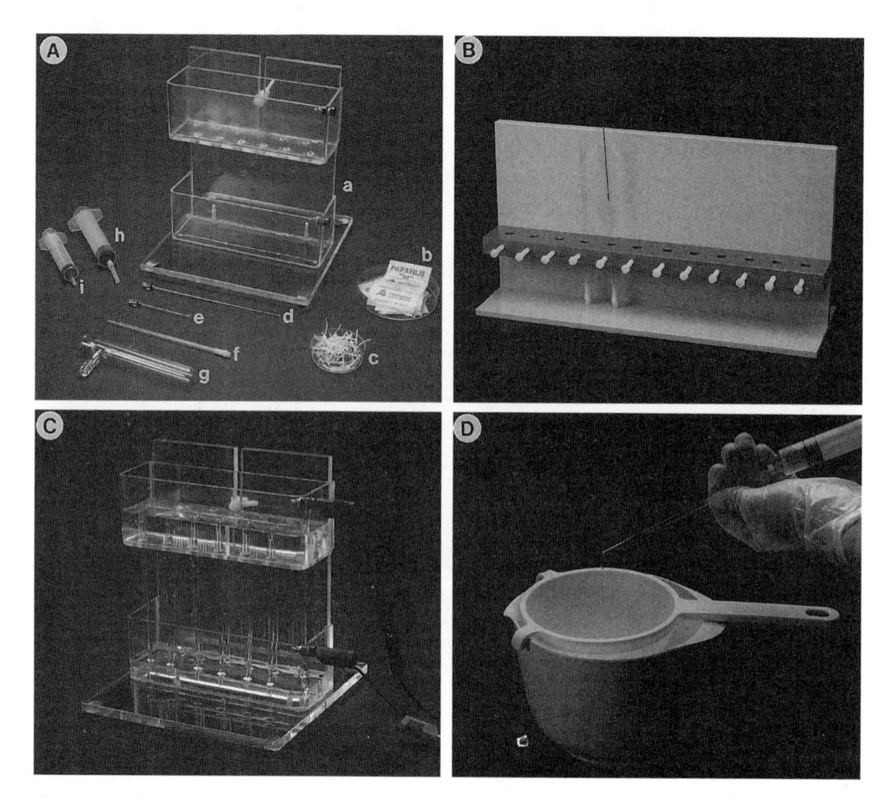

FIGURE 1 (A) First-dimension chamber and accessories for first dimension. (a) First-dimension chamber, (b) Parafilm, (c) paper strips, (d) long needle for filling the tubes, (e) short needle for extruding the gel, (f) first-dimension tubes, (g) vacuum tube, (h) syringe connected to a piece of rubber tubing, (i) syringe. (B) Filling the first-dimensional glass tubes with gel solution. (C) First-dimension chamber filled with tubes. (D) Extruding the first-dimension gel.

8. *1 M H_3PO_4 stock:* To make 100 ml, take 6.74 ml of H_3PO_4 (87%) and complete to 100 ml with distilled water. Keep at room temperature.

9. *20 mM NaOH:* To make 500 ml, take 10 ml of 1 *M* NaOH and complete to 500 ml with distilled water. Prepare fresh.

10. *10 mM H_3PO_4:* To make 500 ml, take 5 ml of 1 *M* H_3PO_4 and complete to 500 ml with distilled water. Prepare fresh.

Steps

1. Mark the glass tubes with a line (use a diamond-tipped pencil) 12.5 cm from the bottom (Fig. 1A, f). Seal the bottom end of the tube by wrapping with Parafilm and place it standing up in a rack (Fig. 1B).

2. Mix the solution containing urea, H_2O, acrylamide, NP-40, and ampholytes (kept at −20°C in 1-ml aliquots) in a tube containing a vacuum outlet (Fig. 1A, g). Swirl the solution gently until the urea is dissolved. The solution should not be heated. Add ammonium persulfate and TEMED, mix gently, and degas using a vacuum pump. Use a clean rubber stopper to control the vacuum.

To make 12 first-dimension IEF gels, use 4.12 g urea; 0.975 ml of acrylamide solution; 1.5 ml of 10% NP-40; 1.5 ml of H_2O; 0.30 ml of carrier ampholytes, pH range 5–7; 0.10 ml of carrier ampholytes, pH range 3.5–10; 7.5 μl of 10% ammonium persulfate; and 5 μl of TEMED.

To make 12 first-dimension NEPHGE gels, use 4.12 g urea; 0.975 ml of acrylamide solution; 1.5 ml of 10% NP-40; 1.5 ml of H_2O; 0.190 ml of carrier ampholytes, pH range 7–9; 0.190 ml of carrier ampholytes, pH range 8–9.5; 15 μl of 10% ammonium persulfate; and 10.5 μl of TEMED.

3. Pour the solution into a 58-mm culture dish. Aspirate the liquid with a 10-ml syringe and add to the thin glass tubes (Fig. 1A, f) placed in a rack using a long needle (Fig. 1A, d). Insert the tip of the needle to the bottom of the tube and slowly fill to the mark to avoid air bubbles while moving up the needle (Fig. 1B).

4. Overlay the gel mix with 10 μl of glass-distilled water and leave to polymerize for 45 min. In the meantime, fill the lower chamber of the first dimension (Fig. 1C) with 250 ml of 10 m*M* H_3PO_4 (IEF gels) or 250 ml of 20 m*M* NaOH (NEPHGE gels).

5. Take the tubes from the rack and remove the Parafilm using a scalpel. Remove excess liquid from the upper part of the tube by shaking and dry using a thin strip of Whatman 3MM paper (Fig. 1A, c). Insert the tubes into the chamber, which holds up to 12 tubes (Fig. 1C). Tap the tubes to remove trapped air bubbles.

6. Prerun IEF gels before adding the sample. First add 10 μl of lysis solution and then 10 μl of overlay. Use a Gilson Microman pipette to apply the solutions. Fill the tubes as well as the upper chamber with 20 m*M* NaOH. Prerun gels at room temperature for 15 min at 200 V, 30 min at 300 V, and 60 min at 400 V. After prerunning, disconnect the power supply and discard the upper and bottom solutions. Remove the tubes and wash the top of the gels with distilled water. Dry with a thin strip of Whatmann 3MM paper and apply the sample (up to 50 μl in lysis solution, in this case about one million hot trichloracetic acid-precipitable counts of [^{35}S]methionine-labeled proteins from transformed human amnion cells; see also the article by Julio E. Celis, Jette B. Lauridsen, and Bodil Basse). Add 10 μl of overlay solution and fill the tubes with 20 m*M* NaOH. Fill the upper chamber with 20 m*M* NaOH and the bottom one with 10 m*M* H_3PO_4. Run for 18 hr at 400 V at room temperature.

7. NEPHGE gels are not prerun. Add the sample in lysis solution (up to 50 μl, in this case about one million hot trichloracetic acid-precipitable counts of [^{35}S]methionine-labeled proteins from human epidermal keratinocytes) and cover with 10 μl of overlay solution. Add 250 ml of 20 m*M* NaOH to the bottom chamber and fill the tubes and the upper chamber with 10 m*M* H_3PO_4. Run the gels for 4.5 hr at 400 V at room temperature.

8. Before stopping the run, add 3 ml of equilibration solution to 35-mm tissue culture dishes labeled with the gel number in both the bottom part and the lid. Turn off the power supply and take the gels out with the aid of a syringe (Fig. 1A, h) filled with glass-distilled water. First, use a short needle (Fig. 1A, e) to loosen the gel at both ends of the tube. Then extrude the gel with the aid of pressure applied by a 20-ml syringe (Fig. 1D). Collect the gel in a sieve and place in the 35-mm culture dish containing the equilibration solution. Leave 2–5 min at room temperature and store at −20°C until use. Samples can be stored for at least 1 month under these conditions.

B. SECOND DIMENSION: SDS–POLYACRYLAMIDE (15%) GEL ELECTROPHORESIS

This procedure is performed according to Laemmli (1970). See also the article by Julio E. Celis and Eyδfinnur Olsen.

Solutions

1. *Solution A:* To make 500 ml, add 150 g of acrylamide and 0.75 g of bisacrylamide. After dissolving, complete to 500 ml with distilled water. Filter if necessary. Aliquot 100-ml portions and store at 4°C.

2. *Solution B:* To make 1 liter of 1.5 *M* Tris–HCl, pH 8.8, add 181.6 g of Trizma base and titrate with HCl. Complete to 1 liter with distilled water. Aliquot 200-ml portions and store at 4°C.

3. *Solution C:* To make 1 liter of 1 *M* Tris–HCl, pH 6.8, add 121.1 g of Trizma base and titrate with HCl. Complete to 1 liter with distilled water. Aliquot in 200-ml portions and store at 4°C.

4. *Solution D:* To make 100 ml, add 10 g of acrylamide and 0.5 g of bisacrylamide. Complete to 100 ml with distilled water. Filter if necessary and store at 4°C.

5. *10% SDS:* To make 1 liter, add 100 g of SDS and complete to 1 liter with distilled water. Filter if necessary. Store at room temperature.

6. *10% ammonium persulfate:* To make 10 ml, weigh 1 g of ammonium persulfate and complete to 10 ml with distilled water. This solution should be prepared just before use.

7. *Electrode buffer:* To make 1 liter of a 5× solution, add 30.3 g of Trizma base, 144 g of glycine, and 50 ml of 10% SDS solution. Complete to 1 liter with distilled water. Store at room temperature.

Steps

1. Store clean glass plates in dust-free boxes (see Fig. 1A in the article by Julio E. Celis and Eyδfinnur Olsen). One of the plates is 16.5 cm wide and 20 cm high and has a notch 2 cm deep and 13 cm wide. Cover the edges of the plate with vaseline. Use a 10-ml syringe filled with vaseline and fitted with a Gilson tip (Fig. 2A). Place 1-mm-thick polystyrene spacers at the edges of the plate and cover with vaseline (Fig. 2A). Place a small piece of paper without lines containing the gel number (written with pencil) at the corner of the plate (Fig. 2A).

2. Assemble the rectangular glass plate 16.5 cm wide and 20 cm high together with the notched plate and the spacers. Make sure that the vertical spacers are in contact with the horizontal one at the bottom. Hold the assembled plates together with the aid of fold-back clamps. Mark a line 2.5 cm from the top of the notched plate.

3. To make six 15% separation gels, mix the following solutions in a 250-ml filter flask containing a magnetic stirrer: solution A (acrylamide:bisacrylamide 30:0.15), 75.0 ml; 10% SDS, 1.5 ml; solution B (1.5 *M* Tris–HCl, pH 8.8), 37.5 ml; H_2O, 35.22 ml; 10% ammonium persulfate, 750 μl; TEMED, 30 μl.

4. Add ammonium persulfate and TEMED to the separation gel solution just before degassing using a vacuum pump. Pour the solution into the assembled plates until the marked line and overlay with distilled water. Leave the gels to polymerize for approximately 1 hr.

5. Remove the excess liquid and dry the top of the gel with a strip of Whatman 3MM paper (2 × 9 cm).

6. To make 5% stacking solution for six gels, mix the following solutions: solution D (acrylamide:bisacrylamide 10:0.5), 15.0 ml; 10% SDS, 0.3 ml;

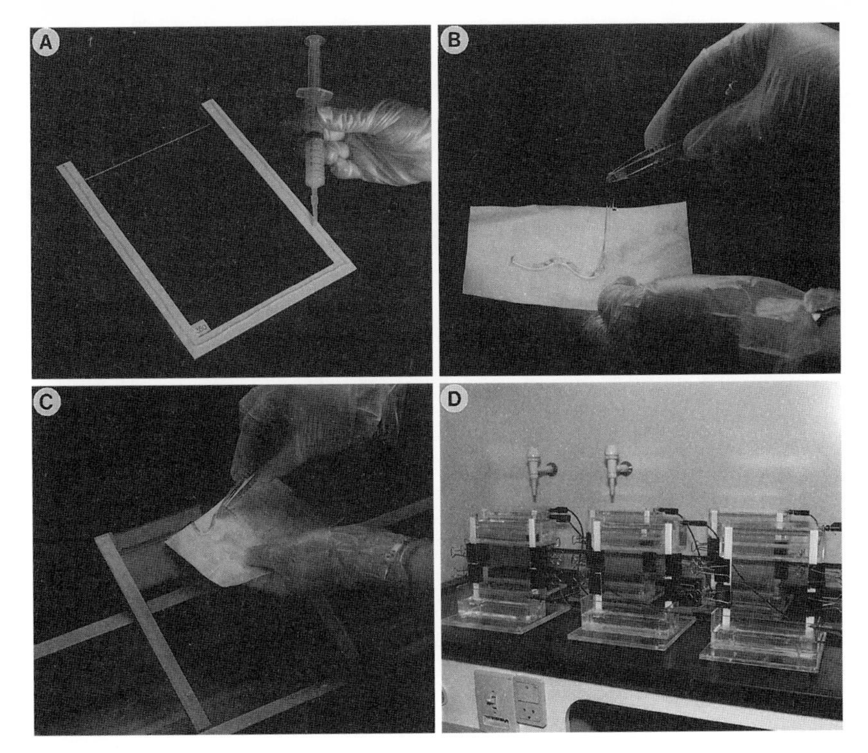

FIGURE 2 (A) Covering the spacers with vaseline. (B) First-dimension gel prior to application to second-dimension gel. (C) Application of first-dimension gel to second-dimension gel. (D) Second-dimension chambers.

solution C (1.0 *M* Tris–HCl, pH 6.8), 3.6 ml; H_2O, 10.8 ml; 10% ammonium persulfate, 0.24 ml; TEMED, 12 μl.

7. After degassing, add the stacking gel solution and insert a polystyrene spacer a few millimeters into the assembled plates. Keep in place with the aid of a fold-out clamp. Leave the gels to polymerize for approximately 1 hr.

8. When the gel has polymerized, remove the top spacer and clean the top of the gel with a strip of Whatman 3MM paper. Remove the clamps as well as the horizontal spacer at the bottom with the aid of a spatula. Clean the space between the two glass plates using a thin spatula covered with tissue paper.

9. Lay the gels at an angle to facilitate the application of the first dimension. Remove the culture dishes containing the first-dimension gels from the freezer 20 min before application. Once they are defrosted, melt the agarose solution in a microwave oven and immediately cover the top of the stacking gel with a small amount of agarose to fill the space left by the spacer.

10. Collect the first-dimension gel into a sieve and place it on a piece of Parafilm (Fig. 2B). Place the gel carefully on top of the second dimension with the aid of plastic tweezers (Fig. 2C). Do not stretch the gel. Cover the gels with 2–3 ml of melted agarose. Eliminate air bubbles by pushing them out with the same pipette.

11. Clamp the gel plates to the homemade electrophoresis chambers, which have been prefilled with 1× electrode buffer. Fill the upper chamber with enough electrode buffer to cover the agarose. Remove air bubbles at the bottom of the gel with electrode buffer using a 10-ml syringe joined to a bent needle (see Fig. 1D in the article by Julio E. Celis and Eyδfinnur Olsen).

12. Connect the electrodes to the power supply. Run the gels at 3 mA

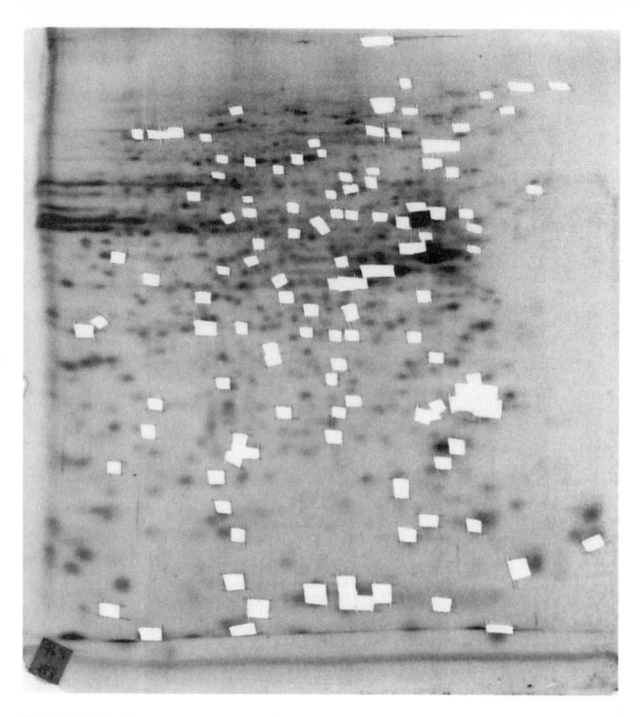

FIGURE 3 Cutting radioactive polypeptides from a 2D gel. Spots are identified with the aid of a fluorogram. The fluorogram is aligned on top of the dry gel with the aid of marks (X) made with radioactive ink.

overnight at room temperature (until the tracking dye has reached 1 cm from the bottom) (Fig. 2D). At the end of the run turn off the power supply, disassemble the plates, and remove the stacking gel with the aid of a scalpel. Process the separation gel for fluorography or for staining with either silver (see article by Carl R. Merril, Janet E. Joy, and G. Joseph Creed) or Coomassie brilliant blue (see article by Julio E. Celis and Eyðfinnur Olsen). Gels can be used directly for blotting (see article by Julio E. Celis, Jette B. Lauridsen, and Bodil Basse).

C. FLUOROGRAPHY

This procedure is from Laskey and Mills (1975).

Solutions

1. *Fixation solution:* To make 1 liter, add 450 ml of methanol and 75 ml of acetic acid. Complete to 1 liter with distilled water.
2. *PPO/DMSO:* To make 1 liter, weigh 4–5 g of diphenyloxazole (PPO) and complete to 1 liter with DMSO.

Steps

1. Place the gel in a rectangular pie dish (24 × 19 cm) and fix for 60 min at room temperature in fixative solution. Shake while fixing.
2. Place gel in 120 ml of DMSO and shake for 20 min.
3. Change to fresh DMSO and shake for 20 min.
4. Place gel in 120 ml of PPO/DMSO solution and shake for 2 hr.
5. Remove PPO/DMSO (save as it can be reused several times) and wash two times with water (15 min wash each time).

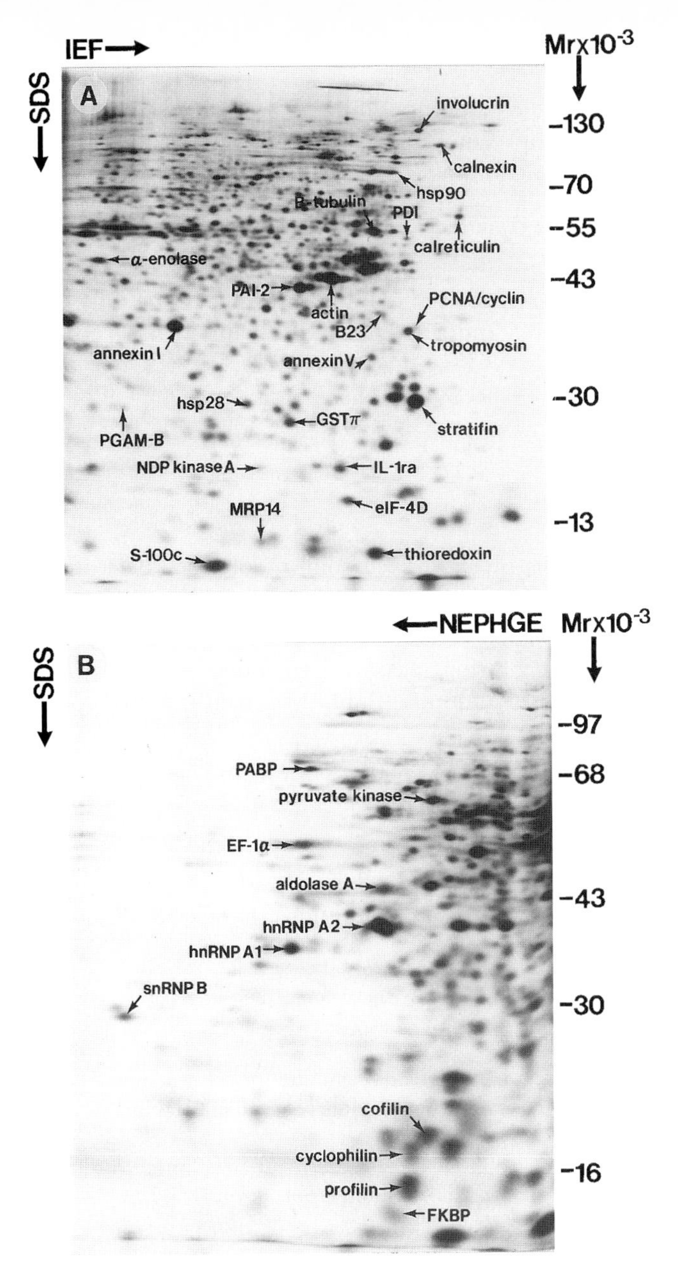

FIGURE 4 Two-dimensional gel fluorograms of [^{35}S]methionine-labeled proteins from primary normal human keratinocytes: (A) IEF, (B) NEPHGE. The identity of a few proteins is indicated for reference.

6. Dry gels as described in the article by Julio E. Celis and Eyðfinnur Olsen in this volume.
7. Preflush X-ray films in the dark (see the article by Amandio Vieira, Robert G. Elkin, and Karl Kuchler) and expose at −80°C in cassettes. Use intensifying screens for ^{3}H.

D. QUANTITATION OF [^{35}S]METHIONINE-LABELED PROTEIN SPOTS EXCISED FROM TWO-DIMENSIONAL GELS

Steps

1. Protein spots are localized with the aid of the X-ray film (Fig. 3). Before exposing, make four crosses at the corner of the gels using radioactive ink. Excise proteins from dry gels using a scalpel.

2. Place gel pieces in counting vials containing 4 ml of Filter-Count, leave for 1 hr, and count for 5 min in a scintillation counter.

IV. Comments

Using the protocol described in this article, it is possible to resolve proteins having apparent molecular weights between 8.5 and 230 kDa and p*I* values from 4 to 12. Representative fluorograms of IEF and NEPHGE gels of human keratinocyte proteins are shown in Figs. 4A and B, respectively. The identity of a few spots is indicated for reference (Celis *et al.,* 1993).

V. Pitfalls

1. Do not heat the sample when dissolving in lysis solution or when defrosting.

2. For optimal results titrate the ampholytes. Mix in various proportions, maintaining the final percentage fixed, and run first and second dimensions. Select the combination that gives the best separation (well-focused spots, no streaking, etc.). Store them at −20°C in 1- or 2-ml aliquots. Ampholytes can be stored for many years at −20°C.

3. Make sure that all glassware is washed properly. Rinse with glass-distilled water before drying.

4. The pH of the 1.5 *M* Tris-HCl, pH 8.8, solution should be checked carefully.

5. Use sterile, disposable pipettes to dispense the solutions. Do not allow other colleagues to use your solutions.

REFERENCES

Anderson, N. L., and Anderson, N. G. (1978) Analytical technique for cell fractions. XXII. Two-dimensional analysis of serum and tissue proteins. Multiple gradient-slab gel electrophoresis. *Anal. Biochem.* **85**, 341–354.

Bravo, R. (1984) Two-dimensional gel electrophoresis: A guide for the beginner. *In* "Two-Dimensional Gel Electrophoresis of Proteins: Methods and Applications" (J. E. Celis and R. Bravo, eds.), pp. 3–36. Academic Press, New York.

Celis, J. E. (ed.) (1991) Two-dimensional gel electrophoresis in cell biology. *Electrophoresis* **11.**

Celis, J. E., and Bravo, R. (eds.) (1984) "Two-Dimensional Gel Electrophoresis of Proteins: Methods and Applications." Academic Press, New York.

Celis, J. E., Rasmussen, H. H., Olsen, E., Madsen, P., Leffers, H., Honoré, B., Dejgaard, K., Gromov, P., Hoffmann, H. J., Nielsen, M., Vassilev, A., Vintermyr, O., Hao, J., Celis, A., Basse, B., Lauridsen, J. B., Ratz, G. P., Andersen, A. H., Walbum, E., Kjærgaard, I., Puype, M., Van Damme, J., and Vandekerckhove, J. (1993) *Electrophoresis* **14**, 1091–1198.

Klose, J. (1975) Protein mapping by combined isoelectric focusing and electrophoresis of mouse tissues. A novel approach to testing for induced point mutations in mammals. *Humangenetik* **26**, 231–243.

Laemmli, U. K. (1970) Cleavage of structural proteins during the assembly of the head of bacteriophage T4. *Nature* **227**, 680–685.

Laskey, R. A., and Mills, A. D. (1975) Quantitative film detection of ^{3}H and ^{14}C in polyacrylamide gels by fluorography. *Eur. J. Biochem.* **56**, 335–341.

O'Farrell, P. H. (1975) High resolution two-dimensional electrophoresis of proteins. *J. Biol. Chem.* **250**, 4007–4021.

O'Farrell, P. Z., Goodman, H. M., and O'Farrell, P. H. (1977) High resolution two-dimensional electrophoresis of basic as well as acidic proteins. *Cell* **12**, 1133–1142.

High-Resolution Two-Dimensional Electrophoresis of Proteins Using Immobilized pH Gradients

Angelika Görg

I. Introduction

Classical high-resolution two-dimensional (2D) electrophoresis originally described by O'Farrell (1975) has been modified by using immobilized pH gradients (IPGs) instead of carrier ampholytes (CAs) for first-dimensional isoelectric focusing (Görg *et al.*, 1988). IPGs were introduced to overcome the variabilities of isoelectric focusing patterns due to batch variations of CAs and pH gradient instability with time. As IPGs are an integral part of the polyacrylamide matrix (Bjellqvist *et al.*, 1982; Righetti, 1990), the problem of cathodic drift is eliminated and reproducible focusing patterns of polypeptides with isoelectric points up to the basic end are obtained (Görg, 1991). Meanwhile, highly diverse samples such as proteins from human cells of blood and skin, as well as yeast cell proteins, seed and tissue proteins of plants (Görg *et al.*, 1988), and human liver (Hochstrasser *et al.*, 1992), have been successfully separated by 2D electrophoresis with IPGs (IPG-Dalt) following the protocol we established in 1988 (Görg *et al.*, 1988): IEF is performed in individual IPG gel strips, and after equilibration, the strip is applied to a horizontal or vertical SDS gel. With the introduction of readymade IPG gel strips and horizontal SDS gels on plastic backing, 2D electrophoresis can be facilitated, leaving the gel casting procedures to manufacturers.

II. Materials and Instrumentation

Immobilines (p*K* 3.6, 4.6, 6.2, 7.0, 8.5, and 9.3, Cat. Nos. 80125570–80125575), Pharmalyte pH 3–10 (Cat. No. 17-0456-01), Immobiline DryStrips pH 4–7 (Cat. No. 17-1233-01), pH 3–10 linear (Cat. No. 17-1234-01) and pH 3–10 nonlinear (Cat. No. 17-1235-01), ExcelGel SDS and buffer strips (Cat. No. 80-5062-50), repel silane (Cat. No. 80-1129-42), IEF electrode strips (Cat. No. 18-1004-40), and kerosene (Cat. No. 80-1006-35) were obtained from Pharmacia Biotech. Acrylamide (Cat. No. 10675), *N,N'*-methylenebisacrylamide (Cat. No. 29195), SDS (Cat. No. 20763), ammonium persulfate (Cat. No. 13375), glycine (Cat. No. 23390), Triton X-100 (Cat. No. 46252), and ion exchanger (Amberlite MB-1, Cat. No. 40701) were purchased from Serva. Trizma base (Cat. No. T-1503), DTT (Cat. No. D-0632), and iodoacetamide (Cat. No. I-6125) were from Sigma. Glycerol (Cat. No. 4093), urea (Cat. No. 84879), and a serin protease inhibitor (Pefabloc, Cat. No. 24839) were obtained from Merck. *N,N,N',N'*-tetramethylethylenediamine (TEMED, Cat. No. 1610800) and electrode wicks (ultrapure, Cat. No. 1704127) were from Bio-Rad. GelBond PAGfilms (Cat. No. 54786) were purchased from FMC. Water was deionized using the Milli-Q system of Millipore.

Chambers for isoelectric focusing (IEF) and horizontal SDS electrophoresis (Multiphor II, Cat. No. 18-1018-06), Power supply (Multidrive XL, cat. no. 18-1013-68), thermostatic circulator (Multitemp II, Cat. No. 18-1013-77), magnetic stirrer (Cat. No. 80-5027-90), Immobiline DryStrip kit (Cat. No. 18-1004-30), gradient gel kit (including plain glass plates, glass plates with a 0.5-mm-thick U-frame, gradient maker, and clamps, Cat. No. 80-1013-74) and reswelling cassette (Cat. No. 18-1013-74) were obtained from Pharmacia. Prior to use the glass plates are thoroughly washed with a mild detergent, rinsed with deionized water, and air-dried. If new glass plates are used, pipette 1–2 ml of repel silane on the glass plate that bears the U-frame and distribute it evenly with fuzz-free filter paper (Kimwipe). Let it dry for a few minutes, rinse again with water, and let it air-dry. Repeat this procedure occasionally to prevent the gels from sticking to the glass plates.

III. Procedures

A. PREPARATION AND RUNNING OF FIRST-DIMENSIONAL IPG GEL STRIPS

Solutions

1. *Lysis solution:* 9.5 *M* urea, 2% (w/v) Triton X-100, 0.8% (w/v) Pharmalyte pH 3–10, 1% DTT. To prepare 50 ml of lysis buffer, dissolve 30.0 g of urea in deionized water and make up to 50 ml. Add 0.5 g of Amberlite MB-1, stir for 10 min, and filter. Add 1.0 g of Triton X-100, 0.5 g DTT, 1.0 ml of Pharmalyte pH 3–10 (40% w/v), and 50 mg of Pefabloc to 48 ml of the urea solution. Lysis buffer should always be prepared freshly. Alternatively, small aliquots (1 ml) can be stored at −80°C. Lysis buffer thawed once should not be refrozen again. Never heat urea solutions above 37°C!

2. *Acrylamide/bisacrylamide solution (30% T, 4% C):* 28.8% (w/v) acrylamide, 1.2% (w/v) *N,N′*-methylenebisacrylamide. To make 100 ml of the solution dissolve 28.8 g of acrylamide and 1.2 g of bisacrylamide in deionized water and fill up to 100 ml. Add 1 g of Amberlite MB-1, stir for 10 min, and filter. This solution can be stored for 1 week at 4°C; however, for optimum results it is advisable to prepare it freshly the day you use it.

3. *Ammonium persulfate solution:* 40% (w/v) in deionized water. To prepare 1 ml of the solution, dissolve 0.4 g of ammonium persulfate in 1 ml of deionized water. This solution should be prepared freshly just before use.

4. *Rehydration solution:* 8 *M* urea, 0.5% (w/v) Triton X-100, 10 m*M* DTT, 0.2% (w/v) Pharmalyte pH 3–10. To prepare 50 ml of the solution, dissolve 25.0 g of urea in deionized water and complete to 50 ml. Add 0.5 g of amberlite MB-1, stir for 10 min, and filter. To 48 ml of this solution add 0.25 g of Triton X-100, 0.25 ml Pharmalyte pH 3–10 (40% w/v), and 77 mg of DTT and complete to 50 ml with deionized water. Rehydration solution should be prepared freshly the day you use it. Do not heat urea solutions above 37°C. Otherwise protein carbamylation may occur.

5. *Solutions for casting immobiline gels:* To prepare 15 ml each of acidic and basic solutions mix chemicals and reagent solutions as described in Table I. A huge selection of recipes for any type of narrow or broad pH gradient have been calculated (Righetti, 1990; Righetti and Tonani, 1991). Table I describes our favorite pH gradients for 2D electrophoresis.

TABLE I Recipes for Casting IEF Gels with Immobilized pH Gradients[a]

Linear pH gradient	pH 4–7 Acidic solution pH 4	pH 4–7 Basic solution pH 7	pH 4–9 Acidic solution pH 4	pH 4–9 Basic solution pH 9	pH 6–10 Acidic solution pH 6	pH 6–10 Basic solution pH 10
Immobiline pK 3.6	578 μl	302 μl	829 μl	147 μl	941 μl	100 μl
Immobiline pK 4.6	110 μl	738 μl	235 μl	424 μl	—	—
Immobiline pK 6.2	450 μl	151 μl	232 μl	360 μl	273 μl	333 μl
Immobiline pK 7.0	—	269 μl	22 μl	296 μl	243 μl	361 μl
Immobiline pK 8.5	—	—	250 μl	71 μl	260 μl	239 μl
Immobiline pK 9.3	—	876 μl	221 μl	663 μl	282 μl	326 μl
Acrylamide/bisacrylamide (28.8/1.2)	2.0 ml	2.0 ml	2.0 ml	2.0 ml	2.0 ml	2.0 ml
Deionized water	8.9 ml	10.7 ml	8.3 ml	11.1 ml	8.1 ml	11.7 ml
Glycerol (100%)	3.75 g	—	3.75 g	—	3.75 g	—
Final volume	15 ml	15 ml	15 ml	15 ml	15 ml	15 ml

[a] For effective polymerization, acidic and basic solutions are adjusted to pH 7 with 1 N sodium hydroxide and 1 N acetic acid, respectively, before adding the polymerization catalysts. *Source:* Pharmacia-LKB Instruction Manual for Casting IPG Gels.

Steps

IPG slab gels for 18-cm separation distance (250 $\times$ 180 $\times$ 0.5 mm^3) are cast on GelBond PAGfilm. After polymerization, the IPG gels are extensively washed with deionized water and then dried. Instead of laboratory-made gels, readymade gels (Immobiline DryPlate or Immobiline DryStrip) can be used. Prior to the first dimension, the desired number of IPG gel strips is cut off the slab gel and rehydrated to their original thickness. The rehydrated strips are then placed on the cooling block of the electrofocusing chamber and samples are applied into cups placed directly on the surface of the IPG gel strips.

Preparation of the IPG gel strips

1. To assemble the polymerization cassette, wet the plain glass plate (size 260 $\times$ 200 mm^2) with a few drops of water. Place the Gelbond PAGfilm, hydrophilic side upward, on the wetted surface of the plain glass plate. The GelBond PAGfilm should overlap the upper edge of the glass plate for 1–2 mm to facilitate filling of the cassette. Expel excess water with a roller. Place the glass plate which bears the U-frame (0.5 mm thick) on top of the Gelbond PAGfilm and clamp the cassette together (Fig. 1A). Put it in the refrigerator for 30 min.

2. To cast the IPG gel, pipette 12.0 ml of the acidic, dense solution into the mixing chamber of the gradient mixer. Outlet and connecting line between the mixing chamber and reservoir have to be closed! Add 7.5 μl of TEMED and 12 μl of ammonium persulfate and mix. Open the connecting line between the chambers for a second to release any air bubbles.

3. Pipette 12.0 ml of the basic, light solution into the reservoir of the gradient mixer. Add 7.5 μl of TEMED and 12 μl of ammonium persulfate and mix with a spatula.

4. Switch on the magnetic stirrer at a reproducible and rapid rate; however, avoid excessive vortex. Remove the polymerization cassette from the refrigerator

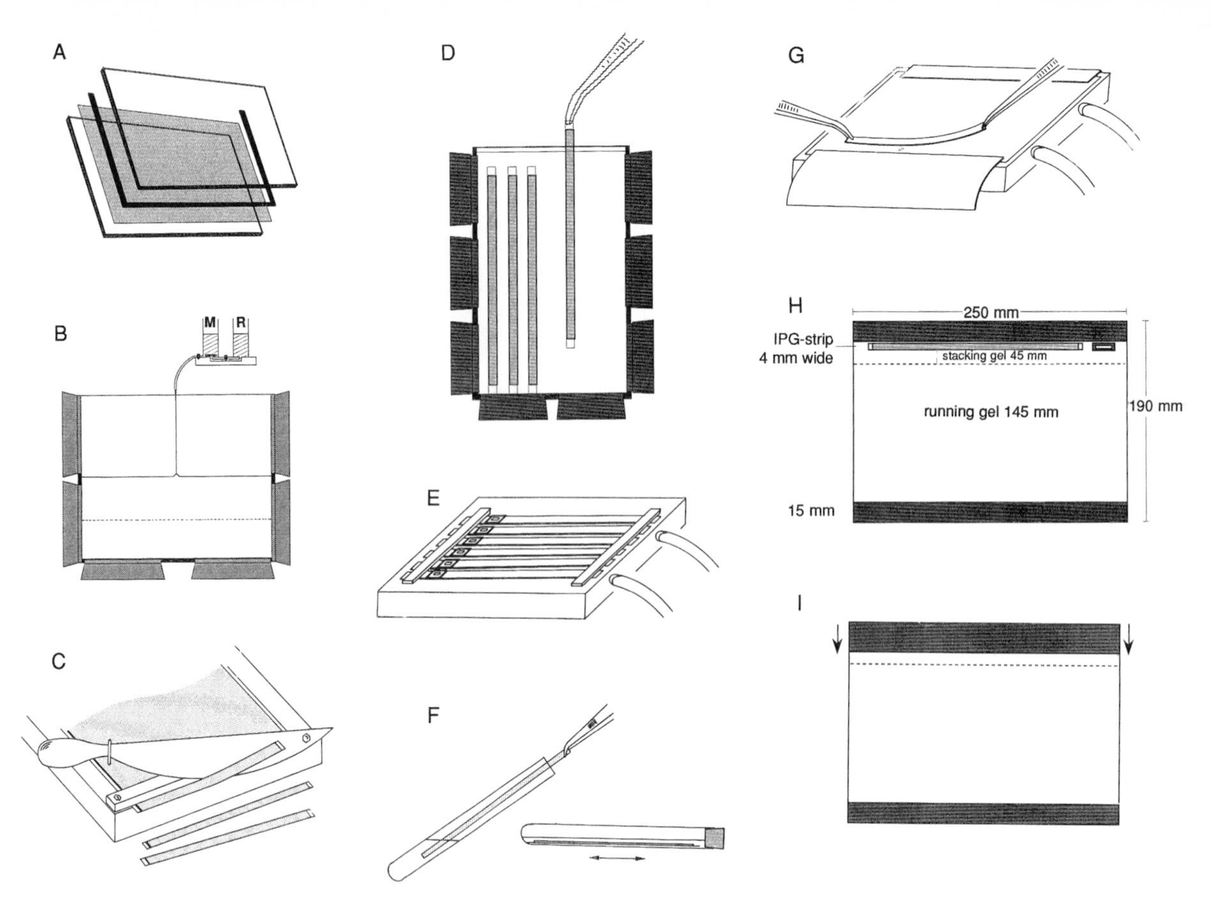

FIGURE 1 Procedure of horizontal IPG-Dalt with laboratory-made gels. (A) Assembly of the polymerization cassette for the preparation of IPG and SDS gels cast on plastic backings (Glass plates, GelBond PAGfilm, U-frame 0.5 mm thick). (B) Casting of pH and/or pore gradient gels. (C) Cutting of washed and dried IPG slab gels (or Immobiline DryPlates) into individual IPG gel strips. (D) Rehydration of individual IPG gel strips. (E) IEF in individual IPG gel strips. (F) Equilibration of IPG gel strips prior to SDS–PAGE. (G) Transfer of equilibrated IPG gel strips onto the surface of the horizontal SDS gel along the cathodic electrode wick. (H) Geometry of the second dimension. (I) Removal of the IPG gel strip after the proteins have migrated into the SDS gel. The electrode wick or strip is moved forward so that it overlaps the former application area of the IPG gel strip.

and put it underneath the outlet of the gradient mixer. Open the valve connecting the chambers and, immediately afterward, the pinchcock on the outlet tubing so that the gradient mixture is applied centrally into the cassette from a height of about 5 cm just by gravity flow. Formation of the gradient is completed in 3–5 min (Fig 1B).

NOTE

If a pH plateau for anodic sample application is desired, pipette an extra portion of dense solution into the mold prior to pouring the gradient.

5. Keep the mold at room temperature for 15 min to allow adequate leveling of the density gradient. Then polymerize the gel for 1 hr at 50°C in a heating cabinet.

6. After polymerization, wash the IPG gel for 1 hr with 10-min changes of

deionized water (500 ml each) in a glass tray on a rocking platform. Then equilibrate the gel in 2% (w/v) glycerol for 30 min and dry it overnight at room temperature, using a fan, in a dust-free cabinet. Afterward, protect the surface of the dry gel with a sheet of plastic film. The dried IPG gel can be stored in a sealed plastic bag at −20°C for at least several months without loss of function. Dried IPG gels in several pH ranges are also commercially available (Immobiline DryPlate).

7. For IEF in individual IPG gel strips, cut the dried IPG gels—or the readymade Immobiline DryPlates–into 3- to 4-mm-wide strips with the help of a paper cutter (Fig. 1C). Alternatively, ready-cut IPG strips (Immobiline DryStrip) can also be used.

Rehydration of laboratory-made and readymade IPG gel strips

1. To rehydrate the IPG gel strips to their original thickness (0.5 mm), take two layers of Parafilm and cut off a U-frame that has the same shape and size as the glass plate's U-frame. Assemble the rehydration cassette in such a way that a 0.7-mm-thick U-frame (0.5-mm original thickness plus two layers of Parafilm, 0.1 mm each) is obtained. Clamp the cassette together and pipette in the rehydration solution.

2. Take an appropriate number of dry IPG gel strips and pull off their protective covers. Lower them carefully, but without delay, into the rehydration cassette, gel side toward the glass plate bearing the U-frame. Allow the strips to rehydrate overnight (Fig. 1D).

Isoelectric focusing in individual IPG gel strips

1. After the IPG gel strips have been rehydrated, pour the rehydration solution out of the reswelling cassette, remove the clamps, and open the cassette. Using clean forceps, place the rehydrated IPG gel strips, gel side up, on a sheet of water-saturated filter paper. Wet a second sheet of filter paper with deionized water, blot it slightly to remove excess water, and put it onto the surface of the IPG gel strips. Blot them gently for a few seconds to remove excess rehydration solution, to prevent urea crystallization on the surface of the gel during focusing.

2. Cover the flat-bed cooling block with 2–3 ml of kerosene and place the IPG gel strips (up to 40) side by side, 1–2 mm apart, on it (Fig. 1E). The acidic end of the IPG gel strips must face toward the anode.

3. Cut two IEF electrode strips (or paper strips prepared from 3-mm-thick filter paper MN 440, Macherey & Nagel) to a length corresponding to the width of all IPG gel strips lying on the cooling plate. Soak the electrode strips with deionized water and remove excessive moisture by blotting with filter paper.

4. Place the IEF electrode strips on top of the alligned IPG gel strips at the cathode and anode. Add paper strips soaked in 5 *N* NaOH to the chamber to diminish the carbon dioxide content in the chamber.

5. Apply silicone rubber frames (2×5 mm^2 inner diameter) onto the gel surface, 5 mm apart from anode or cathode, for sample application (Fig. 1E).

6. Pipette the samples (20 μl each, preferably dissolved in lysis buffer) into the silicone frames. When the sample cups of the Immobiline DryStrip kit are used, up to 100 μl can be applied. Sample load is 60–100 μg protein per strip for silver-stained 2D patterns. For preparative purposes, however, up to 1 mg (or even more) of protein from a cell lysate can be loaded onto a single IPG gel strip (Hanash *et al.*, 1991).

TABLE II Running Conditions for First-Dimensional IEF with IPG Gel Strips

Temperature	20°C		
Current maximum	0.05 mA per strip, 2 mA max in total		
Power maximum	3.0–5.0 W		
Voltage maximum	150 V	30 min	Sample entry
	300 V	60 min	Sample entry
	3500 V	See below	To the steady state
Separation distance		11 cm	18 cm
IPG 4–7		22000 Vh	42000 Vh
IPG 4–9		17000 Vh	28000 Vh
IPG 6–10		21000 Vh	35000 Vh
IPG 3–10.5		11000 Vh	18000 Vh

Reprinted, with permission, from Görg (1993).

7. Position the electrodes and press them down on top of the IEF electrode strips.

8. Place the lid on the electrofocusing chamber, connect the cables to the power supply, and start IEF. Running conditions depend on the pH gradient and the length of the IPG gel strip used. An appropriate time schedule for orientation is given in Table II (Görg, 1993). For improved sample entry, voltage is limited to 150 V (30 min) and 300 V (60 min) at the beginning. Then continue with maximum settings of 3500 V to the steady state. Optimum focusing temperature is 20°C (Görg *et al.*, 1991).

9. After IEF, those IPG gel strips that are not used immediately for second-dimension run and/or are kept for further reference are stored between two sheets of plastic film at −80°C up to several months (Fig. 2).

NOTE

IEF can also be performed using the Pharmacia DryStrip kit where IPG gel strips are protected from oxygen and carbon dioxide by a layer of silicon oil (see Pharmacia DryStrip Instruction Manual).

B. SECOND DIMENSION: HORIZONTAL SDS–POLYACRYLAMIDE GEL ELECTROPHORESIS

Solutions

1. *Stacking gel buffer:* 0.5 *M* Tris–HCl, pH 6.8, 0.4% (w/v) SDS. To make 100 ml, dissolve 6.05 g of Trizma base and 0.4 g of SDS in about 80 ml of deionized water. Adjust the pH of the solution with 4 *N* HCl and fill up to 100 ml with deionized water. Add 10 mg of sodium azide and filter. The buffer can be stored at 4°C for 2 weeks.

2. *Resolving gel buffer:* 1.5 *M* Tris–HCl, pH 8.8, 0.4% (w/v) SDS. To make 250 ml, dissolve 45.5 g of Trizma base and 1 g of SDS in about 200 ml of deionized water. Adjust the pH of the solution with 4 *N* HCl and fill up to 250 ml with deionized water. Add 25 mg of sodium azide and filter. The buffer can be stored at 4°C up to 2 weeks.

3. *Acrylamide/bisacrylamide solution (30% T, 4% C):* 28.8% (w/v) acrylamide and 1.2% (w/v) methylenebisacrylamide in deionized water. To make 500 ml, dissolve 144 g of acrylamide and 6 g of methylenebisacrylamide in deionized water and fill up to 500 ml. Add 1 g of Amberlite MB-1, stir for 10 min, and filter. The solution can be stored up to 2 weeks in a refrigerator.

4. *Electrode buffer stock solution:* To make 1000 ml of a 10× solution, add 30.3 g of Trizma base, 144 g of glycine, 10.0 g of SDS, and 100 mg of sodium azide. Dissolve in deionized water, fill up to 1000 ml, and filter. Electrode buffer stock solution can be kept at room temperature for up to 2 weeks. Before use, mix 100 ml of the buffer with 900 ml of deionized water.

5. *Equilibration buffer:* 6 *M* urea, 30% (w/v) glycerol, 2% (w/v) SDS in 0.05 *M* Tris–HCl buffer, pH 8.8. To make 500 ml, add 180 g of urea, 150 g of glycerol, 10 g of SDS, and 16.7 ml of resolving gel buffer. Dissolve in deionized water and fill up to 500 ml. The buffer can be stored at room temperature up to 2 weeks.

6. *Bromphenol blue solution:* 0.25% (w/v) of bromphenol blue in stacking gel buffer. To make 10 ml, dissolve 25 mg of bromphenol blue in 10 ml of stacking gel buffer. Store at 4°C.

7. *Ammonium persulfate solution:* 40% (w/v) ammonium persulfate in deionized water. To prepare 1 ml of the solution, dissolve 0.4 g of ammonium persulfate in 1 ml of deionized water. This solution should be prepared freshly just before use.

Steps

For the second dimension, a laboratory- or readymade SDS pore gradient gel (0.5 mm thick on GelBond PAGfilm) is placed on the cooling block of the horizontal electrophoresis unit. Electrode wicks (Bio-Rad) or buffer strips from acrylamide are then applied. The equilibrated IPG gel strip is simply placed gel side down onto the surface of the horizontal SDS gel without any embedding procedure. Horizontal setups are perfectly suited for the use of readymade gels on film supports.

1. Horizontal SDS–PAGE with Laboratory-Made Gels on Plastic Backing

a. Casting of SDS pore gradient gels and preparation of the electrophoresis unit

1. Assemble the polymerization cassette consisting of two glass plates, one covered with the GelBond PAGfilm, the other bearing the U-frame (0.5 mm thick) as described in Section A for casting IPG gels (Fig. 1A). GelBond PAGfilms should be washed 6 × 10 min with deionized water prior to use to avoid spot streaking on silver staining.

2. Immediately before casting add 5 μl of TEMED and 10 μl of ammonium persulfate to the gel solutions (see Table III). For casting an SDS gel (size 250 × 195 × 0.5 mm^3) with a stacking gel length of 50 mm, pipette 6.0 ml of stacking gel solution into the precooled (4°C) mold. Then cast the pore gradient on top of the stacking gel by mixing 9.0 ml of the dense solution (12% T, 25% glycerol) and 9.0 ml of the light solution (15% T, no glycerol) with the help of a gradient maker similarly as described in Section A for casting IPG gels. The high glycerol concentration of the stacking gel solution allows overlaying of the pore gradient mixture without an intermediate polymerization step (see Fig. 1B).

TABLE III Recipe for Casting SDS Pore Gradient Gel (12–15% T, 4% C)

		Resolving gel	
	Stacking gel 6% T	Dense solution 12% T	Light solution 15% T
Glycerol (100%)	3.75 g	2.50 g	—
Stacking gel buffer	2.5 ml	—	—
Resolving gel buffer	—	2.5 ml	2.5 ml
Acrylamide/bisacrylamide solution	2.0 ml	4.0 ml	5.0 ml
Deionized water	2.5 ml	1.5 ml	2.5 ml
Final volume	10.0 ml	10.0 ml	10.0 ml
TEMED	5.0 μl	5.0 μl	5.0 μl
Ammouium persulfate	10.0 μl	10.0 μl	10.0 μl

NOTE

Instead of pore gradient gels, homogeneous SDS–PAGE gels may be cast for the second dimension.

3. After pouring, leave the cassette for 15 min at room temperature to allow adequate leveling of the density gradient. Then place it in a heating cabinet at 50°C for 30 min for polymerization. The polymerized gel can be stored in a refrigerator overnight.

4. Fill the buffer tanks of the electrophoresis unit with electrode buffer. Soak four sheets of filter paper (size 250 × 110 mm^2) in electrode buffer and put them on the cooling block (15°C). Soak the electrode wicks (size 250 × 100 mm^2) in electrode buffer. Place them at the edges of the buffer-soaked filter papers and perform a prerun (600 V, 30 mA) for 3 hr to remove impurities from the electrode wicks. Then remove the filter papers and discard them; the purified electrode wicks remain in the electrode buffer tanks and are used repeatedly.

b. Equilibration of the IPG gel strips

The IPG gel strips are equilibrated twice, each time for 15 min. During the second equilibration, 260 m*M* iodoacetamide is added to the equilibration buffer to remove excess DTT (responsible for the "point streaking" in silver-stained patterns).

1. Dissolve 100 mg of DTT in 10 ml of equilibration buffer (= equilibration buffer I). Take out the focused IPG gel strips from the freezer and place them into individual test tubes (200 mm long, 20 mm i.d.). Add 10 ml of equilibration buffer I and 50 μl of the bromphenol blue solution. Seal the test tubes with Parafilm, rock them for 15 min on a shaker (Fig. 1F), and then pour off the equilibration buffer.

2. Dissolve 480 mg of iodoacetamide in 10 ml of equilibration buffer (=equilibration buffer II). Add equilibration buffer II and 50 μl of bromphenol blue solution to the test tube as above and equilibrate for another 15 min on a rocker.

3. After the second equilibration, place the IPG gel strip on a piece of filter paper to remove excess equilibration buffer. The strip should be turned up at one edge for a few minutes to help it drain.

c. Horizontal SDS–PAGE

1. During the equilibration step of the IPG gel strips, open the polymerization

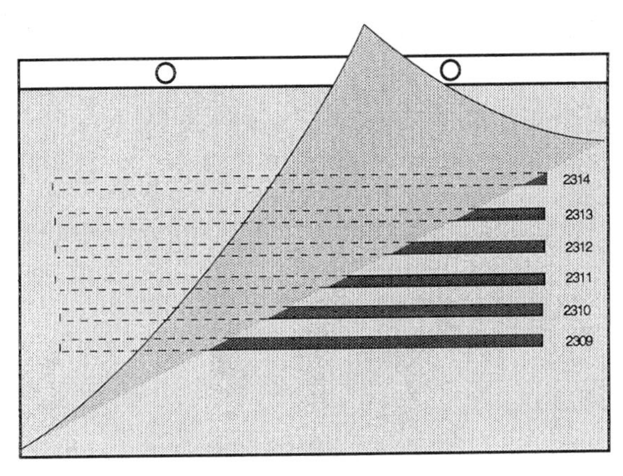

FIGURE 2 After IEF, IPG strips not used immediately can be stored at −80°C for further reference.

cassette, pipette a few milliliters of kerosene on the cooling block (15°C) of the electrophoresis unit, and put the SDS gel (gel side up) on it. Lay the electrode wicks on the surface of the SDS gel so that they overlap the cathodic and anodic edges of the gel by about 10 mm.

2. Place the blotted IPG gel strips gel side down onto the SDS gel surface adjacent to the cathodic wick (Fig. 1G). No embedding of the IPG gel strip is necessary. If it is desired to coelectrophorese molecular weight (M_r) marker proteins, put a silicone rubber frame onto the SDS gel surface alongside the IPG gel strip and pipette in 5 μl of molecular weight marker proteins dissolved in equilibration buffer.

3. Place a glass plate across the electrode wicks, providing a moist atmosphere over the gel without making contact with it.

4. Put the lid on the electrophoresis unit and start SDS–PAGE at 200 V for about 70 min with a limit of 20 mA. When the bromphenol blue tracking dye has completely moved out of the IPG gel strip, interrupt the run, remove the IPG gel strip, and move the cathodic electrode wick forward for 4–5 mm so that it now overlaps the former sample application area (Fig. 1H, I). Then continue the run at 600 V with a limit of 30 mA until the tracking dye has migrated into the anodic electrode wick. Total running time is approximately 6 hr. The gel is then fixed and stained with either silver nitrate (Fig. 3) or Coomassie blue. Alternatively, it can be removed from the plastic backing with the help of a film remover (Pharmacia, Cat. No. 18-1013-75) and used for blotting.

2. Horizontal SDS–PAGE with Readymade Gels

Readymade SDS gels (ExcelGel, 250 × 200 × 0.5 mm^3, on plastic backing) in combination with polyacrylamide buffer strips are used.

1. Equilibrate the IPG gel strips as described above (Fig. 1F).

2. While the strips are equilibrating, begin the assembly of the SDS ExcelGel for the second dimension: Remove the ExcelGel from its foil package. Pipette 2–3 ml of kerosene on the cooling plate of the horizontal electrophoresis unit (15°C). Remove the protective cover from the top of the ExcelGel and place the gel on the cooling plate, cut-off edge toward the anode. Avoid trapping air bubbles between the gel and the cooling block.

3. Peel back the protective foil of the cathodic SDS buffer strip. Wet your

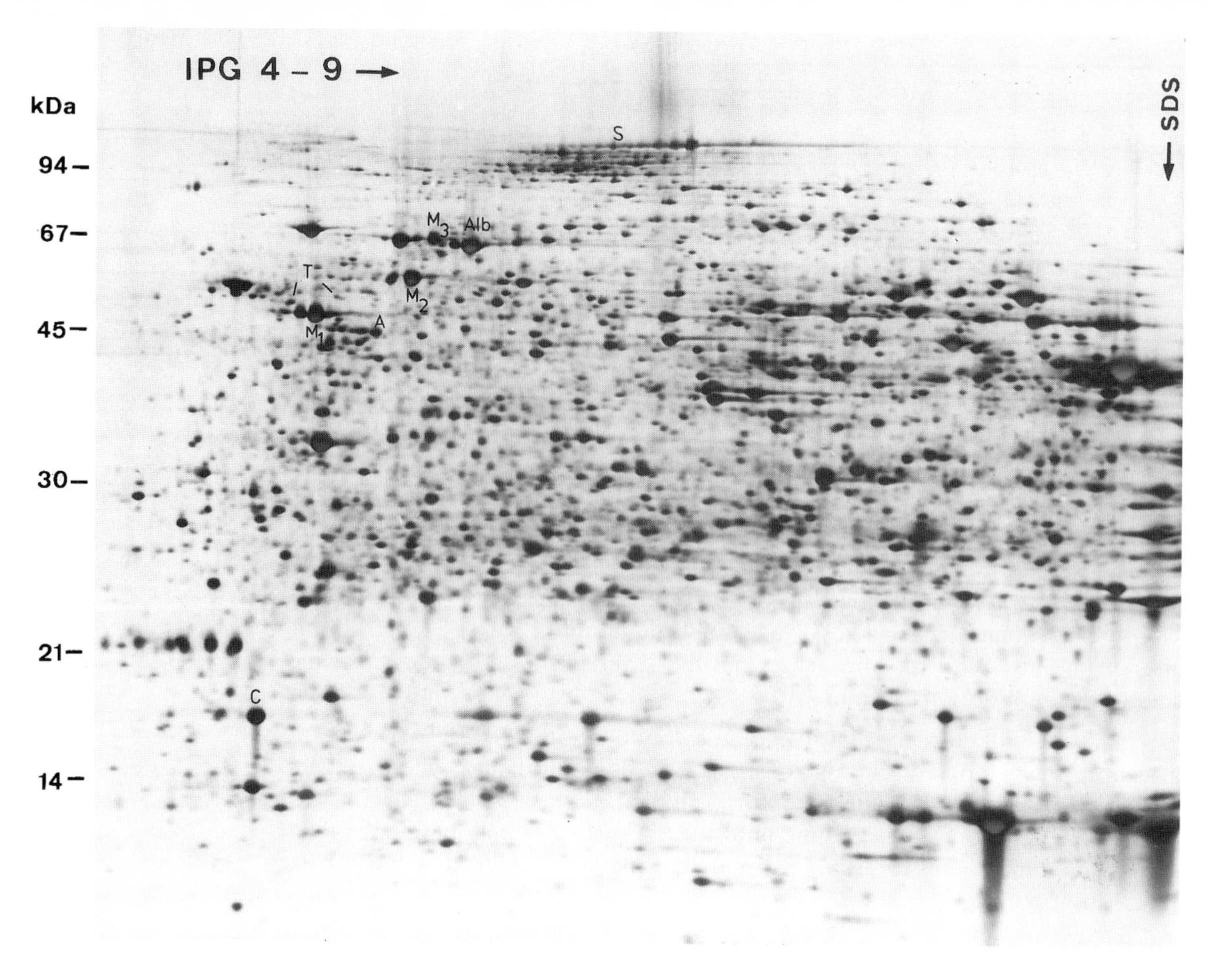

FIGURE 3 Horizontal IPG-Dalt of mouse liver proteins. First dimension: IEF with IPG 4–9; separation distance: 18 cm; sample application: anode. Focusing time: 35,000 V·hr. Second dimension: horizontal SDS–PAGE, 12–15% T. Silver stain. A, actin; Alb, albumin; C, cytochrome b_5; M_1, M_2, M_3, mitochondrial proteins; S, carbamyl phosphate synthetase; T, tubulin (Reprinted with permission from Görg, 1993).

gloves with a few drops of deionized water and place the buffer strip on the cathodic end of the gel. Avoid trapping air bubbles between gel surface and buffer strip.

4. Repeat this procedure with the anodic buffer strip.

5. Place the equilibrated IPG gel strips gel side down on the surface of the ExcelGel, 1 mm apart from the cathodic buffer strip (Fig. 4).

6. Press gently on top of the IPG gel strips with forceps to remove any trapped air bubbles.

7. Align the electrodes with the buffer strips and lower the electrode holder carefully onto the buffer strips.

8. Start SDS–PAGE at 200 V for about 45 min with a limit of 20 mA. When the bromphenol blue tracking dye has moved 4–5 mm from the IPG gel strip, interrupt the run, remove the IPG gel strip, and move the cathodic buffer strip forward so that it just covers the former contact area of the IPG gel strip. Readjust the electrodes and continue with electrophoresis at 800 V and 40 mA for about 180 min until the bromphenol blue dye front has reached the anodic buffer strip.

9. Proceed with silver or Coomassie blue staining or with blotting.

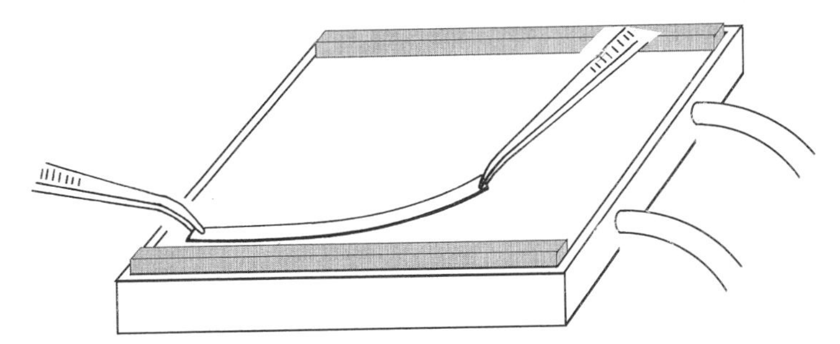

FIGURE 4 Horizontal IPG-Dalt using readymade SDS gels and buffer strips made of polyacrylamide.

C. SECOND DIMENSION: VERTICAL SDS–POLYACRYLAMIDE GEL ELECTROPHORESIS

Solutions

See Section B.

Steps

First-dimension IEF is performed as described in Section IIIA. After equilibration, the IPG gel strip is placed on top of the vertical SDS gel. A stacking gel is not necessary.

1. Cast vertical SDS–PAGE gels and prepare the electrophoresis chamber as described (see article by Julio E. Celis, Gitte Ratz, Bodil Basse, Jette B. Lauridsen, and Ariana Celis). Support the SDS gel cassette in a vertical position to facilitate the application of the first-dimension IPG gel strip.
2. Equilibrate the IPG gel strips as described above (Fig. 1F).
3. Suspend 0.5% (w/v) agarose in electrode buffer and melt it. Place 1 ml of agarose solution at 90°C onto the surface of the SDS gel and immediately immerse the IPG gel strip in the agarose solution. Carefully press the IPG strip with a spatula onto the surface of the SDS gel to achieve complete contact. Allow the agarose to solidify for 5 min and then place the slab gel into the electrophoresis apparatus.

NOTE

Embedding is not absolutely necessary but ensures better contact between the IPG gel strip and the top of the SDS gel.

4. Fill the upper chamber with electrode buffer and start electrophoresis. In contrast to the procedure of horizontal SDS–PAGE, it is not necessary to remove the IPG gel strips from the surface of the vertical SDS gel once the proteins have migrated out of the IPG gel strip.
5. Run the SDS–PAGE gels overnight (100–150 V maximum setting).
6. Terminate the run when the bromphenol blue tracking dye has reached the lower end of the gel and begin protein staining.

IV. Comments

Using the protocols described in this article, it is possible to resolve proteins having apparent molecular masses between 10 and 200 kDa and p*I* values from 4 to 10. It is possible to expand the p*I* range to pH 2.5 at the acidic end and to pH 11.7 at the basic end if three additional Immobiline species (p*K* 1.0, 10.3, and 12.0) are used for gel casting (Righetti and Tonani, 1991).

Two-dimensional electrophoresis with IPG has not only been successfully used for analytical 2D analysis but also for preparative purposes followed by protein sequencing due to its high protein loading capacity. Between 1 mg (Hanash *et al.*, 1991) and 10 mg (B. Bjellqvist, personal communication) of a crude protein preparation have been applied onto a single IPG gel strip without loss of resolution in the 2D map.

V. Pitfalls

1. Blot the rehydrated IPG gel strips to remove excess rehydration solution; otherwise, urea crystallization on the surface of the IPG gel strips might occur which will desturb IEF patterns or prolong focusing time to the steady state.

2. Make sure that the orientation of the IPG gel strips on the cooling block of the IEF chamber is correct (acidic end toward anode). Check the temperature of the cooling block (20°C).

3. Sample solution should not be too concentrated to avoid protein precipitation at the sample application point. If you are in doubt, dilute the sample with lysis solution and apply a larger volume (>20 μl) instead.

4. For better sample entry, start IEF at low voltage (150 V for 30 min, followed by 300 V for 60 min).

5. Remove the IPG gel strip from the surface of the horizontal SDS–PAGE gel as soon as the bromphenol blue dye front has migrated 4–5 mm off the IPG gel strip. Then move the cathodic electrode wick (or buffer strip) forward so that it overlaps the area the IPG gel strip once covered.

REFERENCES

Bjellqvist, B., Ek, K., Righetti, P. G., Gianazza, E., Görg, A., Westermeier, R., and Postel, W. (1982) Isoelectric focusing in immobilized pH gradients: Principle, methodology and some applications. *J. Biochem. Biophys. Methods* **6**, 317–339.

Görg, A. (1991) Two-dimensional electrophoresis. *Nature* **349**, 545–546.

Görg, A. (1993). Two-dimensional electrophoresis with immobilized pH gradients: Current state. *Biochem. Soc. Trans.* **21**, 130–132.

Görg, A., Postel, W., Friedrich, C., Kuick, R., Strahler, J. R., and Hanash, S. M. (1991) *Electrophoresis* **12**, 653–658.

Görg, A., Postel, W., and Günther, S. (1988) The current state of two-dimensional electrophoresis with immobilized pH gradients. *Electrophoresis* **9**, 531–546.

Hanash, S. M., Strahler, J. R., Neel, J. V., Hailat, N., Melham, R., Keim, D., Zhu, X. X., Wagner, D., Gage, D. A., and Watson, J. T. (1991) Highly resolving two-dimensional gels for protein sequencing. *Proc. Natl. Acad. Sci. USA* **88**, 5709–5713.

Hochstrasser, D. F., *et al.* (1992) Human liver protein map: A reference database established by microsequencing and gel comparison. *Electrophoresis* **13**, 992–1001.

O'Farrell, P. H. (1975) High resolution two-dimensional electrophoresis of proteins. *J. Biol. Chem.* **250**, 4007–4021.

Righetti, P. G. (1990) "Immobilized pH Gradients. Theory and Methodology." *Elsevier*, Amsterdam.

Righetti, P. G., and Tonani, C. (1991) Immobilized pH gradients (IPG) simulator—An additional step in pH gradient engineering. *Electrophoresis* **12**, 1011–1027.

Mini Two-Dimensional Gel Electrophoresis

Mario Gimona, Barbara Galazkiewicz, and Markus Niederreiter

I. Introduction

Capillary nonequilibrium pH gradient gel electrophoresis in conjunction with mini slab polyacrylamide electrophoresis is a rapid, cost-effective, and easy-to-handle system for the two-dimensional analysis of complex protein mixtures in one day.

II. Materials and Instrumentation

Ampholytes Servalyt (pH 2–11, Cat. No. 42900; pH 3–5, Cat. No. 42903; pH 4–6, Cat. No. 42904; pH 5–8, Cat. No. 42949; pH 7–9, Cat. No. 42907), acrylamide (Cat. No. 10674), SDS (Cat. No. 20760), glycine (Cat. No. 23390), agarose (Cat. No. 11400), and DTE (Cat. No. 20697) were purchased from **Serva.** Bisacrylamide (Cat. No. 161-0200), TEMED (Cat. No. 161-0800), and ammonium persulfate (APS, Cat. No. 161-0700) were from Bio-Rad, and Tris (Cat. No. 8382) was from Merck. Urea was obtained from U.S. Biochemicals (USB, Cat. No. 23040), and Nonidet P-40 (NP-40, Cat. No. 74385) from Fluka. Ampholytes pH 2.5–4 (Cat. No. A-5299), glycerol (99%, Cat. No. G-7757), and Fluorinert FC-40 (Cat. No. F-9755) were from Sigma. Plastic tubes (Cat. No. 55484) and tops (Cat. No. 65722) were from Sarstedt.

First-dimension glass capillaries from Bio-Rad (Cat. No. 165-2966) were cleaned by boiling in 0.1 *N* NaOH for 15 min, followed by 15 min in boiling 0.1 *N* HCl, extensively rinsed with distilled water, and finally cleaned with ethanol and distilled water. Glass plates for second dimensions were custom cut (dimensions 10.2 × 8.2 cm) and were cleaned in chromic acid for 60 min, rinsed extensively with distilled water, and dried at 40°C. First-dimension chambers and the tube gel ejector were from Bio-Rad (Cat. No. 165-2961), chambers for SDS–PAGE were homemade based on the design of Matsudaira and Burgess (1978). Spacers (0.6 × 11 cm) were cut from 0.5-mm Teflon sheets. The multiple casting chamber for second dimensions was homemade.

III. Procedures

A. PREPARATION OF FIRST DIMENSIONS FOR NEPHGE

Solutions

See article by Julio E. Celis, Gitte Ratz, Bodil Basse, Jette B. Lauridsen, and Ariana Celis.

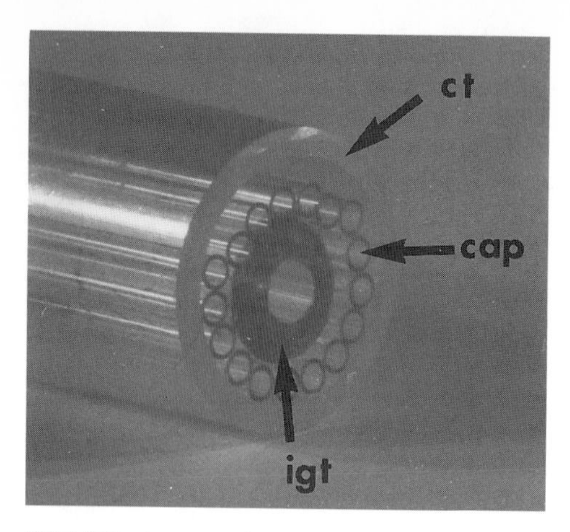

FIGURE 1 "**Gatling**"-type array of first-dimension capillaries (cap) around the inner glass tube (igt) within the casting tube (ct). This figure shows the base of the assembly after sealing with Parafilm.

Steps

1. Seal one end of the Bio-Rad casting tube with several layers of Parafilm and insert the second glass tube.

2. Circularly arrange the capillaries in the space between the two tubes (Fig. 1).

3. Mix 2.75 g urea, 0.665 ml acrylamide solution, 1.000 ml NP-40, and 0.985 ml H_2O.

4. Degas carefully for 1 min, then add 25 μl carrier ampholytes, pH range 2–11; 50 μl carrier ampholytes, pH range 3–5; 50 μl carrier ampholytes, pH range 4–6; 50 μl carrier ampholytes, pH range 7–9; 75 μl carrier ampholytes, pH range 5–8; 10 μl APS; and 5 μl TEMED.

5. Insert a 10-ml syringe equipped with a needle (0.8 $\times$ 80 mm) into the inner glass tube (Fig. 2).

6. Pour the solution into the syringe, add the plunger, and inject the gel solution into the central tube. Gently lift the inner tube to release the liquid until the solution reaches the desired height (ideally 0.5 cm from the end of the capillary).

7. Allow the solution to polymerize (without overlaying) for 2 hr.

8. Cut the Parafilm from the base with a blade and push out inner tube and capillaries using the wide end of a blue tip of a 1000-μl Gilson pipette. Separate the capillaries, rinse the outside with distilled water, clean with tissue paper, and insert the capillaries into the capillary holders (supplied with the Bio-Rad kit).

9. Fill the bottom tank of the Bio-Rad chamber with 800 ml of 20 m*M* NaOH and insert the rack holding the capillaries.

10. Wash the top of the capillaries with distilled water.

11. Apply the sample (up to 50 μl) using a pipette fitted with Geloader tips from Eppendorf (Cat. No. 0030 001.222), overlay with 10 μl of lysis buffer and 25 μl of overlay buffer, and fill the reservoir with 10 m*M* H_3PO_4.

12. Connect the electrodes. Prerun (upper chamber, +; lower chamber, −) for 10 min at 400 V, 10 min at 500 V and then for 75 min at 750 V.

13. Before opening the chamber, pipette 1.5 ml of equilibration buffer in 3-ml plastic tubes labeled with the number of the run.

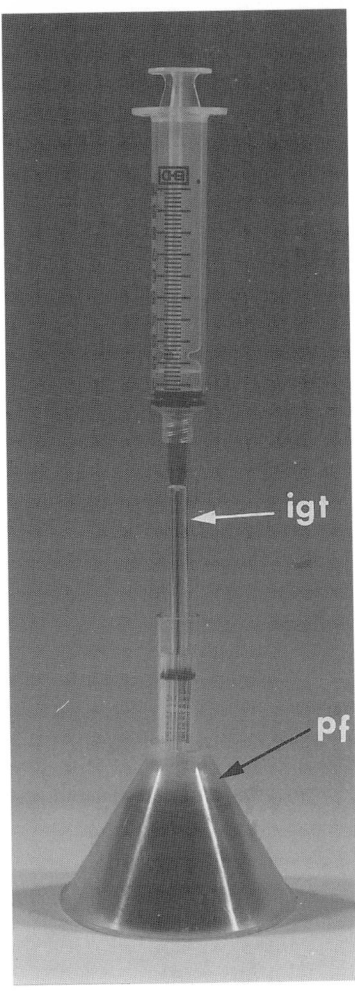

FIGURE 2 Insertion of the needle into the inner glass tube (igt). The assembly is supported by a truncated plastic funnel (pf).

14. Extrude the gels with the aid of the Bio-Rad tube gel ejector filled with equilibration buffer directly into the tubes.

15. Close tubes and store at −20°C.

B. SECOND-DIMENSION PAGE ON MINI SLAB GELS

Solutions

1. *750 mM Tris, pH 8.8:* Add 18.17 g to 200 ml distilled water, adjust pH with HCl, and sterile-filter.

2. *Acrylamide:bisacrylamide 50:1.33%:* Add 50 g acrylamide and 1.33 g bisacrylamide to 100 ml water (final volume), dissolve, and sterile-filter. Store at room temperature.

3. *n-Butanol overlay solution:* Mix 100 ml of *n*-butanol with 100 ml of 750 m*M* Tris, pH 8.8, buffer, shake well, and let saturate at room temperature for 30 min.

To cast 18 second-dimension 8–22% gradient gels, mix:

8%	22%
21.00 ml 750 m*M* Tris buffer, pH 8.8	21.00 ml 750 m*M* Tris buffer, pH 8.8
14.28 ml distilled water	18.48 ml acrylamide solution
6.72 ml acrylamide solution	2.52 ml glycerol

Steps

1. Fill the multiple casting chamber with 18 slab gel assemblies.
2. Mix the solution and store in the refrigerator after thorough degassing.
3. Pump *n*-butanol (saturated with the separation gel buffer) from the bottom with a peristaltic pump until the solution reaches 1 cm into the glass plates.
4. Add 0.42 ml 10% SDS, 0.16 ml APS (10%), and 6 μl TEMED.
5. Fill the solutions into a gradient mixer.
6. Pump in the acrylamide solution at a flow rate of 15 ml/min.
7. Pump Fluorinert FC-40 until the gels reach the desired height.
8. Allow polymerization for at least 6 hr (but not longer than 10 hr).
9. Remove the butanol from the top with a Pasteur pipette and collect the Fluorinert from the bottom.
10. Open the chamber and cut polymerized material from the bottom of the stacked glass plates with a razor blade.
11. Push out the gel assembly with the back of a pair of forceps or a strong spatula, and wash the gel top with distilled water and once with 1:1 separation gel buffer:water.
12. Wrap the gels in wet, waxed paper soaked with separation gel buffer and then in a plastic bag to prevent drying, and store at 4°C.
13. Remove gels from stack as required by inserting a razor blade between adjacent gel sets.

Stacking Gel

1. Wash with distilled water, dry the inside with a piece of filter paper, and assemble the running chamber.
2. Seal the space between the glas plates and the running chamber with 2% hot agarose in running buffer and prepare the stacking gel mix.
3. For three gels, mix 2.01 ml distilled water, 2.50 ml Tris (250 m*M*, pH 6.8), and 0.40 ml acrylamide solution (50%:1.33%).
4. Apply the solution with a pipette and fill gel completely.
5. Polymerize for 30 min without overlay.
6. Thaw the frozen first dimensions 10 min before use at room temperature.
7. Drain away unpolymerized material from the top of the mini slab gel with a piece of filter paper.
8. Pour the first-dimension gel together with the equilibration buffer in a petri dish, remove the gel with a needle, and place it on the freshly exposed side of a Parafilm.
9. Use a clean spatula to straighten the gel.

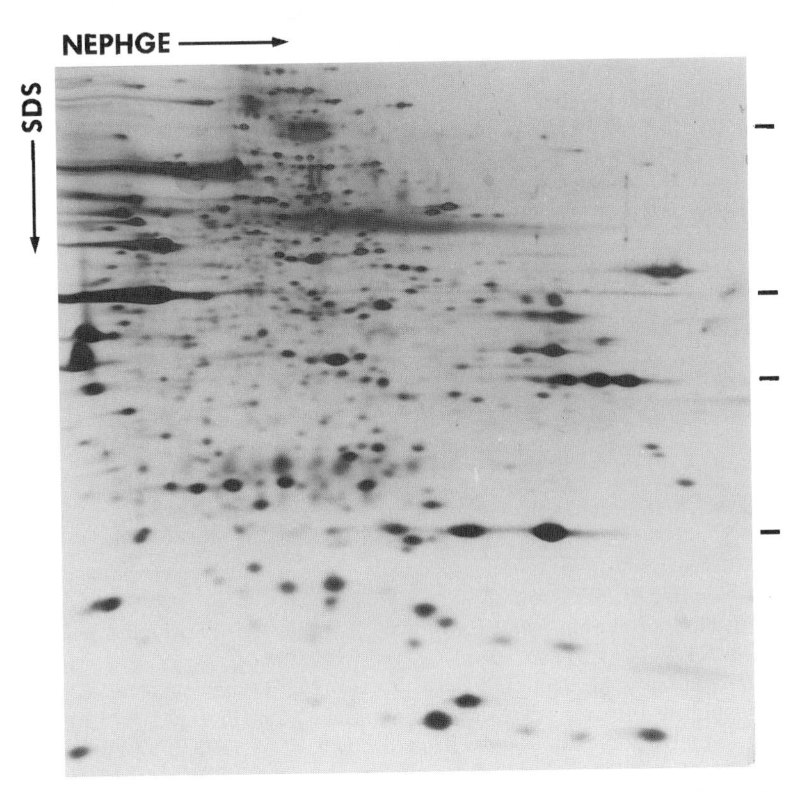

FIGURE 3 Silver-stained mini two-dimensional NEPHGE. Sample: pig bladder whole muscle extract. Resolved p*I* values range from 4.7 (tropomyosin) to 9.82 (mammalian calponin α-variant).

10. Fill the last millimeter with hot agarose containing bromphenol blue and quickly apply the tube gel.
11. Overlay with agarose, fill the chamber with buffer, and run the second dimension with constant 100 V through the stacking gel and then at constant 160 V for separation.
12. Remove the gel and process for Coomassie blue stain, silver stain (Fig. 3), or Western blotting.

IV. Comments

The method described provides a quick and efficient tool for determining p*I* values of proteins in complex mixtures like those expressed in *Escherichia coli.* Information about the p*I* of recombinant proteins can help in the design of purification procedures.

Changes in the crosslinking and acrylamide percentages in first and second dimensions allow observation of proteins of molecular weights up to 250 kDa.

The reduced thickness of first- and second-dimension gels makes this method also useful for monitoring radioactively labeled proteins from cell culture extracts.

V. Pitfalls

Handling of first-dimension capillary tubes requires some practice as the capillaries tend to break when pushed with too much force into the tube connectors.

REFERENCE

Matsudaira, P., and Burgess, D. R. (1978) SDS microslab linear gradient polyacrylamide gel electrophoresis. *Anal. Biochem.* **87**, 383–396.

SUGGESTED READING

Gimona, M., Sparrow, M. P., Strasser, P., Herzog, M., and Small, J. V. (1992) Calponin and SM 22 isoforms in avian and mammalian smooth muscle. *Eur. J. Biochem.* **205**, 1067–1075.

Laemmli, U. K. (1970) Cleavage of structural proteins during the assembly of the head of bacteriophage T4. *Nature* **277**, 680–685.

O'Farrell, P. H. (1975) High resolution two-dimensional electrophoresis of proteins. *J. Biol. Chem.* **250**, 4007–4021.

O'Farrell, P. Z., Goodman, H. M., and O'Farrell, P. H. (1977) High resolution two-dimensional electrophoresis of basic as well as acidic proteins. *Cell* **12**, 1133–1142.

Strasser, P., Gimona, M., Herzog, M., Geiger, B., and Small, J. V. (1993) Variable and constant regions in the C-terminus of vinculin and metavinculin. *FEBS Lett.* **317**, 189–194.

Two-Dimensional Gel Analysis of Posttranslational Modifications

Scott D. Patterson and James I. Garrels

I. Introduction

Two-dimensional (2D) gel electrophoresis provides the ability to separate thousands of gene products in a single experiment (see also articles by Julio E. Celis, Gitte Ratz, Bodil Basse, Jette B. Lauridsen, and Ariana Celis; by Angelika Görg; and by Mario Gimona, Barbara Galazkiewicz, and Markus Niederreiter). Linking many such experiments and quantitating them by computer analysis can reveal patterns of coordinate regulation (Garrels and Franza, 1989). With appropriate *in vivo* metabolic and *in vitro* labeling strategies, a large number of posttranslational modifications can be identified on many proteins at once. Therefore, not only can protein regulation be analyzed, so can the posttranslational modification status of these proteins. In this article we describe methods to identify phosphorylated, glycosylated (N-linked), and terminal O-linked N-acetylglucosamine (O-GlcNAc) and prenylated and fatty acylated proteins in human lymphoblast cells. These modifications are then mapped into ^{35}S-radiolabeled 2D gel patterns by comigration.

II. Materials and Instrumentation

Jurkat T lymphoblasts (Clone E6-1, ATCC TIB 152) were obtained from the American Type Culture Collection. Jurkat cells are maintained in RPMI-1640 (Cat. No. 320-1875AJ) and streptomycin–penicillin (Cat. No. 600-5140AG) from Gibco-BRL/Life Technologies and in fetal bovine serum (FBS, characterized, Cat. No. A-1115-L) from Hyclone Laboratories, Inc. The following, obtained from Gibco-BRL/Life Technologies, are used for various *in vivo* radiolabeling experiments: dialyzed fetal bovine serum (dFBS, Cat. No. 220-6300AG), sodium phosphate-free RPMI-1640 (Cat. No. 329-1877AJ), and L-methionine free RPMI-1640 (Cat. No. 320-1876PJ). Deoxyribonuclease I (DNase, bovine pancreas, EC 3.1.21.1, >2000 U/mg, Cat. No. LS06330, DPFF) and ribonuclease A (RNase, bovine pancreas, EC 3.1.27.5, >3000 U/mg, Cat. No. LS05679, RASE) were obtained from Worthington Biochemical Corporation. Phosphate-buffered saline (PBS) in tablet form (Cat. No. P-4417), galactosyltransferase (bovine milk, EC 2.4.1.22, Cat. No. G-5507), UDP-galactose Na (Cat. No. U-4500), aprotinin (Cat. No. A-4529), and adenosine 5′-monophosphate (5′-AMP, type III, equine muscle, Cat. No. A-1877) were from Sigma Chemical Company. Nalgene filter units (0.2 μm, 500 ml, Cat. No. 450-0020) were from Baxter.

The following radiolabels were from NEN Products: EXPRE^{35}S^{35}S [^{35}S]methionine/cysteine mix (>1000 Ci/mmole, Cat. No. NEG-072), [^{32}P]orthophosphate (~9000 Ci/

mmole, Cat. No. NEX-053), [9, 10-^{3}H(N)]palmitic acid (~60 Ci/mmole, Cat. No. NET-043), and [9, 10-^{3}H(N)]myristic acid (~30 Ci/mmole, Cat. No. NET-830). [5-^{3}H]Mevalonolactone, RS (MVA, 50–60 Ci/mmole, Cat. No. ART-315), and D-[2, 6-^{3}H]mannose (60 Ci/mmole, Cat. No. ART-319) were from American Radiolabeled Chemicals, Inc. Uridine diphospho-D-[6-^{3}H]galactose ammonium salt (UDP-[^{3}H]-galactose, 18 Ci/ml, Cat. No. TRK.513) was from Amersham Corporation. Lovastatin was a gift of Mr. A. W. Alberts (Merck & Co., Inc.). All chemicals for 2D gel electrophoresis were from Millipore Corporation, except for carrier ampholytes which were from Pharmacia LKB Biotechnology and Serva (Crescent Chemical Co.). All other chemicals and reagents were of the highest grade available.

Images of fluorographed, ^{3}H-radiolabeled 2D gel patterns are visualized using Kodak X-ray film (X-Omat AR-5, 10 × 12 in., Cat. No. 152 4065, Eastman Kodak Company) following fluorography or autoradiography as described in the text.

III. Procedures

A. SAMPLE PREPARATION

Modified from Garrels (1983) and Garrels and Franza (1989).

Solutions

1. *dSDS:* 0.3% SDS, 1% β-mercaptoethanol, 0.05 *M* Tris, pH 8.0. To make 1 liter, solubilize 3 g of SDS, 4.44 g Tris–HCl, 2.65 g Trisbase, and 10 ml β-mercaptoethanol (β-ME) in distilled water (dH_2O) and adjust to 1 liter. Aliquot this into 500-μl lots and store at −70°C.

2. *DNase/RNase:* 1 mg/ml DNase, 0.5 mg/ml RNase, 0.5 *M* Tris, 0.05 *M* $MgCl_2$, pH 7.0. To make 5 ml, add 5.0 mg of DNase I, 2.5 mg of RNase A, 1585 μl of 1.5 *M* Tris–HCl, 80 μl of 1.5 *M* Tris base, and 250 μl of 1.0 *M* $MgCl_2$ to 2.96 ml of dH_2O. This solution is stored at −70°C as 50-μl aliquots.

3. *Low-salt lysis buffer (LSLB):* 1% Triton X-100, 0.01 *M* $MgCl_2$, 0.03 *M* Tris–HCl, pH 7.5. To make 100 ml, add 1 ml of Triton X-100, 1 ml of 1.0 M $MgCl_2$, 1.72 ml of 1.5 *M* Tris–HCl, and 273 μl of 1.5 *M* Tris base to distilled water and bring to a total volume of 100 ml. Store at −70°C as 1-ml aliquots.

Steps

Whole cell lysate

1. Wash cells in a microfuge tube with PBS twice.

2. Add an approximately equal volume of hot (just boiled) dSDS to the pelleted cells.

3. Immediately place the tube into boiling water for 1–3 min, gently swirl, and then cool on ice.

4. Add a volume of DNase/RNase equal to one-tenth that of the dSDS, and gently swirl the tube while keeping it on ice for a couple of minutes or by repeatedly pipetting or vortexing (ensuring no bubble formation). This volume of DNase/RNase is usually sufficient for the sample to lose its viscosity (easily determined by pipetting) and the solution to look clear. If this is not the case, add more dSDS and RNase/DNase.

5. Snap-freeze the sample in liquid nitrogen, and store at −70°C.

Nucleus enrichment/postnuclear supernatant

1. Wash the cells in PBS twice and resuspend them in an equal volume of LSLB in a microfuge tube on ice.

2. Pass the mixture through a 28-gauge needle several times and then centrifuge at 325 *g* (2000 rpm) in a microfuge for 2 min to pellet the nuclei.

3. View an aliquot of the nuclei under a phase-contrast microscope to determine the extent of enrichment (i.e., are the nuclei morphologically satisfactory? devoid of plasma membrane?) and, if necessary, repeat the shearing.

4. Remove the supernatant (postnuclear supernatant, PNS), and wash the nuclei once with LSLB and once with PBS prior to lysis of the nuclei with dSDS as above (whole cell lysate). For this lysis use two-tenths volume of DNase/RNase.

5. Snap-freeze the sample in liquid nitrogen, and store at −70°C.

B. METABOLIC LABELING

1. Methionine-Containing Proteins

Solutions

1. *Complete culture medium:* 90% RPMI-1640, 10% FBS, streptomycin–penicillin. Make the medium by mixing 900 ml RPMI-1640, 100 ml fetal bovine serum, and 10 ml streptomycin–penicillin (100×). Sterilize immediately by filtration using a 0.2-μm filter and store at 4°C. Maintain Jurkat T lymphoblasts in this medium at a concentration of 10^5 to 10^6 cells/ml.

2. *Methionine-free medium:* 90% methionine-free RPMI-1640, 10% dFBS. Mix methionine-free RPMI (90%) with dFBS (10%), filter-sterilize using a 0.2-μm filter, and store at 4°C.

Step

Label protein by adding the methionine/cysteine radiolabel (EXPRE^{35}S^{35}S), at 50–250 μCi/ml, to the methionine-free medium for variable labeling periods, from 3 to 24 hr. The labeling period is usually matched to the labeling period of the specific posttranslational modification radiolabeling experiment.

2. Phosphorylation Labeling

Solution

Sodium phosphate-free medium: 90% Na phosphate-free RPMI-1640, 10% FBS. Mix sodium phosphate-free RPMI (90%) with FBS (10%), filter-sterilize using a 0.2-μm filter, and store at 4°C.

Steps

1. For some experimental protocols it may be necessary to preincubate the cells for 30 min at a density of 1–10 × 10^6 cells/ml in sodium phosphate-free medium. If this is the case, the experiment should be carefully controlled to see whether this affects cell growth.

2. Initiate labeling by adding [^{32}P]orthophosphate to the phosphate-free medium at a concentration of 100 μCi/ml for 3 hr.

3. Wash the cells in PBS and lyse as described above.

3. N-Linked Sugar Labeling

Solution

[^{3}H]Mannose solution: The [^{3}H]mannose is supplied in ethanol. Following drying of the appropriate amount of radiolabel under vacuum, resuspend the label in complete culture medium. The label can also be dried by passive evaporation as described below for [^{3}H]MVA labeling.

Steps

1. Label by adding the equivalent of 250 μCi/ml of this [^{3}H]mannose solution to cells at a density of $1-10 \times 10^6$ cells/ml in complete culture medium and incubating for 3 hr.

2. Wash the cells with PBS and lyse as described above.

4. Lipid Labeling

This procedure follows that of Mumby and Buss (1990).

Solutions

1. *Lovastatin solution:* Prepare Lovastatin as follows (conversion of lactone to sodium salt). Dissolve 4 mg of lovastatin in 100 μl ethanol (95–100%), add 150 μl of 0.1 *N* NaOH, and heat for 2 hr at 50°C. Neutralize the solution with HCl to approximately pH 7.2, bring up to a 1-ml volume (5 m*M*) with dH_2O, and store frozen. This solution cannot be filter-sterilized.

2. *[^{3}H]MVA solution:* Add the [^{3}H]MVA label (50–100 μCi/ml) to a tissue culture well and dry by passive evaporation in a tissue culture hood. Resuspend the label by washing the well twice with a half-volume of RPMI-1640 (90%), dFBS (10%) containing lovastatin at 12.5 μ*M*.

3. *[^{3}H]Palmitic acid and [^{3}H]myristic acid solutions:* Both radiolabels, [^{3}H]palmitic acid and [^{3}H]myristic acid, are supplied in ethanol. Following drying of the appropriate amount of radiolabel under vacuum, resuspend the label in complete culture medium. The label can also be dried by passive evaporation as described above for [^{3}H]MVA labeling.

Steps

Prenylation
This procedure is modified from that of Maltese *et al.* (1990).

1. Following washing in PBS, add the cell pellet to the well containing the [^{3}H]MVA solution, giving a cell density of $1-10 \times 10^6$ cells/ml, and incubate for 24 hr.

2. Transfer the cells from the well to a microfuge tube, wash in PBS, and lyse as described above.

Fatty Acids
1. Label cells at a density of $1-10 \times 10^6$ cells/ml for 24 hr (palmitic acid) or 3 hr (myristic acid), both at 500 μCi/ml.

2. Wash the cells in PBS and lyse as described above.

C. O-GlcNAc DETECTION OF NUCLEAR PROTEINS

This procedure is modified from those of Torres and Hart (1984) and Jackson and Tjian (1988).

Solutions

1. *Autogalactosylation buffer:* To make the standard 59-μl volume of the autogalactosylation buffer, mix (in a microfuge tube) 50 μl of 100 m*M* Tris–HCl/10 m*M* $MnCl_2$, pH 7.4, 5 μl of 8 m*M* UDP-galactose Na (25 mg/ml dH_2O), 2 μl of aprotinin (10 mg/ml dH_2O), and 2 μl of β-ME (50 m*M* stock, 3.5 μl β-ME/ml dH_2O).

2. *Labeling buffer:* To make the standard 55-μl volume of the labeling buffer, mix 37.5 μl 10 m*M* Hepes–NaOH (pH 7.3), 0.15 *M* NaCl, 0.3% NP-40, 10 μl of autogalactosylated galactosyltransferase (50 U/ml), 2.5 μl of galactose buffer (0.1 *M* D-galactose, 0.1 *M* Hepes–NaOH (pH 7.3), 0.15 *M* NaCl, 50 m*M* $MgCl_2$, 5% NP-40), and 5 μl of UDP-[^{3}H]galactose in 5'-AMP (250 μCi label dried under vacuum and resuspended in 250 μl 25 m*M* 5'-AMP).

Steps

Enzyme preparation

1. Autogalactosylate galactosyltransferase by first dissolving the enzyme (10 U) in 100 μl dH_2O and adding half (store remainder at $-20°C$) of this to a microfuge tube (1.5 ml) containing 59 μl of the autogalactosylation buffer.

2. Incubate this autogalactosylation mixture for 1 hr at 37°C, and then chill on ice.

3. Add solid ammonium sulfate (61 mg, 85% final concentration) to the mix piecemeal with vortexing, and then leave the mix to stand at 4°C overnight.

4. Pellet the mix by centrifugation in a microfuge at 16,000 *g*. Resuspend the precipitate in 25 m*M* Hepes–NaOH (pH 7.3), 5 m*M* $MnCl_2$ and dialyze against this buffer for 4 hr at 4°C. Mix the dialysate (autogalactosylated galactosyltransferase) with 50 μl glycerol, yielding a final volume of 100 μl (50 U/ml).

In vitro *labeling reaction*

1. Resuspend enriched nuclei (from approximately 1×10^7 cells), prepared as described above, in 55 μl of the labeling buffer.

2. Incubate the reaction mix at 37°C for 30 min, then precipitate the protein with 55 μl TCA (20%) and wash once with 80% acetone. It is also useful to include a control experiment without the galactosyltransferase.

3. Dissolve the protein in hot dSDS, boil for 1–3 min, and store at $-70°C$ prior to electrophoresis.

D. HIGH-RESOLUTION TWO-DIMENSIONAL GEL ELECTROPHORESIS, DETECTION, AND IDENTIFICATION OF CELLULAR PROTEIN CARRYING SPECIFIC POSTTRANSLATIONAL MODIFICATIONS

This procedure follows those of Garrels (1983) and Garrels and Franza (1989). See also articles by Julio E. Celis, Gitte Ratz, Bodil Basse, Jette B. Lauridsen, and Ariana Celis and by Angelika Görg.

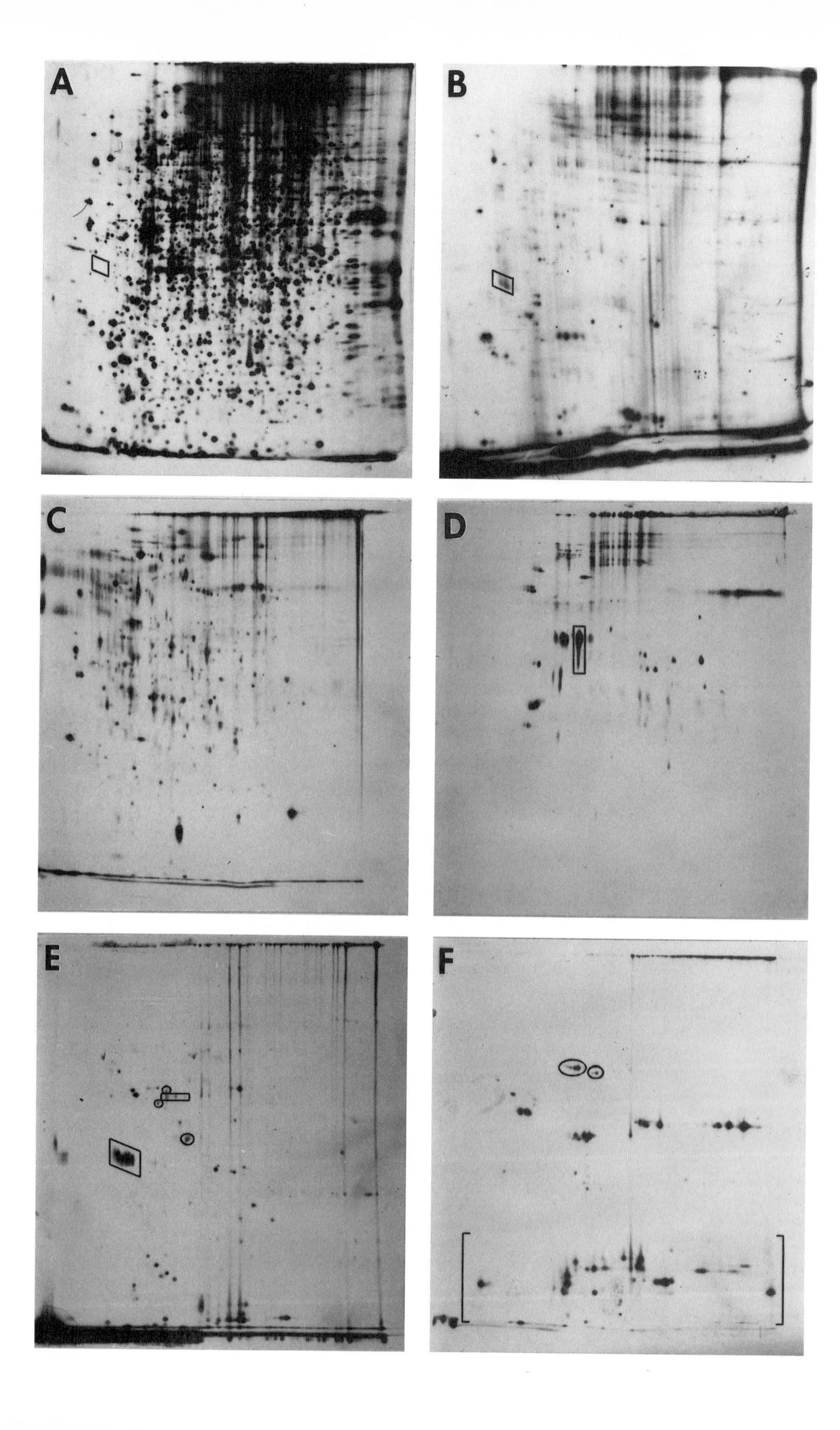
A
B
C
D
E
F

1. 2D-Gel Electrophoresis

Samples frozen at $-70°C$ are either vacuum dried ([^{35}S]methionine or [^{32}P]-orthophosphate) or acetone precipitated (all other labels). (To acetone precipitate, add 4 vol acetone to sample and leave for 1 hr at ambient temperature, then microfuge for 15 min at 16,000 *g* at 4°C, remove supernatant carefully, and let pellet air dry.) The dried samples are resuspended carefully (heating to 37°C for a short period, only if necessary) in a volume of sample buffer [SB: 9.95 *M* urea, 4% NP-40, 2% ampholytes pH 6–8, 100 m*M* dithiothreitol (Garrels and Franza, 1989)] equal to that of the original sample volume. The exception to this is postnuclear supernatants which are resuspended in half of their original volume with SB containing 0.3% SDS (SBS). Any further dilution of the sample prior to loading is made in SBS. TCA precipitates of aliquots (2 μl) of the sample are subjected to liquid scintillation counting as described (Garrels, 1983), and the activity (dpm/μl) is determined. We routinely load 500,000 dpm of ^{35}S-labeled protein, 200,000 dpm ^{32}P-labeled protein, and 1,000,000 dpm ^{3}H-labeled protein to each gel. The electrophoresis conditions are as described in Garrels (1983). Total protein load is limited to less than 20 μg protein in this system.

2. Detection Methods

All ^{3}H-labeled samples (including mixes) are visualized using fluorography with either PPO/DMSO as described by Garrels (1983) or EN^{3}HANCE^{TM} (NEN Products, Boston, MA) according to the manufacturer's directions. The ^{35}S- and $^{35}S/^{32}P$-labeled mixed samples are visualized by fluorography. Fluorographs are exposed to film for generally 1 week and then 1 month or longer. ^{32}P-labeled samples are visualized by autoradiography for 6 hr and 1 day.

3. Identifying Cellular Proteins Carrying Specific Posttranslational Modifications

This is achieved by mixing the general protein-labeled sample (^{35}S-labeled) with the specific modifying group-labeled sample. The ratios (and exposure times) that we use are approximately 500,000 dpm ^{35}S label to 1,000,000 dpm ^{3}H label (1 week and 1 month) or 200,000 dpm of ^{32}P label (2 days). If time permits, it is also

FIGURE 1 Fluorographs of whole cell lysates and a nucleus-enriched lysate, radiolabeled to display various posttranslational modifications. Jurkat T lymphoblasts were radiolabeled for the indicated time, lysed, and loaded on a 2D gel. The resulting fluorographs were imaged for the time shown in parentheses: (A) [^{35}S]methionine/cysteine mix for 3 hr (37 days); (B) [^{32}P]orthophosphate for 8 hr (6 hr) (gel autoradiographed, not fluorographed); (C) [^{3}H]-mannose for 3 hr (60 days); (D) [^{3}H]galactose (100 days) (enzymatic labeling of nucleus-enriched fraction after lysis); (E) [^{3}H]myristate for 3 hr (90 days); and (F) [^{3}H]mevalonate for 24 hr (120 days). Most of the protein spots visible on these exposures were also visible at imaging times a third the length of those shown. The gels are oriented with basic proteins to the right and high mass proteins at the top of the image. The boxes in the acidic region of A, B, and E show a protein labeled by myristate and phosphate but not methionine—a candidate MARCKS protein family member. The box in D shows the inverted teardrop shape characteristic of a heavily O-GlcNAc-modified protein. The small rectangular box in E shows the labeling of $p56^{lck}$, a myristate-modified protein-tyrosine kinase (identified using antiserum kindly supplied by Drs. Aebersold and Watts). The myristate-labeled sample in E was vacuum dried, and the faint images of actin and the tubulins, due to nonspecific binding, have been circled. Acetone-precipitated samples show greatly decreased nonspecific binding. In F, lamins B and B_2 are circled, and the lower mass protein region that is bracketed shows the small GTP-binding proteins.

of advantage to allow the ^{35}S label to decay one half-life (87 days) between exposures of $^{3}H/^{35}S$ mixes, and the ^{32}P to decay two half-lives (28 days) for the $^{32}P/^{35}S$ mixes. This will assist in determining which proteins are carrying the label. For ^{32}P labeling it is also possible to shield the β-induced light emission from the ^{35}S label in fluorographs by using thin black cardboard placed between the gel and the film. This will yield superimposable images which greatly facilitates identifying which proteins are phosphorylated.

IV. Comments

All radioactive work should be performed carefully and according to the radiosafety guidelines of the institution (also see article by Richard W. Davies). Using the labeling strategies and protocols described in this article, it is possible to identify ^{35}S-labeled proteins in whole cell lysates, nucleus enrichments, and postnuclear supernatants that are posttranslationally modified with phosphate, sugar, or lipid. Representative fluorographs are shown in Fig. 1. Once modifications are mapped to specific ^{35}S-labeled protein spots, further investigation of their regulation can be followed by [^{35}S]methionine labeling experiments. In the past, 2D gels have been underutilized for the analysis of posttranslational modification changes in response to cellular regulatory events.

V. Pitfalls

1. When identifying cellular proteins that carry specific posttranslational modifications, in the first instance, ensure that the labeling period for the ^{35}S labeling is the same as that for the specific ($^{3}H/^{32}P$) labeling. Remember that labeling reflects protein turnover (synthesis/degradation or secretion) and that required label concentration can vary between cell types due to differences in the endogenous pool of the precursor. The radiolabel concentrations reported here should serve only as a guide for initial labeling studies.

2. Myristate has been shown to be turned over rapidly to palmitate (Vidal *et al.*, 1991). We have used labeling times for palmitate and myristate of 24 and 3 hr. These gave us efficient labeling and only one protein labeled by both palmitate and myristate. Without extracting the labeled protein and characterizing the labeled moiety, a mix of both labelings (myristate/palmitate) can confirm whether the protein of interest could have been inappropriately labeled due to this turnover. Another consideration in this regard is that myristoylation is a stable modification and palmitoylation is a dynamic process; therefore, the specific activity of the myristate-labeled protein reflects that of the precursor pool over the labeling period, whereas the palmitate labeled protein may only reflect that of the precursor pool at the end of the labeling period (Linder *et al.*, 1993).

3. Duplicate exposures of double-labeled gel patterns that are separated in time by the half-life of the shortest-lived isotope should be for the same period (e.g., 1 week initially, then 1 week after one half-life). This will allow easier determination of which spots have decreased in intensity between the two exposures.

4. An important factor to address when labeling with terminal O-GlcNAc residues is that the mass of the protein is increased by 180 Da with each labeled galactose moiety added (see spot shape boxed in Fig. 1D). With heavily O-GlcNAc-modified proteins this can make identification of the ^{35}S-labeled protein impossible. This can be overcome by galactosylating a ^{35}S-labeled lysate with

"cold" UDP-galactose to observe which proteins disappear compared with an untreated lysate. If less sensitive detection is sufficient, then lectin blotting can be performed using succinylated wheat germ agglutinin to detect glycoproteins with terminal GlcNAc residues (Patterson and Bell, 1990).

5. When labeling prenylated proteins it is important to keep the lovastatin concentration low, as it has been observed to arrest some cells in a cell cycle-dependent manner and induce others to undergo apoptosis (S. D. Patterson, unpublished data).

6. Acetone precipitation, rather than vacuum drying of the cell lysate, will decrease the amount of free unincorporated label from being noncovalently bound to abundant proteins nonspecifically, i.e., actin and tubulins (see circled proteins in Fig. 1E).

7. Ensure that following resuspension of the sample in SB or SBS, the sample is not subjected to heating above 37°C. SB and SBS contain urea and heating in this solution will cause carbamylation and the artifactual generation of charged isoforms.

REFERENCES

Garrels, J. I. (1983) Quantitative two-dimensional electrophoresis of proteins. *In* "Methods in Enzymology" (R. Wu, L. Grossman, and K. Moldave, eds.), Vol. 100, pp. 411–423. Academic Press, San Diego.

Garrels, J. I., and Franza, B. R., Jr. (1989) The REF52 protein database. *J. Biol. Chem.* **264**, 5283–5298.

Jackson, S. P., and Tjian, R. (1988) O-Glycosylation of eukaryotic transcription factors: Implications for mechanisms of transcriptional regulation. *Cell* **55**, 125–133.

Linder, M. E., Middleton, P., Hepler, J. R., Taussig, R., Gilman, A. G., and Mumby, S. M. (1993) Lipid modifications of G proteins: a subunits are palmitoylated. *Proc. Natl. Acad. Sci. USA* **90**, 3675–3679.

Maltese, W. A., Sheridan, K. M., Repko, E. M., and Erdman, R. A. (1990) Post-translational modification of low molecular mass GTP-binding proteins by isoprenoid. *J. Biol. Chem.* **265**, 2148–2155.

Mumby, S. M., and Buss, J. E. (1990) Metabolic radiolabeling techniques for identification of prenylated and fatty acylated proteins. *In* "Methods: A Companion to Methods in Enzymology" (J. N. Abelson and M. I. Simon, eds.), Vol. 1, pp. 216–220. Academic Press, San Diego.

Patterson, S. D., and Bell, K. (1990) The carbohydrate side chains of the major plasma serpins of horse and wallaby: Analyses of enzymatic and chemically treated (including 'Smith degradation') protein blots by lectin binding. *Biochem. Int.* **20**, 429–436.

Torres, C.-R., and Hart, G. W. (1984) Topography and polypeptide distribution of terminal *N*-acetylglucosamine residues on the surfaces of intact lymphocytes. *J. Biol. Chem.* **259**, 3308–3317.

Vidal, M., Murgue, B., Basse, F., and Bienvenue, A. (1991) Fatty acylation of human platelet proteins: Evidence for myristoylation of a 50 kDa peptide. *Biochem. Int.* **23**, 1175–1184.

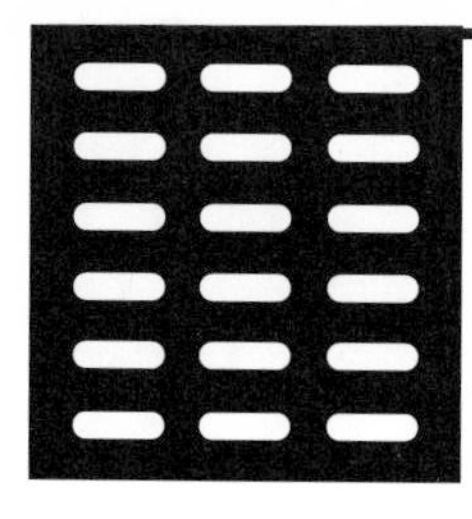

Detection of Protein Kinase Activity after Renaturation of Proteins Transferred from Sodium Dodecyl Sulfate–Polyacrylamide Gels to Membranes

Deborah A. Shackelford, Richard Y. Yeh, and Justin A. Zivin

I. Introduction

Proteins denatured and separated by SDS–polyacrylamide gel electrophoresis can often be renatured and regain enzymatic activity. This has proved a useful and effective method of (1) detecting enzymatic activities in crude homogenates, (2) demonstrating that a purified protein or protein expressed from a cloned gene has activity, or (3) demonstrating that a subunit of a multisubunit enzyme complex has intrinsic activity. Initially protocols relied on extensive washing to remove the SDS from the polyacrylamide gel to allow renaturation of the proteins and detection of enzymatic activity by a gel overlay technique (Heeb and Gabriel, 1984; Hutchcroft *et al.*, 1991). Detection of protein kinases generally has relied on autophosphorylation of the enzyme. Substrates have also been incorporated into the gel or into a blocking solution to augment the phosphorylation signal or to detect other types of enzymes, including nucleases and DNA polymerase. The sensitivity of the gel overlay method was increased by denaturing proteins with guanidine hydrochloride or urea after SDS–PAGE followed by renaturation in buffer. A further modification that makes the procedure more versatile is electroblotting proteins separated by SDS–PAGE onto a nitrocellulose (Celenza and Carlson, 1991) or PVDF (Ferrell and Martin, 1991) membrane before denaturation, renaturation, and phosphorylation *in situ*. This article describes the *in situ* renaturation method adapted for the detection of Ca^{2+}/calmodulin-dependent protein kinase II (CaM kinase II) in crude tissue homogenates (Shackelford and Zivin, 1993). CaM kinase II is a ubiquitous oligomeric enzyme but is particularly enriched in the brain, from which four homologous isoforms and an alternatively spliced isoform have been isolated and cloned (Colbran and Soderling, 1990; Hanson and Schulman, 1992). CaM kinase II is activated by elevation of intracellular Ca^{2+} and phosphorylates many substrates regulating a wide variety of cellular functions. The *in situ* renaturation procedure described has been used to analyze the changes in activity and subcellular distribution of CaM kinase II that occur in spinal cord and brain in response to ischemic injury (Shackelford *et al.*, 1993).

II. Materials

Immobilon-P membrane (Cat. No. IPVH) is purchased from Millipore. Guanidine hydrochloride (Cat. No. BP178), Tris base (Cat. No. BP152), NaCl (Cat. No. S671), EDTA (disodium salt, Cat. No. S311), $MgCl_2$ (Cat. No. M33), KOH (Cat. No. P250), dithiothreitol, (DTT, Cat. No. BP172), and heat-sealable pouches (Cat. No. 01-812-17) are purchased from Fisher Scientific. Hepes (sodium salt, Cat. No. H-1016), $CaCl_2$ (Cat. No. C-3881), and calmodulin (phosphodiesterase 3′:5′-cyclic nucleotide activator, Cat. No. P-2277) are purchased from Sigma. Guanidine–HCl (Cat. No. G-4505) can also be obtained from Sigma. Nonidet P-40 (NP-40, Cat. No. 19628) is purchased from U.S. Biochemical Corporation; $ZnSO_4$ (Cat. No. 8880) is from Mallinckrodt; and SDS (Cat. No. 44244) is from Gallard–Schlesinger. [γ-^{32}P]ATP (Cat. No. 35001X) is purchased from ICN. Hyperfilm-MP (Cat. No. RPN 1678) is from Amersham.

III. Procedures

Solutions

1. *1 M Tris–HCl, pH 8.3:* To make 1 liter, solubilize 121.1 g of Tris base in distilled water, adjust pH to 8.3 with HCl, and bring to a total volume of 1 liter. Store at 4°C.

2. *0.5 M EDTA, pH 8.0:* To make 100 ml, dissolve 18.6 g of EDTA, disodium salt, in distilled water, adjust pH to 8.0 to aid in solubilization, and adjust to a total volume of 100 ml.

3. *10% Nonidet P-40 (v/v):* Dilute 10 ml of NP-40 in 90 ml of distilled water. Store at 4°C.

4. *1 M HEPES, pH 7.3:* To make 100 ml, solubilize 26 g Hepes, sodium salt, in distilled water, adjust pH to 7.3 with NaOH, and bring to a total volume of 100 ml. Store at 4°C.

5. *1 M $MgCl_2$.*

6. *50 mM $CaCl_2$.*

7. *2 M NaCl.*

8. *1 M KOH.*

9. *Denaturation buffer:* 7 *M* guanidine–HCl, 50 m*M* Tris–HCl, pH 8.3, 2 m*M* EDTA, 50 m*M* DTT. To make 100 ml, dissolve 66.85 g guanidine–HCl in distilled water. Add 5 ml 1 *M* Tris–HCl, pH 8.3, and 0.4 ml 0.5 *M* EDTA, pH 8.0. Allow the mixture to warm to room temperature with stirring and adjust to a total volume of 100 ml. Add 0.77 g solid DTT. It is essential to add the DTT fresh for every use.

10. *Tris-buffered saline:* 10 m*M* Tris–HCl, pH 7.5, 0.14 *M* NaCl. To make 1 liter, solubilize 9 g of NaCl in distilled water. Add 10 ml of 1 *M* Tris–HCl, pH 7.5, and adjust to a total volume of 1 liter.

11. *Renaturation buffer:* 140 m*M* NaCl, 10 m*M* Tris–HCl, pH 7.5, 2 m*M* EDTA, 0.1% NP-40, 2 m*M* DTT. To make 100 ml, combine 7 ml 2 *M* NaCl, 1 ml 1 *M* Tris–HCl, pH 7.5, 0.4 ml 0.5 *M* EDTA, pH 8.0, 1 ml 10% NP-40, 0.031 g DTT, and 90.6 ml H_2O.

12. *Kinase buffer A:* 40 m*M* Hepes, pH 7.3, 5 m*M* $MgCl_2$, 0.15 m*M* $CaCl_2$, 14 μg/ml calmodulin, 10 μCi/ml [γ-^{32}P]ATP). To make 10 ml, combine 0.4 ml 1

M Hepes, pH 7.3, 0.05 ml 1 *M* $MgCl_2$, 0.030 ml 50 m*M* $CaCl_2$, 0.028 ml 5 mg/ml calmodulin, 0.010 ml 10 mCi/ml [γ-^{32}P]ATP, and 9.48 ml H_2O.

13. *Kinase buffer B:* 40 m*M* Hepes, pH 7.3, 5 m*M* $MgCl_2$, 5 m*M* $ZnSO_4$, 10 μCi/ml [γ-^{32}P]ATP. To make 10 ml, combine 0.4 ml 1 *M* Hepes, pH 7.3, 0.05 ml 1 *M* $MgCl_2$, 0.05 ml 1 *M* $ZnSO_4$, 0.010 ml 10 μCi/ml [γ-^{32}P]ATP, and 9.49 ml H_2O.

Steps

1. Fractionate proteins by SDS–polyacrylamide gel electrophoresis (Laemmli, 1970; see also article by Julio E. Celis and Eyδfinnur Olsen) and electrophoretically transfer to Immobilon-P membrane in transfer buffer (192 m*M* glycine, 25 m*M* Tris base, 20% v/v methanol) (Towbin *et al.*, 1979; see also article by Julio E. Celis, Jette B. Lauridsen, and Bodil Basse) for 4 hr at 140 mA. The presence of methanol does not interfere with subsequent procedures.

2. After transfer, place the blot in denaturation buffer (50 ml per blot). (The volumes indicated are for a typical 14 × 14-cm membrane.) Incubate for 1 hr at room temperature with gentle shaking. The membrane will turn translucent.

3. Decant the denaturation buffer and rinse the blot three times with Tris-buffered saline. The membrane will turn opaque again.

4. Add 50 ml of renaturation buffer per blot and incubate the membrane at 4°C for approximately 16 hr with gentle rocking.

5. Decant renaturation buffer and incubate the membrane in 50 ml of 30 m*M* Tris–HCl, pH 7.5, per blot for 30–60 min at room temperature. This wash can be replaced with 40 m*M* Hepes, pH 7.3, buffer with no effect on renaturable kinase activities.

6. Place blot into a heat-sealable pouch. Add 5 ml of kinase buffer A or kinase buffer B per blot. Seal pouch and carefully trap and seal bubbles away from blot. This step can also be done in a tray dedicated to radioactive samples but may require a greater volume of kinase buffer. Incubate for 30 min at room temperature with gentle shaking.

7. Pour off kinase buffer into appropriate radioactive waste receptacle. Wash each blot twice for 10 min with 50 ml of 30 m*M* Tris–HCl, pH 7.5; once with 30 m*M* Tris–HCl, pH 7.5, containing 0.1% NP-40; and once more with 30 m*M* Tris–HCl, pH 7.5.

8. Wash each blot once for 10 min with 50 ml of 1 *M* KOH to hydrolyze unreacted ATP, and rinse with water, 10% acetic acid, and again with water. Dispose of all washes as radioactive waste.

9. Without allowing membrane to dry, wrap blot in Saran wrap and expose to X-ray film with an intensifying screen at −70°C for approximately 0.5–2 days. The blot can be rewashed with 1 *M* KOH if the background is too high.

IV. Comments

In situ renaturation of homogenates from rat or rabbit brain or spinal cord tissue revealed three major kinase activities. The phosphoproteins at M_r = 58,000–62,000 and 50,000–52,000 comigrated with the purified CaM kinase isoforms β, β', and α, respectively, and were recognized by monoclonal antibodies to the respective subunits by immunoblotting and immunoprecipitation (Shackelford and Zivin, 1993). Unlike the CaM kinase isoforms, phosphorylation of the 90,000- to 95,000-dalton kinase did not require Ca^{2+} and calmodulin. The ratio of incorporation of

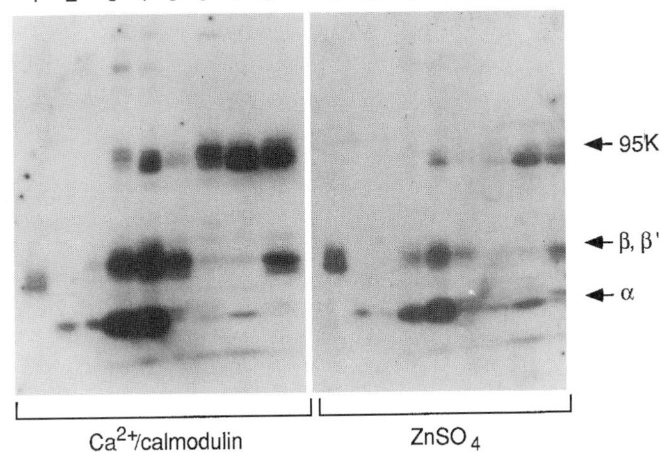

FIGURE 1 Autoradiograph of CaM kinase α and β isoforms autophosphorylated after *in situ* renaturation. Identical samples were analyzed on each half of the blot. The left half was phosphorylated with kinase buffer A containing Ca^{2+} and calmodulin, and the right half was phosphorylated with kinase buffer B containing $ZnSO_4$. Lane 1, purified recombinant *Xenopus* CaM kinase β (490 ng); lane 2, purified recombinant mouse brain CaM kinase α (174 ng); lane 3, rat forebrain (50 μg of particulate fraction); lane 4, rabbit forebrain (50 μg of particulate fraction); lane 5, rabbit spinal cord (50 μg of particulate fraction); lane 6, rat forebrain (50 μg of cytosol fraction); lane 7, rabbit forebrain (50 μg of cytosol fraction); lane 8, rabbit spinal cord (50 μg of cytosol fraction). The exposure times were 15 hr (left half) and 30 hr (right half). Purified CaM kinase isoforms were provided by Drs. Debra Brickey and Thomas Soderling (Brickey *et al.*, 1990).

label into CaM kinase α and β from the rat forebrain correlates well with their relative expression in this brain region. CaM kinase α and β could be detected in as little as 2–5 μg of a crude particulate fraction and 10 μg of the cytosolic fraction of rabbit or rat brain. We routinely use 10 and 50 μg of the particulate and cytosolic fractions, respectively, of brain tissue to detect CaM kinase II by *in situ* renaturation and autoradiography of the blot for 16 hr.

It was reported that $ZnSO_4$ inhibits basal and Ca^{2+}/calmodulin-stimulated phosphorylation of substrates in crude tissue homogenates, but also stimulates the Ca^{2+}/calmodulin-independent autophosphorylation of CaM kinase II (Weinberger and Rostas, 1991). We compared the ability of $ZnSO_4$ and Ca^{2+}/calmodulin to stimulate CaM kinase II autophosphorylation after *in situ* renaturation (Fig. 1). Ca^{2+}/calmodulin-stimulated autophosphorylation of CaM kinase α and β was 2 to 10 times greater than the Zn^{2+}-stimulated activity, depending on the sample; however, $ZnSO_4$ had the added advantages of inhibiting the phosphorylation of the 90,000- to 95,000-dalton kinase present in the crude homogenates and being less expensive than using calmodulin in the assay. The components of the kinase buffer (e.g., metal ions, cofactors) can be varied to optimize detection of a particular kinase.

The incorporation of phosphate into the α and β subunits on the membrane was linear with respect to time from 10 to 30 min of incubation with kinase buffer A (Ferrell and Martin, 1991; Shackelford and Zivin, 1993).

There are several advantages to performing the denaturation, renaturation, and kinase procedures with the proteins electroblotted onto a membrane rather than with the SDS–polyacrylamide gel. First, after phosphorylation, the same blot can be used for immunoblotting depending on the antibody and the integrity of the epitope recognized. We were able to successfully use monoclonal antibodies to CaM kinase α and β and the Amersham Enhanced Chemiluminescence (ECL) Western blotting detection system to detect the isoforms after *in situ* renaturation (Shackelford and Zivin, 1993). Because detection of the chemiluminescence required only a 30 sec to 5 min exposure, the ^{32}P-labeled proteins on the blot did not interfere. Alternatively, colorimetric substrates can be used for visualization of antibodies bound in immunoblotting. Second, renatured protein kinases detected on the membrane can be subjected directly to peptide mapping or to phosphoamino acid analysis (Kamps and Sefton, 1989) to confirm that radiolabeling of the blotted proteins is due to kinase activity and not just nonspecific ATP binding. The use of PVDF membrane, rather than nitrocellulose, permits the use of a strong base to remove unincorporated label and a strong acid to hydrolyze the protein for amino acid analysis. Third, the volume of buffers used and the volume of radioactive waste liquid from the washes are greatly reduced.

The *in situ* renaturation procedure can also be adapted to measure kinase activity as incorporation of phosphate into exogenously added peptide substrate (Shackelford and Zivin, 1993). This allows detection of CaM kinase II that may be enzymatically active but has the sites of autophosphorylation altered by mutagenesis, proteolysis, or posttranslational modification. By the judicious choice of peptide substrate and required activators, the method can be used to selectively detect different protein kinases.

V. Pitfalls

1. Omission of the denaturation and renaturation steps results in no detectable kinase activities on the blot. Omission of just the denaturation step reduces the incorporation of phosphate into the CaM kinase subunits tenfold.

2. It has been noted previously (Heeb and Gabriel, 1984), and our own experience has shown, that impurities in the SDS used for gel electrophoresis can inhibit renaturation of activity. Using electrophoretic or molecular biology-grade SDS should avoid this problem.

3. We found that inclusion of 1, 10, or 100 μM unlabeled ATP in kinase buffer A progressively reduced the label incorporated into the blotted proteins, although Celenza and Carlson (1991) reported that addition of 0.1 μM ATP reduced the background without compromising the signal. Unlabeled ATP (1–10 μM) can be included in the kinase buffer to determine the stoichiometry of incorporation of phosphate into the CaM kinase subunits.

4. It should be noted that the efficiency of incorporation of phosphate into the CaM kinase II subunits subjected to *in situ* renaturation is lower than autophosphorylation of the native enzyme in solution (Shackelford and Zivin, 1993). This appeared to be due to immobilization of the enzyme on the membrane and not to the processes of electrophoresis, denaturation, and renaturation.

5. BSA was not included in the renaturation buffer nor was the membrane blocked with 5% BSA or other proteins as described elsewhere (Ferrell and Martin, 1991; Celenza and Carlson, 1991) because this reduced the signal observed from CaM kinase II. Incubation of the membrane with BSA or other proteins may, however, increase the signal from other kinases by providing a substrate. Other procedures have employed incorporation of microtubule-associated protein 2 (MAP-2) into the gel matrix to augment detection of CaM kinase II (Kameshita and Fujisawa, 1989) using the gel overlay method; however, MAP-2 is a substrate for multiple kinases, thus reducing the specificity of the assay.

REFERENCES

Brickey, D. A., Colbran, R. J., Fong, Y. L., and Soderling, T. R. (1990) Expression and characterization of the alpha-subunit of Ca^{2+}/calmodulin-dependent protein kinase II using the baculovirus expression system. *Biochem. Biophys. Res. Commun.* **173,** 578–584.

Celenza, J. L., and Carlson, M. (1991) Renaturation of protein kinase activity on protein blots. *In* "Methods in Enzymology" (T. Hunter and B. M. Sefton, eds.), Vol. 200, pp. 423–430, Academic Press, San Diego.

Colbran, R. J., and Soderling, T. R. (1990) Calcium/calmodulin-dependent protein kinase II. *In* "Current Topics in Cell Regulation" (B. L. Horecker, E. R. Stadtman, P. B. Chock, and A. Levitzki, eds.), Vol. 31, pp. 181–221, Academic Press, San Diego.

Ferrell, J., and Martin, G. S. (1991) Assessing activities of blotted protein kinases. *In* "Methods in Enzymology" (T. Hunter and B. M. Sefton, eds.), Vol. 200, pp. 430–435. Academic Press, San Diego.

Hanson, P. I., and Schulman, H. (1992) Neuronal Ca^{2+}/calmodulin-dependent protein kinases. *Annu. Rev. Biochem.* **61,** 559–601.

Heeb, M. J., and Gabriel, O. (1984) Enzyme localization in gels. *In* "Methods in Enzymology" (W. B. Jakoby, ed.), Vol. 104, pp. 416–439. Academic Press, New York.

Hutchcroft, J. E., Anostario, J., Harrison, M. L., and Geahlen, R. L. (1991) Renaturation and assay of protein kinases after electrophoresis in sodium dodecyl sulfate–polyacrylamide gels. *In* "Methods in Enzymology" (T. Hunter and B. M. Sefton, eds.), Vol. 200, pp. 417–423. Academic Press, San Diego.

Kameshita, I., and Fujisawa, H. (1989) A sensitive method for detection of calmodulin-dependent protein kinase II activity in sodium dodecyl sulfate–polyacrylamide gel. *Anal. Biochem.* **183,** 139–143.

Kamps, M. P., and Sefton, B. M. (1989) Acid and base hydrolysis of phosphoproteins bound to immobilon facilitates analysis of phosphoamino acids in gel-fractionated proteins. *Anal. Biochem.* **176,** 22–27.

Laemmli, U. K. (1970) Cleavage of structural proteins during assembly of the head of bacteriophage T4. *Nature* **227,** 680–685.

Shackelford, D. A., Yeh, R., and Zivin, J. A. (1993) Inactivation and subcellular redistribution of Ca^{2+}/calmodulin-dependent protein kinase II following spinal cord ischemia. *J. Neurochem.* **61,** 738–747.

Shackelford, D. A., and Zivin, J. A. (1993) Renaturation of calcium/calmodulin-dependent protein kinase activity after electrophoretic transfer from sodium dodecyl sulfate–polyacrylamide gels to membranes. *Anal. Biochem.* **211,** 131–138.

Towbin, H., Staehelin, T., and Gordon, J. (1979) Electrophoretic transfer of proteins from polyacrylamide gels to nitrocellulose sheets: Procedure and some applications. *Proc. Natl. Acad. Sci. USA* **76,** 4350–4354.

Weinberger, R. P., and Rostas, J. A. P. (1991) Effect of zinc on calmodulin-stimulated protein kinase II and protein phosphorylation in rat cerebral cortex. *J. Neurochem.* 57, 605–614.

Zymography of Proteases

Christian Paech and Teresa Christianson

I. Introduction

Zymography, also known as activity staining, is a technique by which a specific enzyme or a class of enzymes can be detected in a protein mixture after electrophoretic separation on a suitable matrix (for recent reviews see Gabriel and Gersten, 1992; Gersten and Gabriel, 1992). Zymograms have become invaluable tools for identifying multiple forms of the same enzyme (isozymes) or multiple enzymes of the same class (e.g., proteases or cellulases), for studying activators and inhibitors of enzymes, and for designing purification strategies. Prerequisite for successful activity staining are (1) adequate electrophoretic resolution of the critical proteins; (2) minimum effect of the electrophoretic system on enzyme activity; (3) substrates leading directly or through a secondary reaction to a specific, stable, and sensitive signal at the location of the investigated enzyme; and (4) ability to restore enzyme activity after protein separation under denaturing conditions.

Most of the methods for producing zymograms of proteases fall into two categories: (1) the indicator signal is produced on an overlay of the electrophoresis matrix; (2) a substrate is embedded in the electrophoresis matrix and a signal appears as soon as the masking agent of the protease is removed, or the pro form of the protease is processed. In an intermediate to these two approaches a protease substrate is applied to the polyacrylamide gel after completion of the separation.

This article describes three zymogram techniques for proteases: (A) An overlay method using a slab of agarose containing a protein—proteases present in the electrophoresis gel produce clearing zones on the agarose overlay which is stained for residual protein (Every, 1981); (B) an overlay method using developed X-ray film—the gelatin layer of the film is digested by proteases present in the electrophoresis gel, resulting in the release of silver particles and, thus, in clearing zones (Paech *et al.*, 1993a,b); (C) a direct method using polyacrylamide gels with embedded protein—Electrophoresis is carried out under denaturing conditions; after renaturation of the protease clearing zones appear within the gel when the gel is stained for protein (Heussen and Dowdle, 1980). The first two methods are compatible with any conventional polyacrylamide electrophoresis on slab gels. The last method requires a homemade gel, although some companies now offer a limited variety of "zymogram" gels (Bio-Rad, NOVEX, Integrated Separation Systems, and others).

II. Materials and Instrumentation

Whenever possible, commercially prepared polyacrylamide gels were used. This avoids exposure to toxic chemicals and at the same time enhances reproducibility of results. Standard methods for preparing polyacrylamide gels are described here and elsewhere in this volume.

Homogeneous 12.5% gels from Pharmacia LKB Biotechnology (PhastGel, Cat. No. 17-0623-01) were used. Film material with clear base for overlay zymograms was purchased from Eastman Kodak Corporation (X-Omat C and EMC 1) and from E. I. du Pont de Nemours (MRF-34). MRF-34 and EMC 1 film was briefly exposed to bright light, then developed for 15 min with Eastman Kodak GBX film developer (3.8-liter concentrate, Cat. No. 190 0984), fixed for 15 min with Eastman Kodak GBX fixing solution (3.8-liter concentrate, Cat. No. 190 2485), washed with running water for 15 min, and then air-dried. X-Omat C film was processed similarly, except that the film was not exposed to light. Acrylamide (Cat. No. 161-0101), *N,N'*-methylene bisacrylamide (bisacrylamide, Cat. No. 161-0201), ammonium persulfate (Cat. No. 161-0700), and *N,N,N',N'*-tetramethylenediamine (TEMED, Cat. No. 161-0800) were products of Bio-Rad Laboratories. Agarose was purchased from FMC (SeaKem GTG agarose, Cat. No. 31079). Casein according to Hammarsten was supplied by E. Merck (Cat. No. 2242). SDS (Cat. No. 28312) and Brij 35 (10% w/v solution, Cat. No. 28316 G) was a product of Pierce Chemical Company. Ammonium sulfate (Cat. No. A-2939), bromphenol blue (sodium salt, Cat. No. B-7021), calcium chloride (dihydrate, Cat. No. C-3881), collagenase (Cat. No. C-7657), gelatin (Cat. No. G-2500), glycerol (Cat. No. G-7893), glycine (Cat. No. G-7403), hemoglobin (bovine, Cat. No. H-2500), Mes (Cat. No. M-8250), Sigmacote (Cat. No. SL-2), sodium chloride (Cat. No. S-9888), subtilisin BPN' (Cat. No. P-4789), Tris (Cat. No. T-1503), Triton X-100 (Cat. No. X-100), and trypsin (Cat. No. T-8642) were purchased from Sigma Chemical Company.

Automated polyacrylamide gel electrophoresis (PAGE) was performed with a PhastSystem from Pharmacia LKB Biotechnology (Cat. No. 18-1018-23). Homemade polyacrylamide gels were run with a Mighty Small II (Hoefer Scientific Instruments, Model SE 250) or with a Mini-PROTEAN II (Bio-Rad Laboratories, Cat. No. 165-2940) gel electrophoresis apparatus.

III. Procedures

A. ZYMOGRAPHY OF PROTEASES WITH AGAROSE OVERLAY GEL OF A NONDENATURING POLYACRYLAMIDE GEL

This procedure is adapted from Every (1981).

Solutions

1. *Overlay buffer solution:* 20 m*M* Tris–HNO_3, pH 8.8, containing 1 m*M* $NiCl_2$ and 0.02% (w/v) sodium azide. Dissolve 242 mg of Tris in 95 ml of water, titrate to pH 8.8 at room temperature with 1 *N* HNO_3, add 24 mg $NiCl_2 \cdot 6H_2O$ and 20 mg sodium azide, and complete with water to 100 ml. Keep solution at room temperature.

2. *Saturated ammonium sulfate solution:* Stir 380 g of ammonium sulfate into 500 ml of water. Heat to 80°C for 15 min, then allow to cool to room temperature. Crystal formation indicates saturation. Filter solution through Whatman paper No. 54. Keep solution at room temperature.

3. *Gel fixing solution:* Methanol/water/acetic acid, 5/5/1 (v/v/v). To make 550 ml of fixing solution, add 250 ml of methanol to 250 ml of water and stir briefly. Then add slowly, with stirring, 50 ml of glacial acetic acid. Keep solution at room temperature.

Steps

1. Coat a set of glass plates of the size of the separating gel with Sigmacote, a silanizing reagent. Wear protective gloves and work under a hood! Rapidly pour 1 to 2 ml of Sigmacote onto the glass plate and distribute solution quickly with a wad of paper towels over the entire surface. Allow to air-dry for a few minutes. Coating of the plates is required only once.

2. Assemble two coated glass plates to a chamber, closed on three sides by a silicon rubber strip (0.75 mm thick and 5 mm wide) and held in place by binder clips. Place assembled glass plates in a water bath at 80°C.

3. Suspend 300 mg of agarose and 100 mg of gelatin in 20 ml of overlay buffer in a small suction flask. Heat mixture in a microwave oven until the agarose is dissolved. Vacuum degas solution briefly. Pour solution into preheated glass plate assembly.

4. Remove glass plate assembly from water bath and allow to cool to room temperature. When the gel has set, seal the chamber with tape and store in an airtight box at 4°C until used.

5. Load sample and perform slab gel electrophoresis by any desired method. After electrophoresis, remove one (glass or plastic) plate from the separation gel.

6. Remove one glass plate from the overlay gel. Spread a sheet of clear plastic wrap over the gel. Allow for a large margin of wrap on all four sides of the gel. Turn sandwich upside down and lift the other glass plate off the overlay gel.

7. Place the overlay gel onto the separation gel. Displace trapped air bubbles by gently rubbing over the plastic wrap. Wrap up into an airtight package.

8. Incubate this sandwich for 30 min at 37°C in a standard laboratory incubator or drying oven.

9. Carefully separate the sandwich and submerse the overlay gel in saturated ammonium sulfate solution for 10 min. Place the separation gel in gel fixing solution and process for staining with Coomassie blue or with silver.

10. The overlay gel turns opaque, with clear zones indicating the position of the protease. View (photograph) the overlay gel against a black background. For representative examples, see Every (1981).

B. ZYMOGRAPHY OF PROTEASES WITH DEVELOPED FILM AFTER NONDENATURING POLYACRYLAMIDE GEL ELECTROPHORESIS ON PHASTSYSTEM GELS

This procedure is adapted from Paech *et al.* (1993a,b).

Solutions

1. *Gel fixing solution:* Methanol/water/acetic acid, 5/5/1 (v/v/v). To make 550 ml of fixing solution add 250 ml of methanol to 250 ml of water and stir briefly. Then add slowly, with stirring, 50 ml of glacial acetic acid. Keep solution at room temperature.

2. *Developing buffer:* 0.1 *M* glycine–NaOH, pH 10, for subtilisin BPN′ and trypsin. To make 250 ml of the solution, dissolve 1.87 g of glycine in 220 ml of water, adjust to pH 10 with 2 *N* NaOH at room temperature, and complete to 250 ml with water. Keep solution refrigerated.

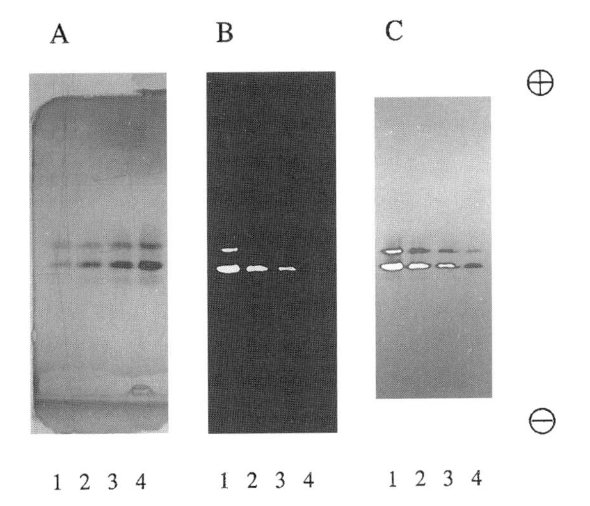

FIGURE 1 Nondenaturing PAGE of subtilisin BPN′ prepared in 20 m*M* Mes–NaOH, pH 5.8. Lanes 1 to 4: 15, 30, 60, and 120 ng of protein (A) Silver-stained 12.5% PhastGel. (B) Zymogram (mirror image) of gel shown in A. The contact time of the film overlay (MRF-34) was 8 min. The film was developed with 0.1 *M* glycine, pH 10, at 50°C for 30 sec, and photographed under transmitting light conditions. (C) The zymogram shown in B photographed under reflecting light conditions.

Steps

1. Perform polyacrylamide gel electrophoresis with 12.5% homogeneous gels under nondenaturing conditions on a PHastSystem.

2. Prior to use soak a piece of film, 50 × 60 mm, in water for at least 5 min.

3. When the electrophoresis is terminated briefly blot the piece of film between paper towels and place it on a glass plate (gelatin layer up). Then roll the PhastGel onto the film and squeeze out trapped air bubbles by rubbing over the gel backing with a spatula. Place a second glass plate over the gel and weigh it down with 500 to 1000 g (glass bottle, chemicals container, etc.).

4. Separate the sandwich after 8 min. Place the gel into 25 ml of gel fixing solution and prepare for staining with Coomassie blue or with silver. Place the film into a dry petri dish (for best contrast on a light box) and slowly pour 30 ml of developing buffer into the dish. Do not agitate the dish. Temperature and pH of the buffer depend on type and amount of the protease investigated and should reflect optimal reaction conditions.

5. Wait until clearing zones become visible, then stop the reaction by slowly filling the petri dish with cold water. Remove the film from the petri dish, rinse several times with running water, and air-dry. Examples with subtilisin BPN′ and trypsin are shown in Figs. 1 and 2.

C. ZYMOGRAPHY OF PROTEASES IN DENATURING POLYACRYLAMIDE GELS

This procedure is adapted from Heussen and Dowdle (1980).

Solutions

1. *Acrylamide solution:* 30% (w/v) acrylamide, 0.8% (w/v) bisacrylamide. Dissolve 30.0 g of acrylamide and 0.80 g of bisacrylamide in 55 ml of water and complete with water to 100 ml. Keep solution refrigerated in a brown bottle.

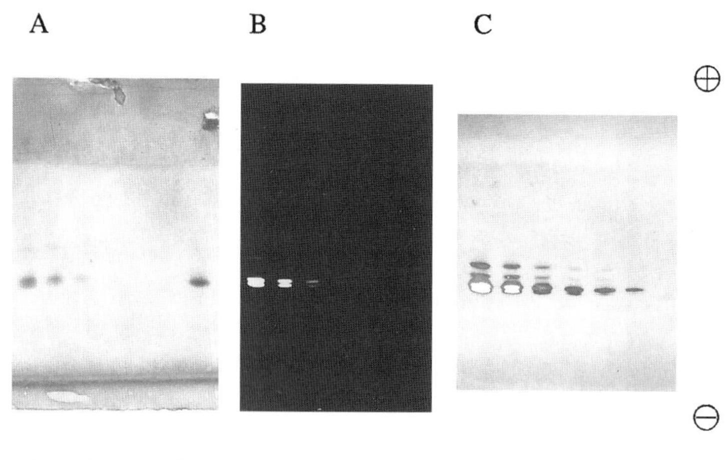

FIGURE 2 Nondenaturing PAGE of trypsin prepared in 20 m*M* Mes–NaOH, pH 5.8. Lanes 1 to 6: 480, 240, 120, 60, 30, and 15 ng of protein. Lane 7: 480 ng of trypsin inhibited with phenylmethylsulfonyl fluoride. (A) Silver-stained 12.5% PhastGel. (B) Zymogram of gel shown in A. The contact time of the film overlay (MRF-34) was 8 min. The film was developed with 0.1 *M* glycine–NaOH, pH 10, at 37°C for 30 sec. (C) The zymogram shown in B photographed under reflecting light conditions.

2. *Separating gel buffer solution:* 1.5 *M* Tris–HCl, pH 8.8, containing 0.4% (w/v) SDS. Dissolve 18.2 g of Tris and 400 mg of SDS in 60 ml of water. Add 24 ml of 1 *N* HCl and complete with water to 100 ml. Keep solution at room temperature.

3. *Stacking gel buffer solution:* 0.5 *M* Tris–HCl, pH 6.8, containing 0.4% (w/v) SDS. Dissolve 6.05 g of Tris and 400 mg of SDS in 90 ml of water. Titrate solution at room temperature to pH 6.8 with 6 *N* HCl using a combination glass electrode. Complete with water to 100 ml. Keep solution at room temperature.

4. *Indicator protein solution:* 1% (w/v) protein. Dissolve 1 g of the desired protein (such as gelatin, casein, hemoglobin) in 100 ml of water containing 400 mg of SDS. Keep solution refrigerated.

5. *Ammonium persulfate solution:* Dissolve 100 mg ammonium persulfate in 1 ml of water. Prepare solution freshly and discard after use.

6. *Reservoir buffer solution:* Prepare a 10-fold concentrate of the reservoir buffer by dissolving 30.3 g of Tris, 144 g of glycine, and 10 g of SDS in water to a final volume of 1 liter. Keep solution at room temperature. Prior to use, dilute 1 vol of concentrate with 9 vol of water.

7. *Renaturation solution:* 2.5% (v/v) Triton X-100. Dissolve 2.5 ml of Triton X-100 in 97.5 ml of water. Keep solution at room temperature.

8. *Sample preparation buffer:* 0.125 *M* Tris–HCl, pH 6.8, containing 4% (w/v) SDS, 0.01% bromphenol blue, 20% glycerol. Prepare 10 ml of this solution from 2.5 ml of 0.5 *M* Tris, adjusted to pH 6.8 with HCl, 4 ml of 10% (w/v) SDS in water, 1 ml of 0.1% (w/v) bromphenol blue in water, and 2 ml of glycerol. Keep solution at room temperature.

9. *Developing buffer solution:* 50 m*M* Tris–HCl, 0.2 *M* NaCl, 10 m*M* $CaCl_2$, 0.02% (w/v) Brij 35, pH 7.5. Dissolve 6.06 g of Tris, 11.7 g of sodium chloride, and 1.47 g of $CaCl_2 \cdot 2H_2O$ in 950 ml of water. Titrate with 6 *N* HCl to pH 7.5. Add 2 ml of a 10% (w/v) Brij 35 solution and complete with water to 1 liter. Keep solution refrigerated.

10. *Gel fixing solution:* Methanol/water/acetic acid, 5/5/1 (v/v/v). To make 550 ml of fixing solution add 250 ml of methanol to 250 ml of water and stir briefly. Then add slowly, with stirring, 50 ml of glacial acetic acid. Keep solution at room temperature.

Steps

1. Cast two 12% polyacrylamide separating gels (80 mm wide, 60 mm high, 0.75 mm thick) into chilled glass plates from the following mixture of solutions at room temperature. In a small suction flask, mix 3.0 ml of acrylamide solution, 3.75 ml of separating gel buffer, 1.5 ml of indicator protein solution, and 6.68 ml of water. Swirl gently, degas for 3 min at low vacuum (water aspirator), add 50 μl of ammonium persulfate solution and 20 μl of TEMED, and mix again. Pour solution into a disposable 20-ml syringe equipped with a luer-lock stopcock and a blunt 20-gauge needle. Tilt the assembled glass plates and fill space between glass plates by running solution down the spacer. When the appropriate volume has been added, carefully layer water on top of the gel solution. The polymerization is completed after 30 to 45 min. Decant the water layer.

2. Cast the stacking gel by mixing 2.5 ml stacking gel buffer, 1.25 ml acrylamide solution, and 5.5 ml of water. Degas solution. Add 0.75 ml of ammonium persulfate solution and 5 μl of TEMED. Pipette solution between the plates and insert a well-forming comb. Avoid trapping of air bubbles as they might prevent polymerization.

3. Store gels for several hours, preferably overnight, in a sealed tank at saturated humidity.

4. Prepare protease sample by mixing equal volumes of the starting material and the protein preparation buffer. Incubate at room temperature for 15 min. Do not heat.

5. Run electrophoresis at 4°C at a constant current of 10 mA per gel until the tracking dye has traveled close to the bottom of the separating gel.

6. Disassemble the glass plates, and place each gel in 50 ml of renaturation solution for 30 min with one change of the solution after 15 min. Gently agitate trays on a shaker.

7. Replace the renaturation solution with 100 ml of developing buffer. Close tray and place in a shaker-incubator set at 37°C for 2 to 16 hr.

8. Rinse gel briefly with water, place in gel fixing solution, and finish by staining gel with Coomassie blue. Proteolytic activity is indicated by clearing zones on blue background. For representative examples see Heussen and Dowdle (1980) and Brown *et al.* (1990).

IV. Comments

PROCEDURE A

The detection limit for several proteases separated on 1.8-mm-thick gels is approximately 1 μg (Every, 1981). On PhastGels, the lower limit for trypsin and subtilisins is 50 to 100 ng (C. Paech and T. Christianson, unpublished).

For the purpose of preheating the casting chamber a water bath at 80°C may be replaced by an ice bucket filled with water preheated in a microwave oven.

For casting multiple overlay gels, use Hoefer's gel casting stand (Model SE 215 for 80 × 100-mm plates or Model SE 615 for 160 × 180-mm plates).

PROCEDURE B

The detection limit of this method for subtilisins is approximately 1 ng. The method works exceptionally well with PhastGels due to the support on which they are cast. Their ultrathin structure facilitates rapid diffusion of the protease onto the gelatin layer of the film, thereby reducing transfer time and, consequently, retaining resolution on both the gel and the zymogram. The method is not limited to PhastGels, although the minimum amount of protease needed to elicit zymograms on 60 × 80-mm gels (0.75 mm thick) is on the order of 10 ng (C. Paech and T. Christianson, unpublished).

PROCEDURE C

Casein and gelatin containing polyacrylamide gels are commercially available in a limited selection. However, their use may require specialized equipment; e.g., precast homogeneous 10% gels containing 0.1% gelatin ("zymogram" gel) from Novex (Cat. No. EC6175) require the Novex Xcell Mini-Cell (Novex, Cat. No. E16001).

V. Pitfalls

PROCEDURE A

1. If only white plaques but no clearing zones appear on the overlay gel, the buffering capacity of the overlay gel may be insufficient. In this case, transfer the overlay gel briefly into a buffer optimal for the protease under investigation. Shortly, the white zones will turn into clearing zones. Stop the reaction by returning the gel to the saturated ammonium sulfate solution. An intermediate acid bath may be necessary to accelerate the quenching process.

PROCEDURE B

1. Diminished sensitivity of the film overlay was observed with aged X-ray film in both undeveloped and developed form. Presumably air oxidation hardens the gelatin, reducing susceptibility to proteolytic degradation. No apparent change in quality over at least 2 months was observed with freshly developed film kept in a closed box in the dark.

2. Diminished sensitivity may also result from aged buffer, particularly at elevated pH. We typically replace the glycine buffer every 2 weeks.

REFERENCES

Brown, P. D., Levy, A. T., Margulies, I. M. K., Liotta, L. A., and Stetler-Stevenson, W. G. (1990) Independent expression and cellular processing of M_r 72,000 type IV collagenase and interstitial collagenase in human tumorigenic cell lines. *Cancer Res.* **50**, 6184–6191.

Every, D. (1981) Quantitative measurement of protease activities in slab polyacrylamide gel electrophoretograms. *Anal. Biochem.* **116**, 519–523.

Gabriel, O., and Gersten, D. M. (1992) Staining for enzymatic activity after gel electrophoresis. I. *Anal. Biochem.* **203**, 1–21.

Gersten, D. M., and Gabriel, O. (1992) Staining for enzymatic activity after gel electrophoresis. II. Enzymes modifying nucleic acids. *Anal. Biochem.* **203**, 181–186.

Heussen, C., and Dowdle, E. B. (1980) Electrophoretic analysis of plasminogen activators in polyacrylamide gels containing sodium dodecyl sulfate and copolymerized substrates. *Anal. Biochem.* **102**, 196–202.

Paech, C., Christianson, T., and Bläsig, S. (1993a) Enhanced zymograms of proteases. *Anal. Biochem.* **213**, 440–441.

Paech, C., Christianson, T., and Maurer, K.-H. (1993b) Zymogram of proteases made with developed film from nondenaturing polyacrylamide gels after electrophoresis. *Anal. Biochem.* 208, 249–254.

Electroelution of Proteins from Two-Dimensional Gels

Julio E. Celis, Gitte Ratz, and Bodil Basse

I. Introduction

There are many situations in which one would like to recover proteins from acrylamide gels for further analysis. For example, polypeptides extracted from gels can be readily used to immunize rabbits or mice to prepare antibodies (see articles by Christian Huet and by Ariana Celis, Kurt Dejgaard, and Julio E. Celis). Here we present a simple protocol for electroeluting proteins from fixed, unstained and Coomassie brilliant blue-stained dry two-dimensional (2D) gels (IEF or NEPHGE).

II. Materials and Instrumentation

NH_4HCO_3 (Cat. No. 09832) was obtained from Fluka and SDS (Cat. No. 20763) from Serva. Simian virus 40 (SV40)-transformed keratinocytes were kindly provided by U. Jensen from the Institute of Human Genetics, Aarhus University.

The Electro-Eluter Assembly (Model 422) and accessories were obtained from Bio-Rad (Cat. No. 165-2976). The magnetic stirrer (Framo-Gerätetechnik, Model M 20/1) was purchased from Holm & Halby. All other reagents and materials were as described in the article by Ariana Celis and Julio E. Celis in Volume 1.

III. Procedure

Solution

Volatile buffer: 50 m*M* NH_4HCO_3, 0.1% SDS. To make 1 liter, weigh 3.95 g of NH_4HCO_3 and 1 g of SDS. Complete to 1 liter with distilled water. Keep at room temperature.

Steps

1. Run 2D gels (IEF, NEPHGE) as described in the article by Julio E. Celis, Gitte Ratz, Jette B. Lauridsen, Bodil Basse, and Ariana Celis.
2. Cut spots from the dry, Coomassie brilliant blue-stained gels using a

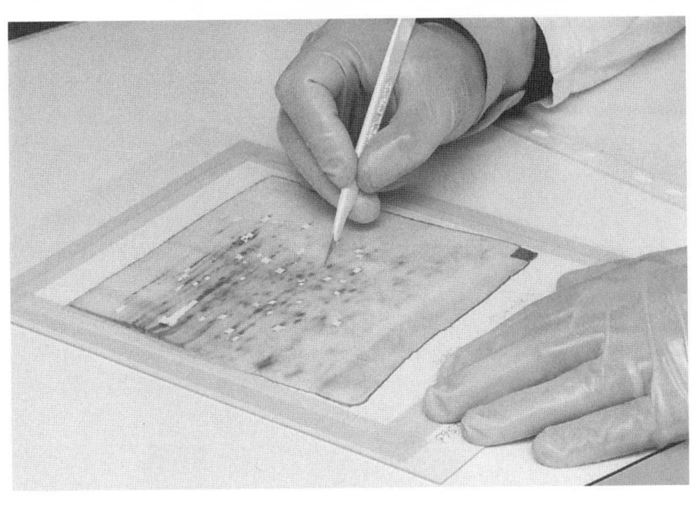

FIGURE 1 Cutting polypeptides from a dry Coomassie brilliant blue-stained IEF 2D gel of SV40-transformed human keratinocytes.

scalpel (Fig. 1) (see article by Julio E. Celis and Eyδfinnur Olsen concerning staining and drying). In this particular case we have cut glutathione *S*-transferase π from a Coomassie brilliant blue-stained gel of SV40-transformed human keratinocytes. If the gels are to be fixed but not stained, run the sample together with a small amount of [^{35}S]methionine-labeled proteins (total cellular extract). Proteins are localized with the aid of an X-ray film (see Fig. 3 in the article by Julio E. Celis, Gitte Ratz, Jette B. Lauridsen, Bodil Basse, and Ariana Celis).

3. Soak the membrane caps (Fig. 2A, a) for 1 hr at 60°C in volatile buffer. Wear gloves throughout the procedure.

4. Place a frit on the bottom of a glass tube (Fig. 2A, c).

5. Place the membrane cap in the bottom of a silicone adaptor (Fig. 2A, b) and fill the adaptor with volatile buffer.

6. Slide the adaptor containing the cap (Fig. 2B, a) onto the glass tube with the frit (Fig. 2B, b). Pull the adaptor off and on a couple of times to expel air bubbles.

7. Fill the tube with volatile buffer and place it in the chamber holder (Fig. 2A, e).

8. Fill the buffer chamber (Fig. 2A, d) with 600 ml of volatile buffer and place a magnetic stirrer in the bottom of the chamber.

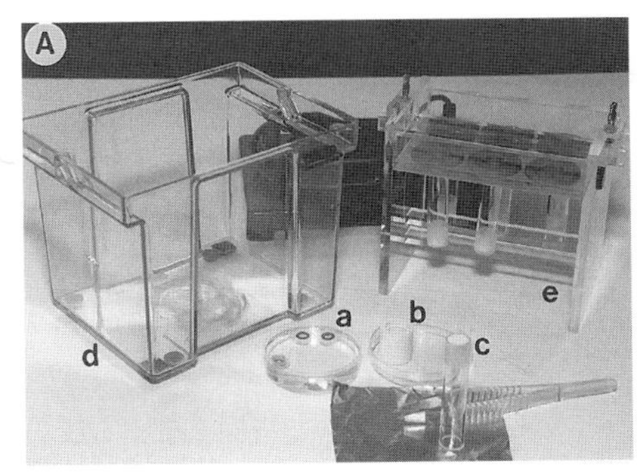

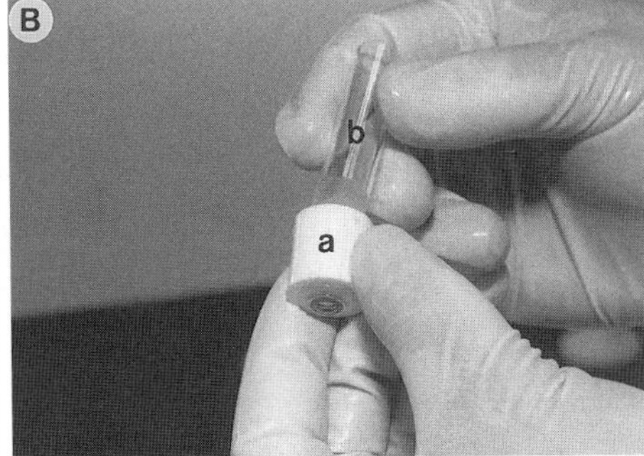

FIGURE 2 Equipment and materials for electroelution. (A) (a) Membrane caps; (b) silicone adaptor; (c) frit placed in the glass tube; (d) chamber holder; (e) buffer chamber. (B) Sliding the adaptor containing the cap onto the glass tube with the frit.

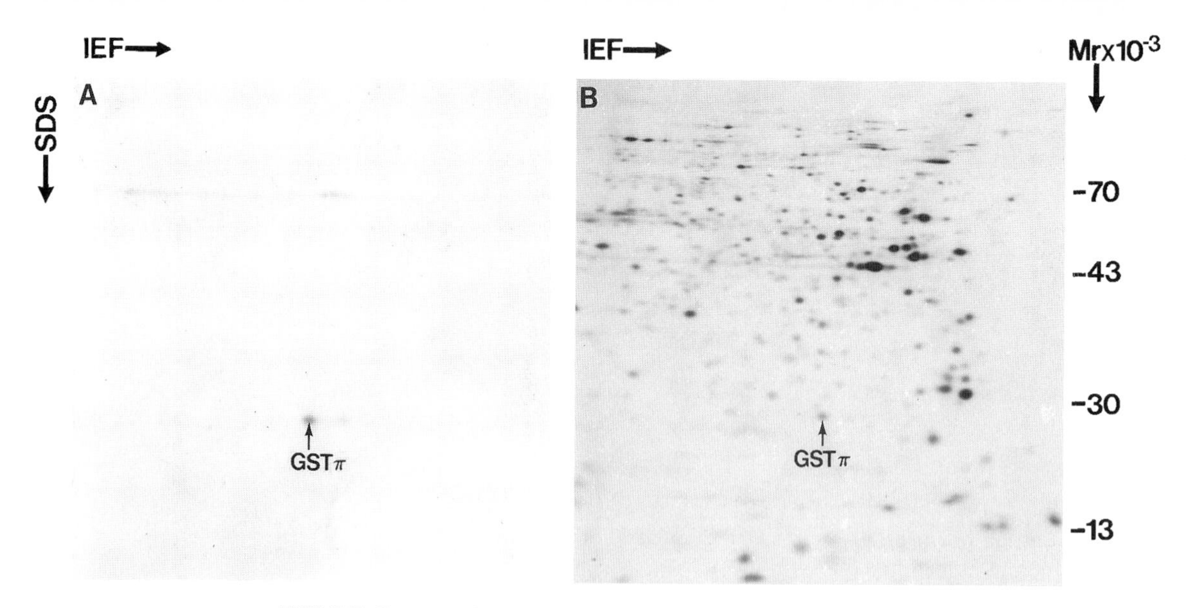

FIGURE 3 (A) Silver-stained IEF 2D gel of glutathione *S*-transferase π electroeluted from a Coomassie brilliant blue-destained 2D gel of SV40-transformed keratinocyte proteins. (B) Autoradiogram of [^{35}S]methionine-labeled SV40-transformed keratinocyte proteins co-run with the electroeluted protein.

9. Place the holder in the buffer chamber.

10. Add small pieces of gels (dry or wet) into the glass tubes.

11. Fill the glass tubes and the chamber with volatile buffer and attach the lid with cables. Push down gel pieces if they float. Usually, we electroelute several samples at a time and therefore use all six glass tubes. If necessary, cover the unused holes in the holder with rubber stoppers.

12. Turn on the magnetic stirrer (slow) and run at 8–10 mA per glass tube for 2–3 hr.

13. At the end of the run, aspirate the volatile buffer in the upper chamber and in the tubes with a Pasteur pipette connected to a water pump. Take out the holder and recover the silicone adaptor with the cap.

14. Remove the volatile buffer remaining in the adaptor just above the cap with the aid of a Pasteur pipette.

15. Collect the liquid remaining in the cap by pipetting up and down a couple of times. Add the solution to a sterile conical tube. Wash the cap with a small volume of volatile buffer and pool.

16. Dialyze the solution against three changes of distilled water (1 liter at a time). Freeze-dry an aliquot of the preparation separately and use it to assess the purity of the preparation by 2D gel electrophoresis (Fig. 3). Resuspend in 10–20 μl of O'Farrel's lysis solution (O'Farrel, 1975) and run 2-D gels as described in the article by Julio E. Celis, Gitte Ratz, Jette B. Lauridsen, Bodil Basse, and Ariana Celis and by Angelika Görg in this volume.

IV. Comments

Figure 3 A shows a silver-stained gel of electroeluted glutathione *S*-transferase π (GST-π) cut from a dry Coomassie brilliant blue-stained 2D gel of SV40-transformed keratinocytes. The sample was co-run with a small amount of [^{35}S]methionine-labeled proteins from the same cell type and the autoradiogram is shown in Fig. 3B. As can be seen, the eluted protein migrates at the same position as the [^{35}S]-methionine-labeled GST-π.

V. Pitfalls

1. Make sure you stir the solution in the buffer chamber to prevent bubbles from sticking to the bottom of the dialysis membrane.
2. The dialysis membranes can be used several times. Wash well after using and keep in volatile solution at 4°C.
3. Sometimes, electroeluted proteins give rise to artifactual variants.

REFERENCE

O'Farrel, P. H. (1975) High resolution two-dimensional electrophoresis of proteins. *J. Biol. Chem.* 250, 4007–4021.

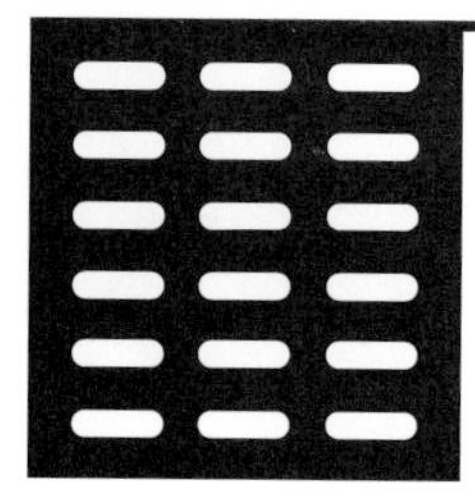

Monitoring Sodium Dodecyl Sulfate Contamination

Michael Arand, Thomas Friedberg, and Franz Oesch

I. Introduction

Sodium dodecyl sulfate is a potent detergent of pronounced cytotoxicity that strongly interferes with many enzyme-catalyzed processes. Because of its wide application in the life sciences it represents a common potential contaminant of laboratory samples. Both insufficient removal of the compound after application in experimental protocols and accidental contamination may cause severe problems. To provide a simple yet sensitive method for scrutinizing suspicious samples, we have developed the protocol given in the following as also described earlier (Arand *et al.,* 1992). The procedure is based on formation of the ion pair SDS and methylene blue and subsequent extraction of this complex with chloroform.

Determining if a protein of interest is heavily contaminated with SDS, and that this is why, for example, no successful proteolytic digest can be obtained with the preparation, is one step forward but does not solve the problem. We therefore include in the following a method for protein precipitation developed by Wessel and Flügge (1984) that, in our hands, has proved to be extremely efficient in the removal of SDS. We recommend this procedure for the purification of contaminated samples wherever denaturation of the protein in question is not critical.

II. Materials and Instrumentation

Methylene blue (Cat. No. 6040), sodium sulfate (anhydrous, Cat. No. 6643), sulfuric acid (95–98%, Cat. No. 713), chloroform (Cat. No. 2445), and methanol (Cat. No. 6009) were obtained from Merck. Sodium dodecyl sulfate (Cat. No. L-5750) was purchased from Sigma. Safe-lock Eppendorf cups, 2.0 ml (Cat. No. 0030 120.094) and 1.5 ml (Cat. No. 0030 120.086), from Eppendorf Gerätebau, Netheler + Hinz, were obtained through Mitlacher.

A Biofuge A (Heraeus), equipped with rotors 1386 and 1378 for the 2.0 and 1.5-ml cups, respectively, was used for the centrifugation steps. Spectrophotometric analyses were carried out on a Shimadzu MPS-2000 spectrophotometer (Shimadzu Europa GmbH).

III. Procedures

A. QUANTIFICATION OF SDS

Solution

Methylene blue reagent: Dissolve 50 g of anhydrous sodium sulfate in 900 ml of double-distilled water. Carefully add 10 ml of concentrated sulfuric acid and, after gentle but thorough mixing, add 250 mg of methylene blue. Bring up the volume to 1 liter with water. The reagent prepared this way can be stored in a stoppered glass bottle for more than a year at room temperature without significant impairment of performance. Storage over chloroform is optional but, in our hands, did not substantially improve the quality of the preparation.

Steps

1. Transfer the sample to be analyzed to a 2.0-ml Eppendorf cup. Bring the volume to 300 μl by adding water. Add an equal volume of methylene blue reagent.

2. Extract the mixture with 1.2 ml chloroform by thorough vortexing. Separate the phases by centrifugation in a bench-top centrifuge for 1 min at 10,000 *g*.

3. Using a Pasteur pipette, transfer the chloroform phase (lower phase) to a 1.5-ml Eppendorf cup containing approximately 50–100 mg anhydrous sodium sulfate. Invert the tube several times to allow for the absorption of residual water dissolved in the chloroform by the sodium sulfate. Pellet the solid material by brief centrifugation in a bench-top centrifuge.

4. Determine the OD_{651} of the supernatant in a 1-ml glass cuvette against chloroform as a reference on a spectrophotometer.

For an accurate quantification, prepare a standard curve using 0, 0.3, 0.6, 0.9, 1.5, and 3 μg of SDS.

B. REMOVAL OF SDS FROM PROTEIN PREPARATIONS BY METHANOL–CHLOROFORM PRECIPITATION

Steps

1. To 100 μl of sample in a 1.5-ml Eppendorf cup add 400 μl of methanol and subsequently 100 μl of chloroform. Mix well after each addition of reagent.

2. Add 300 μl of water and vortex thoroughly. Spin in a bench-top centrifuge for 5 min at 10,000 *g*. This should result in separation of the chloroform phase (about 100 μl in volume) and formation of a protein precipitate at the interphase that is not necessarily visible at this step, depending on the initial protein concentration of the sample.

3. Immediately remove most of the upper phase, taking care not to aspirate any of the precipitated protein. This is best achieved by leaving a residual amount of about 50 μl of the upper phase. Add 300 μl of methanol and vortex thoroughly. Pellet the protein by centrifugation at 10,000 *g* for 5 min.

4. Completely remove the supernatant. Add 1 ml of ice-cold acetone (stored at −20°C) and spin again for 1 min at 10,000 *g*.

5. Completely remove the supernatant and air-dry the pellet by leaving the inverted tube for 15 min on a paper towel. The sample is now ready for further processing. Because of its potential insolubility it may be necessary to use strong denaturing agents like high concentrations of urea to dissolve it. These may later be removed by dialysis or sufficient dilution, if necessary.

IV. Comments

After our first report on what we believed to be an entirely new approach, namely, the colorimetric quantification of SDS, it was kindly brought to our attention by

Professor Takagi, Osaka University, that essentially the same strategy had already been applied for the same purpose by others much earlier. Therefore, it is our particular desire to acknowledge here these earlier reports, especially the work of Epton (1947), Mukerjee (1956), and Hayashi (1975), as we regretfully did not do so in our original publication.

V. Pitfalls

The colorimetric method for the quantification of SDS is extremely useful for monitoring the presence of minute amounts of the detergent in samples of interest, as the interaction with the dye appears to be quantitative in all circumstances, even in the presence of large amounts of protein. It must, however, be underlined that the method of detection is rather indirect and that a number of other compounds are known to form chloroform-extractable ion pairs with methylene blue. Among these, a variety of other organic sulfate esters behave very similarly to SDS, whereas other compounds like iodine salts and trichloroacetic acid give a strong yet not quantitative response. Of practical implication is the moderate interference observed with phospholipids from biological membranes and with chloride ions present in many buffers. A more detailed list of interfering compounds is given in Arand *et al.* (1992). Thus, preparation of a proper blank is crucial to the correct quantification of possible contamination. It should, however, be borne in mind that only overestimation of the SDS concentration in the sample may occur but, to our present experience, an underestimation may not be expected.

REFERENCES

Arand, M., Friedberg, T., and Oesch, F. (1992) Colorimetric quantitation of trace amounts of sodium lauryl sulfate in the presence of nucleic acids and proteins. *Anal. Biochem.* **207**, 73–75.

Epton, S. R. (1947) A rapid method of analysis for certain surface-active agents. *Nature* **160**, 795–796.

Hayashi, K. (1975) A rapid determination of sodium dodecyl sulfate with methylene blue. *Anal. Biochem.* **67**, 503–506.

Mukerjee, P. (1956) Use of ionic dyes in the analysis of ionic surfactants and other ionic organic compounds. *Anal. Chem.* **28**, 870–873.

Wessel, D., and Flügge, U. I. (1984) A method for the quantitative recovery of protein in dilute solution in the presence of detergents and lipids. *Anal. Biochem.* **138**, 141–143.

SECTION D

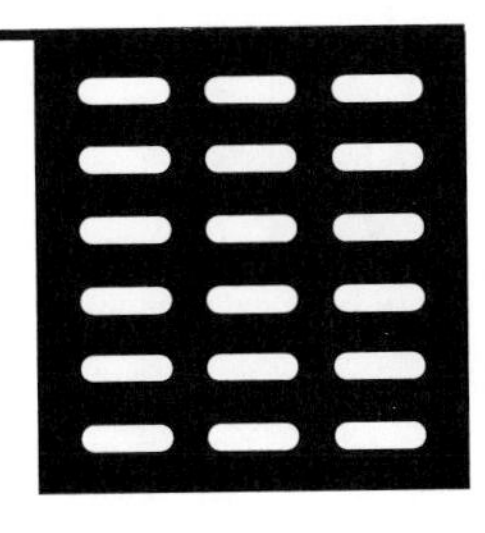

Staining

Ultrasensitive Silver-Based Stains for Protein Detection

Carl R. Merril, Janet E. Joy, and G. Joseph Creed

I. Introduction

Silver stains have proven to be more than 100-fold more sensitive than the most commonly used organic stains, such as Coomassie blue, for the detection of proteins separated on gels (Merril *et al.*, 1979; Switzer *et al.*, 1979). With silver staining, large numbers of proteins can be visualized in high-resolution two-dimensional electrophoretograms (Fig. 1). Detection of proteins by silver staining depends on the reduction of silver ions to form metallic silver images (Merril, 1986). The use of this reduction reaction to create an image of the protein distribution in a gel depends on oxidation–reduction potential differences between the sites occupied by the proteins and adjacent sites in the gel. It is possible to alter these relative oxidation–reduction potentials by changing the staining procedure such that proteins separated on polyacrylamide gels will stain negatively or positively (Merril, 1986).

Silver stain protocols for protein detection can be divided into three general categories: diamine or ammoniacal stains, nondiamine chemical reduction stains, and stains based on photodevelopment. The diamine or ammoniacal stains have been designed to release silver ions in a controlled manner to facilitate the selective reduction of metallic silver (Merril, 1986, 1990). The silver ion concentration is maintained at a low level in these stains by the formation of silver diamine complexes with ammonium hydroxide. Image development is initiated by acidification of the ammoniacal silver solution, usually with citric acid in the presence of formaldehyde. The addition of citric acid lowers the concentration of free ammonium ions, which results in the liberation of silver ions for reduction by formaldehyde to metallic silver. The diamine or ammoniacal silver stains generally have high sensitivity and they have proven to be particularly useful for the staining of proteins separated on polyacrylamide gels thicker than 1 mm.

Nondiamine chemical reduction stains use silver nitrate to provide silver ions for reaction with protein and nucleic acid sites under acidic conditions (Merril, 1986, 1990). Image development is initiated by placing the gel in an alkaline solution, using sodium carbonate and/or hydroxide or other bases to maintain the alkaline pH, while the silver ions are selectively reduced to metallic silver with formaldehyde. The formic acid, produced by the oxidation of formaldehyde, is buffered by the sodium carbonate. This type of stain is relatively rapid and simple to perform. The nondiamine stains generally work best with gels 1 mm or less in thickness.

Photodevelopment silver stains depend on the energy from photons of light to reduce ionic silver to metallic silver (Merril, 1986). Proteins enhance the photoreduction of ionic to metallic silver in gels impregnated with silver chloride. While the photodevelopment stains are very rapid and can permit the visualization of protein

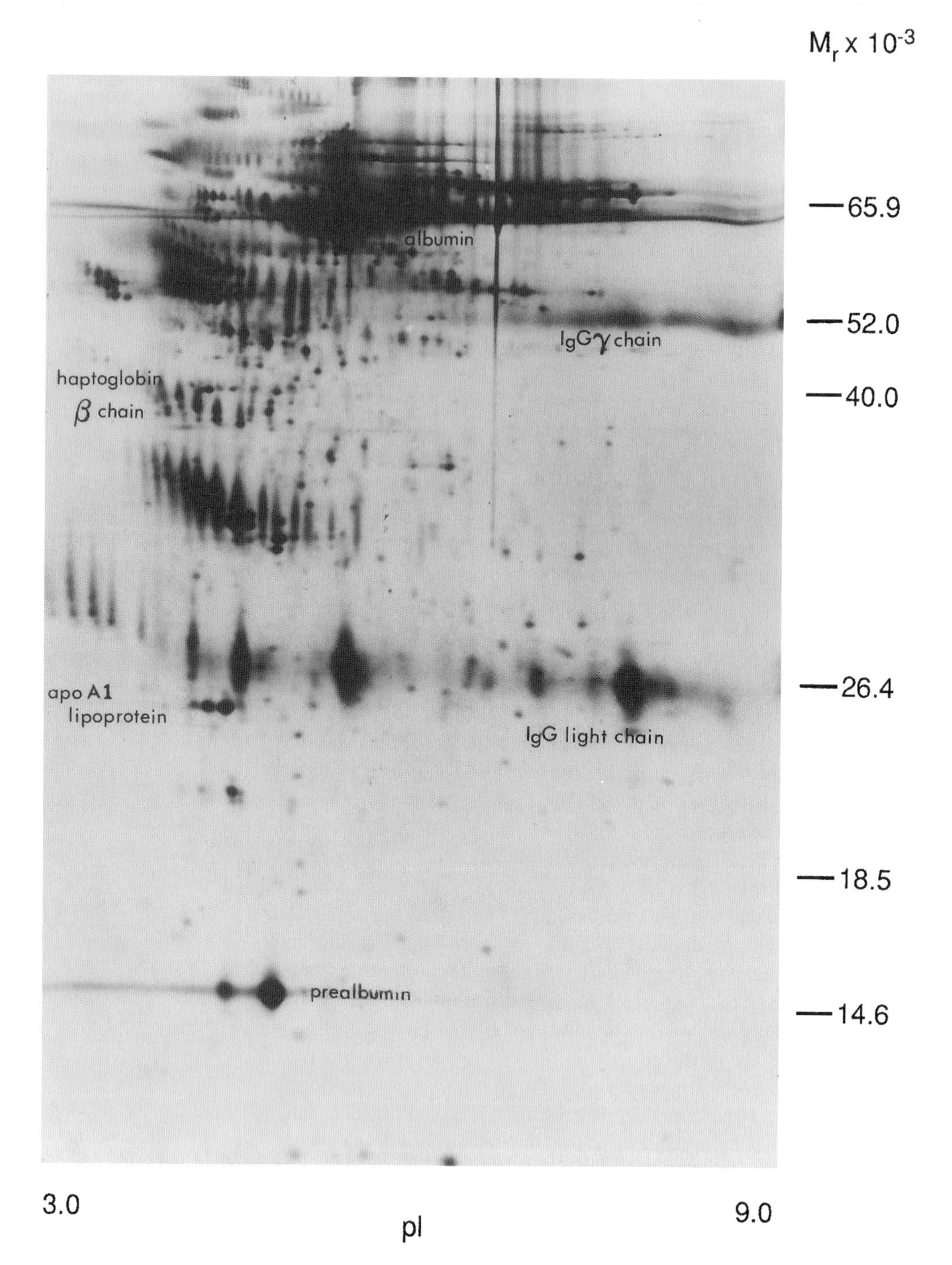

FIGURE 1 More than 800 proteins can be visualized with silver staining of high-resolution two-dimensional electrophoretograms of unconcentrated human cerebrospinal fluid (40 μl).

patterns within 10 min of an electrophoretic separation, they lack the sensitivity of the other silver staining methods. Furthermore, image preservation, which is very good with chemical reduction methods, is poor with photodevelopment stains. This type of silver stain should be reserved for studies of dense protein bands or spots.

It is possible to combine the chemical and photodevelopment methods. For example, one silver stain protocol, which was developed to detect proteins and nucleic acids on membranes, uses light to initiate the formation of silver nucleation centers with silver halides, followed by the use of chemical development to deposit additional silver on the silver nucleation centers. This protocol provides a stain which is rapid and sensitive. It can detect proteins and nucleic acids in the nanogram range on thin membranes in under 15 min (Merril and Pratt, 1986).

II. Materials

The chemicals used in these stains are common, high-purity laboratory reagents that may be purchased from any reputable chemical supply company. Those required for the silver diamine stain are glacial acetic acid, concentrated ammonium hydroxide, citric acid, absolute ethanol, 37% (w/w) formaldehyde, glutaraldehyde, silver nitrate, and 10 *N* sodium hydroxide. Those required for the silver dichromate stain are glacial acetic acid, 37% (w/w) formaldehyde, glutaraldehyde, absolute methanol, concentrated nitric acid, potassium dichromate, silver nitrate, and anhydrous sodium carbonate. We recommend the use of diacrylylpiperazine (PIP) as the acrylamide crosslinker to provide low background when staining with silver (Hochstrasser and Merril, 1988). This compound may be purchased under the name piperazine diacrylamide (PDA, Cat. No. 161-0202) from Bio-Rad.

III. Procedures

A. DIAMINE SILVER STAIN

This procedure is modified from those of Merril *et al.* (1979), Switzer *et al.* (1979), and Hochstrasser and Merril, (1988). This stain is recommended for gels thicker than 1 mm.

Solutions

Volumes are given for the staining of six 16 × 16-cm gels.

1. *Fixation solution:* 40% (v/v) ethanol, 10% (v/v) acetic acid. To make 1 liter of the solution, add 100 ml of glacial acetic acid to 400 ml of absolute ethanol. Bring to final volume with deionized water. Store at room temperature.

2. *Rehydration solution:* 5% (v/v) ethanol, 5% (v/v) acetic acid. To make 1 liter of the solution, add 50 ml of glacial acetic acid to 50 ml of absolute ethanol. Bring to final volume with deionized water. Store at room temperature.

3. *Glutaraldehyde solution:* 2% (v/v) glutaraldehyde. To make 1 liter of the solution, dilute 20 ml of anhydrous glutaraldehyde to final volume with deionized water. Prepare just prior to use. Store stock glutaraldehyde at 4°C. Glutaraldehyde is a hazardous material and should not be used in solutions greater than 2%. Avoid skin contact, and particularly avoid breathing vapors. Therefore, make up only the volume needed to fix the number of gels being stained.

4. *Silver diamine solution:* 0.047 *M* silver nitrate, 0.2 *M* ammonium hydroxide, 0.02 *M* sodium hydroxide. This diamine solution is made by combining a silver nitrate solution with an ammonium/sodium hydroxide solution. To make the silver nitrate solution, add 6 g of silver nitrate to 30 ml of deionized water in a small graduated cylinder or beaker. To make the ammonium/sodium hydroxide solution, add 10 ml of concentrated NH_4OH and 1.5 ml of 10 *M* NaOH to 160 ml of deionized water in a 1-liter graduated cylinder. After preparation of each of the above solutions, slowly add the silver

nitrate solution to the ammonium/sodium hydroxide solution. A brown precipitate may form which should quickly dissolve, leaving a colorless solution. If the silver nitrate is added too rapidly, the brown precipitate may not redissolve. After mixing, bring to a final volume of 750 ml with deionized water. Prepare just prior to use.

5. *Reducing solution:* 0.0005 *M* citric acid, 0.007 *M* formaldehyde. To make 1 liter of the solution, add 0.1 g of anhydrous citric acid and 1 ml of 37% (w/w) formaldehyde to 900 ml of deionized water. After dissolving, bring to final volume with deionized water. Cold water (approximately 4°C) is not essential for this solution, but it may help reduce background staining. Prepare just prior to use.

6. *Stopbath solution:* 5% (v/v) acetic acid. To make 2 liters of the solution, add 100 ml of glacial acetic acid to 1800 ml of deionized water. After dissolving, bring to final volume with deionized water. Store at room temperature.

Steps

1. Perform all staining steps in glass trays (up to four gels per tray) on a rocker or shaker at a very gentle speed. Perform all steps at room temperature. From the development step onward, use clean trays for each solution. For each solution, use volumes sufficient to fully immerse the gels.

2. After electrophoresis, place gels into a tray containing 500 ml of fixation solution. Soak the gels in this solution for approximately 1 hr.

3. Transfer gels from the fixation solution into 500 ml of rehydrating solution. Soak the gels in this solution for a minimum of 3 hr. Gels may be left in this solution for extended periods, i.e., several days.

4. Transfer gels from the rehydrating solution into 500 ml of deionized water. Wash the gels for 5 min.

5. Discard the rehydration solution and add 500 ml of the glutaraldehyde solution to each tray. Soak the gels in this solution for 30 min.

6. Discard the glutaraldehyde solution. Wash gels three times with 500 ml of deionized water for 10 min each wash.

7. Wash gels four times with 500 ml of deionized water for 30 min each wash.

8. Transfer gels to the ammoniacal silver. Soak the gels in this solution for 5 to 30 min.

9. Pour off the silver nitrate solution and rinse the gels two times with 500 ml of deionized water for 15 sec each, followed by three rinses for 5 to 10 min each. This rinsing schedule may be varied, but two factors must be kept in mind: inadequate rinsing may leave a metallic sheen on the surface of the gels, but rinsing for more than 30 min may result in the gels sticking to the bottom of the trays.

10. Develop image with the citric acid/formaldehyde solution until the proteins are sufficiently stained. Proteins normally become visible in 1 to 2 min.

11. Stop development with 500 ml of 5% (v/v) acetic acid. Soak the gels in this solution for 15 min.

12. Wash gels three times with 500 ml of deionized water for 5 min each wash.

13. Store gels moist in sealed clear plastic bags.

B. NONDIAMINE SILVER STAIN

This procedure is modified from that of Merril *et al.* (1981). This stain is recommended for gels less than 1 mm in thickness.

Solutions

Volumes are given for the staining of six 16 × 16-cm gels.

1. *Fixation solution:* 50% (v/v) methanol, 10% (v/v) acetic acid. To make 1200 ml of the solution, add 120 ml of glacial acetic acid to 600 ml of absolute methanol. Bring to a final volume of 1200 ml with deionized water. Store at room temperature.

2. *Rehydration solution:* 10% (v/v) methanol, 5% (v/v) acetic acid. To make 1200 ml of the solution, add 60 ml of glacial acetic acid to 120 ml of absolute methanol. Bring to final volume with deionized water. Store at room temperature.

3. *Glutaraldehyde solution:* 2% (v/v) glutaraldehyde. To make 1200 ml of the solution, dilute 24 ml of anhydrous glutaraldehyde to final volume with deionized water. Prepare just prior to use. Store stock glutaraldehyde at 4°C. Glutaraldehyde is a hazardous material and should not be used in solutions greater than 2% because of the vapor pressure of stronger solutions. Avoid skin contact, and particularly avoid breathing vapors. Therefore, make up only the volume needed to fix the number of gels being stained.

4. *Dichromate solution:* 0.034 *M* potassium dichromate, 0.032 *M* nitric acid. To make 1 liter of a stock solution, add 10 g of potassium dichromate and 2 ml of concentrated nitric acid to 750 ml of deionized water. After dissolving, bring to a final volume with deionized water. This solution may be stored at room temperature for months in a tightly capped dark bottle. To make a working solution of 0.1% dichromate, dilute 120 ml of the above stock solution to a final volume of 1200 ml.

5. *Staining solution:* 0.118 *M* silver nitrate. To make 1 liter of a stock solution, add 20 g of silver nitrate to 800 ml of deionized water. After dissolving, bring to final volume with deionized water. Store this stock solution at room temperature in a dark bottle. To make a working solution of 0.2% (w/v) silver nitrate, dilute 120 ml of the stock solution to a final volume of 1200 ml.

6. *Reducing solution:* 0.283 *M* sodium carbonate, 0.007 *M* formaldehyde. To make 2 liters of the solution, add 60 g of anhydrous sodium carbonate and 1 ml of 37% (w/w) formaldehyde to 1800 ml of deionized water. After dissolving, bring to a final volume with deionized water. Prepare fresh, approximately 30 min prior to use, to allow for the dissolution of the carbonate.

7. *Stopbath solution:* 3% (v/v) acetic acid. To make 1500 ml of the solution, add 45 ml of glacial acetic acid to 1000 ml of deionized water. After dissolving, bring to final volume with deionized water. Store at room temperature.

Steps

1. Perform all steps in glass trays, staining one gel per tray. Place the trays on a rocker or shaker at a very gentle speed. Perform all steps at room temperature.

2. After electrophoresis, place each gel into 200 ml of fixation solution. Soak the gels in this solution for 1 hr. Gels can be stained 1 hr after fixation; however, the gels may remain in this solution overnight if necessary.

3. Transfer each gel from the fixation solution into 200 ml of rehydrating solution. Soak the gels in this solution for 10 min.

4. Discard the rehydration solution and add 200 ml of glutaraldehyde solution to each tray. Soak the gels in this solution for 30 min.

5. Discard the glutaraldehyde solution. Wash each gel with 200 ml of deionized water for 15 min.

6. Discard the wash and add to each gel 200 ml of 0.1% (w/v) potassium dichromate. Soak the gels in this solution for 5 min.

7. Discard the dichromate solution and add to each gel 200 ml of 0.2% (w/v) silver nitrate. Soak the gels in this solution for 25 min.

8. Discard the silver nitrate solution, wash each gel briefly (approximately 15 sec) with 50 ml of the sodium carbonate/formaldehyde solution, and discard this wash as soon as it turns gray with colloidal particles. Follow this initial rinse with 250 ml of the sodium carbonate/formaldehyde solution. If colloidal particles collect in the solution prior to full image development, it may be necessary to replace the carbonate/formaldehyde solution. Continue the development in this solution until the proteins are sufficiently stained. Proteins should become visible within 1 to 3 min.

9. To stop the image development, discard the carbonate solution and add 250 ml of 3% (v/v) acetic acid. Soak the gels in this solution for 5 min.

10. Discard the acetic acid solution. Wash each gel two times with 250 ml of deionized water for 10 min each wash.

11. Store gels moist in sealed clear plastic bags.

IV. Comments

Most protein silver stains may be analyzed quantitatively, provided that the methodological limitations of silver staining are respected. It is critical in such applications to be aware that the relationship between the density of silver staining and protein concentration is protein specific. Such specificity, which is a function of the staining reaction and the reactive groups contained in each protein, is not limited to silver detection methods (Merril, 1986, 1990). It has also been demonstrated with Coomassie blue and the commonly used Lowry protein assay. While most silver stains produce monochromatic brown or black colors with proteins, other colors may be produced. Lipoproteins may stain with a bluish hue, while some glycoproteins may stain yellow, brown, or red. This color effect is due to the diffractive scattering of light by the microscopic silver grains (Merril *et al.*, 1988). Thus, while quantitative comparisons can be made between equivalent proteins on different gels of similar samples, comparisons between different proteins are not valid.

General background staining has been demonstrated to be due in part to the chemistry of the polyacrylamide gels. Alterations in the chemistry of the polyacrylamide gels, such as in the use of the crosslinker diacrylylpiperazine (piperazine diacrylamide), results in reduced background for the diamine silver stain. (Hochstrasser and Merril, 1988). In addition, the use of sodium thiosulfate in the second-dimension gels will also help to reduce background staining.

V. Pitfalls

1. If the proteins are radioactively labeled, silver staining may interfere with the detection of the radioactivity (Van Keuren *et al.*, 1981). While quenching of

^{35}S- and ^{14}C-labeled proteins is minimal with most nondiamine silver stains, diamine methods may cause as much as a 50% decrease in autoradiography image density. All types of silver stains severely quench the detection of ^{3}H-labeled proteins. Destaining may restore some of the ability to detect ^{3}H-labeled proteins fluorographically, providing that the initial staining was performed with a nondiamine silver stain.

2. Artifactual bands with molecular weights ranging from 50,000 to 68,000 are often observed in silver-stained gels. Evidence has been presented indicating that these bands are due to contamination by keratin-type proteins (Ochs, 1983). These bands may be more prominent in the presence of certain reducing agents, such as mercaptoethanol.

3. The sensitivity of the stain may be diminished unless the deionized water is of good quality, with a conductivity of less than 1 mho.

REFERENCES

Hochstrasser, D. F., and Merril, C. R. (1988) 'Catalysts' for polyacrylamide gel polymerization and detection of proteins by silver staining. *Appl. Theor. Electrophor.* **1,** 35–40.

Merril, C. R. (1986) Development and mechanisms of silver stains for electrophoresis. *Acta Histochem. Cytochem.* **19,** 655–667.

Merril, C. R. (1990) Silver staining of proteins and DNA. *Nature (London)* **343,** 779–780.

Merril, C. R., Bisher, M. E., Harrington, M., and Steven A. C. (1988) Coloration of silver-stained protein bands in polyacrylamide gels is caused by light scattering from silver grains of characteristic sizes. *Proc. Natl. Acad. Sci. USA* **85,** 453–457.

Merril, C. R., Goldman, D., Sedman, S. A., and Ebert, M. H. (1981) Ultra-sensitive stain for proteins in polyacrylamide gels shows regional variation in cerebrospinal fluid proteins. *Science* **211,** 1437–1438.

Merril, C. R., and Pratt, M. (1986) A rapid sensitive protein silver stain and assay system for proteins on membranes. *Anal. Biochem.* **156,** 96–110.

Merril, C. R., Switzer, R. C., and Van Keuren, M. L. (1979) Trace polypeptides in cellular extracts and human body fluids detected by two-dimensional electrophoresis and a highly sensitive silver stain. *Proc. Natl. Acad. Sci. USA* **76,** 4335–4339.

Ochs, D. (1983) Protein contaminants of sodium dodecyl sulfate–polyacrylamide gels. *Anal. Biochem.* **135,** 470–474.

Switzer, R. C., III, Merril, C. R., and Shifrin, S. (1979) A highly sensitive silver stain for detecting proteins and peptides in polyacrylamide gels. *Anal. Biochem.* **98,** 231–237.

Van Keuren, M. L., Goldman, D., and Merril, C. R. (1981) Detection of radioactively labeled proteins is quenched by silver staining methods: Quenching is minimal for ^{14}C and partially reversible for ^{3}H with a photochemical stain. *Anal. Biochem.* **116,** 248–255.

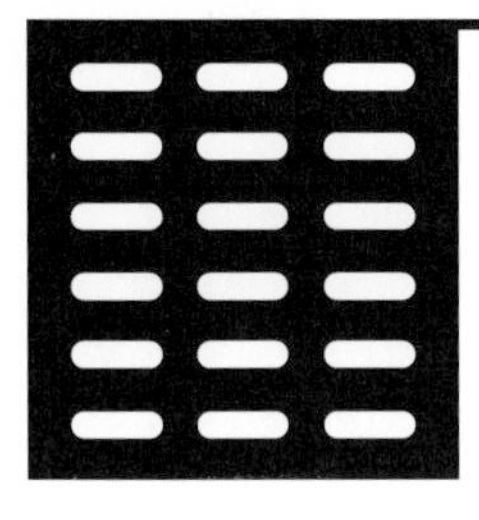

Detection of Subpicogram Quantities of Protein in Polyacrylamide Gels

Andrew Wallace and Hans Peter Saluz

I. Introduction

Here we describe a highly sensitive procedure to detect proteins within SDS gels. This method facilitates the characterization of rare proteins (Wallace and Saluz, 1992a,b), occurring in unique or limited sources. Another application is the ability to detect certain types of synthetic peptides that conventional procedures fail to stain (Wallace and Saluz, 1992b).

The procedure is based on photochemical reactions in which very small amounts of silver are deposited around proteins and in a series of steps are converted to silver sulfide. With minor modifications this technique should also be applicable to the detection of other biopolymers, such as nucleic acids (Boulikas and Hancock, 1981).

The first step of the procedure is "staining" with silver nitrate (Ansorge, 1985), which results in the diffusion of the silver salt throughout the gel matrix. Thereby silver ions tend to associate with the trapped protein, which results in a higher concentration of silver around the protein bands than in the gel matrix. At this stage, in contrast to conventional silver staining, no visible signals are obtained.

In the second step, developing, silver nitrate is reacted with formaldehyde under basic conditions to produce metallic silver (Glafkides, 1987). Proteins act as catalysts in this reaction, leading to faster deposition of silver metal in the area of the protein bands, compared with that in the rest of the gel. The nonreduced silver has to be washed away at this stage, otherwise it contributes to the background.

The third step, known as bleaching (Fig. 1), converts the deposited silver to AgBr (Glafkides, 1987). Finally, the silver bromide is transformed to silver sulfide by reaction with [^{35}S]thiourea (Owunwanne *et al.*, 1982), resulting in a deposit of radioactive silver sulfide at the sites of proteins (Figs. 2 and 3).

II. Materials and Instrumentation

Dichlorodimethylsilane, Tris base (Trizma), and SDS were obtained from Sigma. Carbon tetrachloride (CCl_4), methanol (H_3COH), ethanol (H_3CCH_2OH), acetic acid (H_3CCOOH), glycine (H_2NCH_2COOH), silver nitrate AR ($AgNO_3$), potassium carbonate AR (K_2CO_3), 37% formaldehyde solution (stabilized with 10% methanol and Dolomite dust, HCHO), potassium ferricyanide AR ($K_3[Fe(CN)_6]$), potassium bromide AR (KBr), sodium hydroxide AR (NaOH), 2-mercaptoethanol, and DTT were obtained from Merck. Radioactive [^{35}S]thiourea (H_2NCSNH_2, product code SJ 33, specific activity 29.3 mCi/mmole, supplied as dry powder; on receipt, 1 ml of water was added and after dissolution, it was stored frozen at -20°C in 100-μl

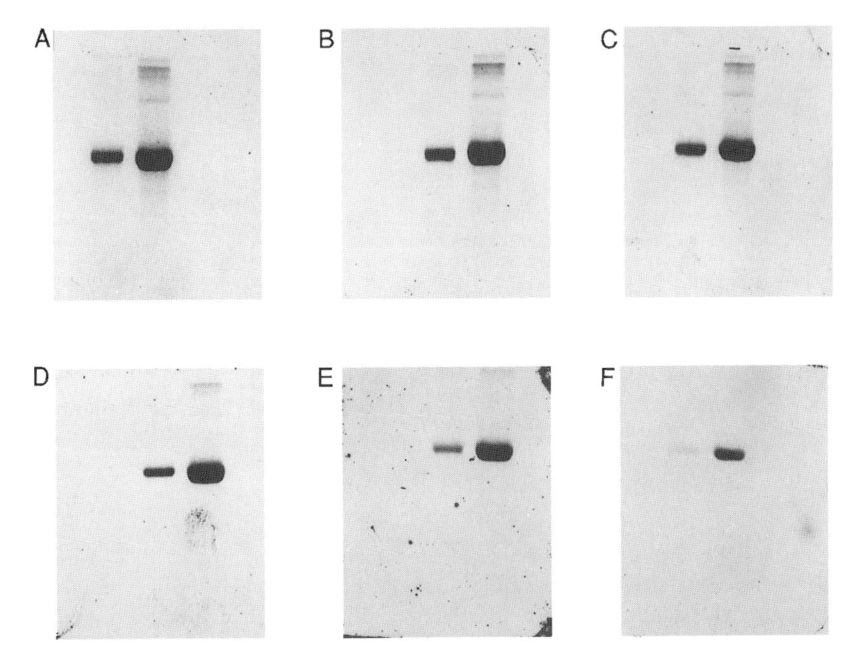

FIGURE 1 Effect of different bleach bath concentrations on the protein–silver radioactivation procedure. For each panel (A–F) two different BSA amounts were loaded: 50 ng at the left, 100 ng at the right. The following increasing concentrations were used: (A) $K_3Fe(CN)_6$, 0.5 g/liter; KBr, 0.05 g/liter. (B) $K_3Fe(CN)_6$, 0.1 g/liter; KBr, 0.01 g/liter. (C) $K_3Fe(CN)_6$, 1 g/liter; KBr, 0.1 g/liter. (D) $K_3Fe(CN)_6$, 10 g/liter; KBr, 1 g/liter. (E) $K_3Fe(CN)_6$; 20 g/liter; KBr; 2 g/liter; (F) $K_3Fe(CN)_6$, 40 g/liter; KBr, 4 g/liter. Increasing bleach bath concentrations resulted in a decreasing signal strength and very faint bands became invisible. The exposure time was 10 hr. Copyright Academic Press, 1992. Reprinted, with permission, from Wallace and Saluz (1992a).

aliquots) and Amplify (product code NANP 100) were supplied by Amersham. For all solutions and washing steps, deionized, double-distilled water (Milli-Q quality or equivalent) was used. Proteins were purchased from Pharmacia (gel filtration calibration kit). Lubrificated microcentrifuge tubes for handling the protein samples were obtained from MulTI-Technology, Inc. (1.7-ml Natural Multi-Lube Tubes, Cat. No. I301726N090, 250 Tubes/Pack).

Electrophoresis was performed using the Bio-Rad Mini-Protean II dual slab cell gel apparatus. Acrylamide, *N,N'*-methylenebisacrylamide, ammonium persulfate (APS), bromphenol blue (BPB), and TEMED were purchased from Bio-Rad (electrophoresis-grade reagents).

The gel fixing and treatment procedures can be carried out in any suitably sized glass or plastic dish, even the plastic lids from autoclavable pipette tip racks. No special equipment is required, but care should be taken to handle and dispose of radioactive solutions according to the appropriate safety regulations.

III. Procedures

A. SDS–POLYACRYLAMIDE GEL ELECTROPHORESIS

SDS–polyacrylamide gels (up to 9 cm × 5 cm × 0.75–1.0 mm thick, with slot sizes of 5 × 1 mm) were prepared according to Laemmli (1970). (see also article by Julio E. Celis and Eydfinnur Olsen.)

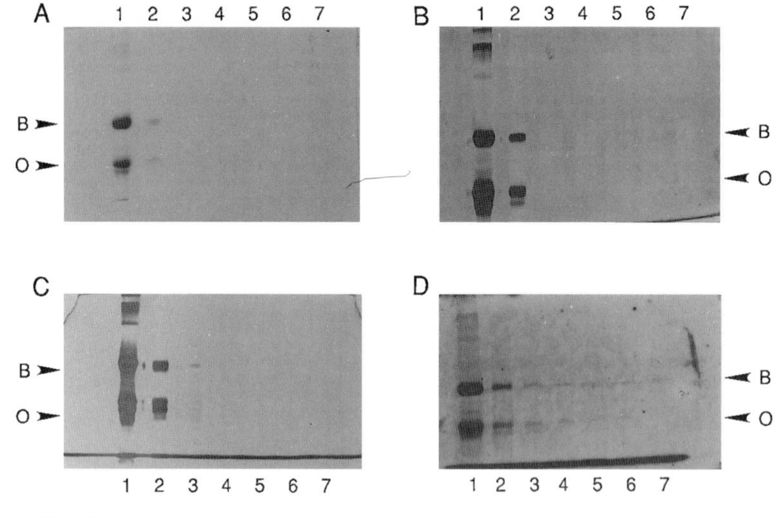

FIGURE 2 Sensitivity comparison between different detection procedures on 10%, 1-mm-thick SDS–gels with slot sizes 6 mm wide. (A) Coomassie blue staining. (B) Silver staining. (C) Coomassie and silver staining. (D) Radioactivation procedure involving [^{35}S]thiourea, exposed for 3 weeks. Lanes 1–7: 400 ng, 40 ng, 4 ng, 400 pg, 40 pg, 4 pg, and 400 fg of each protein, i.e., bovine serum albumin (B) and ovalbumin (O). Coomassie blue staining (A) detected down to 40 ng of each protein, silver staining (B) down to 4 ng in the best case, Coomassie plus silver staining (C) down to 4 ng but with higher signal intensity, and with radioactivation (D) down to 400 fg. Copyright Academic Press, 1992. Reprinted, with permission, from Wallace and Saluz (1992a).

Solutions

1. *Acrylamide solution:* To make 300 ml, dissolve 87.6 g acrylamide and 2.4 g of *N,N′*-methylenebisacrylamide in distilled water. This gives a 30% (w/v) T, 2.67% (w/v) C solution. Filter and store at 4°C in the dark.

2. *Separating gel buffer:* To make 150 ml, dissolve 27.23 g Tris base in approximately 80 ml of distilled water. Adjust the pH to 8.8 with 1 *M* HCl, make up to 150 ml with distilled water, and store at room temperature (RT). Final concentration is 1.5 *M* Tris–Cl, pH 8.8.

3. *Stacking gel buffer:* To make 100 ml, dissolve 6 g Tris base in approximately 60 ml of distilled water. Adjust the pH to 6.8 with 1 *M* HCl, make up to 100 ml with distilled water, and store at RT. Final concentration is 0.5 *M* Tris–Cl, pH 6.8.

4. *10% (w/v) SDS:* To make 100 ml, dissolve 10 g of SDS in approximately 80 ml of distilled water. Adjust the volume to 100 ml with distilled water and store at RT.

5. *Bromphenol blue solution:* To make 10 ml, dissolve 5 mg of bromphenol blue in 10 ml of distilled water. Filter and store at RT. Final concentration is approximately 0.05% (v/v).

6. *Sample buffer (5×):* To make 1 ml of 5× concentrate, mix 0.1 g SDS with 250 μl of stacking gel buffer, then add 200 μl glycerol, 200 μl bromphenol blue solution, and 280 μl of distilled water. Mix well and, just before use, add 70 μl of 2-mercaptoethanol (final concentration 1 *M*).

7. *Running buffer (5×), pH 8.3 (RT):* To make 600 ml of 5× concentrate, dissolve 9 g Tris base, 43.2 g glycine, and 3 g SDS in 600 ml of distilled water. Check the pH, which should be around 8.3. If it is less than 7 or more than 9, discard the solution. Do not attempt to adjust the pH or add any chloride-

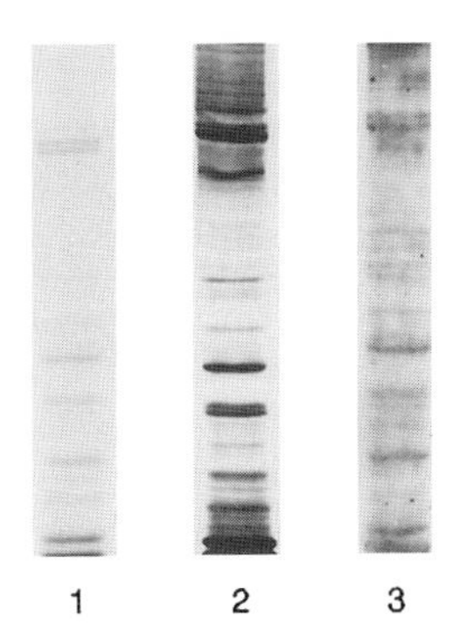

FIGURE 3 Comparison of different sensitive protein staining procedures with respect to resolution and detectability of proteins in a sample of yeast extract on 7.5%, 1-mm-thick SDS–gels with slot sizes 6 mm wide. In each track shown, the total amount of protein loaded was 4.2 μg. The tracks shown in each panel were obtained as follows: Staining with Commassie brilliant blue (lane 1), Coomassie plus silver staining (lane 2), and radioactivation with overnight exposure (lane 3). The background in lane 1 is slightly grayer than that in the other panels due to the photographic exposure required to reveal the fainter Coomassie-stained bands. Copyright Academic Press, 1992. Reprinted, with permission, from Wallace and Saluz (1992a).

containing salts. Store at RT. Before use, dilute 60 ml of 5× buffer with 240 ml of distilled water. This is sufficient for one run.

8. *Ammonium persulfate solution (APS):* To prepare 1 ml of 10% APS, dissolve 100 mg of ammonium persulfate in 1 ml of distilled water. Always prepare this solution freshly.

9. *Silanizing solution:* To prepare 100 ml, dilute 1 ml of dimethyldichlorosilane to 100 ml with carbon tetrachloride. Wear gloves when handling this solution and work in a well-ventilated area.

10. *Water-saturated butan-1-ol:* To prepare 10 ml, add 2 ml of water to 8 ml of butan-1-ol. Shake well and allow the two phases to separate.

Steps

1. Wash the gel glass plates with water and ethanol.

2. Lay the clean plates on a layer of tissue paper and wipe the surface with a tissue moistened with silanizing solution.

3. Wipe the plates with a tissue moistened with ethanol (no water) and allow them to dry.

4. Assemble the glass plate sandwich. Lay the larger rectangular plate on a clean surface and place two equal spacers up to 1 mm thick along the short edges of the plate. Place the smaller glass plate on top of the spacers so that the bottom ends of the spacers and glass plates are aligned (do not use any kind of grease).

5. Loosen the four screws on the clamp assembly and stand it upright with the screws facing away from you.

6. Grip the glass plate sandwich by the edges, with the larger plate facing away from you, and slide it into the clamp assembly along the front face of the plastic pressure plate. Gently tighten the top two screws of the assembly.

7. Set up the casting stand on a level surface with the alignment slot facing you. Put the gray silicon rubber gaskets into position on top of the red foam pads of the casting stand.

8. Put the clamp assembly into the alignment slot with the clamp screws facing away from you. Loosen the screws and allow the spacers and glass plates to set firmly against the base of the slot. If necessary, use the alignment card provided with the apparatus to hold the spacers in place. Gently tighten the clamp screws until you can see Newtonian rings at the edge of the glass plate sandwich.

9. Clean the inner surfaces of the sandwich by blowing a stream of compressed air or nitrogen gas into the assembled sandwich.

10. Remove the assembled sandwich from the alignment slot and transfer it to one of the casting slots in the stand. With the glass plate sandwich facing outward, press the bottom of the plate assembly against the gray silicon rubber gasket and snap the plastic plate into place under the overhang of the casting slot.

11. Prepare 10 ml of separating gel solution (enough for two 10% SDS gels) by combining 4.01 ml distilled water, 2.5 ml separating gel buffer, 100 μl SDS solution, 3.33 ml acrylamide solution, 50 μl APS, and 5 μl TEMED.

12. Mix well and pipette the solution into the gel sandwich up to 2 cm below the upper edge of the shorter glass plate.

13. Overlay the gel solution with a few drops of butan-1-ol (saturated with water).

14. Allow the solution to polymerize for 1 hr (RT).

15. Remove butan-1-ol overlay and rinse well with water.

16. Prepare 10 ml of stacking gel solution (enough for two SDS gels) by combining 6.1 ml distilled water, 2.5 ml stacking gel buffer, 100 μl SDS solution, 1.3 ml acrylamide solution, 50 μl APS, and 10 μl TEMED.

17. Mix well and pipette the solution into the gel sandwich up to the top edge of the shorter glass plate.

18. Insert the comb carefully to avoid trapping air bubbles below the teeth.

19. Allow the solution to polymerize for 1 hr (RT).

20. Carefully remove the comb by pulling straight up slowly and gently. If the slots start to distort, rock the comb gently back and forth to allow air to enter below the teeth.

21. Remove the gel assembly from the casting stand and attach it to the electrode assembly.

22. Prepare 300 ml of diluted running buffer.

23. Place the complete assembly in the buffer tank and fill the inner space of the electrode assembly with running buffer. Add the remaining buffer to the outer tank.

24. Clean the wells with a stream of running buffer using a Pasteur pipette.

25. Prepare the samples by adding 0.2 vol of 5× sample buffer to the protein solution in Lubrificated microcentrifuge tubes (final sample volume 10 μl, but up to 30 μl if necessary). Heat at 95°C for 5 min.

26. Load samples into the wells using siliconized capillaries.

27. Close the tank and run the gel at 170 V (constant voltage) until the bromphenol marker reaches the bottom of the gel. This takes about 1 hr.

28. Switch off the current and take out the gel assembly.

29. Remove the gel sandwiches and open them carefully.

B. FIXING AND STAINING

Solutions

1. *0.1 M sodium hydroxide solution:* Prepare 1 liter of a 0.1 *M* sodium hydroxide stock solution by dissolving 4 g NaOH in 1 liter of water.

2. *[^{35}S]Thiourea stock solution:* To prepare a 1 μCi/μl stock solution, dissolve the contents of the vial (1 mCi) in 1 ml of distilled water. Make aliquots of 100 μl and store them frozen at −20°C.

3. *Amplify solution:* This is purchased from Amersham (product code NAMP 100) and is ready for use; store in dark at room temperature and *Do not freeze.*

4. *Fixing solution:* To prepare 1 liter, mix 400 ml methanol with 100 ml acetic acid and 500 ml water. Prepare fresh.

5. *Ethanol solution:* To prepare 1 liter, mix 100 ml absolute ethanol, 50 ml acetic acid, and 850 ml water. Prepare fresh.

6. *Silver nitrate solution:* To prepare 1 liter, first dissolve 0.1 g $AgNO_3$ in 100 ml water to form a 0.1% solution, then dilute 0.5 ml of this to 1 liter with water to form a 0.5 mg/liter solution of $AgNO_3$.

NOTE

These solutions must be freshly prepared immediately before use; do not attempt to store or reuse them.

7. *Developing solution:* To prepare 500 ml, dissolve 10 g potassium carbonate in 500 ml water. **Immediately before use,** add 140 μl of 37% formaldehyde solution and mix well. This gives enough developing solution for two gels.

8. *Bleach bath solution:* To prepare 500 ml, dissolve 0.25 g potassium ferricyanide and 0.05 g potassium bromide together in 500 ml water (enough for two gels).

NOTE

This solution must be freshly prepared immediately before use; do not attempt to store or reuse it.

9. *Radioactivating solution:* Prepare the [^{35}S]thiourea radioactivating solution as follows. Add 25 ml of 0.1 *M* sodium hydroxide solution to 24 ml water. Add 50 μl (50 μCi) of [^{35}S]thiourea stock solution to 950 μl water, mix well, add this 1 ml of diluted [^{35}S]thiourea to the 49 ml of diluted NaOH, and dilute the whole mixture to 200 ml with water.

NOTE

This solution must be freshly prepared immediately before use; do not attempt to store or reuse it.

TABLE I Procedure for Radioactivation of Protein Bands

Step	Treatment time (1-mm-thick gels)
40% Methanol, 10% acetic acid	1 hr
10% Ethanol, 5% acetic acid	5 min
10% Ethanol, 5% acetic acid	5 min
Water	5 min
Water	5 min
0.00005% $AgNO_3$	20 min
Rinse with water	1–10 sec
0.01% Formaldehyde in 2% K_2CO_3	10 min
Water	5 min
Water	5 min
Water	5 min
Water	5 min
0.05% $K_3Fe(CN)_6$ in 0.01% KBr	10 min
Water	5 min
Water	5 min
Water	5 min
Water	5 min
50 μCi of [^{35}S]thiourea in 50 ml of 12.5 m*M* NaOH	30 min
Water (50 ml)	5 min
Water (50 ml)	5 min
Water (50 ml)	5 min
50 ml of Amplify solution	30 min
Rinse with water	1 min
Dry the treated gels onto filter paper (Whatman 3) under vacuum at 80°C	1 hr
Expose the dried gels on an X-ray film that is sensitive to blue light (Kodak X-Omat AR or equivalent) at −80°C (with intensifying screens, if required) until the desired signals appear on film development	As required to visualize signals

Steps

See also Table I.

1. Run protein samples to be detected on a normal SDS–polyacrylamide gel using the Laemmli (1970) buffer system as described above.
2. Fix gels in fixing solution for 1 hr, using 250 ml solution per gel.
3. Remove fixing solution.
4. Incubate gels in ethanol solution for 5 min (250 ml per gel).
5. Remove ethanol solution.
6. Repeat steps 4 and 5.
7. Incubate gels in water for 5 min (250 ml per gel).
8. Remove water.
9. Repeat steps 7 and 8.
10. While carrying out the water wash steps above, prepare the silver nitrate solution as described above.
11. Incubate gels in the silver nitrate solution for 20 min (250 ml per gel). Add the silver solution while gently shaking the gels.
12. During the silver nitrate treatment, prepare the developing solution.

13. Remove the silver nitrate solution and briefly rinse the gels in 20–30 ml of water or developing solution.
14. Add the developing solution described above (total volume 250 ml per gel). Incubate for 10 min.
15. Remove the developing solution.
16. Incubate the gels in water for 5 min (250 ml per gel) and then remove the water.
17. Repeat step 16 three times (total water wash time: 20 min).
18. During the water wash steps, prepare the bleach bath solution.
19. After the last water wash step, remove the water and incubate each gel in 250 ml of the bleach bath solution for 10 min. Add the solution while gently shaking the gels.
20. Remove the bleach bath solution.
21. Incubate the gels in water for 5 min (250 ml per gel) and then remove the water.
22. Repeat step 21 three times (total water wash time: 20 min). Shorter washing times can be used, but at the expense of higher final background.
23. During the water wash steps, prepare the [^{35}S]thiourea radioactivating solution.
24. After the last water wash step, remove the water and incubate each gel in 200 ml of the [^{35}S]thiourea radioactivating solution described above for 30 min.
25. Remove the [^{35}S]thiourea radioactivating solution.
26. Incubate the gels in water for 5 min (250 ml per gel) and then remove the water.
27. Repeat step 26 two or three times (total water wash time: 15–20 min).

The following treatment with fluorographic enhancer is optional, depending on the signal strength required.

28. Remove the water and incubate each gel in 50 ml of Amplify solution for 30 min with shaking.
29. Wash the Amplify treated gel with water for up to 1 min.
30. Dry the treated gels onto filter paper under vacuum for 1 hr at 80°C.
31. Expose the dried gels to an X-ray film that is sensitive to blue light (Kodak X-Omat AR or equivalent) at −80°C (with intensifying screens, if required) until the desired signals appear on film development.

IV. Comments

This method is capable of detecting **400 fg** of bovine serum albumin after 7 days of exposure. For any semiquantification, the signal response of the X-ray film must be linearized before exposure.

V. Pitfalls

A. HIGH BACKGROUND WITHIN THE SAMPLE TRACKS

1. Do not use sample dyes or protein buffer solutions containing DTT or other substances that react with thiourea. 2-Mercaptoethanol should be used as a reducing agent in the sample buffer.

B. OVERALL HIGH BACKGROUND

1. Avoid the use of any compound in the gel solutions that reacts with thiourea.

2. Do not use glutaraldehyde-containing solutions to fix the gel if glycine is used in the running buffer. In such cases, try using Tricine instead of glycine.

3. If using Amplify solution, rinse the gel well with water before drying.

4. Try increasing the water washing time after development and bleach bath treatments.

5. Follow all steps in the protocol carefully. Do not omit any treatment in an attempt to save time.

C. NO SIGNALS FROM THE SEPARATED PROTEINS

1. Try increasing the exposure time or using a more sensitive film.

2. Do not cover the gel with Saran wrap or other coverings while exposing the gel to film.

3. Try using Amplify solution or increasing the Amplify treatment time.

4. Use 10–100 ng of bovine serum albumin as an internal or external standard to have a reference that gives readily detected signals (see Figs. 2 and 4).

5. Use only silanized or coated materials to handle the protein samples.

6. Negative staining may be observed if excessive amounts of protein are used.

D. WEAK SIGNALS

1. Protein amounts might be below the detection limit or the protein may not be easily stainable. Increase the protein concentration in the sample. Use a BSA dilution series as a reference.

2. Increase exposure time.

3. Try using a more sensitive film and/or preflash (Laskey and Mills, 1977) or treat the film with "forming gas" (Smith *et al.,* 1985a,b).

4. Check or change developing conditions for the X-ray film being used. Deep-tank developing can increase the signal.

A

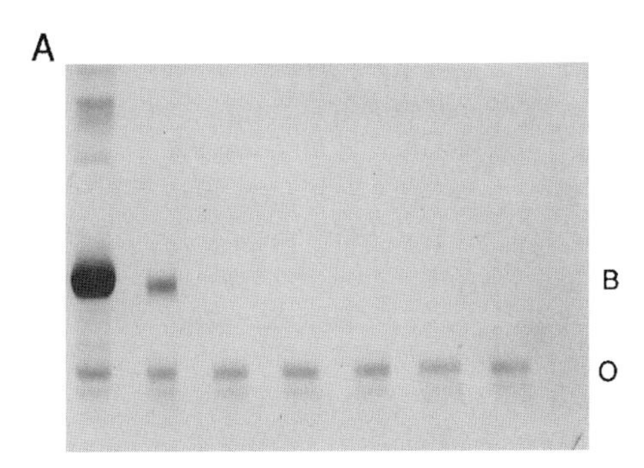

B

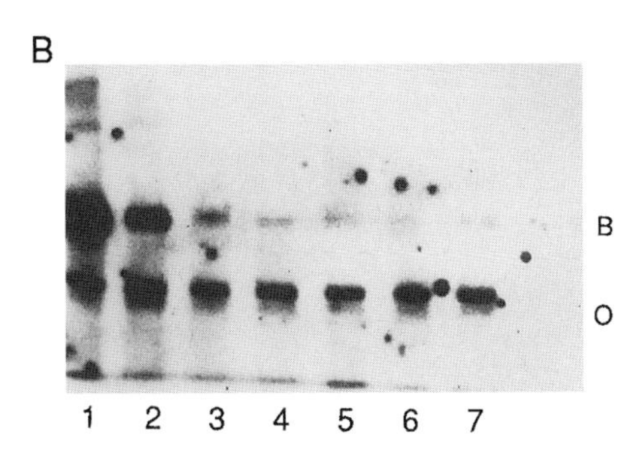

FIGURE 4 Sensitivity comparison between different detection procedures on 10% SDS–gels. (A) Coomassie blue staining. (B) Radioactivation procedure. Lanes 1–7: 400 ng of ovalbumin (internal standard) in each track (O) and 400 ng, 40 ng, 4 ng, 400 pg, 40 pg, 4 pg, and 400 fg of BSA (B). Reprinted, with permission, from Wallace and Saluz (1992b). Copyright Macmillan Magazines Ltd., 1992.

E. IRREGULAR BACKGROUND OR "HOT SPOTS"

1. Try increasing the washing time after thiourea treatment. Thiourea is a known "fogging" agent and can chemically darken the film.

2. "Hot spots" may be caused by dust on the gel surfaces or in the solutions. Clean and silanize the glass plates more carefully and filter all solutions if problems persist. Use only clean tanks for gel treatment.

ACKNOWLEDGMENTS

We thank Inge Obergfoell of the Friedrich Miescher Institute in Basel, Switzerland, for the reproduction of the photographs. The yeast extract used in the experiment illustrated in Fig. 3 was kindly provided by Dr. Alessandra Vitelli of IRBM.

REFERENCES

Ansorge, W. (1985) Fast and sensitive detection of protein and DNA bands by treatment with potassium permanganate. *J. Biochem. Biophys. Methods* **11**, 13–20.

Boulikas, T., and Hancock, R. (1981) A highly sensitive technique for staining DNA and RNA in polyacrylamide gels using silver. *J. Biochem. Biophys. Methods* **5**, 219–228.

Glafkides, P. (1987) "Affaiblisseurs superficiels au ferricyanure de potassiumin, in Chimie et physique photographiques," Vol. 1, pp. 228–230. Editions de l'Usine, Paris.

Laemmli, U. K. (1970) Cleavage of structural proteins during the assembly of the head of bacteriophage T4. *Nature* **227**, 680–685.

Laskey, R. A., and Mills, A. D. (1977) Enhanced autoradiographic detection of ^{32}P and ^{125}I using intensifying screens and hypersensitized film. *FEBS Lett.* **82**, 314–316.
Owunwanne, A., Wheaton, L. E., Carroll, B. H., and O'Mara, R. E. (1982) Autoradiographic intensification method: Effect of increasing the amount of nonradioactive thiourea in the radioactivating solution. *J. Appl. Photogr. Eng.* **8**, 104–106.
Smith, A. G., Phillips, C. A., and Hahn, E. J. (1985a) X-ray films: Suppression of reciprocity failure by astronomical techniques. *J. Imag. Technol.* **11**, 27–32.
Smith, A. G., Phillips, C. A., Hahn, E. J., and Leacock, R. J. (1985b) Hypersensitization and astronomical tests of X-ray films. *Am. Astron. Soc. Photo-Bull.* **39**, 8–14.
Wallace, A., and Saluz, H. P. (1992a) Ultramicrodetection of proteins in polyacrylamide gels. *Anal. Biochem.* **203**, 27–34, and references therein.
Wallace, A., and Saluz, H. P. (1992b) Beyond silver staining. *Nature* **357**, 608–609.

SECTION E

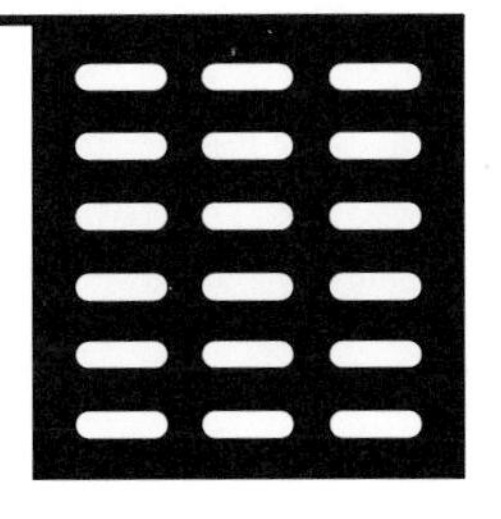

Overlay Techniques and Others

Blot Overlay Assay: A Method to Detect Protein–Protein Interactions

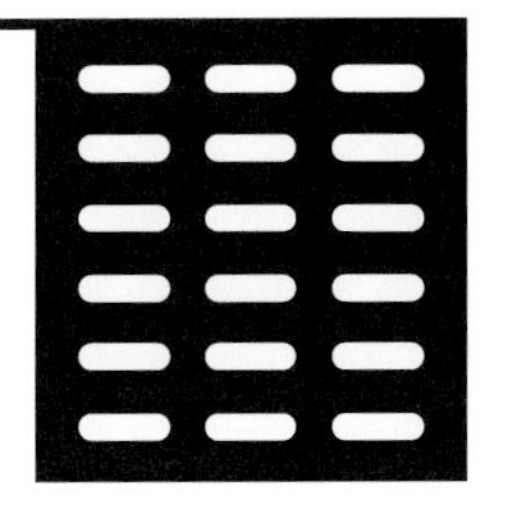

Aaron W. Crawford and Mary C. Beckerle

I. Introduction

The blot overlay assay is a powerful method used to study protein–protein interactions and provides an especially useful means by which to identify potential protein ligands. In this approach, a radiolabeled protein probe is used to overlay protein samples immobilized on nitrocellulose. Because this assay allows detection of protein–protein interactions within the context of a complex mixture of proteins, this method is also useful to investigate the specificity of an interaction between two ligands. The blot overlay assay may also be used to define specific domains of a ligand involved in protein–protein interactions; for example, proteolytic fragments of proteins or nested deletion fragments may be probed to determine which portion of a molecule contains the interactive site (Crawford *et al.*, 1992; Gilmore *et al.*, 1992). In addition, the blot overlay procedure may be modified to probe cDNA libraries to identify bacterially expressed proteins that interact with labeled probes (Cicchetti *et al.*, 1992; Blanar and Rutter, 1992).

II. Materials and Instrumentation

Iodo-Gen reagent (1,3,4,6-tetrachloro-3α,6α-diphenylglycouril) was obtained from Pierce. $Na^{125}I$ (100 mCi/ml, in NaOH solution) was purchased from ICN. Disposable fractionation columns (0.7 × 20 cm) and 2-mercaptoethanol were obtained from Bio-Rad, and plastic collection tubes (~8 ml) came from Falcon. Sephadex G-50 chromatography matrix was obtained from Pharmacia. Nitrocellulose (Immobilon-NC with a pore size of 0.45 μm) was purchased from Millipore, and the Transfor electrophoresis unit was obtained from Hoeffer Scientific. All other chemicals were obtained from Sigma.

III. Procedures

A. PROTEIN IODINATION

Solutions

All stock solutions should be prepared in distilled water.

1. *Dialysis buffer:* 150 m*M* NaCl, 50 m*M* Tris–HCl, pH 7.6. To make 4 liters of dialysis buffer, use 120 ml of 5 *M* NaCl stock solution and 200 ml of 1 *M*

Tris–HCl, pH 7.6, stock solution. Bring this solution to a final volume of 4 liters. Store at 4°C.

2. *Reaction stop solution:* 10 mg/ml tyrosine. To make 5 ml of this solution, add 50 mg tyrosine to 5 ml of distilled water. Because this is a saturated solution, not all of the tyrosine will dissolve.

3. *Column elution/equilibration buffer:* 150 m*M* NaCl, 50 m*M* Tris–HCl, pH 7.6, 0.2% gelatin, 0.1% 2-mercaptoethanol, 1 m*M* EDTA, 0.1% sodium azide. To make 500 ml, add 15 ml of 5 *M* NaCl stock solution, 25 ml of 1 *M* Tris–HCl, pH 7.6 stock solution, 1 g gelatin, 500 μl 2-mercaptoethanol, 2.5 ml of 200 m*M* EDTA stock solution, and 5 ml of 10% sodium azide stock solution. Gelatin may be dissolved first in 50–100 ml of warm distilled water. Bring the final volume of the solution to 500 ml.

Steps

The protein iodination procedure described here was introduced by Fraker and Speck (1978) and is an efficient solid-phase method for labeling exposed tyrosine residues under relatively mild conditions.

1. The day before the iodination reaction, prepare Iodo-Gen-coated tubes by dissolving Iodo-Gen in chloroform at a concentration of 1 mg/ml; use these reagents with caution in a ventilated fume hood. Add 40 μl of the Iodo-Gen/chloroform solution to Eppendorf tubes and let the tubes dry overnight in the fume hood. (Alternatively, the tubes may be dried in the hood under a stream of nitrogen). Seal the tubes and store in a desiccation chamber at room temperature; these Iodo-Gen-coated tubes, which serve as the reaction vial for the iodination reaction, may be used for up to 2 months after preparation when stored in this manner.

2. The purified protein to be iodinated should be at a concentration between 0.2 and 1.0 mg/ml. (Protein samples below 0.2 mg/ml may also be iodinated effectively; however, the reaction time may need to be increased for less concentrated samples.) Place the protein into dialysis buffer; the concentration of the protein must be determined after dialysis to calculate the specific activity of the labeled protein, as discussed below (step 7). If the protein is not very concentrated (i.e., <0.2 mg/ml), minimize the dialysis time to prevent nonspecific adsorption of the protein to the dialysis tubing. Because the iodination procedure described here is an oxidative reaction, it is necessary to remove reducing agents from the protein sample to ensure effective labeling. A dialysis time of 4 to 6 hr, using a volume of 1 liter with multiple changes of the dialysis buffer, is sufficient to remove excess reducing agent. More concentrated protein samples can be dialyzed for longer periods, though the dialysis buffer should still be changed multiple times.

3. Prepare a gel filtration column to separate radiolabeled protein from free iodine and iodotyrosine. Boil Sephadex G-50 column matrix for 0.5 hr in deionized water; 2 g of G-50 matrix will be sufficient for more than five columns. Equilibrate Sephadex matrix in elution buffer, and pour a 0.7 × 15-cm column in a disposable column. Attach rubber tubing to the outflow of the column that can be clamped off to regulate the outflow. Remove excess buffer from the top of the column matrix to allow the sample to enter the matrix immediately and not be diluted by excess buffer. Remove excess buffer just prior to applying the sample so that the column matrix does not dry out, taking care not to disturb the top surface of the matrix. Wrap the column in a flexible lead shield, making sure

that the top surface of the column matrix is just visible above the shielding, and set aside.

NOTE

Caution: Because unconjugated radioactive iodide is extremely volatile, it should be handled only in a well-ventilated fume hood using extreme caution. Take appropriate precautions when handling radioactive iodide; work behind protective shielding, and wear protective clothing, gloves, eyeglasses, and personal monitoring devices (see also article by R. W. Davies). Open the vial containing the radioactivity according to the manufacturer's instructions; use a syringe needle to puncture the rubber cap to vent pressure.

4. Perform the iodination reaction as follows. Set up the appropriate lead shielding devices in a fume hood, with a dry waste receptacle readily accessible. Behind the shielding, position the column support holding the gel filtration column (wrapped in lead) and a rack containing plastic tubes to collect fractions. Place the Iodo-Gen-coated tube on ice in an ice bucket, behind the shielding. Add 100 μl of dialyzed protein to the Iodo-Gen-coated tube. Add 1 mCi $Na^{125}I$ to the reaction vial; allow the reaction to proceed on ice for 5–10 min. When half of the reaction time has elapsed, mix the solution by slowly pipetting the mixture up and down a few times, being careful not to generate bubbles. The length of the reaction time can be varied depending on the desired specific activity of the labeled protein, the concentration of the protein, and the availability of reactive tyrosine groups in the protein. Conjugate unreacted $Na^{125}I$ by adding 50 μl of saturated tyrosine (stop solution) to the reaction vial; let the reaction proceed on ice for 5 min. Terminate the reaction by removing the reaction mixture from the Iodo-Gen-coated tube, and transfer it to the gel filtration column set up behind the protective lead shielding. If a pipetman is too wide to penetrate the column opening, use a long-shanked Pasteur pipette to transfer the reaction mixture. Layer the reaction mixture on top of the column matrix, which should be visible just above the protective shielding.

5. Unclamp the outflow tubing to begin eluting the column and start collecting fractions. After the reaction mixture enters the matrix completely (~0.5–1 min) slowly add elution buffer to the top of the column matrix. Collect 400- to 500-μl fractions into sterile, plastic (~8-ml) fraction tubes (these are easier and safer to handle than smaller Eppendorf tubes). When using a 15 × 0.7-cm bed volume, radioiodinated proteins begin to elute from the column at approximately 2500–3000 μl.

6. Monitor the material as it is eluted from the column with a hand-held gamma counter to determine when the peak radioactive fractions are collected. The first detectable radioactive peak corresponds to labeled protein; the second radioactive peak is residual-free iodine and iodotyrosine. Terminate fraction collection once the first peak of radioactivity is detected. Leave the unincorporated counts (second radioactive peak) in the column by clamping off the rubber tubing connected to the outflow. Discard the used column in the dry radioactive waste receptacle.

7. Estimate the specific activity (cpm/mg) of the radiolabeled protein. Using an accurate micropipettor, pipette 1 μl of each collected fraction onto filter paper that has been positioned in a gamma counter fraction tube. Cap the tube, and count samples for 1 min in a gamma counter to determine the radioactivity (cpm/μl) for each fraction. The protein concentration was determined earlier (step 2); assume that all of the protein loaded onto the column is present in the peak

fractions of radioactivity. Measure the volume of each fraction collected. Use these values to determine the total radioactivity (cpm) present in the protein fractions; divide this number by the total amount of protein (μg) used in the iodination reaction to estimate the specific activity of the labeled protein. *Note:* To be reliable, this method depends on a reproducible, high recovery of the protein after gel filtration. Protein recovery should be evaluated in pilot experiments with unlabeled protein. If protein recovery is variable, it will be necessary to determine the protein concentration in the radioiodinated fractions directly to define the specific activity of the labeled protein.

8. Prepare protein samples for SDS–PAGE to evaluate the homogeneity of the radiolabeled probe. Place 1–5 μl of each fraction into 30 μl SDS–PAGE sample buffer and boil the samples in a fume hood. Resolve protein samples by SDS–PAGE (Laemmli, 1970; see also article by Julio E. Celis and Eydfinnur Olsen) using appropriate shielding while resolving the proteins on the gel. Stain and fix the gel briefly, and then dry the gel onto filter paper under vacuum; expose the dried gel to autoradiographic film. A sample containing 150,000 cpm yields a strong signal when exposed to autoradiographic film with an intensification screen for 1 hr.

9. Store the radiolabeled protein fractions at 4°C until ready to perform the blot overlay assay; for best results, it is recommended that the protein be used as soon after labeling as possible. However, depending on the stability of the radiolabeled probe, it may be used for several weeks after labeling. Resolve the radiolabeled probe on a polyacrylamide gel immediately prior to use to ensure that it is still intact and has not undergone proteolysis.

B. BLOT OVERLAY ASSAY

The blot overlay assay was first described as a method to detect interacting protein ligands resolved on polyacrylamide gels (Glenney and Weber, 1980; Otto, 1983). In the procedure described here, potential protein ligands are transferred from polyacrylamide gels to nitrocellulose before incubating with labeled probes.

Solutions

All stock solutions should be prepared in distilled water.

1. *Transfer buffer:* 20% methanol, 192 m*M* glycine, 25 m*M* Tris base. To make 10 liters of transfer buffer, use 2 liters methanol, 144 g glycine (be careful not to use glycine–HCl), and 30 g Tris base. Bring this to a final volume of 10 liters with distilled water. The resulting solution should have a pH of 8.2–8.4.

2. *Blocking buffer:* 150 m*M* NaCl, 50 m*M* Tris–HCl, pH 7.6, 0.05% sodium azide, 2.0% BSA. To make 500 ml of blocking buffer, add 15 ml 5 *M* NaCl stock solution, 25 ml 1 *M* Tris–HCl, pH 7.6, stock solution, 2.5 ml 10% sodium azide stock solution, and 10 g BSA. Bring the solution to a final volume of 500 ml with distilled water.

3. *Overlay solution:* 20 m*M* Hepes, pH 7.5, 0.5% BSA, 0.25% gelatin, 1% Nonidet-P 40, 10 m*M* NaCl, 1 m*M* EGTA, 0.1% 2-mercaptoethanol. To make 100 ml of overlay solution, add 10 ml of 200 m*M* Hepes, pH 7.5, stock solution, 0.5 g BSA, 0.25 g gelatin, 10 ml 10% Nonidet-P 40 stock solution, 200 μl 5 *M* NaCl stock solution, 500 μl 200 m*M* EGTA stock solution, and 100 μl 2-mercaptoethanol; bring to a final volume of 100 ml with distilled water. *Note:* To

more closely approximate physiological conditions, 100 m*M* NaCl may be used in the overlay buffer.

4. *Washing buffer:* 50 m*M* Tris–HCl, pH 7.6, 150 m*M* NaCl, 0.05% Tween-20 (polyoxyethylene-sorbitan laurate), 0.1% sodium azide, 0.2% gelatin. To make 1 liter of washing buffer, use 30 ml of 5 *M* NaCl stock solution, 50 ml 1 *M* Tris–HCl, pH 7.6, stock solution, 10 ml 5% Tween-20 stock solution, 10 ml 10% sodium azide stock solution, and 2 g gelatin.

Steps

1. Protein samples to be assayed in the blot overlay procedure should be resolved on SDS–polyacrylamide gels (Laemmli, 1970; see article by Julio E. Celis and Eyδfinmar Olsen). Prepare duplicate samples: one of these will be used for the overlay assay; the other will be stained with Coomassie blue to enable evaluation of sample complexity and binding specificity.

2. Transfer one gel sample to nitrocellulose using a Transphor electrophoresis unit. Transfer at 0.5 A for 1.5–3 hr in transfer buffer; high-molecular-weight proteins may require longer transfer times. Radioactive molecular weight markers may be resolved on the gel transferred to nitrocellulose to aid in estimating the molecular weight of proteins identified in the overlay assay.

3. After the electrophoretic transfer of proteins is complete, place the nitrocellulose strip with the transferred proteins in 100–150 ml of blocking buffer. Leave the nitrocellulose strips in this solution a minimum of 4 hr to inhibit nonspecific background binding.

4. To perform the blot overlay assay, place overlay buffer into a small container with a tight-fitting lid. To the overlay buffer, add radiolabeled probe to a final concentration of 250,000 cpm/ml; mix the solution well, and add the nitrocellulose strip. Because the radiolabeled protein is often available in limited quantity, it may be necessary to perform the blot overlay assay in a small volume. For a 5 × 10-cm nitrocellulose strip, 10 ml of solution is usually sufficient for the assay, as long as the container does not exceed these dimensions significantly. One should make sure that there is sufficient volume of the overlay solution to prevent the nitrocellulose strips from drying out during the incubation. Place the container with the nitrocellulose strip and the radiolabeled probe on an orbital shaker under moderate speed, appropriately shielded with lead, for 4 hr at room temperature. Multiple strips may be incubated at the same time as long as sufficient volume is present such that the nitrocellulose strips do not adhere to one another and inhibit accessibility of the radiolabeled probe. If multiple strips are probed simultaneously it is recommended that the position of the strips in the container (from bottom to top) be changed every hour or so.

5. After 4 hr of incubation, decant the radioactive overlay solution into a liquid radioactive waste receptacle, and rinse the nitrocellulose strips briefly with 10–20 ml of washing buffer. Perform three or four additional washes (in 50–100 ml), each for 5 min in washing buffer. Decant washes into liquid radioactive waste. Dry the nitrocellulose strip on filter paper at room temperature for 10–15 min. Wrap the nitrocellulose strips in plastic and expose them to autoradiographic film. Generally, overnight exposures will be informative, but the length of exposure will likely need to be adjusted.

IV. Comments

An attractive feature of the blot overlay assay is that it is a useful method to investigate the specificity of protein–protein interactions. For example, the selective

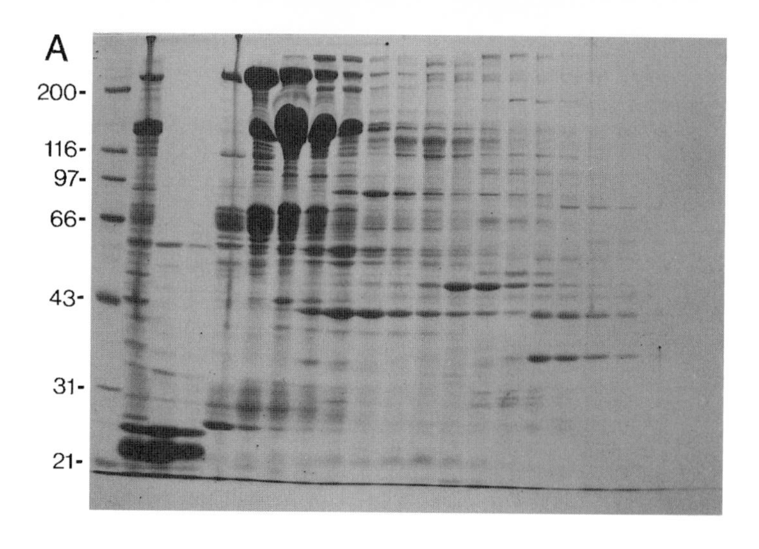

FIGURE 1 A typical blot overlay experiment to detect protein binding partners. Many proteins are present in the Coomassie blue-stained gel (A); however, ^{125}I-zyxin recognizes predominantly a 23-kDa protein (the cysteine-rich protein) from this complex protein sample (B). The purity of ^{125}I-zyxin used in this assay is shown in C (750,000 cpm, exposed for 10 min).

association of zyxin with cCRP (chicken cysteine-rich protein) using the blot overlay assay is shown in Fig. 1.

The length of the iodination reaction can be modified to increase or decrease the specific activity of the labeled protein; however, there is a trade-off between achieving a protein of higher specific activity and the possibility of either protein denaturation or modification of key tyrosine residues that may affect the protein's activity. We have used reaction times of 5–10 min with successful results. In addition, we have performed assays under various conditions of specific activity (from 2.0×10^5 to 1.3×10^6 cpm/μg), with no apparent effect on the specificity of the interaction (see Crawford *et al.*, 1992).

It may be necessary to modify the overlay buffer to detect some protein–protein interactions. For example, divalent cations in the overlay buffer may enhance certain protein–protein interactions (see Glenney and Weber, 1980; Fowler, 1987).

If the recognized ligand can be purified to homogeneity, the blot overlay assay may be performed under more native conditions. For example, the purified protein may be adsorbed to nitrocellulose under vacuum and probed (see Sadler *et al.*, 1992). A Hybridot manifold apparatus (BRL-Life Technologies) may be used for this purpose; however, in our hands this method was not as effective as electrophoretic transfer for stably immobilizing proteins on nitrocellulose. Consequently, protein samples adsorbed to nitrocellulose by nonelectrophoretic methods should be probed soon after they are prepared.

A number of control experiments can be performed to strengthen the interpretation of the results obtained from blot overlay assays: (A) A heat-denatured probe (i.e., 95°C for 10 min) should be significantly reduced in its ability to interact with the immobilized ligand (see Crawford *et al.*, 1992). (B) If possible, excess unlabeled protein should be used in the overlay assay to competitively inhibit protein–protein interactions (see Gilmore *et al.*, 1992). (C) If both proteins can be purified to homogeneity, the blot overlay may be performed using each protein as the radiolabeled probe (see Crawford *et al.*, 1992).

V. Pitfalls

1. It is essential to use a highly purified radiolabeled probe in these assays.

2. When preparing purified protein for the iodination reaction, it is important to remove reducing agents, as this is an oxidative reaction.

3. The blot overlay assay is not a native assay. Thus, it is recommended that interactions detected by this approach be confirmed by employing solution binding assays under native conditions.

4. Low-abundance ligands may not be detected in the blot overlay assay. To increase the possibility of detecting low-abundance ligands by this method, enriching for specific proteins by selective biochemical fractionation of protein samples (e.g., ammonium sulfate fractionation, anion exchange chromatography) is suggested.

ACKNOWLEDGMENTS

This work was supported by funds from the National Institutes of Health. M.C.B. is an Established Investigator of the American Heart Association.

REFERENCES

Blanar, M. A., and Rutter, W. J. (1992) Interaction cloning: Identification of a helix–loop–helix zipper protein that interacts with c-Fos. *Science* **256**, 1014–1018.

Cicchetti, P. B., Mayer, J., Thiel, G., and Baltimore, D. (1992) Identification of a protein that binds to the SH3 region of Abl and is similar to Bcr and GAP-rho. *Science* **257**, 803–806.

Crawford, A. W., Michelsen, J. M., and Beckerle, M. C. (1992) An interaction between zyxin and α-actinin. *J. Cell Biol.* **116**, 1381–1393.

Fowler, V. M. (1987) Identification and purification of a novel M_r 43,000 tropomyosin-binding protein from human erythrocyte membranes. *J. Biol. Chem.* **262**, 12792–12800.

Fraker, P. J., and Speck, J. C. (1978) Protein and cell membrane iodinations with a sparingly soluble chloramide, 1,3,4,6-tetrachloro-3α-6α-diphenylglycoluril. *Biochem. Biophys. Res. Commun.* **80**, 849–857.

Gilmore, A. P., Jackson, P., Waites, G. T., and Critchley, D. R. (1992) Further characterization of the talin-binding site in the cytoskeletal protein vinculin. *J. Cell Sci.* **103**, 719–731.

Glenney, J. R., and Weber, K. (1980) Calmodulin-binding proteins of the microfilaments present in isolated brush borders and microvilli of intestinal epithelial cells. *J. Biol. Chem.* **255**, 10551–10554.

Laemmli, U. K. (1970) Cleavage of structural proteins during the assembly of the head of bacteriophage T4. *Nature* **227**, 680–685.

Otto, J. J. (1983) Detection of vinculin-binding proteins with an ^{125}I-vinculin gel overlay technique. *J. Cell Biol.* **97**, 1283–1287.

Sadler, I., Crawford, A. W., Michelsen, J. W., and Beckerle, M. C. (1992) Zyxin and cCRP: Two interactive LIM domain proteins associated with the cytoskeleton. *J. Cell Biol.* **119**, 1573–1587.

Calcium Overlay Assay

Hans Jürgen Hoffmann and Julio E. Celis

I. Introduction

The calcium overlay assay (Maruyama *et al.*, 1984) as described here is essentially a specific application of a general metal ion binding assay (Aoki *et al.*, 1986). The method has been used to identify calcium-binding proteins that contain EF hands (Hoffmann *et al.*, 1993) as well as other types of calcium-binding proteins (Son *et al.*, 1993) transferred to nitrocellulose from either one- or two dimensional gels (see article by Julio E. Celis, Jette B. Lauridsen, and Bodil Basse). The procedure can be performed at room temperature within 24 hr and can detect as little as 20 pmole of calcium binding sites.

II. Materials and Instrumentation

Imidazole (Cat. No. I-0250) and amido black (C.I. 20470, Cat. No. N-3393) were purchased from Sigma. $^{45}CaCl_2$ (Cat. No. CES3) was obtained from Amersham. Most sources of water, including the water used to wash laboratory glassware, are contaminated with metal ions. Use, preferably, one set of dishes and bottles to store solutions and to perform the experiments. A shaker (Certomat/B. Braun) is needed for the incubation, and a plastic sealing device is required to seal the membranes in plastic pouches. Rectangular glass pie dishes (19 × 24 cm) were obtained from Corning (Cat. No. PX385687). Strips of one-dimensional blots were processed in a small immunoblot incubation and staining tray (Pierce). X-ray films (X-Omat DS, 18 × 24 cm, Cat. No. 508 7838) were obtained from Kodak. All other reagents and materials were as described in the article by Ariana Celis and Julio E. Celis.

III. Procedures

A. PROBING WESTERN BLOTS WITH RADIOACTIVE CALCIUM

This procedure is adapted from that of Maruyama *et al.* (1984).

Solutions

The volumes given in these procedures are for one two-dimensional (2D) gel blot (14 × 16 cm) and, in parentheses, for one strip of a 1D Western blot (6 mm × 16 cm).

1. *Washing buffer:* 60 m*M* KCl, 5 m*M* $MgCl_2$, 10 m*M* imidazole–HCl, pH

6.8. Prepare stock solutions in glass-distilled water. To make 1 liter of 3 *M* KCl, dissolve 223.6 g in 700 ml of water and bring to 1 liter. To make 1 liter of 1 *M* $MgCl_2$ dissolve 203.1 g in 700 ml water and bring to 1 liter. Just before use, prepare 40 ml of the 1 *M* imidazole solution in a 50-ml Falcon plastic tube; dissolve 2.72 g of imidazole in 20 ml of distilled water and adjust the pH to 6.8 with HCl. Complete to 40 ml with water. To make 500 ml (20 ml) of washing buffer, enough for one 14 × 16-cm (6-mm × 14-cm) membrane, combine the following: 3 *M* KCl, 10 ml (0.4 ml); 1 *M* $MgCl_2$, 2.5 ml (0.1 ml); 1 *M* Imidazole, 5 ml (0.2 ml); Distilled water, 482.5 ml (19.7 ml)

2. *Probing buffer:* Add 15 μl (2 μl) of $^{45}CaCl_2$ to 15 ml (2 ml) of washing buffer (final concentration of 1 μCi/ml).

3. *Aqueous ethanol:* Prepare 150 ml (5 ml) of 67% aqueous ethanol per membrane. Add 50 ml (1.67 ml) of distilled water to 100 ml (3.33 ml) of ethanol.

Steps

1. Wear gloves throughout the procedure. See article by Richard W. Davies in this volume concerning the use of isotopes.

2. Proteins are transferred to the nitrocellulose membrane either by diffusion or by electrotransfer from a gel (as described by Julio E. Celis, Jette B. Lauridsen, and Bodil Basse).

3. Remove the membrane from the blotting apparatus and wash it briefly with blotting buffer to remove residual acrylamide. Dry the membrane.

4. Soak the membrane in 150 ml (2 ml) of washing buffer (see Fig. 1A of the article by Julio E. Celis, Jette B. Lauridsen, and Bodil Basse in this volume). Shake for 20 min.

5. Pour off the buffer, and add 150 ml (2 ml) fresh washing buffer. Shake for 20 min.

6. Repeat step 5.

7. Place the membrane or strip in a plastic bag and add 15 ml (2 ml) of probing buffer. Seal the bag and shake for 10 min. Alternatively, incubate the membrane in 150 ml of the ^{45}Ca solution in a rectangular glass pie dish (see Fig. 1A of the article by Julio E. Celis, Jette B. Lauridsen, and Bodil Basse). The incubation can be extended up to 1 hr without adverse effects.

8. Pour off the radioactive solution from the plastic bag, and transfer the membrane to a dish containing 150 ml (2 ml) aqueous ethanol. Shake for 5 min. Hang the membrane on a drying line for a few hours. Discard radioactive solutions and plastics according to the regulations in your laboratory (see also the article by R. W. Davies).

9. Expose the dried membrane to X-ray film for 1 hr to 3 days at room temperature.

B. STAINING OF PROTEINS ON NITROCELLULOSE MEMBRANES WITH AMIDO BLACK

This procedure is adapted from that of Rasmussen *et al.* (1991).

Solution

Staining solution: 0.1% Amido black in 45% methanol and 9% acetic acid. To make 1 liter of staining solution, dissolve 1 g of amido black in 450 ml methanol.

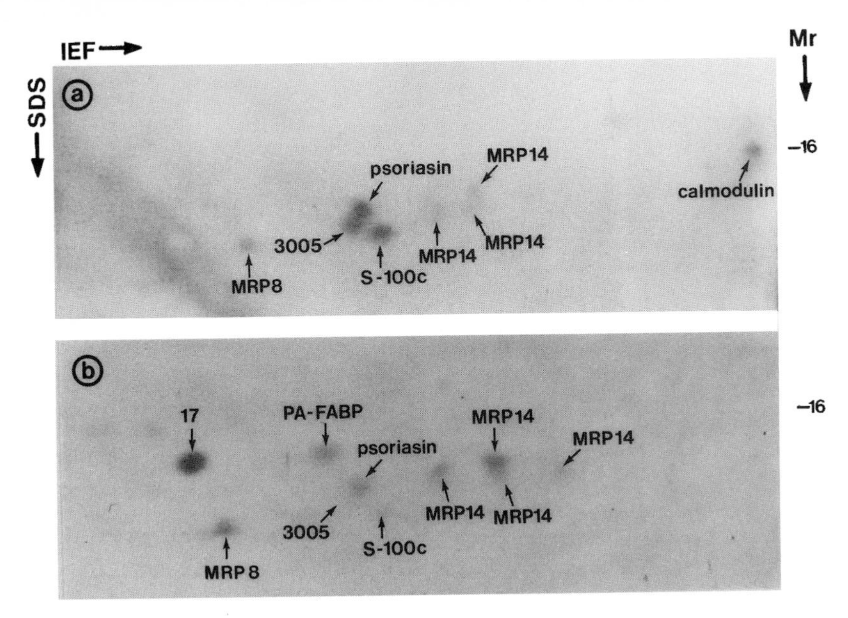

FIGURE 1 Calcium binding by psoriasin and other members of the S100 protein family. (a) $^{45}Ca^{2+}$ gel overlay of a two-dimensional gel blot of total protein from noncultured, unfractionated psoriatic keratinocytes. Calcium-binding proteins were visualized by autoradiography. (b) As in a, but stained with amido black to relate the autoradiogram to known proteins in the two-dimensional gel database of keratinocyte proteins (Celis *et al.*, 1992).

Add 460 ml of distilled water and 90 ml of acetic acid. Store at room temperature.

Steps

1. Wet the nitrocellulose membrane with water (see Fig. 1A of the article by Julio E. Celis, Jette B. Lauridsen, and Bodil Basse). Wear gloves throughout the procedure. Do not handle the membrane with bare fingers as the fingermarks will stain the membrane.
2. Immerse the wet membrane for 1 min in a glass dish containing just enough amido black stain to cover the membrane. The solution can be reused several times.
3. Transfer the membrane to a dish containing distilled water and shake gently.
4. Dry the membrane for a few hours.

IV. Comments

Figure 1a shows an IEF 2D gel of total protein extracts from psoriatic keratinocytes blotted to nitrocellulose (see the article by Julio E. Celis, Jette B. Lauridsen, and Bodil Basse) and probed with $^{45}CaCl_2$ (Hoffmann *et al.*, 1993). The membrane was stained with amido black (Fig. 1b) after autoradiography to aid the identification of the polypeptide spots.

We have not noticed any differences in calcium binding between membranes that had been dried before probing and membranes that had been used directly after blotting.

Competing metal ions (Ca^{2+}, Mg^{2+}, etc.) may be added in steps 4–7 to a final concentration of 10 m*M*.

V. Pitfalls

1. Use fresh imidazole solution. In our hands, calcium binding by S100 proteins is inversely related to the age of the imidazole solution.
2. Do not dry the membrane between sheets of filter paper as this procedure gives severe background problems.
3. The membranes must be completely dry before exposing to X-ray film.

REFERENCES

Aoki, Y., Kunimoto, M., Shibata, Y., and Suzuki, K. T. (1986) Detection of metallothionein on nitrocellulose membrane using Western blotting technique and its application to identification of cadmium-binding proteins. *Anal. Biochem.* **157**, 117–122.

Celis, J. E., Rasmussen, H. H., Madsen, P., Leffers, H., Honoré, B., Dejgaard, K., Gesser, B., Olsen, E., Gromov, P., Hoffmann, H. J., Nielsen, M., Celis, A., Basse, B., Lauridsen, J. B., Ratz, G. P., Nielsen, H., Andersen, A. H., Walbum, E., Kjærgaard, I., Puype, M., Van Damme, J., and Vandekerckhove, J. (1992) The human keratinocyte two-dimensional gel protein database (update 1992): Towards an integrated approach to the study of cell proliferation, differentiation and skin diseases. *Electrophoresis* **13**, 893–959.

Hoffmann, H. J., Olsen, E., Etzerodt, M., Madsen, P., Thøgersen, H.-C., Kruse, T., and Celis, J. E. (1993) Psoriasin binds calcium and is differentially regulated with respect to other members of the S100 protein family. *J. Invest. Dermatol.* **103**, in press.

Maruyama, K., Mikawa, T., and Ebashi, S. (1984) Detection of calcium binding proteins by ^{45}Ca autoradiography on nitrocellulose membrane after sodium dodecyl sulfate gel electrophoresis. *J. Biochem.* **95**, 511–519.

Rasmussen, H. H., Van Damme, J., Puype, M., Gesser, B., Celis, J. E., and Vandekerckhove, J. (1991) Microsequencing of proteins recorded in human two-dimensional gel protein databases. *Electrophoresis* **12**, 873–882.

Son, M., Gundersen, R. E., and Nelson, D. L. (1993) A 2nd member of the novel Ca^{2+}-dependent protein-kinase family from paramecium-tetraurelia—Purification and characterization. *J. Biol. Chem.* **268**, 5940–5948.

Blot Overlay Assay for the Identification of GTP-Binding Proteins

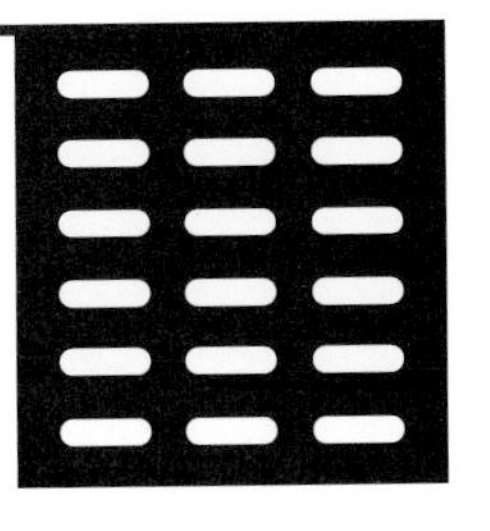

Pavel S. Gromov and Julio E. Celis

I. Introduction

Low-molecular-weight GTP-binding proteins constitute a rapidly increasing family of monomeric regulatory proteins that play a key role in signaling for various cellular activities such as proliferation, differentiation, protein transport, cytoskeletal organization, and secretion (Hall, 1993; Bokoch and Der, 1993). Unlike oligomeric G proteins, which have an α,β,γ subunit structure, these proteins bind GTP specifically when separated by SDS–PAGE and blotted onto nitrocellulose membranes. Here we describe a nitrocellulose blot overlay nucleotide binding assay (McGrath *et al.*, 1984; Bhullar and Haslam, 1987; Doucet and Tuana, 1991; Gromov and Celis, 1994) that allows detection of low-molecular-weight GTP-binding proteins in polypeptide mixtures separated by one-dimensional SDS–PAGE (see article by Julio E. Celis and Eyδfinnur Olsen in this volume) or high-resolution two-dimensional (2D) gel electrophoresis (see articles by Julio E. Celis, Gitte Ratz, Bodil Basse, Jette B. Lauridsen, and Ariana Celis and by Angelika Görg).

II. Materials and Instrumentation

Tween 20 (Cat. No. 822 184) and $MgCl_2$ (Cat. No. 5833) were purchased from Merck. DTT (Cat. No. D-0632), Trizma base (Cat. No. T-1503), and ATP (Cat. No. A-2383) were obtained from Sigma. [α-^{32}P]GTP (Cat. No. PB 201) and nitrocellulose sheets (Hybond C, Cat. No. RPN.203C) were purchased from Amersham. X-ray films (X-Omat DS, 18 × 24 cm, Cat. No. 508 7838) were obtained from Kodak.

Rectangular glass pie dishes (19 × 24 cm, Cat. No. PX385687) were purchased from Corning. The orbital shaker was obtained from Hoefer.

III. Procedure

This procedure is modified from those of McGrath *et al.* (1984) and Bhullar and Haslam (1987).

Solutions

The volumes given in this procedure are for nitrocellulose blot sheets (14 × 16 cm, 1D or 2D).

1. *Washing buffer:* 50 m*M* Tris–HCl, pH 7.6, 10 μM $MgCl_2$, 0.3% Tween 20. To make 1 liter of the solution, add 6.055 g of Trizma base to 800 ml of distilled H_2O and titrate with HCl. Add 30 ml of a 10% stock solution of Tween 20 and 100 μl of a 0.1 *M* stock solution of $MgCl_2$. After dissolving, complete to 1 liter with distilled H_2O. Store at 4°C.

2. *ATP overlay buffer:* 50 m*M* Tris–HCl, pH 7.6, 10 μM $MgCl_2$, 0.3% Tween 20, 100 m*M* DTT, 100 μM ATP. To make 100 ml of the solution, dissolve 1.54 g DTT in 90 ml of washing buffer and add 100 μl of a 0.1 *M* stock solution of ATP. After dissolving complete to 100 ml with washing buffer. Store at 4°C.

3. *Binding buffer:* 50 m*M* Tris–HCl, pH 7.6, 10 μM $MgCl_2$, 0.3% Tween 20, 100 m*M* DTT, 100 m*M* ATP, 1 n*M* [α-^{32}P]GTP (1 μCi [α-^{32}P]GTP/ml). To make 100 ml of the solution, add 50 μl of a 2 mCi/ml solution of [α-^{32}P]GTP to ATP overlay buffer. Prepare directly in the blotting container prior to use (see step 4).

4. *10% Tween 20:* To make 50 ml of the solution, weigh 5 g of Tween 20 and complete to 50 ml with distilled H_2O. Store at room temperature.

5. *100 mM ATP:* To make 1 ml of the solution, add 55.1 mg of ATP and complete to 1 ml with distilled water. Aliquot in 100-μl portions and store at −20°C.

6. *0.1 M $MgCl_2$:* To make 50 ml of the solution, weigh 0.102 g of $MgCl_2 \cdot 6H_2O$ and complete to 50 ml with distilled H_2O. Store at 4°C.

Steps

1. Transfer the proteins separated by 1D (see article by Julio E. Celis and Eyðfinnur Olsen in this volume) or 2D (see articles by Julio Celis, Gitte Ratz, Bodil Basse, Jette B. Lauridsen, and Ariana Celis and by Angelika Görg) gel electrophoresis to a nitrocellulose sheet as described in the article by Julio E. Celis, Jette B. Lauridsen, and Bodil Basse.

2. Place the nitrocellulose sheet in a rectangular glass pie dish (19 × 24 cm) containing 100 ml of washing buffer. Wear gloves when handling the membrane. The nitrocellulose sheet should be placed with the protein-bearing side facing upwards. Rinse the nitrocellulose sheet twice with washing buffer.

3. Remove the washing buffer from the container and fill it with 50 ml of ATP overlay buffer. Place the container on an orbital shaker and incubate for 10 min with gentle agitation at room temperature.

4. Remove the blotting container from the orbital shaker platform and add 50 μl of a 2 mCi/ml solution of [α-^{32}P]GTP. Place the container on the orbital shaker and incubate with gentle agitation for 60 min at room temperature. Handle radioactive material with care (see article by R. W. Davies).

5. Remove the binding buffer from the container and fill it with 50 ml of washing buffer. Soak the nitrocellulose sheet for 10 min at room temperature. Dispose radioactive solutions according to the safety procedures in your laboratory.

6. Repeat the washing step twice at room temperature (10 min per wash). Use as much washing buffer as possible.

7. Carefully remove the nitrocellulose sheet from the container using plastic tweezers and air-dry for at least 4 hr at room temperature.

8. Place the air-dried nitrocellulose sheet into a cassette for autoradiography (12–72 hr at −80°C) using X-ray film and an intensifying screen.

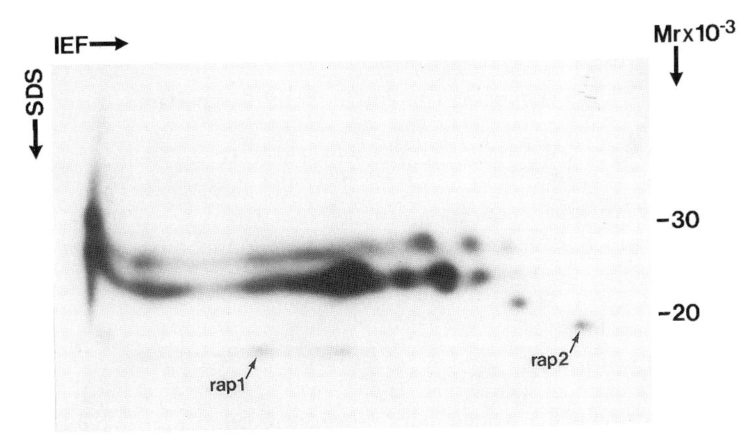

FIGURE 1 Two-dimensional blot autoradiograph of human keratinocyte [α-^{32}P]GTP-binding proteins separated by IEF.

IV. Comments

The use of a rotating roller system (see Fig. 1 in the article by Julio E. Celis, Jette Lauridsen, and Bodil Basse) for incubation of the nitrocellulose sheet is recommended instead of the usual containers, as it considerably reduces the volume of reagents used and avoids uneven detection. In the rotating system the nitrocellulose sheet is placed on the inner wall of the blotting cylinder with the protein-bearing side facing the center. All incubation steps are carried out on the rotating platform.

DTT (100 m*M* final concentration in steps 3 and 4) enhances the GTP binding ability of low-molecular-weight GTP-binding proteins. This improves considerably the signal-to-noise ratio as well as the sensitivity of the procedure (Gromov and Celis, 1994).

To reduce the background, we recommend ATP as an effective competitor for nonspecific GTP binding to the nitrocellulose. If this is not possible, *e.g.*, specificity of nucleotide binding by proteins is unknown, use bovine serum albumin (BSA, 0.3% final concentration) in the overlay and binding buffers as recommended by McGrath *et al.* (1984) and Doucet and Tuana (1991).

Bound [α-^{32}P]GTP can be removed from the nitrocellulose blot without visible loss of proteins by incubation in a solution containing 50 m*M* Tris–HCl, pH 7.4, and 1% SDS for 30 min at room temperature.

Using the protocol described here, it is possible to detect several low-molecular-weight GTP-binding proteins. A representative ^{32}P autoradiograph of low-molecular-weight GTP-binding proteins detected in an IEF 2D gel blot of total human keratinocyte proteins is shown in Fig. 1.

V. Pitfalls

1. Do not dry the nitrocellulose sheet after protein transfer as it substantially reduces the efficiency of GTP binding.
2. Make sure that the solution covers the whole nitrocellulose sheet surface during agitation. Avoid scratching or tearing of the nitrocellulose membrane during manipulation.
3. Use high-grade ATP. Small traces of unlabeled GTP, which may contaminate commercial ATP, decrease the efficiency of [α-^{32}P]GTP binding.
4. Make sure that the blotting containers are washed properly.

REFERENCES

Bokoch, G. M., and Der, C. J. (1993) Emerging concepts in the Ras superfamily of GTP-binding proteins. *FASEB J.* **7**, 750–759.

Bourne, H. R., Sanders, D. A., and McCormick, F. (1990) The GTPase superfamily: A conserved switch for diverse cell functions. *Nature (London)* **348**, 125–132.

Doucet, J.-P., and Tuana, B. S. (1991) Identification of low molecular weight GTP-binding proteins and their sites of interaction in subcellular fractions from skeletal muscle. *J. Biol. Chem.* **266**, 17613–17620.

Gromov, P. S., and Celis, J. E. (1994) Some small GTP-binding proteins are strongly down regulated in SV40 transformed human keratinocytes. *Electrophoresis*, **15**, 474–481.

Hall, A. (1993) Ras-related proteins. *Current Opin. Cell Bio.* **5**, 265–268.

McGrath, J. P., Capon, D. J., Goeddel, D. V., and Levinson, A. D. (1984) Comparative biochemical properties of normal and activated human *ras* p21 protein. *Nature (London)* **310**, 644–649.

Two-Dimensional Gel-Based Mapping of *in Situ* Crosslinked GTP-Binding Proteins

Marcus E. Peter and Lukas A. Huber

I. Introduction

A method is described to label GTP-binding proteins in permeabilized eukaryotic cells. To this end, cells are perforated for 5 min at 0°C with lysophosphatidylcholine and then incubated with 1 μM [α-^{32}P]GTP for an extended period at 37°C during which the radiolabeled GTP is hydrolyzed to GDP. The nucleotide then displaces the endogenous bound G nucleotide of a GTP-binding protein (Fig. 1, I). Next, sodium periodate is added to oxidize the ribose moiety of the bound GDP (II), resulting in the formation of a reactive dialdehyde (GDP_{oxi}, III). A Schiff base formed between the *in situ* oxidized nucleotide and the ϵ-amino group of the lysine residue in the vicinity of the respective nucleotide binding site (IV) is specifically stabilized with sodium cyanoborohydride, yielding a *N*-morpholine derivative-modified protein (V). To prevent dissociation of GTP_{oxi} from the protein, which would result in unspecific modification of surface lysine residues, it is imperative to limit the *in situ* treatment with $NaIO_4$ and $NaCNBH_3$ to 1 min (Peter *et al.*, 1988). Finally, excess dialdehyde is reduced to $GDP_{oxi\text{-}red}$ by addition of sodium borohydride (VI). Using this method several proteins of the human leukemic T-cell line Jurkat could be selectively labeled with either [α-^{32}P]ATP_{oxi} or [α-^{32}P]GTP_{oxi} (Peter *et al.*, 1993a). The method can be used for identification of novel GTP binding structures such as the T-cell receptor ζ chain (Peter *et al.*, 1992) or for detection of well-characterized GTP-binding proteins such as the p21^{ras} oncogene product or G-protein α subunits (Peter *et al.*, 1993a). In one case the method allowed direct labeling of a receptor coupling to an as yet unknown G-protein (Peter *et al.*, 1993b). Very recently we demonstrated that *ras*-like GTPases of the *rab* and *rap* families can be identified by combining the labeling technique with high-resolution two-dimensional (2D) IEF/SDS–PAGE (Fig. 2) (Huber and Peter, 1994).

II. Materials and Instrumentation

Media and reagents for cell culture are purchased from Gibco Biocult and Biochrom. Growth medium for Madin–Darby canine kidney strain II (MDCKII) cells consists of EME with Earle's salts (E-MEM) supplemented with 10 mM Hepes, pH 7.3, 10% FCS, 100 U/ml penicillin, and 100 mg/ml streptomycin. MDCKII cells are grown and passaged as described previously (Matlin *et al.*, 1983).

L-α-Lysophosphatidylcholine (Cat. No. L-5254), leupeptin (Cat. No. L-2884), chymostatin (Cat. No. C-7268), pepstatin A (Cat. No. P-4265), antipain (Cat. No.

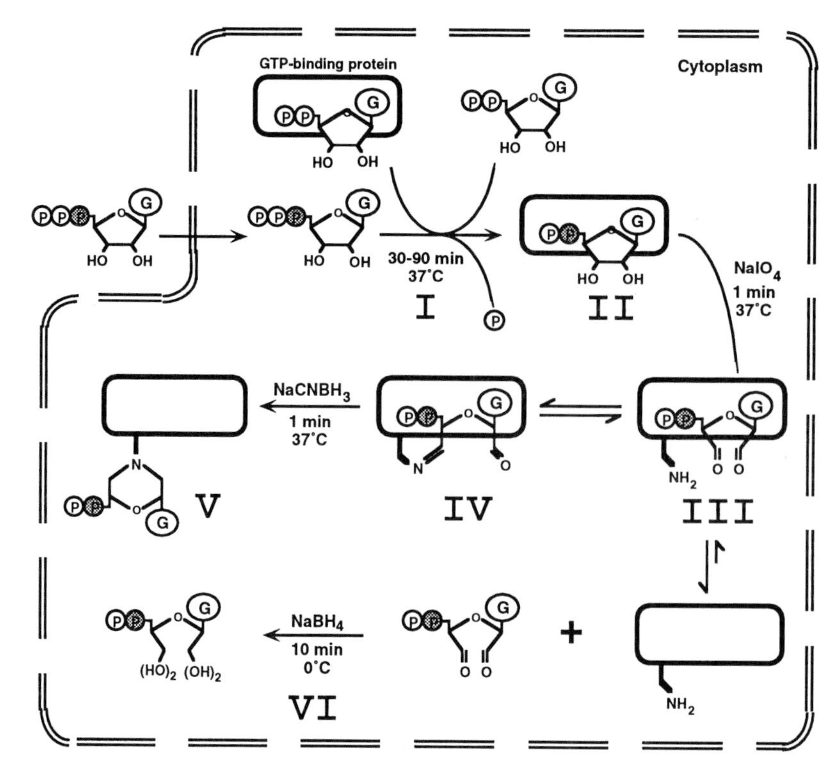

FIGURE 1 Schematic representation of the labeling of a GTP-binding protein in a permeabilized cell using [α-^{32}P]GTP. For further information refer to the text.

A-6271), $NaIO_4$ (Cat. No. S-1878), $NaCNBH_3$ (Cat. No. S-8628), and $NaBH_4$ (Cat. No. S-9125) are from Sigma. GTP stock, pH 7.0 (100 m*M*, Cat. No. 1140 957) is from Boehringer-Mannheim. Protein A (PA)–Sepharose (Cat. No. 17-0780-01) is from Pharmacia.

III. Procedures

A. CELL PERMEABILIZATION

For cell permeabilization various methods can be applied. Treatment with L-α-lysophosphatidylcholine (LPC) has proven to be a cheap, easy, and versatile way to perforate cells. If soluble cytoplasmic proteins need to be labeled other reagents generating smaller holes, such as *Staphylococcus aureus* α-toxin, can be used. If only the plasma membrane needs to be permeabilized the LPC concentration should be adjusted to obtain 95% trypan blue-stainable cells.

The LPC permeabilization technique reproducibly permeabilizes numerous cell types including human and murine T cells, T-cell lines, NK cells, B cells, B-cell lines, fibroblasts, Chinese hamster ovary cells, baby hamster kidney cells, MDCK cells, murine neurons, and COS African green monkey kidney cells, using identical conditions.

Solutions

1. *Phosphate-buffered saline (PBS) without Mg^{2+} or Ca^{2+}.*
2. *Labeling buffer (L-buffer):* To make 100 ml, combine 1.04 g 140 m*M* KCl

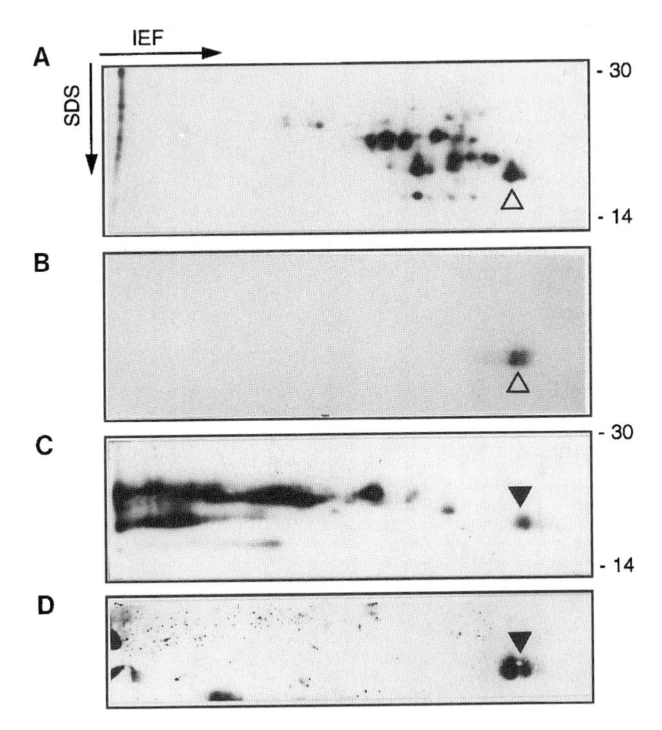

FIGURE 2 Comparison of the *in situ* GTP_{oxi} labeling technique with the GTP ligand binding method (Huber and Peter, 1994). (A) GTP_{oxi}-labeled lysate proteins from MDCKII cells. (B) Identification of GTP_{oxi}-labeled rap2 by immunoprecipitation using a rap2-specific anti-peptide rabbit antibody (Huber and Peter, 1994). (C) Detection of GTP-binding proteins in MDCKII cells using the GTP ligand binding assay. (D) Identification of rap2 by Western blotting after the GTP ligand binding assay. Anti-rap2 antiserum was the kind gift from Dr. Maridonneau-Parini and was used as described recently (Maridonneau-Parini and de Gunzburg, 1992).

(MW 74.55), 58.4 mg 10 m*M* NaCl (MW 58.44), 23.8 mg 2.5 m*M* $MgCl_2$ (MW 95.21), and 476 mg 20 m*M* Hepes–KOH, pH 7.8 (MW 238.3).

3. *LPC solution:* 2.5 mg L-α-lysophosphatidylcholine in 1 mL L-buffer. Prepare fresh and keep at room temperature.

Steps

1. Grow MDCKII cells to confluency in a 75-cm^2 culture flask (any other cell in liquid culture can also be taken).
2. Wash cells twice in PBS and trypsinize for 5 min at 25°C (trypsin treatment will not interfere with the labeling reaction).
3. Transfer dissociated cells into 15-ml tube and wash with 10 ml PBS.
4. Add 10 ml PBS and count cells.
5. Spin down cells and resuspend 10^7 cells in 1 ml ice-cold L-buffer.
6. Transfer to Eppendorf tube (with screw cap).
7. Add 20 μl LPC solution and mix cells.
8. Keep on ice for 5 min.
9. Spin down cells in a minifuge at 6000 rpm for 15 sec (during this step most of the cytosolic proteins and excess LPC will be removed).
10. Resuspend cells in 500 μl L-buffer.

B. *In situ* GTP_{oxi} LABELING

Solutions

1. *Lysis buffer:* Labeling buffer with the following supplements. To make 100 ml, combine 1 ml NP-40, 1 ml 100 m*M* PMSF in ethanol, 1 mg leupeptin, 1 mg chymostatin, 1 mg pepstatin A, and 1 mg antipain.

2. *Labeling reagents:* To prepare 1 ml each of (I) 50 m*M* $NaIO_4$, (II) 50 m*M* $NaCNBH_3$, and (III) 1 *M* $NaBH_4$, dissolve 10.7, 62.8, and 38.7 mg, respectively, of the reagents in water. Do not close the lid of solution III (extensive H_2 release!).

3. *Nucleotide solution:* Dilute a 100 m*M* GTP stock, pH 7.0, 1:1000 in L-buffer (100 μM stock). Any vendor will supply satisfactory [α-^{32}P]GTP (specific activity >3000 Ci/mmole). Use only nucleotides prepared in water or an aqueous buffer without addition of any stabilizers such as 2-mercaptoethanol, which will inhibit the reaction. Mix 20 μl of radiolabeled nucleotide with 10 μl of the 100 μM GTP stock.

Steps

The protocol should be used when immunoprecipitation of labeled GTP-binding proteins is intended. If only lysate proteins are to be analyzed, 10^6 cells will be sufficient to label.

1. Take 500 μl cell suspension (10^7 cells) and add 15 μl of the 100 μM GTP solution.
2. Incubate on heating block for 30–90 min at 37°C (depending on the GDP exchange kinetics of the protein to be labeled). For labeling of ATP-binding proteins a 5-min incubation is sufficient.
3. Add 10 μl solution I, mix, and incubate for 1 min at 37°C.
4. Add 10 μl solution II, mix, and incubate for 1 min at 37°C.
5. Stop reaction by adding 10 μl of solution III (before addition it is advisable to mix the solution rigorously to remove all H_2 bubbles).
6. Transfer immediately on ice and leave for approximately 10 min. Reduction with $NaBH_4$ is not crucial and should be used only when labeled proteins will be immunoprecipitated to avoid modification of the antibody used by free reactive aldehydes.
7. Mix cell suspension to remove bubbles and spin down cells in minifuge for 3 min at 6000 rpm.
8. Discard supernatant into radioactive waste container.
9. Add 1 ml of lysis buffer, mix, and leave on ice for 15 min.
10. Remove nuclei by centrifugation (14,000 rpm for 15 min at 4°C).
11. Take supernatant for immunoprecipitation.

C. IMMUNOPRECIPITATION AND 2D IEF/SDS–POLYACRYLAMIDE GEL ELECTROPHORESIS

The following steps need to be carried out at 4°C.

1. Couple the desired anti-GTP-binding protein antibody to 30 μl of 50% (v/v) protein A (PA)–Sepharose for 4–8 hr.

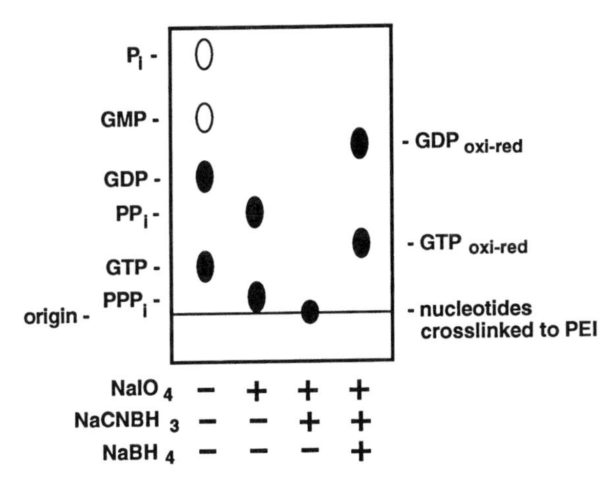

FIGURE 3 PP_i corresponds to the formation of GDP_{oxi} and PPP_i to the formation of GTP_{oxi}. They are generated by complete hydrolysis of the nucleotide involving β-elimination of the phosphate moiety on polyethyleneimine (PEI).

2. Wash PA–Sepharose three times with washing buffer (same as lysis buffer containing 0.1% NP-40).
3. Preclear lysates for 1 hr with PA–Sepharose-coupled normal rabbit serum.
4. Immunoprecipitate with specific antibody for 4–8 hr.
5. Wash immunoprecipitate six times with washing buffer and remove supernatant from beads.
6. Add a standard sample buffer used for isoelectric focusing and incubate for 30 min at 30°C.
7. Perform two-dimensional separation of labeled proteins as described by Huber *et al.* (1993). See also the articles by Julio E. Celis, Gitte Ratz, Bodil Basse, Jette B. Lauridsen, and Ariana Celis; by Angelika Görg; and by Mario Gimona, Barbara Galazkiewicz, and Markus Niederreiter.

IV. Comments

Efficiency and specificity of the labeling technique are guaranteed if the following recommendations are considered. Do not treat cells with reagents containing free *cis*-diol groups (such as glycerol), as they will inhibit the periodate oxidation. Prepare all reagents fresh each time. $NaCNBH_3$, in particular, tends to decompose. Do not use a jar longer than 6 months. The pH of the labeling buffer can be varied but under alkaline conditions crosslinking yield will be higher. Labeling efficiency at pH 7.0:7.4:7.8 = 1:2:4. Proteins can be labeled using any radiolabeled di- or triphosphorylated ribonucleotide. ^{14}C-, ^{3}H-, ^{32}P-, ^{33}P-, and ^{35}S- (as in GTPγS)-labeled nucleotides will work.

V. Pitfalls

A. NO LABELING AT ALL

Possible cause
Cells were not permeabilized.

Solution

Try higher LPC concentration. We have used LPC up to 500 μg/ml without diminishing the labeling efficiency.

Alternative cause

One of the reagents did not work. To determine which one, each step of the labeling reaction can be easily monitored by thin-layer chromatography: Load 0.5 μl of sample after each labeling step on polyethyleneimine cellulose sheets (Macherey and Nagel No. 801 053). Run a 20-cm ascending chromatography in 0.8 *M* LiCl/ 1.5 *M* formic acid. The spots shown in Fig. 3 should be seen after autoradiography.

B. NO SPECIFICALLY LABELED PROTEINS

Possible cause

Hydrolysis of either the unlabeled GTP stock or the radiolabeled GTP. As GMP will not bind to GTP-binding proteins [α-^{32}P]GMP will yield the same unspecific labeling pattern as [α-^{32}P]AMP.

REFERENCES

Huber, L. A., and Peter, M. E. (1994) Mapping small GTP-binding proteins on high resolution two-dimensional gels by a combination of GTP binding and labeling with *in situ* periodate-oxidized GTP. *Electrophoresis* **15**, 283–288.

Huber, L. A., Pimplikar, S., Parton, R. G., Virta, H., Zerial, M., and Simons, K. (1993) rab8, a small GTPase involved in vesicular traffic between the TGN and the basolateral plasma membrane. *J. Cell Biol.* **123**, 35–45.

Matlin, K., Bainton, D. F., Personen, M., Louvard, D., Genty, N., and Simons, K. (1983) Transepithelial transport of a viral membrane glycoprotein implanted into the apical plasma membrane of Madin–Darby canine kidney cells. I. Morphological evidence. *J. Cell Biol.* **97**, 627–637.

Maridonneau-Parini, I., and de Gunzburg, J. (1992) Association of rap1 and rap2 proteins with the specific granules of human neutrophils. *J. Biol. Chem.* **267**, 6396–6402.

Peter, M. E., Hall, C., Rühlmann, A., Sancho, J., and Terhorst, C. (1992) The T-cell receptor ζ chain contains a GTP/GDP-binding site. *EMBO J.* **11**, 933–941.

Peter, M. E., She, J., Huber, L. A., and Terhorst, C. (1993a) Labeling of adenine and guanine nucleotide-binding proteins in permeabilized cells with *in situ* periodate-oxidized nucleotides. *Anal. Biochem.* **210**, 75–82.

Peter, M. E., Wileman, T. E., and Terhorst, C. (1993b) Covalent binding of guanine nucleotides to the CD3-γ chain of the T-cell receptor/CD3 complex. *Eur. J. Immunol.* **23**, 461–466.

Peter, M. E., Wittmann-Liebold, B., and Sprinzl, M. (1988) Affinity labeling of the GDP/GTP-binding site in *Thermus thermophilus* elongation factor Tu. *Biochemistry* **27**, 9132–9139.

Protein-Blot Analysis of Glycoproteins and Lectin Overlays

Shoshana Bar-Nun and Jonathan M. Gershoni

I. Introduction

One of the most prevalent modifications of proteins is their glycosylation. This process is by no means random and is accomplished through the consecutive activity of a variety of enzymatic systems. Two major types of complex glycosylation have been recognized: (1) *N*-glycosylation taking place on asparagine residues that comply with the sequence motif Asn–X–Ser/Thr, and (2) O-glycosylation that can occur on serine or threonine residues. These glycomoieties can themselves undergo maturation processes that reflect stepwise trimming and addition of saccharide residues to the branched structures, each of these events characteristic of a discrete intracellular compartment (Alberts *et al.,* 1989). In addition, dynamic monosaccharides have been found recently on a multitude of regulatory nuclear and cytoplasmic proteins (Halttwanger *et al.,* 1992).

The "reason" for glycosylation or the function of the glycomoieties is not all that clear. Complex glycoproteins have no obvious functions in housekeeping activities but they appear to play a role during development (Alberts *et al.,* 1989). Due to the polar nature of these molecules, they add markedly to the hydrophilicity of the proteins they decorate, making them more soluble. Indeed, one can generally assume that most proteins secreted from cells are glycosylated to some degree. Furthermore, the extracellular domains of membrane proteins are routinely glycosylated as well. Specific modification of glycomoieties can assist in the trafficking of proteins intracellularly. Thus, for example, phosphorylation of mannose to produce mannose 6-phosphate is the signal that directs appropriate enzymes to lysosomes (Alberts *et al.,* 1989). There is also evidence indicating that the integrity of the glycomoiety of serum proteins is what keeps them circulating, and deterioration of the sugar structures is a signal for the liver cells to dispose of such proteins (Alberts *et al.,* 1989).

Whatever their functions are, one thing is certain. For the cell biologist, the glycomoieties are extremely useful for the characterization and identification of glycoproteins and also provide excellent handles and markers to follow intracellular transport. One means that enables us to accomplish these tasks is the use of lectins. Lectins are traditionally defined as multivalent sugar-binding proteins (Sharon, 1993). Most common lectins are plant derived, although more examples from the animal kingdom are rapidly being recognized. The characteristic nature of lectins is that they are sugar specific. Thus, concanavalin A (Con A) binds mannose or glucose residues, whereas peanut agglutinin (PNA) and *Ricinus communis* agglutinin (RCA) bind galactose. Therefore, by choosing the lectin used in a given procedure one can learn something about the glycoprotein structure and its pathway of synthesis.

The following protocols describe the use of lectins combined with protein blotting and have been chosen to illustrate different aspects of the elucidation of glycoprotein natural history.

II. Materials and Instrumentation

Avidin–horseradish peroxidase (Cat. No. A-3151), biotinamidocaproylhydrazide (Cat. No. B-3770), biotin conjugates of Con A (Cat. No. C-2272), RCA (Cat. No. L-2641), wheat germ agglutinin (WGA, *Triticum vulgaris,* Cat. No. L-5142), BSA (Cat. No. A-8022), 4-chloro-1-naphthol (Cat. No. C-8890), Con A (Cat. No. C-2010), horseradish peroxidase (HRP, Cat. No. P-6782), periodic acid (Cat. No. P-7875), streptavidin–HRP (Cat. No. S-5512), and Trizma base (Cat. No. T-6791) were purchased from Sigma.

Compartmentalized plastic boxes can be obtained from Althor Products; an alternative is your local supermarket or grocery store.

It is assumed that those interested in this article are familiar with SDS–polyacrylamide gel electrophoresis and protein blotting. For details on protein blotting in general, the reader is referred to Gershoni (1987, 1988).

The only equipment required for the effective processing of blots is a shaker and a flat-bottom container to perform the various incubations and washes. Shakers can be orbital or reciprocal; however, the blot should be placed in a volume of reagent/buffer so as to ensure good mixing and exchange of reagents over the entire surface of the blot. Care should be taken not to allow the blot to stick to the bottom or sides of the container, and incubation of more than one blot per container should be avoided. Rockers as opposed to shakers are advantageous as they often enable effective incubation in smaller reagent volumes.

III. Procedures

A. GENERAL SUGAR STAINING ON BLOTS: HYDRAZIDE CONJUGATES

Standard sugar stains are normally based on the selective oxidation of vicinal-hydroxyls, thus producing aldehydes that are subsequently reacted with an amine containing dye *via* a Schiff base. Such procedures are referred to as periodic acid–Schiff (PAS) staining, and the classical Schiff reagent is a fuchsin derivative that generates a pink color at the reactive sugar. Unfortunately, this reagent is not compatible with most membrane filters and thus cannot be used in protein blot assays. Therefore, alternative reagents have been developed for PAS staining of blots that are basically hydrazide conjugates. Enzyme–hydrazides are easily prepared (Gershoni *et al.*, 1985), yet most readily available is biotinamidocaproylhydrazide and thus it is more convenient to use. This procedure has also been adapted for selective cell surface staining (Fig. 1) (Keren *et al.*, 1986).

Solutions

1. *Periodic acid:* Prepare 10 m*M* periodic acid by dissolving 22.8 mg in 10 ml distilled water. Prepare fresh (for total sugar stain). Selective staining of sialic acid residues can be achieved by using a 1 m*M* periodic acid solution (Gershoni *et al.*, 1985).

2. *Biotin–hydrazide:* Dissolve biotinamidocaproylhydrazide in phosphate-

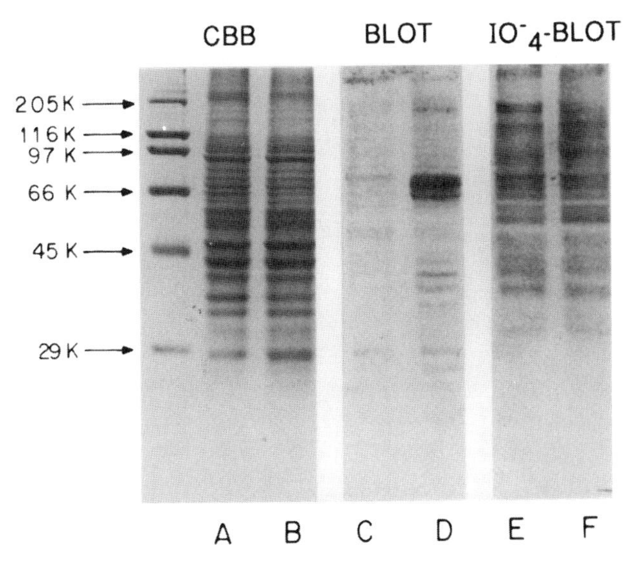

FIGURE 1 Selective labeling of cell surface glycoproteins. Murine leukemia cells were either treated with periodic acid (lanes B, D, and F) or not treated (lanes A, C, and E). Detergent lysates of the cells were prepared and the protein mixtures were run on SDS–polyacrylamide gels and stained with Coomassie brilliant blue (CBB) (lanes A and B) or blotted, quenched, and reacted with alkaline phosphatase hydrazide (lanes C and D). Oxidation of blots (lanes E and F) was done prior to the addition of enzyme. Note that signals develop in lane D (compared with lack of signals in lane C), indicating the cell surface orientation of those peptides. Complete oxidation of all the glycoproteins, irrespective of the surface orientation, is demonstrated in lanes E and F, where no differences are found. Reprinted, with permission, from Keren *et al.* (1986).

buffered saline (PBS, see below) to make a 20 μg/ml solution and then dilute with an equal volume of BSA quench (see below).

3. *BSA quench:* 2% (w/v) BSA in PBS. Often it is convenient to prepare a 10% stock solution to be diluted as required. This can be prepared by carefully applying 10 g of dry powdered BSA to the surface of 100 ml PBS in a 100- to 200-ml beaker. Cover the beaker and then simply place it in the refrigerator, allowing the protein to dissolve spontaneously *without* any stirring. This will produce a golden yellow clear solution without clumps of BSA or formation of bubbles or froth.

4. *Streptavidin–HRP conjugate:* Dilute 1–10 mg/ml of streptavidin–HRP in PBS 1:500 to 1:1000 in BSA quench.

5. *Enzyme substrate:* Prepare 4-chloro-1-naphthol as a 3 mg/ml stock solution in methanol and dilute just before use with PBS containing 0.01% H_2O_2 to give 0.5 mg/ml (Hawkes *et al.*, 1982).

6. *PBS:* Dissolve 8 g NaCl, 0.2 g KCl, 1.35 g $Na_2HPO_4 \cdot 2H_2O$, and 0.2 g KH_2PO_4 in 1 liter of distilled water.

Steps

1. Rinse (briefly incubate) blot in PBS.
2. Quench blot in BSA quench solution, 1 hr at 37°C [or a few hours at room temperature (RT)] to block all unoccupied sites on the filter.
3. Incubate blot (rock or shake in a suitable volume of solution, enough to allow the blot to float) in periodic acid (freshly prepared), 30 min at RT.

4. Rinse blot in PBS.
5. Incubate blot in biotin–hydrazide, 1 hr at RT.
6. Wash blot in PBS, 2–3 × 10 min at RT.
7. Incubate blot with streptavidin–HRP, 1 hr at RT.
8. Wash blot in PBS, 2–3 × 10 min at RT.
9. Incubate blot in enzyme substrate until desired signal develops (HRP substrates are often light sensitive and thus reaction should be performed in the dark, i.e., wrapped in aluminum foil or in low light or in your top drawer).
10. Rinse and store blot.

B. DETECTION OF N-LINKED GLYCOPROTEINS: CON A OVERLAYS

The N-linked glycomoiety can be distinguished from O-linked structures in that the former is exclusive for mannose residues. Mannose is recognized by the lectin Con A. Moreover, the enzyme HRP is also an N-linked glycoprotein. Therefore, the simple procedure developed by Clegg (1982) is suggested for Con A overlays.

Solutions

1. *Tris–Ca–Mg buffer:* 25 m*M* Tris–HCl, pH 7.4, 150 m*M* NaCl, 1 m*M* $CaCl_2$, 0.5 m*M* $MgCl_2$. To make 1 liter, dissolve in 500 ml distilled water 3.03 g Trizma base, 8.77 g NaCl, 0.11 g $CaCl_2$, and 0.10 g $MgCl_2 \cdot 6H_2O$. Titrate to pH 7.4 with HCl and adjust volume to 1 liter with distilled water. Con A requires calcium and magnesium for efficient binding; thus, a Tris buffer is preferable to PBS.

2. *BSA quench:* 2% BSA in Tris–Ca–Mg buffer.

3. *Con A:* 10 μg/ml Con A in 2% BSA in Tris–Ca–Mg buffer.

4. *HRP:* 10 μg/ml HRP in 2% BSA in Tris–Ca–Mg buffer.

5. *HRP substrate:* Prepare 4-chloro-1-naphthol as a 3 mg/ml stock solution in methanol and dilute just before use with PBS containing 0.01% H_2O_2 to give 0.5 mg/ml (Hawkes *et al.*, 1982).

Steps

1. Rinse blot in Tris–Ca–Mg buffer.
2. Quench blot in BSA quench, 1 hr at RT.
3. Incubate blot in Con A solution $\frac{1}{2}$ to 1 hr at RT.
4. Wash blot in Tris–Ca–Mg buffer, 2–3 × 10 min at RT.
5. Incubate blot in HRP solution $\frac{1}{2}$ to 1 hr at RT.
6. Wash blot in Tris–Ca–Mg buffer, 2–3 × 10 min at RT.
7. Incubate blot in HRP substrate until desired signal develops (HRP substrates are often light sensitive and thus reaction should be performed in the dark, i.e., wrapped in aluminum foil or in low light or in your top drawer).
8. Rinse blot and store in dark.

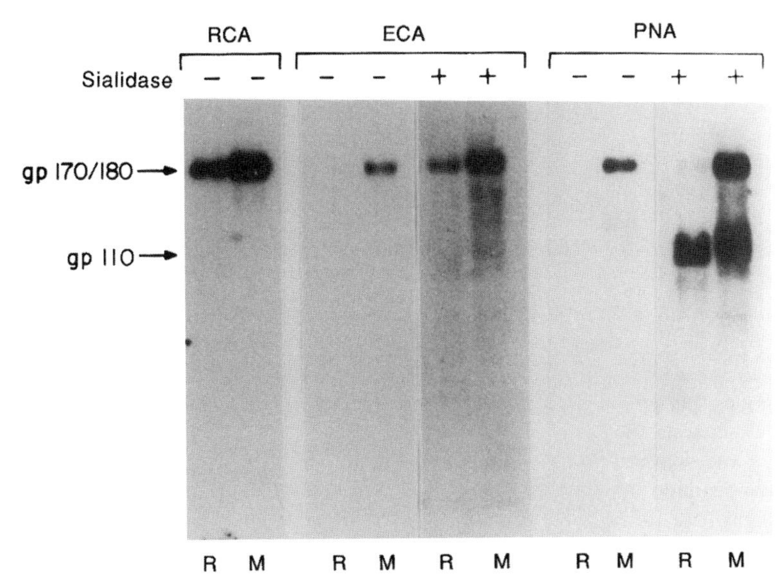

FIGURE 2 Detailed analysis of galacto-glycoproteins. There are many galactose-specific lectins. To the novice they may be wrongly considered to be interchangeable galactose detectors. In fact, they each have their preferred sugar configurations and are thus quite distinct. This is demonstrated in the autoradiogram. Thymocytes were derived from rats (R) or mice (M), homogenized, subjected to SDS–polyacrylamide gel electrophoresis, blotted onto nitrocellulose, and overlaid with ^{125}I-labeled lectins [RCA, *Erythrina crystagalli* agglutinin (ECA), or PNA] with or without *in situ* sialidase treatment (see Section IV). Note the differences in detection of the galactose-containing glycoproteins in different circumstances. Reprinted, with permission, from Gershoni (1987).

C. DISCRIMINATION OF SUGAR STRUCTURES: CLASSICAL PROCEDURE

The structure and composition of glycomoieties are rather complex. Fortunately, a wide variety of lectins exist, each specific for a different sugar and often distinct for their glycosidic linkages (Sharon, 1993). For example, galactose-binding lectins, in general, may bind differently to various glycoproteins, reflecting different orientations and positions of their galactose residues (Fig. 2) (Gershoni, 1987). Therefore, one should try a selection of lectins in characterizing a given glycoprotein. The following serves as the classical lectin staining procedure. A few comments are provided to assist you in custom tailoring the protocol to your specific needs.

As is illustrated in Sections A and B, HRP is a convenient detection system. Many lectins can be purchased directly conjugated to this and other enzymes (e.g., alkaline phosphatase), enabling a single step overlay. Alternatively, iodinated lectins are commonly used (see Fig. 2). In addition, a wide variety of biotin–lectin conjugates are also available and would be used much in the same manner as is described in Section A, i.e., a two-step procedure (see also Section D).

Solutions

1. *Buffer:* 25 m*M* Tris–HCl, pH 7.4, 150 m*M* NaCl (TBS). To make 1 liter, dissolve in 500 ml distilled water 3.03 g Trizma base and 8.77 g NaCl. Titrate to pH 7.4 with HCl and adjust volume to 1 liter with distilled water. PBS (see above) is also suitable.

2. *Quench:* 2% BSA in buffer.

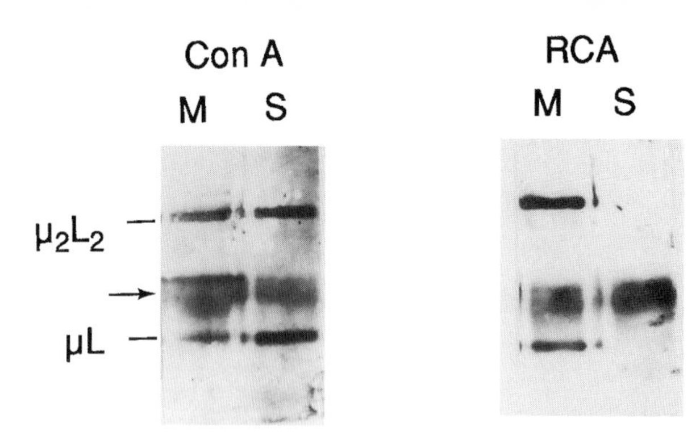

FIGURE 3 Diverging pathways for assembly of membrane and secretory IgM. B cells were fractionated to separate the membrane (M) and secretory (S) forms of IgM. IgM was immunoprecipitated and resolved by 4–10% nonreducing SDS–polyacrylamide gel electrophoresis to preserve disulfide bonds. Nitrocellulose blots were incubated with the biotin–lectin conjugates (Con A or RCA) followed by avidin–HRP conjugate detection. Hemimers (μL); monomers (μ_2L_2). Arrow indicates goat anti-mouse IgM used for immunoprecipitation. Note that Con A reveals monomers of both secretory and membrane forms of IgM. RCA, on the other hand, stains both membrane monomers and their hemimeric precursors, but does not detect any form of secretory IgM. This is interpreted to mean that hemimeric membrane IgM assembles to monomers in or beyond the *trans*-Golgi, while secretory IgM, which fails to reach this compartment, forms monomers nonetheless. Reprinted, with permission, from Shachar *et al.* (1992).

3. *Lectin:* 10 μg/ml in quench buffer is routinely more than enough and one should test greater dilutions when possible.

4. *Second probe:* In instances where biotin–lectin conjugates are used, an enzyme conjugate of streptavidin, avidin, or antibiotin antibody is required and should be suitably diluted in a quench buffer.

5. *Substrate:* Incubate blots in the substrate until the desired signal develops.

Steps

1. Rinse blot in buffer.
2. Quench blot in quench, 1 hr at RT.
3. Incubate blot in lectin solution $\frac{1}{2}$ to 1 hr at RT.
4. Wash blot in buffer, 2–3 × 10 min at RT.
5. Incubate blot in second probe $\frac{1}{2}$ to 1 hr at RT. This step is required only when the lectin is not directly detectable.
6. Wash blot in buffer, 2–3 × 10 min at RT.

7a. Incubate blot in enzyme substrate until desired signal develops; then rinse blot and store.

7b. In instances where the lectin or the second probe is radioiodinated, detection is achieved by autoradiography.

D. LECTINS AS TOOLS TO MONITOR INTRACELLULAR TRAFFIC

Glycoproteins and their related processes can be ascribed to distinct intracellular compartments *via* analysis of their carbohydrate moieties (Figs. 3 and 4). Con A detects mannose residues which are common to all N-linked glycomoieties added

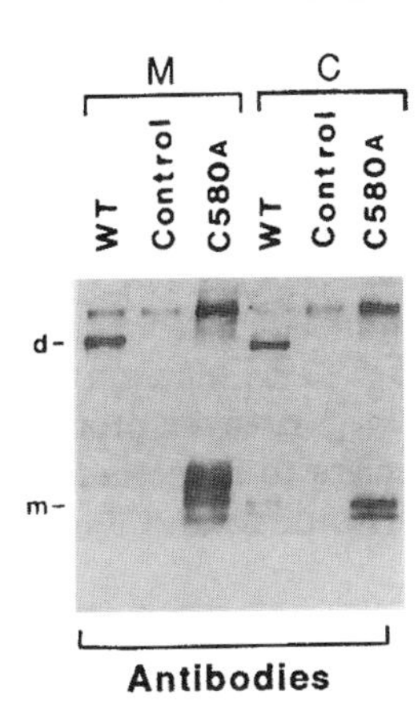

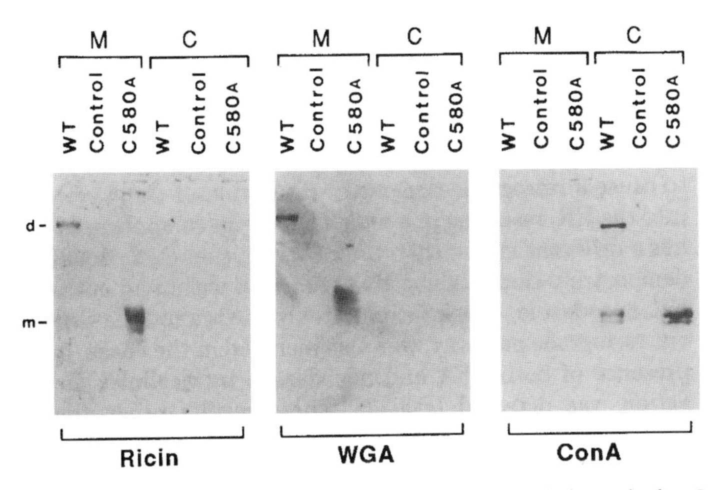

FIGURE 4 Acetylcholinesterase is rapidly shuttled through the Golgi. Kidney cells were transfected with wild-type (WT) or mutant (C580A) forms of acetylcholinesterase or not (control). Cells (C) and medium (M) were separated. Immunoprecipitated esterase was divided into four equal aliquots and resolved by nonreducing 10% SDS–polyacrylamide gel electrophoresis. Nitrocellulose blots were incubated with antiesterase antibodies (top) or with the biotin–lectin conjugate Con A, WGA, or RCA (ricin). Note the immunostaining of steady-state pools of disulfide-bonded dimers (d) and traces of monomers (m) in the wild-type cells, while only dimers are secreted. The mutant, on the other hand, is exclusively monomeric. Con A reveals all of these intracellular assembly species, but does not detect any unprocessed extracellular esterase. Efficient detection by WGA and RCA is of wild-type dimers and mutant monomers in the medium, illustrating that secretion occurs as soon as the esterase acquires galactose residues. Reprinted, with permission, from Kerem *et al.* (1993).

cotranslationally in the endoplasmic reticulum. RCA detects galactose moieties and thus indicates glycoproteins that have passed through the *trans*-Golgi. WGA detects sialic acids and thus serves as a marker for mature glycoproteins.

Solutions

1. *BSA quench:* 2–4% (w/v) BSA in PBS.

2. *Biotin–lectin conjugates:* Dissolve biotin conjugates of Con A, RCA, and WGA in water to 0.5–1 mg/ml and dilute in PBS to give 1 μg/ml.

3. *Avidin–HRP conjugate:* Dissolve avidin–HRP in water to 0.5–1 mg/ml and dilute in PBS to give 1–2 μg/ml.

4. *HRP substrate:* Prepare 4-chloro-1-naphthol as a 3 mg/ml stock solution in methanol and dilute just before use with PBS containing 0.01% H_2O_2 to give 0.5 mg/ml (Hawkes *et al.*, 1982).

Steps

1. *Optional:* Immerse blot in a wide pan of boiling water (make sure that the blot remains flat and does not curl or buckle) for 5 min. This treatment often enhances the signal, probably as a result of better exposure of the hydrophilic glycomoieties.
2. Quench blot in BSA quench, 1 hr at RT.
3. Incubate blot with biotin–lectin conjugate, 30 min at RT.
4. Wash blot in PBS, 3 × 10 min at RT.
5. Incubate blot with avidin–HRP, 30 min at RT.
6. Wash blot in PBS, 3 × 10 min at RT.
7. Incubate blot with HRP substrate and remove when desired signal develops.
8. Rinse in water and store blot.

IV. Comments

Enzymatic treatment of blots.
In view of the fact that lectins are sometimes sensitive to the neighbors and linkages of the detected sugar it can be effective to remove terminal sugars to reveal and make accessible penultimate residues before lectin overlay. This is easily achieved by incubating the blot in an enzyme-containing solution, as is demonstrated for the removal of sialic acid residues with sialidase, allowing binding of ECA or PNA to galactose residues (see Fig. 2).

Sugar competition.
The specificity of the lectin can be confirmed by introducing a competing sugar in the protocol used. For example, coincubation of the blot with the lectin and its corresponding monosaccharide should selectively reduce the specific signal obtained. Alternatively, one can compete off a signal after the fact. This is most effective when radioiodinated lectins are used. In this case, the blot is performed, an autoradiogram is produced, and then the blot is washed in the presence of the appropriate competing sugar followed by a second round of autoradiography.

Enzymes and substrates.
Various enzyme conjugates have been used in blotting assays (e.g., alkaline phosphatase, glucose oxidase). Correspondingly, there are numerous substrates that can be used. It is advisable to consult a textbook on histochemical techniques to identify substrates and protocols that give rise to insoluble products. Interestingly, one should note the recent introduction of chemiluminescent substrates for HRP (ECL, Amersham) which afford greater sensitivity and are amenable to quantification.

V. Pitfalls

1. *Quenchers:* In choosing the most effective quencher one must consider the protocol being used. Thus, for example, hemoglobin has been found to be useful for radioactive probes; however, it would not be suitable for HRP conjugates

because of intrinsic peroxidase activity. Milk may contain sugars and thus enhance background.

2. *Radioiodination:* In preparing radioactive lectins it is often advisable to include competing sugar with the lectin during the iodination. This protects the binding site from tyrosine modifications that might affect activity. The competing sugar would be diluted to an insignificant concentration on use of the lectin during incubation with the blot.

REFERENCES

Alberts, B., Bray, D., Lewis, J., Raff, M., Roberts, K., and Watson, J. D. (1989) "Molecular Biology of the Cell," 2nd ed. Garland Publishing, New York/London.

Clegg, J. C. S. (1982) Glycoprotein detection in nitrocellulose transfers of electrophoretically separated protein mixtures using concanavalin A and peroxidase: Application to arenavirus and flavivirus proteins. *Anal. Biochem.* **127,** 389–394.

Gershoni, J. M. (1987) Protein blotting: A tool for the analytical biochemist. *In* "Advances in Electrophoresis" (A. Chrambach, M. Dunn, and B. J. Radola, eds.), Vol. 1, pp. 141–175. VCH Verlagsgesellschaft, Weinheim.

Gershoni, J. M. (1988) Protein blotting: A manual. *In* "Methods of Biochemical Analysis" (D. Glick, ed.), Vol. 33, pp. 1–58. Wiley, New York.

Gershoni, J. M., Bayer, E. A., and Wilchek, M. (1985) Protein blot analysis of glycoconjugates: Enzyme–hydrazide—A novel reagent for the detection of aldehydes. *Anal. Biochem.* **146,** 59–63.

Halttwanger, R. S., Kelly, W. G., Roquemore, E. P., Blomberg, M. A., Dong, L-Y. D., Kreppel, L., Chou, T-Y., and Hart, G. W. (1992) Glycosylation of nuclear and cytoplasmic proteins is ubiquitous and dynamic. *Biochem. Soc. Trans.* **20,** 264–269.

Hawkes, R., Niday, E., and Gordon, J. (1982) A dot-immunobinding assay for monoclonal and other antibodies. *Anal. Biochem.* **119,** 142–147.

Kerem, A., Kronman, C., Bar-Nun, S., Shafferman, A., and Velan, B. (1993) Interrelations between assembly and secretion of recombinant human acetylcholinesterase. *J. Biol. Chem.* **268,** 180–184.

Keren, Z., Berke, G., and Gershoni, J. M. (1986) Identification of cell surface glycoproteins by periodate–alkaline phosphatase hydrazide. *Anal. Biochem.* **155,** 182–187.

Shachar, I., Amitay, R., Rabinovich, E., Haimovich, J., and Bar-Nun, S. (1992) Polymerization of secretory IgM in B lymphocytes is prevented by a preceding targeting to a degradation pathway. *J. Biol. Chem.* **267,** 24241–24247.

Sharon, N. (1993) Lectin carbohydrate complexes of plants and animals: An atomic view. *Trends Biochem. Sci.* **18,** 221–223.

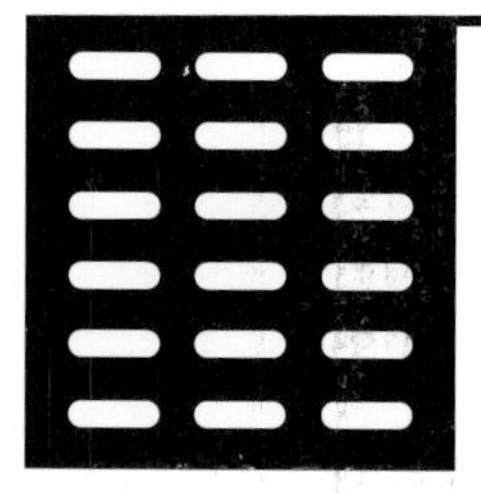

Purification of Lectins and Determination of Their Carbohydrate Specificity

Halina Lis, David Belenky, Aaron Rabinkov, and Nathan Sharon

I. Introduction

Lectins are ubiquitous in nature, being found in animals, plants, and microorganisms (Lis and Sharon, 1986; Drickamer, 1988; Sharon and Lis, 1989; Leffler *et al.*, 1989). Most of the procedures employed for the purification of the different lectins are basically similar, although they may vary somewhat depending on the source (Lotan, 1992; Rudiger, 1993). In particular, a step common to virtually all lectin purification schemes is affinity chromatography on immobilized sugars, which exploits the ability of lectins to combine with carbohydrates specifically and reversibly (Lis and Sharon, 1981).

The isolation of lectins, as a rule, begins with saline (or buffer) extraction of the starting material. Preextraction with organic solvents (e.g., petroleum ether) is often employed to remove lipid or other interfering substances. In most cases prepurification of the lectin (by, e.g., salt or acid precipitation) is required prior to affinity chromatography. In principle, affinity purification of lectins is not different from the purification of other biopolymers with specific combining sites, although it is generally much simpler. This is because lectins do not modify the compounds they bind, nor is the binding very strong (the association constant, K_a, of lectins with monosaccharides is usually in the range 10^3-10^4). As a result, most lectins can readily be displaced from the affinity columns by the sugars for which they are specific. It is also very easy to establish the specificity of a lectin by hapten inhibition of hemagglutination, using simple sugars and crude lectin preparations. Knowledge of the specificity then permits the design of a suitable purification procedure.

A large variety of affinity adsorbents for the purification of lectins have been described. They can be divided in three major types: (1) polysaccharides, either native or modified; (2) matrix-bound glycoproteins; and (3) matrix-bound mono- and oligo (mostly di-) saccharides. Table I lists a selection of supports, ligands, and methods of attachment that are being employed in the preparation of affinity adsorbents for the purification of lectins; many such adsorbents are now commercially available. In the following, we describe in detail purification of the lectin from seeds of the leguminous tree *Erythrina corallodendron* by affinity chromatography on a column of lactose coupled to Sepharose. The procedure, which is a modification of a published one (Lis *et al.*, 1985), is applicable to galactose-specific lectins from other sources as well.

TABLE I Adsorbents for Affinity Chromatography of Lectins[a]

Matrix	Ligand	Coupling method	Application
Type 1: Polysaccharides			
Sephadexes	—	—	Glc/Man-specific lectins
Sepharoses	—	—	Gal-specific lectins
Chitin	—	—	GlcNAc-specific lectins
Insolubilized guaran	—	—	Gal-specific lectins
Type 2: Matrix-bound glycoproteins[b]			
Sepharose	Thyroglobulin	Cyanogen bromide (CNBr) activation	
	Ovomucoid	CNBr activation	
	Fetuin	CNBr activation	
	Bovine submaxillary mucin	CNBr activation	
	Hog gastric mucin	CNBr activation	
Type 3: Matrix-bound mono- and oligosaccharides[c]			
Sepharose	Carbohydrate derivatives with an amino group	CNBr activation	
CH-Sepharose (derivatized with 6-aminohexanoic acid)	Carbohydrate derivatives with an amino group	Carbodiimide coupling	
Epoxy-activated Sepharose	Any sugar	Direct coupling at high pH	
Divinyl sulfone-activated Sepharose	Any sugar	Direct coupling at high pH	

[a] A compilation of procedures for the affinity chromatography of lectins can be found in "Methods in Enzymology," Volumes 28, 34, and 50; see also Lis and Sharon (1981).

[b] Columns of immobilized glycoproteins, preferably desialylated, can be used for the purification of lectins with different sugar specificities and for lectins that do not interact with simple sugars. In the latter case elution is done with solutions of low or high pH (e.g., 0.1 *M* acetic acid or 20 m*M* 2,3-diaminopropane); with lectins that require Ca^{2+} for their activity (as is the case with many animal lectins), desorption can be achieved by the addition of EDTA.

[c] Specificity in this group is determined by the carbohydrate used.

II. Materials and Instrumentation

Sodium carbonate anhydrous (Cat. No. 6392), sodium hydrogen carbonate (Cat. No. 6329), sodium dihydrogen phosphate monohydrate (Cat. No. 6346), and D-galactose (MW 180, Cat. No. 4061) are purchased from Merck. D-Glucose (AnalaR, Cat. No. 10117), lactose (AnalaR, Cat. No. 10139), citric acid (AnalaR, Cat. No. 10081), and sodium citrate (AnalaR, Cat. No. 10242) are from BDH. Divinyl sulfone (vinyl sulfone, Cat. No. V-9501), TPCK-trypsin (Cat. No. T-8642), and NaCl (Cat. No. S-9625) are from Sigma. Sepharose CL-4B (Cat. No. 17-0150-01) and Sephadex G-25 medium (Cat. No. 17-0033-01) are provided by Pharmacia LKB Biotechnology. Acetone (analytical grade, Cat. No. 01035) is from BioLab, ammonium hydrogen carbonate (Cat. No. 09832) from Fluka, and *Vibrio cholerae* sialidase (Test-Neuraminidase, Cat. No. ORKD 04/05) from Behringwerke. Microtiter plates (V-shaped, 96 wells, Cat. No. 651101) are purchased from Greiner Labortechnik, and acetone-resistant polypropylene tubes (Cat. No. 03931) from DuPont.

III. Procedures

A. AGGLUTINATION ASSAY

1. Preparation of Erythrocyte Suspension

Solutions

1. *Phosphate-buffered saline (PBS):* To make 1 liter, dissolve 6.9 g of sodium dihydrogen phosphate monohydrate ($NaH_2PO_4 \cdot H_2O$) and 9 g sodium chloride (NaCl) in distilled water, adjust pH to 7.2, and bring to a total volume of 1 liter.

2. *Saline:* Dissolve 9 g NaCl in 1 liter distilled water.

3. *Alsever's solution:* Dissolve 2 g of glucose, 0.8 g of sodium citrate, and 0.42 g of NaCl in 100 ml of distilled water and bring to pH 6.1 by the addition of solid citric acid.

4. *Anticoagulant:* Dissolve 0.8 g sodium citrate in 10 ml saline; add 5.4 ml of 37% formaldehyde.

5. *Stock rabbit blood suspension:* Add venous whole rabbit blood to an equal volume of Alsever's solution, containing 1/30th volume of the anticoagulant. This suspension can be stored up to 2 weeks at 4°C.

a. *Untreated erythrocytes*

Steps

1. Dilute whole human blood (obtained from a local blood bank) with an equal volume of PBS; stock rabbit blood suspension is used as such.
2. Collect erythrocytes by centrifugation at room temperature in a clinical table centrifuge (2000 rpm, 5 min).
3. Wash three or four times with PBS (5 ml per 1 ml packed cells).
4. Add washed erythrocytes to PBS (4 ml of cells per 100 ml PBS) to give a 4% suspension (3×10^8 cells/ml).

b. *Enzymatically modified erythrocytes: Trypsinized erythrocytes*

Solution

Immediately before use, dissolve TPCK-trypsin in PBS, 1 mg/ml.

Steps

1. Prepare an 8% suspension of washed erythrocytes in PBS.
2. Add trypsin to a final concentration of 100 μg/ml (0.1 ml of trypsin solution to 1 ml of erythrocyte suspension). Incubate for 1 hr at 37°C.
3. Wash the trypsinized erythrocytes four or five times with PBS and prepare a 4% suspension as described above.

Carbohydrate	MIC
Galactose	12.5 mM
GalNAc	3.2 "
Lactose	3.2 "
Mannose	NI
Glucose	NI
MeβGalNDns	24.4 μM
LacNAc	0.8 mM

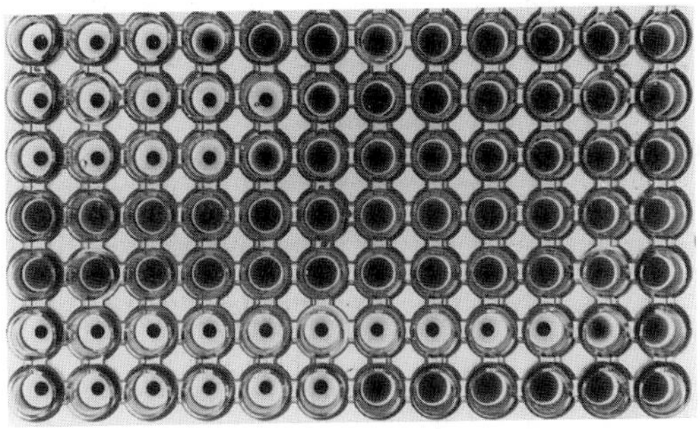

FIGURE 1 Determination of minimum inhibitory concentration (MIC) of various carbohydrates required for the complete inhibition of 4 agglutinating units of ECorL. Each well contains 50 μl of a serial dilution of the tested sugar, 50 μl of lectin solution, and 50 μl of 4% suspension of human erythrocytes. GalNAc, *N*-acetylgalactosamine; MeβGalNDns, methyl β-*N*-dansylgalactosaminide; LacNAc, *N*-acetyllactosamine. The minimum inhibitory concentration is obtained by dividing the starting concentration of the carbohydrate (which was 200 m*M* for galactose and GalNAc, 100 m*M* for lactose, 500 m*M* for mannose and glucose, and 50 m*M* for MeβGalNDns and LacNAc) by the reciprocal of the highest inhibitory dilution, taking into account that due to the addition of lectin, the dilution of the test sugar is 1:2 already in the first well. NI, noninhibitory.

c. *Enzymatically modified erythrocytes: Sialidase-treated erythrocytes*

Steps

1. Prepare a 20% suspension of erythrocytes in PBS.
2. Add sialidase (50 μl, 5×10^{-3} units/ml suspension). Incubate for 1 hr at 37°C.
3. Wash the sialidase-treated cells and prepare a 4% suspension as above.

2. Agglutination Test

Steps

1. Add 50 μl of PBS to each of a row of wells on a microtiter plate, starting with the second well.

2. To each of the first two wells add 50 μl of the solution to be tested for activity, and mix by shaking the plate by hand.

3. Transfer 50 μl of liquid from the second well to the adjacent one, mix, transfer 50 μl from the latter well to the next one, and so on, to the last well. This protocol produces twofold serial dilutions of the tested material, i.e., 1:1, 1:2, 1:4, 1:8, etc.

4. To each well add 50 μl of the 4% erythrocyte suspension, mix, and leave for 1 hr at room temperature.

5. Note the highest dilution at which agglutination is observed. Where agglutination has occurred, a mat of erythrocytes covers the well. In the absence of agglutination, the erythrocytes appear as a button at the tip of the well (Fig. 1). One hemagglutinating unit is arbitrarily defined as the minimal amount of material required to cause full agglutination under the above conditions. The titer

of the tested solution is expressed as the reciprocal of the highest dilution showing agglutination.

B. DETERMINATION OF CARBOHYDRATE SPECIFICITY BY HAPTEN INHIBITION OF HEMAGGLUTINATION

1. Qualitative Determination

Steps

1. Prepare 0.2 *M* solutions in PBS of the sugars to be tested.

2. Determine the titer of the lectin preparation. Dilute the preparation to make its titer 4. Fifty microliters of such a dilution contains by definition 4 agglutinating units of lectin.

3. In wells of a microtiter plate, mix 50 μl of a given carbohydrate solution with 4 agglutinating units of the lectin; let stand 5–10 min.

4. Add 50 μl of a 4% suspension of erythrocytes; after 1 hr determine the degree of agglutination in the different wells. Absence of agglutination indicates that the lectin is specific for the sugar in the well.

2. Quantitative Determination

See Fig. 1.

Steps

1. Prepare twofold serial dilutions of the inhibitory sugar.
2. To each well add 4 agglutinating units of the lectin; wait 5–10 min.
3. Add 50 μl of a 4% suspension of erythrocytes; after 1 hr check agglutination.
4. Note the highest dilution required for complete inhibition.

C. PURIFICATION OF ECorL

1. Preparation of Sepharose–Lactose

Solution

0.5 M Carbonate solution, pH 11: Dissolve 53 g of sodium carbonate in 1 liter distilled water.

Steps

1. Pour the suspension of Sepharose CL-4B (as supplied by the producer) into a cylinder and let stand for 15–30 min. Discard the supernatant.
2. Suspend 100 ml of the sedimented Sepharose in 100 ml 0.5 *M* carbonate solution, pH 11.
3. Add 10 ml vinyl sulfone and keep at room temperature for 70 min with slow stirring with a motor-driven stirrer (not magnetic bar).
4. Wash the activated gel on a glass filter thoroughly with distilled water.

5. Suspend in 100 ml of a 10% solution of lactose in the carbonate buffer and leave overnight in the cold room with slow stirring as above.
6. Wash on a glass filter with 1 liter carbonate–bicarbonate buffer, followed by 2 liters distilled water, and suspend in PBS.

2. Purification of the Lectin

Solutions

1. *0.2 M Galactose:* Dissolve 3.6 g D-galactose in 100 ml of PBS.
2. *0.1 M Ammonium hydrogen carbonate (bicarbonate):* Dissolve 0.79 g ammonium bicarbonate in 100 ml distilled water.

Steps

1. Grind seeds to a fine meal in a Waring blender, 2 × 3 min.

2. Mix 100 g of seed meal with 1 liter PBS and extract for either 3 hr at room temperature or overnight in a cold room with stirring.

3. Filter through cheesecloth and discard insoluble residue.

4. Measure volume of extract, add acetone (precooled at −20°C) to a final concentration of 60% v/v (150 ml of acetone to each 100 ml of extract). Let stand overnight at −20°C.

5. Decant supernatant and collect precipitate by centrifugation in a refrigerated Sorvall RC2-B centrifuge, rotor SS 34, in glass or acetone-resistant plastic tubes, at 3000 rpm for 30 min.

6. Suspend precipitate in minimal volume of PBS (about 100 ml) and dialyze in cold against four or five changes of 3 liters PBS until the acetone odor can no longer be detected.

7. Centrifuge retentate and apply clear supernatant to a column (1.8 × 60 cm) of Sepharose–lactose at a flow rate of 25–30 ml per hour. Collect effluent in fractions of 4–5 ml. Measure OD of fractions at 280 nm.

8. Wash out the unbound proteins with PBS until the effluent shows $OD_{280} < 0.05$.

9. Elute with 0.2 *M* galactose in PBS and collect fractions as above. Pool the fractions containing eluted lectin as determined by OD_{280}.

10. Add glycerol (10% of the pooled volume, which is usually 30–40 ml) and acetone (1%) and apply immediately to a column (1.8 × 60 cm) of Sephadex G-25 medium, preequilibrated with 0.1 *M* NH_4HCO_3.

11. Elute with 0.1 *M* NH_4HCO_3 and measure the OD_{280} of the eluted fractions. Collect the first UV-absorbing peak, which contains the lectin free of PBS and galactose, and lyophilize.

Yield about 100 mg of purified lectin from 100 g of seed meal. On SDS–PAGE the lectin migrates as a single band of M_r 30,000. It agglutinates untreated human A, B, and O erythrocytes at concentrations of 5–10 μg/ml.

IV. Comments

The starting material for the preparation of plant lectins is usually the seeds. They are either collected in the field or purchased from commercial sources. In some cases, seed meal is also available (e.g., jack bean or soybean flour).

Hemagglutination is routinely assayed with native or modified erythrocytes from humans or other animals, usually rabbits and sometimes sheep. Blood group-specific lectins are tested with a panel of typed human erythrocytes. The most common cell modification is mild digestion with trypsin or with sialidase, which renders the cells more sensitive to agglutination. The latter treatment, in which sialic acid is removed from complex carbohydrates, uncovers cryptic galactose residues and is sometimes necessary for agglutination by galactose-specific lectins which do not act on untreated cells (e.g., peanut agglutinin).

In plants, lectins often occur as a group of closely related proteins with the same carbohydrate specificity, or isolectins. Therefore, preparations of affinity-purified plant lectins may contain different molecular species. Isolectins may be products of different genes (Peumans *et al.,* 1982) or of posttranslational processing, either of the protein moiety or, in the case of glycoprotein lectins, of the carbohydrate chains. Different molecular species of the lectin may also result from intramolecular aggregation, possibly occurring during purification. For most purposes, the mixture of isolectins can be used as such. When needed, the isolectins can be separated on the basis of differences in molecular size (gel filtration), carbohydrate structure (chromatography on a suitable lectin, usually concanavalin A), or charge (ion-exchange chromatography, isoelectric focusing).

V. Pitfalls

1. For agglutination, human erythrocytes from outdated blood can be used. If kept at 4°C in the original plastic bags, they are quite stable for several weeks. With time, however, they become hemolytic and should then be discarded.

2. Enzyme-treated erythrocytes should be prepared on the day of the assay.

3. In the preparation of Sepharose–lactose avoid stirring with a magnetic bar, which may disrupt the spherical Sepharose particles.

4. Galactose preparations, even of analytical grade, may contain high-molecular-weight, UV-absorbing material, which will appear as a contaminant of the final product. Use galactose of the highest purity available and check each new batch; the OD_{280} of a 0.2 *M* solution should not exceed 0.05.

5. The volume of the Sephadex G-25 column (last step of ECorL purification) should be four to five times the volume of the applied material.

REFERENCES

Drickamer, K. (1988) Two distinct classes of carbohydrate-recognition domains in animal lectins. *J. Biol. Chem.* **263,** 9557–9560.

Leffler, H., Masiarz, F. R., and Barondes, S. H. (1989) Soluble lactose-binding vertebrate lectins: A growing family. *Biochemistry* **28,** 9222–9229.

Lis, H., Joubert, F. J., and Sharon, N. (1985) Isolation and properties of *N*-acetyllactosamine specific lectin from nine *Erythrina* species. *Phytochemistry* **24,** 2803–2809.

Lis, H., and Sharon, N. (1981) Affinity chromatography for the purification of lectins. *J. Chromatogr.* **215,** 361–372.

Lis, H., and Sharon, N. (1986) Lectins as molecules and tools. *Annu. Rev. Biochem.* **55,** 35–67.

Lotan, R. (1992) β-Galactose-binding vertebrate lectins. *In* "Glycoconjugates" (H. J. Allen and E. C. Kisailus, eds.), pp. 635–671. Marcel Dekker, New York.

Peumans, W. J., Stinissen, H. M., and Carlier, A. R. (1982) A genetic basis for the origin of six different isolectins in hexaploid wheat. *Planta* **154,** 562–567.

Rudiger, H. (1993) Isolation of plant lectins. *In* "Lectins and Glycobiology" (H. J. Gabius and S. Gabius, eds.), pp. 31–46. Springer-Verlag, Heidelberg.

Sharon, N., and Lis, H. (1989) Lectins as recognition molecules. *Science* **246,** 227–234.

Two-Dimensional Northwestern Blotting

Kurt Dejgaard and Julio E. Celis

I. Introduction

Two dimensional (2D) Northwestern blotting complements gel-shift experiments in the identification of specific protein–nucleic acid interactions. The procedures described below, which have been adapted from the protocol described by Schenkel *et al.* (1988), have been valuable in our laboratory for the identification of several hnRNP proteins (our unpublished observations). Here, we demonstrate the technique on 2D gel blots of transformed human amnion (AMA) cell proteins (Fig. 1) using poly(rC), a homopolymer that interacts with hnRNPs K and L (Matunis *et al.*, 1992; Dejgaard *et al.*, 1994), as well as poly(rU), which interact with hnRNPs C and M (Swanson and Dreyfuss, 1988; Dreyfuss *et al.*, 1993). The technique works equally well, however, when sequence-specific deoxyoligonucleotides are used as probes.

II. Reagents

Poly(rU) (Cat. No. 27-4440-02), poly(rC) (Cat. No. 27-4220-02), and Ficoll 400 (Cat. No. 17-0400-01) were purchased from Pharmacia Biotech. Acrylamide (Cat. No. 161-0100), bisacrylamide (Cat. No. 161-0201), ammonium persulfate (APS, Cat. No. 161-0700), TEMED (Cat. No. 161-0800), and xylene cyanol (Cat. No. 161-0423) were obtained from Bio-Rad. *Escherichia coli* tRNA (Cat. No. R-1753), DTT (Cat. No. D-0632), spermidine–tri-HCl (Cat. No. S-2501), polyvinylpyrrolidone (Cat. No. PVP-40T), and bromphenol blue (Cat. No. B-6131) were from Sigma. T4 polynucleotide kinase (10 U/μl, Cat. No. E2021) was from Amersham and [γ-^{32}P]ATP (7000 Ci/mmole, Cat. No. 35020) from ICN. Tris–HCl, EDTA, sodium acetate, and $NaBH_4$ were from Merck. The X-ray films (X-Omat DS, Cat. No. 508 7838) were from Kodak and the Mini-Monitor G-M tube was from Mini-Instruments. All other reagents and materials were as described in the article by Ariana Celis and Julio E. Celis.

III. Procedures

A. LABELING OF PROBES

1. ^{32}P Labeling and Purification of RNA Homopolymers

Solutions

1. *0.5 M EDTA:* To make 100 ml, weigh 18.61 g of EDTA and dissolve in distilled water. Adjust to pH 8.0 and complete to 10 ml with distilled water. Store at 4°C.

FIGURE 1 Incubation of a Northwestern blot in an hybridization oven.

2. *0.1% Spermidine:* To make 100 ml, weigh 100 mg of spermidine–tri-HCl and complete to 100 ml with distilled water. Store at −20°C.

3. *10× Kinase buffer:* To make 10 ml, weigh 0.788 g of Tris–HCl, 203 mg of $MgCl_2 \cdot 6\ H_2O$, and 77 mg of DTT and dissolve in a small amount of distilled water. Add 2.5 μl of 0.1% spermidine–tri-HCl and 20 μl of 0.5 *M* EDTA. Adjust to pH 8.0 and complete to 10 ml with distilled water. Store at −20°C.

4. *3 M Sodium acetate:* To make 100 ml, weigh 40.82 g of NaAc and dissolve in distilled water. Adjust to pH 6.0 with acetic acid and complete to 100 ml with distilled water. Store at 4°C.

5. *TE:* To make 100 ml, weigh 0.158 g Tris–HCl and dissolve in distilled water. Add 20 μl 0.5 *M* EDTA. Adjust to pH 7.5 and complete to 100 ml with distilled water. Store at 4°C.

6. *−20°C Ethanol:* Two ethanol solutions are needed for the purification of polynucleotides, a 99.9% solution and an 80% solution, which is prepared by volumetric dilution of 99.9% ethanol in distilled water. Keep both solutions at −20°C.

Steps

1. Resuspend RNA in sterile glass-distilled water to a final concentration of 0.5 μg/μl.

2. Mix in an Eppendorf tube 1 μl RNA, 1 μl of 10× kinase buffer, and 500 μCi of [γ-^{32}P]ATP. Complete to 9 μl with sterile glass-distilled water in an Eppendorf tube.

3. Add 1 μl of T4 polynucleotide kinase and incubate for 1 hr at 37°C.

4. After incubation, add 77 μl of TE, 10 μl of sodium acetate solution, and 3 μl of 0.5 *M* EDTA. Add 275 ml of 99.9% ethanol kept at −20°C, mix, and leave for 30 min at −20°C.

5. Spin down the labeled RNA in an Eppendorf centrifuge (full speed) for 10–15 min at 4°C (cold room). Carefully aspirate the supernatant and discard it.

6. Wash the pellet by adding 500 μl of 80% ethanol kept at −20°C and centrifuge 5 min in an Eppendorf centrifuge (full speed). Carefully aspirate the supernatant and discard it.

7. Gently resuspend the RNA in 87 μl of TE by pipetting up and down (do not vortex) and transfer to a new Eppendorf tube. Accept loss. Use of more

aggressive means to increase the yield at this step will give rise to an unacceptable high background labeling of the blots.

8. Add 10 μl of the sodium acetate solution, 3 μl of 0.5 *M* EDTA, and 275 μl of 99.9% ethanol at −20°C. Leave for 30 min at −20°C.

9. Centrifuge and wash with 80% ethanol as described in steps 5 and 6.

10. Resuspend the RNA in 1 ml of blocking buffer (see Section B) by pipetting up and down a few times. Store at −20°C if not to be used immediately.

2. ^{32}P Labeling and Purification of Oligonucleotides

Solutions

1. *0.5 M EDTA:* To make 100 ml, weigh 18.61 g of EDTA and dissolve in distilled water. Adjust to pH 8.0 and complete to 10 ml with distilled water. Store at 4°C.

2. *0.1% Spermidine:* To make 100 ml, weigh 100 mg of spermidine–tri-HCl and complete to 100 ml with distilled water. Store at −20°C.

3. *10× Kinase buffer:* To make 10 ml, weigh 0.788 g of Tris–HCl, 203 mg of $MgCl_2 \cdot 6\ H_2O$, and 77.1 mg of DTT and dissolve in a small amount of distilled water. Add 2.5 μl of 0.1% spermidine–tri-HCl and 20 μl of 0.5 *M* EDTA. Adjust to pH 8.0 and complete to 10 ml with distilled water. Store at −20°C.

4. *Acrylamide solution:* To make 500 ml, weigh 190 g of acrylamide and 10 g of bisacrylamide. Complete to 500 ml with distilled water. Store at 4°C.

5. *10× Tris–Borate buffer (10× TBE):* To make 1 liter, weigh 121.1 g of Tris–HCl, 61.8 g of boric acid, and 3.72 g of EDTA. Complete to 1 liter with distilled water. Store at 4°C.

6. *TE:* To make 100 ml, weigh 0.158 g Tris–HCl and dissolve in distilled water. Add 20 μl 0.5 *M* EDTA. Adjust to pH 7.5 and complete to 100 ml with distilled water. Store at 4°C.

7. *0.1% Bromphenol blue and xylene cyanol:* To make 10 ml, weigh 10 mg of bromphenol blue and 10 mg of xylene cyanol. Complete to 10 ml with TE.

8. *Ficoll load:* To make 10 ml, weigh 2 g of Ficoll 400. Add 12 μl of 0.1% bromphenol blue and xylene cyanol and complete to 10 ml with TE.

9. *10% APS:* To make 1 ml, weigh 0.1 g of ammonium persulfate and complete to 1 ml with distilled water (prepare fresh).

10. *10% $NaBH_4$:* To make 1 ml, weigh 0.1 g of $NaBH_4$ and complete to 1 ml with distilled water (prepare fresh).

Steps

1. Label the oligo sample with [γ-^{32}P]ATP (same procedure as for RNA homopolymers, see Section A1, steps 1–3).

2. Assemble glass plates (see the article by Julio E. Celis and Eyδfinnur Olsen) with 1- or 1.5-mm spacers.

3. Mix 25 ml of the acrylamide solution, 5 ml of 10× TBE, 20 ml of distilled water, 25 μl of TEMED, and 250 μl of 10% APS under agitation in a 250-ml side-arm flask. Degas using a vacuum pump.

4. Pour the solution between the glass plates, insert a comb (see the article by

Julio E. Celis and Eyδfinnur Olsen), and leave to polymerize for 1 hr at room temperature.

5. Remove the comb and bottom spacer. Place the gel in a running chamber (see the article by Julio E. Celis and Eyδfinnur Olsen). Fill the upper and lower reservoirs with Tris/borate buffer and prerun the gel for 20 min at 20 W immediately before using.

6. Mix the labeled oligo sample with 12 μl of Ficoll load and load it in one of the gel pockets/slots. Run at 15 W. Check occasionally the bottom reservoir with the Mini-Minotor. Radioactivity in the buffer indicates that the excess [γ-^{32}P]ATP has passed through the gel (~2 hr).

7. Run for additional 10 min. Take out the gel sandwich, remove one of the glass plates, and cover the gel with a thin film of Saran wrap. Tape two or three small pieces of filter paper to the corners of the gel on top of the plastic. Soak the pieces in a 10% solution of $NaBH_4$.

8. Expose an X-ray film by pressing it down on the gel for 5–10 sec. Develop the film. A strong band should be seen (and perhaps a few additional weak bands if the oligonucleotides were not purified by the supplier). The wetted filter paper leaves marks on the film when developed and helps to superimpose the film on top of the gel.

9. Using a scalpel, excise the band from the gel by cutting through the X-ray film.

10. Place the gel piece in an Eppendorf tube and fill it with blocking buffer. Leave at 4°C overnight. This is sufficient to recover the major part of the labeled oligo from the gel.

11. Transfer the blocking buffer, now containing the labeled probe, to a clean Eppendorf tube and centrifuge briefly to eliminate small pieces of acrylamide. Transfer the liquid to a clean tube. Freeze, if not to be used immediately. In contrast to RNA probes, oligo-DNA probes may be reused. Note, however, that ^{32}P has a half-life of 2 weeks, limiting the time span in which the probe can be used.

B. IDENTIFICATION OF SINGLE-STRAND NUCLEOTIDE-BINDING PROTEINS

Solution

Blocking buffer: To make 1 liter, weigh 0.5 g of PVP-40T, 0.5 g of Ficoll 400, 1.58 g of Tris–HCl, and 2.92 g of NaCl and dissolve in distilled water. Adjust to pH 7.5 and complete to 1 liter with distilled water. Store at 4°C.

Steps

1. After blotting 1D or 2D gels onto nitrocellulose sheets (see article by Julio E. Celis, Jette B. Lauridsen, and Bodil Basse), cut the excess nitrocellulose and transfer the blot to a rectangular pie dish (24 × 19 cm) containing 40–50 ml of blocking buffer. Care should be taken that the blot doesn't dry out at any time. Once it is dry, the binding activity of the proteins is irreversibly lost.

2. Shake the blots for at least 1 hr in blocking buffer.

3. After blocking, place the blot on a nylon mesh sheet wetted in blocking

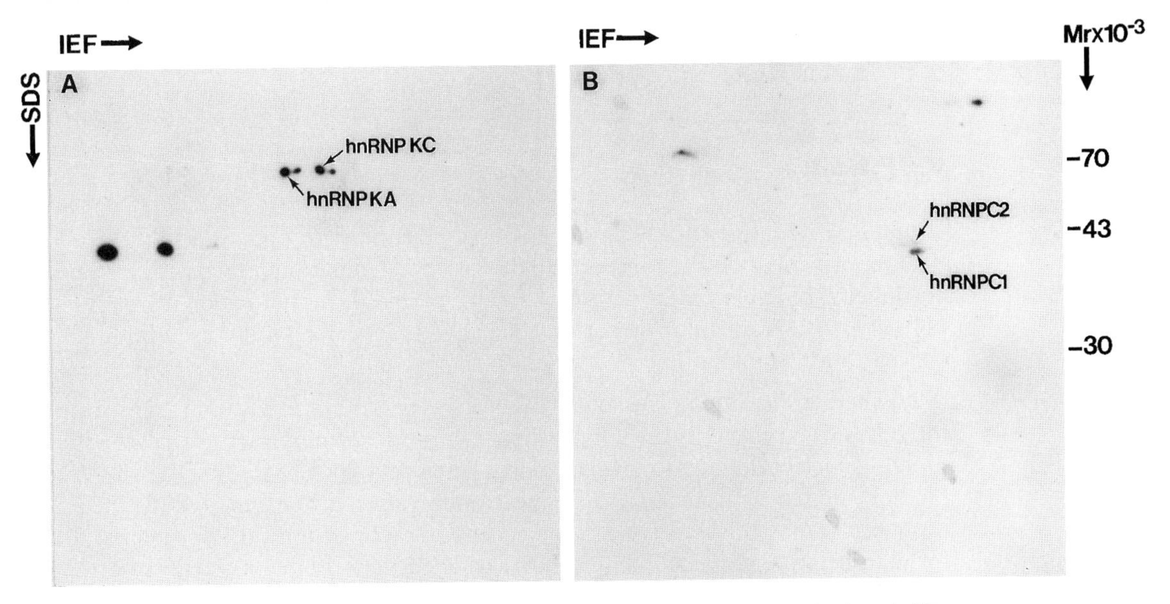

FIGURE 2 Two-dimensional IEF Northwestern blots of AMA proteins probed with ^{32}P-labeled poly(rC) and poly(rU). (A) Poly(rC) binding to the hnRNP-K family. (B) Poly(rU) binding to the hnRNP-C family. IEF gels separate proteins with p*I* < 7.5; therefore, the hnRNP-M family (p*I* 7.5–8.0), which is another major poly(rU)-binding protein family, is not detected on this blot. Blots of NEPHGE gels, covering the basic proteins, show avid binding of poly(rU) to the hnRNP-M family (results not shown).

buffer. Roll it up and place it into a hybridization bottle. If a hybridization oven is not available (see Fig. 2), melt the blot into a plastic bag.

4. Add 20–30 ml of blocking buffer and rotate to ensure that the blot is in contact with the wall of the bottle.

5. Resuspend the labeled RNA/oligo-DNA in 5–10 ml of blocking buffer (5 ml per blot) and add *E. coli* tRNA to a final concentration of 10 μg/ml. This is the labeling probe.

6. Pour out the buffer from the hybridization bottle and replace it with 5 ml of the labeling probe. Place in a hybridization oven and leave it to rotate for 1 hr at room temperature. If plastic bags are used, tape them onto a rotating wheel.

7. Exchange the labeling probe with blocking buffer (do not reuse RNA-based probes, make a new one if needed). Take the blot from the bottle and place it in a rectangular pie dish containing 50 ml of blocking buffer. Place on a shaker and wash three times for 10–15 min in blocking buffer. Check with the Mini-Monitor that the background decreases. If after washing the signal/noise ratio is still too low (if background is above 8–10 dps), wash additionally once or twice.

8. Dry the blot or put it in a plastic bag and expose it to an X-ray film for 4 hr at −80°C. If the signal is too high/low, adjust exposure time and reexpose. Use enhancer screens if available. They enhance the ^{32}P signal up to 10 times. This is convenient if the RNA/DNA probe has a low specific activity or the blots have little protein. We use Kodak X-Omatic, which can be purchased in different sizes.

IV. Comments

As the blocking buffer is protein free, you may choose to stain the blot after exposure with amido black (see article by Hans Jürgen Hoffmann and Julio E. Celis) or Coomassie brilliant blue to determine the molecular weight and isoelectric point of the binding proteins.

V. Pitfalls

1. The amount of tRNA may not always be enough to outcompete the random binding of DNA or RNA. In particular, poly(rG) tends to interact with histones on the blots. Supplementation with herring sperm DNA and/or poly(dI)–poly(dC) DNA can eliminate this problem. We have successfully used both at concentrations ranging from 20 μg/ml to 0.5 mg/ml.

2. There are two main reasons why Northwestern blotting cannot substitute for gel-shift experiments or native affinity chromatography for the analysis of protein–nucleotide interactions: (1) The protein may not have the DNA/RNA binding site reconstituted after SDS electrophoresis and blotting, and (2) the protein may only bind to DNA/RNA when interacting with other protein(s) to form an heterooligomer. It should be mentioned that although Northwestern blotting works for many proteins, it provides no information on other proteins with which the DNA- or RNA-binding proteins may be associated under native conditions.

REFERENCES

Dejgaard, K., Leffers, H., Rasmussen, H. H., Madsen, P., Kruse, T. A., Gesser, B., Nielsen, H., and Celis, J. E. (1994) Identification, molecular cloning, expression and chromosome mapping of a family of transformation upregulated hnRNP-K proteins derived by alternative splicing. *J. Mol. Biol.* **236**, 33–48.

Dreyfuss, G., Matunis, M. J., Piñol-Roma, S., and Burd, C. G. (1993) hnRNP proteins and the biogenesis of mRNA. *Annu. Rev. Biochem.* **62**, 289–321.

Matunis, M. J., Michael, W. M., and Dreyfuss, G. (1992) Characterization and primary structure of the poly(C)-binding heterogeneous nuclear ribonucleoprotein complex K protein. *Mol. Cell. Biol.* **12**, 164–171.

Schenkel, J., Sekeris, C. E., Alonso, A., and Bautz, E. K. F. (1988) RNA-binding properties of hnRNP proteins. *Eur. J. Biochem.* **171**, 565–569.

Swanson, M. S., and Dreyfuss, G. (1988) Classification and purification of proteins of heterogeneous nuclear ribonucleoprotein particles by RNA-binding specificities. *Mol. Cell. Biol.* **8**, 2237–2241.

In Vivo Genomic Footprinting with Dimethyl Sulfate

Jean-Pierre Jost and Hans Peter Saluz

I. Introduction

In vivo footprinting with dimethyl sulfate is a powerful tool to study the *in situ* interaction of proteins with DNA in intact cells. On purpose we consider here only the footprinting of specific genes in intact cells from tissue culture or from cells dissociated from specific tissues. Isolated nuclei will not be considered for *in vivo* footprinting because they may not show the same results as intact cells (Saluz and Jost, 1989a,b, 1990). The use of dimethyl sulfate (DMS) presents one major advantage: because of its small molecular weight it readily penetrates cells, where it reacts with unprotected guanosine residues (Church and Gilbert, 1984). In addition, the use of a dilution series of DMS permits us to establish the endpoint titration of each guanosine residue (Saluz and Jost, 1990). A general review of other possible strategies for *in vivo* genomic footprinting has recently been published (Saluz and Jost, 1993). In the protocol presented here we only consider the detection procedure based on the linear amplification of the reaction product (Saluz and Jost, 1989a,b, 1990). Figure 1 shows the basic steps involved in genomic footprinting with dimethyl sulfate.

II. Materials and Instrumentation

Ammonium acetate (Cat. No. 116), ammonium sulfate (Cat. No. 12019), boric acid (Cat. No. 12015), calcium chloride (Cat. No. 2382) cobalt chloride (Cat. No. 2533), carbon tetrachloride (Cat. No. 2222), chloroform (Cat. No. 2445), *N*-cetyl-*N*,*N*,*N*-triethylammonium bromide (Cat. No. 2342), ethanol (Cat. No. 983), EDTA titriplex III (Cat. No. 8418), formamide (Cat. No. 9684), magnesium chloride (Cat. No. 5833), methanol (Cat. No. 6009), 2-mercaptoethanol (Cat. No. 15433), phenol (Cat. No. 206), potassium chloride (Cat. No. 4936), sodium chloride (Cat. No. 6404), sodium acetate (Cat. No. 1116), Tris base (Cat. No. 8382), urea (Cat. No. 8487), xylene cyanole (Cat. no. 10590), and zinc chloride (Cat. No. 8815) were obtained from Merck.

Acetic acid (Cat. No. 45730), acrylamide (Cat. No. 170111), *N*′,*N*-methylene-bisacrylamide (Cat. No. 66669), bromphenol blue (Cat. No. 18040), dimethyl-dichlorosilane (Cat. No. 40140), EGTA (Cat. No. 03778), Hepes (Cat. No. 54461), Nonidet P-40 (NP-40, Cat. No. 74385), piperidine (Cat. No. 80640), potassium bicarbonate (Cat. No. 60340), spermine (Cat. No. 85605), spermidine (Cat. No.

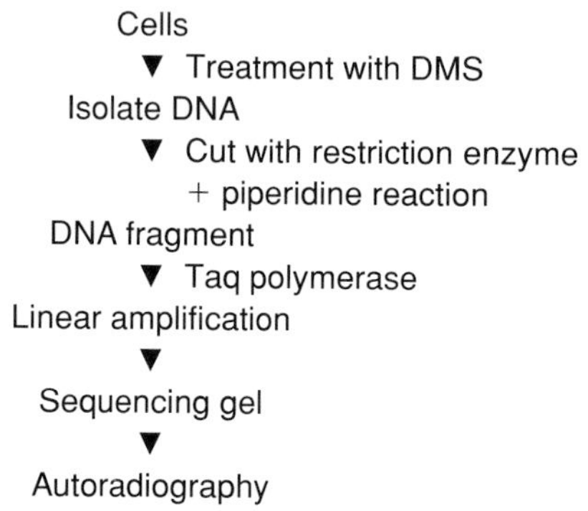

Cells
▼ Treatment with DMS
Isolate DNA
▼ Cut with restriction enzyme
+ piperidine reaction
DNA fragment
▼ Taq polymerase
Linear amplification
▼
Sequencing gel
▼
Autoradiography

FIGURE 1

85578), sucrose (Cat. No. 84100), and TEMED (Cat. No. 87690) were purchased from Fluka Chemie AG.

Collagenase (Cat. No. 103.586), hyaluronidase (Cat. No. 106.518), and proteinase K (Cat. No. 745723) were obtained from Boehringer-Mannheim.

Dimethyl sulfate (Cat. No. 186309) was from Aldrich-Chemie GmbH & Co KG.

Sequenase version 2 (Cat. No. 70775) was purchased from U.S. Biochemicals.

The all deoxynucleotide triphosphate Ultrapur Kit (Cat. No. 272035-01) was obtained from Pharmacia LKB Biotechnology AB.

Deoxy-[α-^{32}P]ATP (3000 Ci/mmole, Cat. No. 10204) was from Amersham International plc.

Bovine serum albumin (Cat. No. ORHD 20/21) was from Behringerwerke AG, Dulbecco's modified Eagle's medium (Cat. No. 07402100) from Gibco-BRL Life Technologies, and sodium dodecyl sulfate (Cat. No. 20760) from Serva Feinbiochemica GmbH & Co KG.

Millipore Ultrafree MC filters (0.45 μm, Cat. No. UFC3 OHVOO) were from Millipore Corporation. X-ray film (Kodak X-Omat-AR) was obtained from the local Kodak supplier. The DNA thermal cycler and Taq polymerase Ampli Taq (Cat. No. 3128) were obtained from Perkin–Elmer–Cetus. All electrophoresis apparatus were conventional homemade (workshop of Ciba-Geigy AG) equipment.

III. Procedures

For all procedures described below, no specific equipment is required. Standard lab equipment is adequate.

A. PREPARATION OF CELL SUSPENSION FROM CHICKEN LIVER, OVIDUCT, AND KIDNEYS

Solutions

1. *Saline solution:* 0.15 *M* NaCl, 20 m*M* Hepes, pH 7.8, 5 m*M* EDTA.

2. *Red blood cell lysis buffer:* 0.13 *M* NH_4Cl, 0.17 *M* Tris–HCl, pH 7.6, 0.01 *M* $KHCO_3$.

3. *Dulbecco's culture medium.*

4. *Digestion buffer:* 1 mg hyaluronidase, 0.5 mg collagenase/ml in 0.15 *M* NaCl, 20 m*M* Hepes, pH 8.0, 1 m*M* $CaCl_2$, 0.1 m*M* $ZnCl_2$, 0.1 m*M* $CoCl_2$.

Sterilize buffer by filtration and keep frozen in aliquots. Add enzymes just before use.

Steps

1. Perfuse livers with saline solution (do not perfuse kidneys and oviducts).

2. Put 10–20 g of tissue into 50 ml of digestion buffer. Mince tissue into small pieces with scissors. Incubate at 37°C for 30–40 min in rotary water shaker.

3. Chill cell suspension. Add 500 μl of 0.5 *M* EDTA, pH 8.0.

4. Filter debris on a nylon grid funnel (mesh size 1 mm).

5. Rinse with saline.

6. Centrifuge cells in Corex tubes at 1000 *g*, 5 min, 0°C.

7. Discard supernatant. Resuspend cells in saline. Filter again and centrifuge as above.

8. Eliminate red blood cells (if necessary) by adding 10 ml of red blood cell lysis buffer. Pipette up and down. Leave cell suspension at room temperature for 5 min (debris and clumps of cells with sediment at the bottom of the tube).

9. Remove cells in suspension with pipette, leaving sediment.

10. Wash cells with cold saline solution and resuspend cells into 3 ml of Dulbecco's medium (~10^8 cells/ml).

NOTE

Monolayer cell cultures can directly be used for footprinting experiments without disturbing the cell-to-cell contacts, which may be important in certain cases. DMS is very toxic and should be handled only in a well-ventilated fume hood.

B. TREATMENT OF CELLS WITH DIMETHYL SULFATE

Solutions

1. *DMS stop buffer:* Phosphate-buffered saline containing 1% bovine serum albumin and 100 m*M* 2-mercaptoethanol.

2. *Nuclear buffer:* 0.3 *M* sucrose, 60 m*M* KCl, 15 m*M* NaCl, 1 m*M* EDTA, 0.5 m*M* EGTA, 15 m*M* Hepes (pH 7.5), 1 m*M* spermidine, 0.3 m*M* spermine.

3. *Nuclear buffer containing 1% Nonidet NP-40.*

4. *2× Proteinase K buffer:* 20 m*M* Tris–HCl, pH 8.0, 20 m*M* EDTA, 20 m*M* NaCl, 1% sodium dodecyl sulfate.

Steps

The cell suspension should contain approximately 10^8 cells/ml, and each reaction mixture contains 1–2 ml of cells in a 15-ml Corex tube.

1. To a series of cell suspensions add 0, 0.5, 0.05, 0.005, and 0.0005% DMS freshly prepared in Dulbecco's medium. Mix slowly.
2. Incubate at 20°C for exactly 5 min.

3. Add 10 ml of ice-cold DMS stop buffer. Mix.
4. Spin 5 min at 1000 *g* and 4°C.
5. Wash cells with 10 ml of DMS stop buffer as outlined above.
6. Resuspend cells in 1.5 ml of cold nuclear buffer and add 1.5 ml of cold nuclear buffer containing 1% NP-40. Mix well.
7. Keep suspension on ice for 5 min. Spin 5 min at 4000 rpm (HB-4 Sorval rotor) at 4°C.
8. Resuspend crude nuclei in 1–1.5 ml of nuclear buffer and add an equal volume of 2× proteinase K buffer containing 600 μg of proteinase K/ml.
9. Incubate overnight at 37°C.
10. Perform five to six phenol extractions and one chloroform extraction.
11. Dialyze 24 hr against 0.5 m*M* EDTA in the cold room.
12. Add 0.1 vol of 3 *M* Na acetate, pH 5.0, and precipitate with 3 vol of ethanol at −20°C for 2 hr.
13. Centrifuge DNA at 16,000 *g* for 20 min. Wash DNA with 75% ethanol and dissolve DNA in minimal volume of 10 m*M* Tris, pH 7.5–8.0, 1 m*M* EDTA (overnight).

C. DIGESTION OF DNA WITH RESTRICTION ENZYMES AND TREATMENT OF DNA WITH PIPERIDINE

For *in vivo* footprinting with Taq polymerase (Saluz and Jost, 1989a,b, 1990), the preparation of a restriction digest is important in reducing the viscosity of the genomic DNA. The restriction endonuclease should, however, not cleave within the target sequence to be studied. The three principal steps in the reaction of DMS with unprotected guanosine residues are the modification of the base, removal of the base from its sugar, and piperidine-induced cleavage at this position.

Solutions

1. *10× buffers for restriction endonucleases:* As recommended by the manufacturer.
2. *1 M piperidine in* H_2O. Prepare freshly.

Steps

1. Determine the $OD_{260\,nm}$ of the purified DNA. Take 15 μg of genomic DNA per 300 μl of incubation mixture. For single-copy genes in genomes of 5×10^9 bp, approximately 50 μg of digested genomic DNA is needed for one reaction.

2. Add 30 μl of 10× restriction buffer to the 15 μg DNA in 270 μl H_2O. Add 45 units of the chosen restriction enzyme. Should restriction enzyme with 4-bp recognition sequence be used, take 150 units. Mix and incubate overnight at 37°C.

3. Perform one phenol and one chloroform extraction.

4. Transfer supernatant to a polyallomer Beckman centrifuge tube. Add 0.1 vol of 3 *M* sodium acetate, 0.05 *M* EDTA, and 2.5 vol of ethanol. Mix and leave at −20°C overnight.

5. Centrifuge 25,000–30,000 rpm in a Beckman centrifuge for 1 hr at 4°C. Decant supernatant and dry DNA sediment.

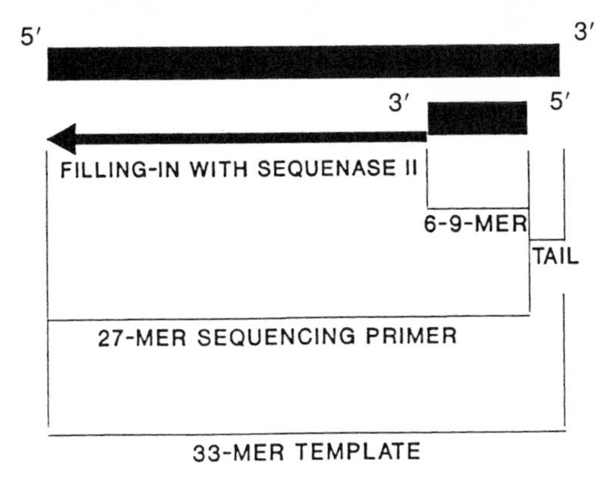

FIGURE 2 Synthesis of the labeled DNA primer by the filling-in reaction with Sequenase version 2.

6. Dissolve DNA into 100 μl of 1 *M* piperidine. Transfer to an Eppendorf tube and incubate for 30 min at 90–95°C.

7. Do repeated lyophilizations under a good vacuum to remove traces of piperidine.

D. SYNTHESIS OF THE RADIOACTIVE PRIMER

The primer must be complementary to the 3′ end of the target sequence to be studied as Taq polymerase elongates a DNA strand in the 5′ to 3′ direction. Good results were obtained with primers of 27 nucleotides. A very high specific radioactivity can be obtained by the filling-in reaction. A synthetic complementary 9-mer segment of the sequencing primer is annealed to the 3′ end of a 33-mer (Fig. 2). This allows, on elongation with one or more radioactively labeled deoxynucleotides, an easy separation of the primer from the 33-mer template on a sequencing gel (Saluz and Jost, 1990).

A very important parameter for amplification is the temperature at which the oligonucleotide primers anneal with the template. It should be performed approximately 2–4°C below the T_m. T_m should be measured in the same buffer used for amplification with Taq polymerase. It should be noted that oligonucleotides with about 50% G + C show a melting temperature of approximately 64°C. A 27-mer primer with 75% G + C residues will give a T_m value of 82°C. If the T_m of an oligonucleotide cannot be physically determined then just empirically start the annealing temperature at 60°C and increase it stepwise by 5°C until no signal of amplification is obtained anymore (Saluz and Jost, 1990); then take the highest temperature where signals are still obtained.

Solutions

1. *Purified synthetic 6- to 9-mer segment of the sequencing primer:* 0.14 μg DNA/μl H_2O.
2. *Purified 33-mer oligonucleotide complementary to the sequence primer:* 0.5 μg DNA/μl H_2O.
3. *Cloned Sequenase version 2.*
4. *Unlabeled dNTPs:* Minus dATP, 10 m*M* each, sequencing grade.
5. *[α-^{32}P]dATP:* 3000 Ci/mmole.

6. *5× sequenase buffer:* 200 m*M* Tris–HCl, pH 7.5, 100 m*M* $MgCl_2$, 250 m*M* NaCl.
7. *Short 15% polyacrylamide sequencing gel.*
8. *Formamide sample dye:* 94% formamide, 10 m*M* NaEDTA, pH 7.5, 0.05% xylene cyanole (XC), 0.05% bromphenol blue (BPB).
9. *Elution buffer:* 0.5 *M* NaCl, 0.5 m*M* EDTA, 0.1 *M* Tris, pH 8.0.

Steps

1. To a sterile Eppendorf tube add consecutively 7 μl of 5× sequenase buffer, 1 μl of the 9-mer and 1 μl of the 33-mer. Mix and heat to 75°C; cool the mixture slowly to anneal the DNA (10–20 min).

2. Put the mixture on ice, add 3 μl of sequencing-grade dNTPs (minus dATP). Add 22 μl (220 μCi) of [α-^{32}P]dATP and 1 μl of Sequenase version 2 (13 units/μl).

3. Incubate 20 min at 23°C.

4. Add 40 μl of formamide sample dye and heat sample 1 min at 90°C. Quick-chill on ice and load immediately on a 15% sequencing gel.

5. Run gel until XC dye has migrated over a distance of about 12 cm.

6. Remove top glass plate and cover gel with Saran wrap.

7. Place labeled markers (or fluorescent marker) onto the gel for orientation and expose 1–5 sec to an X-ray film.

8. Place X-ray film over gel in correct orientation and, using a needle, pierce several holes through the film and gel around the band of interest. Cut out the band with a scalpel blade.

9. Crush gel slice through a 1-ml syringe (no needle) into 500 μl of elution buffer. Heat 30 min at 75°C (alternatively do an electroelution of the labeled primer).

10. Transfer the buffer containing the eluted primer into a Millipore Ultrafree MC 0.45-μm membrane and filter by centrifugation.

11. Add 10 μg of *Escherichia coli* DNA carrier DNA. Dilute NaCl to 0.25 *M* and add 3 vol of ethanol, chill 15 min on dry ice, and centrifuge 15 min at 30,000 *g* in a Sorvall centrifuge.

12. Pour off supernatant. Dry pellet briefly in Speed-Vac and redissolve in 170 μl of H_2O. The primer is sufficient for 10 reactions of linear amplification. Use primer immediately for linear amplification.

E. LINEAR AMPLIFICATION OF CHEMICALLY SEQUENCED DNA

The sequencing reaction is followed by a selective, linear amplification of the gene of interest with Taq polymerase or the heat-stable polymerases using a primer labeled to very high specific activity. The reaction product is then analyzed directly on a sequencing gel by comparison with cloned sequenced control/DNA (Maxam and Gilbert, 1980). The amount of genomic DNA required for a reaction is 25–50 μg for a single-copy gene and a genome size of 3×10^9 nucleotides per haploid genome.

Solutions

1. *Labeled primer, digested, and sequenced genomic DNA. Digested, sequenced, and diluted control DNA.*

2. *10× Taq polymerase reaction buffer:* 166 m*M* $(NH_4)_2SO_4$, 670 m*M* Tris–HCl, pH 8.8, at 25°C, 67 m*M* $MgCl_2$, 100 m*M* β-mercaptoethanol, 2 mg BSA/ml of highest purity (for example BRL). Keep buffer frozen at −20°C in aliquots.

3. *Taq polymerase:* Ampli Taq from Cetus.

4. *dNTPs:* Sequencing grade, Pharmacia. Stock solutions containing all four nucleotides at a concentration of 10 m*M* each.

5. *Sequenced cloned control DNA:* G, A+G, C+T, C.

Steps

1. To an Eppendorf tube (fitting the DNA thermal cycler) add consecutively 69 μl of genomic DNA (50 μg), 17 μl of the radioactively labeled purified primer (approx 10 ng), and 10 μl of 10× Taq polymerase buffer.

2. Prepare the parallel controls with cloned DNA as follows: add to an Eppendorf tube consecutively 76 μl of *E. coli* DNA (50 μg), 1 μl of cloned sequenced control DNA (450 pg), 8.5 μl of labeled primer, and 10 μl of 10× Taq polymerase buffer.

3. Incubate at 95°C for 5 min in a thermal cycler preprogrammed for denaturing DNA.

4. Quick-chill samples in ice/water (1 min, do not interrupt the denaturing program).

5. Spin samples for a few seconds in a microfuge and put back on ice.

6. Add 3 μl of dNTPs.

7. Add 1 μl of Taq polymerase (2–3 units/μl diluted in reaction buffer). Mix and centrifuge briefly. Put samples on ice.

8. If necessary, cover samples with mineral oil.

9. Return samples to the DNA cycler for 1 min at 95°C.

10. Stop denaturing program and start the amplification program: 25–30 cycles each consisting of 1 min denaturation at 94°C, 2 min annealing (2–4°C below the T_m of the oligonucleotide primer duplex, usually around 60°C), and 3 min chain elongation at 72°C.

11. After the last cycle, immediately place the samples on ice/water and do a purification.

F. PURIFICATION OF THE REACTION PRODUCTS

Solutions

1. *1%* N-Cetyl-*N,N,N*-trimethylammonium bromide (CTAB) in H_2O.
2. *0.5 M Ammonium acetate, pH not adjusted.*
3. *3 M sodium acetate, 5 mM EDTA, pH 5.*
4. *100 mM NaOH, 1 mM EDTA.*
5. *8 M Urea, 0.04% xylene cyanole, 0.04% bromphenol blue:* This stock solution has to be stored frozen.

Steps

1. Transfer amplification product to a precooled Eppendorf tube, avoiding contamination from the covering mineral oil. (Trace oil can be removed by filtering the sample on an Ultrafree MC Pharmacia filter.)

2. Add 10 μl of 1% CTAB solution, mix, and keep on ice for 20 min.

3. Centrifuge 15 min at 30,000 *g* at 4°C in Sorval centrifuge.

4. Remove supernatant without disturbing pellet.

5. Without drying the pellet add 100–200 μl of 0.5 *M* ammonium acetate and 0.1 vol of 3 *M* Na acetate, pH 5.0. Precipitate with 3 vol of cold ethanol. Mix, put at −80°C for 15 min, and centrifuge at 30,000 *g* for 15 min at 4°C.

6. Remove supernatant and remove residual solution with a drawn-out capillary.

7. Resuspend pellet in 150 μl of 0.5 *M* ammonium acetate. Add 15 μl of 3 *M* sodium acetate, pH 5.0, and 500 μl of cold ethanol. Mix and leave at −80°C for 15 min.

8. Centrifuge at 30,000 *g* for 15 min at 4°C.

9. Remove the supernatant carefully as indicated above and dry pellet for a few minutes in a Speed-Vac (samples should not be completely dry).

10. Add 4 μl of 100 m*M* NaOH, 1 m*M* EDTA, and 4 μl of 8 *M* urea. Dissolve sample. Just before loading samples onto sequencing gel, heat them for 15 sec at 94°C and load them directly onto the well.

G. GEL ELECTROPHORESIS

The best resolution of the genomic sequence (up to 300 bases) was obtained on an 8% polyacrylamide gel with a ratio of 29:1 acrylamide:bisacrylamide. Prerunning of the gel overnight at low current removes all charged impurities that may interfere with the perfect separation of the genomic DNA fragments.

Materials and Solutions

1. *Power supply:* 2500–3000 V/70 mA.
2. *Glass plates:* 600 × 330 × 5 mm.
3. *Spacers (PVC):* Two 1 × 20 × 600 mm; one 1 × 20 × 400 mm.
4. *Comb (PVC):* 15 teeth (1 × 5 × 25 mm); space between the teeth, 3 mm.
5. *1% Dimethyldichlorosilane in carbon tetrachloride.*
6. *Acrylamide and bisacrylamide recrystallized* 2×.
7. *Ammonium persulfate:* analytical grade.
8. *Urea:* Analytical grade.
9. *TEMED.*
10. *Tris–borate–EDTA (TBE):* 10× TBE: 0.89 *M* Tris base, 0.89 *M* boric acid, 0.02 *M* EDTA, pH 8.3.

Steps

1. Clean glass plates with water and ethanol and treat both plates with 1% dimethyldichlorosilane solution. Clean plates again with ethanol.

2. Assemble plates and spacers as usual.

3. Pour the polyacrylamide solution, placing the plates in a slightly slanted position and filling along one edge. For a 60-cm-long gel (8%), prepare 23.19 g acrylamide, 0.81 g bisacrylamide, 126 g urea (7 *M* final), 30 ml of 10× TBE, and distilled water to 300 ml. Dissolve the ingredients by mixing with magnetic bar. Add 3.9 ml of 10% ammonium persulfate. Mix well. Filter the solution through paper filter. Degas the solution in a Büchner flask under vacuum. Add 60 μl of TEMED. Mix briefly and pour gel as described above. To ensure complete polymerization, store gel overnight at room temperature, then carefully remove the comb and flush the pockets clean with water.

4. Do preelectrophoresis overnight at constant current and approximately 300 V.

5. Change buffer in the upper and lower chambers.

6. Heat the gel for at least 1 hr with constant current (50 mA). The surface of a 60-cm-long gel will be about 50–60°C.

7. Switch power supply off and clean slots with a stream of 1× TBE using a syringe.

8. Load samples with a long drawn-out capillary.

9. Switch the power on and increase the current to 60 mA (for an overnight electrophoresis of 11 hr, use chambers with sufficient capacity, i.e., 2000 ml).

10. Continue electrophoresis until xylene cyanole marker (DNA fragments approximately 90 nucleotides long run with xylene cyanole on a 8% denaturing gel) migrates 55–58 cm from the top of a 60-cm-long gel.

H. FIXATION AND DRYING THE GEL

Solution and Materials

1. *Fixation solution:* 10% methanol, 10% acetic acid, 80% H_2O.
2. *Whatman 17 paper.*
3. *Gel dryer.*

Steps

1. At the end of electrophoresis, remove the gel from the electrophoresis apparatus and take off the upper glass plate. Cover gel with Saran wrap.

2. Mark the piece of gel to be fixed directly on the Saran wrap. Cut out the pieces of gel with a scalpel blade.

3. Place the Saran wrap-covered gel pieces on a glass plate, and transfer the glass plate to a box containing the fixation solution. Remove the Saran wrap.

4. Incubate 30 min at room temperature with slow shaking.

5. Remove solution and put a piece of Whatman 17 paper of appropriate size on top of the gel. Turn the assembly upside down.

6. Remove glass plate from gel/Whatman 17 assembly.

7. Cover gel with Saran wrap and place the gel on a gel dryer.

8. Dry gel under vacuum at 80°C for 1–2 hr.

9. Before exposing the dried gel to X-ray film, remove the Saran wrap and replace with a new one.

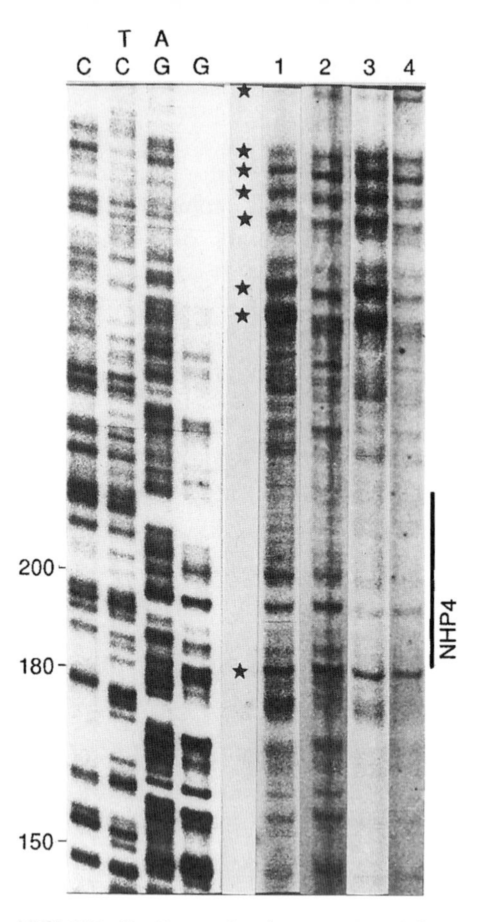

FIGURE 3 Example of *in vivo* DMS footprinting of avian vitellogenin II gene in hen liver cells. Concentrations of DMS were 0.5, 0.05, 0.005, and 0.0005% (lanes 1–4). Lanes C, T, A, and G are the control reactions (Saluz and Jost, 1989a).

IV. Comments

An example of genomic footprinting of avian vitellogenin II gene is shown in Fig. 3. In cases where the genome size exceeds 5×10^9 bases per haploid genome, it may be necessary to first enrich the sequence of interest prior to the piperidine reaction (see Mirkovitch and Darnell, 1991).

V. Pitfalls

1. At the beginning it may be wise to monitor the recovery of DNA after each step of the lengthy procedure because a systematic loss of DNA after each step may jeopardize the success of the experiment. The best way is to adjust the reaction mixture to 25–50 μg DNA just prior to the piperidine reaction (pool duplication or triplicate test if necessary).

2. Success also greatly depends on the quality of the DNA. It is a good idea to test the isolated DNA on agarose before proceeding with further steps.

3. The labeled primer must be used immediately on purification. Overnight storage in ethanol at −20°C, for example, is sufficient to drastically increase the nonspecific background (autoradiolysis).

REFERENCES

Church, G. M., and Gilbert, W. (1984) Genomic sequencing. *Proc. Natl. Acad. Sci. USA* **81**, 1991–1995.

Maxam, A. M., and Gilbert, W. (1980) Sequencing end-labeled DNA with base-specific chemical cleavages. *In* "Methods in Enzymology" (L. Grossman and K. Moldave, eds.), Vol. 65, pp. 499–560. Academic Press, San Diego.

Mirkovitch, J., and Darnell, J. E., Jr. (1991) Rapid in vivo footprinting technique identifies protein bound to the TTR gene in the mouse liver. *Genes Dev.* **5**, 83–93.

Saluz, H. P., and Jost, J. P. (1989a) A simple high resolution procedure to study DNA methylation and in vivo protein/DNA interactions on a single-copy gene level in higher eukaryyotes. *Proc. Natl. Acad. Sci. USA* **86**, 2602–2606.

Saluz, H. P., and Jost, J. P. (1989b) Genomic footprinting with Taq polymerase. *Nature* **338**, 277.

Saluz, H. P., and Jost, J. P. (1990) A laboratory guide for in vivo studies of DNA methylation and protein/DNA interactions. *In* "BioMethods," Vol. 3. Birkhäuser Verlag, Basel.

Saluz, H. P., and Jost, J. P. (1993) Approaches to characterize protein–DNA interactions in vivo. *Crit. Rev. Eukaryotic Gene Expression* 3(1), 1–29.

SECTION F

Microsequencing and Other Techniques

Internal Amino Acid Sequencing of Proteins Recovered from One- or Two-Dimensional Gels

Joël Vandekerckhove and Hanne H. Rasmussen

I. Introduction

SDS–polyacrylamide gel electrophoresis, combined with electroblotting and automated Edman degradation, is routinely used for protein purification and N-terminal amino acid sequence analysis (Vandekerckhove *et al.*, 1985; Aebersold *et al.*, 1986; Matsudaira, 1987; Bauw *et al.*, 1987; Eckerskorn *et al.*, 1988). Unfortunately, a large number of proteins are found to be N-terminally blocked *in vivo*. In addition, development of the amino acid sequencing technology toward higher sensitivities unexpectedly leads to cases where artifactual N-terminal blocking is noted. This causes considerable limitations on the amount of sequence information that can be obtained from the N terminus. Even in cases where N-terminal sequencing is carried out, it is often necessary to generate additional internal sequences to be able to clone the corresponding gene or to characterize the protein in more detail. Internal amino acid sequences are obtained by either in-gel or on-membrane cleavage, followed by separation and sequencing of the peptides generated (Aebersold *et al.*, 1987; Rosenfeld *et al.*, 1992). These methods can be carried out successfully only when the protein concentration in the gel or on the membrane is sufficiently high. For low-abundance proteins it is therefore necessary to use methods that allow concentration of proteins into small volumes or onto small membrane surfaces (Rasmussen *et al.*, 1991). This article describes methods for generating internal sequences from proteins that are either blotted onto membranes or stained inside the gel. In addition a gel concentration system is provided for reeluting and concentrating proteins from multiple combined gel spots into highly concentrated small gel volumes.

II. Materials and Instrumentation

Acrylamide (Cat. No. 161-0100), *N,N′*-methylenebisacrylamide (Cat. No. 161-0201), TEMED (Cat. No. 161-0800), agarose (Cat No. 162-0100), and ammonium persulfate (Cat. No. 161-0700) were from Bio-Rad. DTT (Cat. No. D-0632), glycine (Cat. No. G-7126), Trizma base (Cat. No. T-1503), bromophenol blue (Cat. No. B-6131), Ponceau S (Cat. No. P-3504), and polyvinylpyrrolidone (PVP, Cat. No. PVP-30) were purchased from Sigma. SDS (Cat. No. 20763) was from Serva. Trifluoroacetic acid (TFA, Cat. No. GPS 4040) was obtained from Rathburn. Acetonitrile (LiChrosolv 14291), methanol (analytic grade), boric acid (Cat. No. 165.1000), and ammonium bicarbonate were from Merck. PVDF membranes were either from

Millipore (Immobilon, P15552) or Bio-Rad. Whatmann 3MM Chr paper (Cat. No. 3030917). Trypsin was from Promega (Cat. No. V511a) or Sigma (Cat. No. T-0134). Reverse-phase columns were purchased from Vydac.

Any commercially available or homemade gel electrophoresis apparatus can be used for the elution–concentration system as long as the dimensions do not significantly vary. Electroblotting is carried out in a Bio-Rad Transblot cell or MiniTrans blot. For details on protein sequencing and HPLC peptide separation, reference is made to the article on amino-terminal protein sequence analysis by Heinz Nika and Ruedi Aebersold in this volume. The scalpels (No. 11) were from Paragon and the long needles (Cat. No. V2A 1415 LL-10) from Acufirm. The power supplies were from Pharmacia-LKB (EPS 500/400).

III. Procedures

A. PROTEIN ELUTION–CONCENTRATION GEL SYSTEM

Solutions

1. *Acrylamide solution (Separation gel):* To make 500 ml, add 150 g of acrylamide and 0.75 g of bisacrylamide. After dissolving, complete to 500 ml with distilled water. Filter if necessary. Aliquot in 200-ml portions and store at 4°C.

2. *1.5 M Tris–HCl, pH 8.8:* To make 1 liter of 1.5 *M* Tris–HCl, pH 8.8, add 181.6 g of Trizma base and titrate with HCl. Complete to 1 liter with distilled water. Aliquot in 200-ml portions and store at 4°C.

3. *1 M Tris–HCl, pH 7.1:* To make 1 liter of 1 *M* Tris–HCl, pH 7.1, add 121.1 g of Trizma base and titrate with HCl. Complete to 1 liter with distilled water. Aliquot in 200-ml portions and store at 4°C.

4. *Acrylamide solution (Stacking gel):* To make 500 ml, add 50 g of acrylamide and 2.5 g of bisacrylamide. Complete to 500 ml with distilled water. Filter if necessary. Aliquot in 200-ml portions and store at 4°C.

5. *10% SDS:* To make 1 liter, add 100 g of SDS and complete to 1 liter with distilled water. Filter if necessary. Store at room temperature.

6. *10% ammonium persulfate (APS):* To make 10 ml, weigh 1 g of ammonium persulfate and complete to 10 ml with distilled water. Prepare this solution just before use.

7. *Electrode buffer:* To make 1 liter of a 5x solution, add 30.3 g of Trizma base, 144 g of glycine, and add 50 ml of 10% SDS solution. Complete to 1 liter with distilled water. Store at room temperature.

8. *Protein sample buffer:* 1% SDS, 0.1% bromophenol blue, 50 m*M* dithiothreitol, 60 m*M* Tris–HCl, pH 6.8. To make 50 ml, add 5 ml 10% SDS, 5.7 ml glycerol (87%), 0.386 g DTT, and 3 ml of a 1 *M* stock solution of Tris–HCl, pH 6.8. Complete to 50 ml with distilled water. Store in 1-ml aliquots at −20°C.

9. *1% agarose:* To make 100 ml, add 1 g agarose to 100 ml distilled water and boil in a microwave oven 2–5 min at medium power. Store at room temperature.

Steps

1. Cut the protein spots of interest from Coomassie-stained gels with the aid of a scalpel and collect in an Eppendorf tube. Either dried or wet gels can be

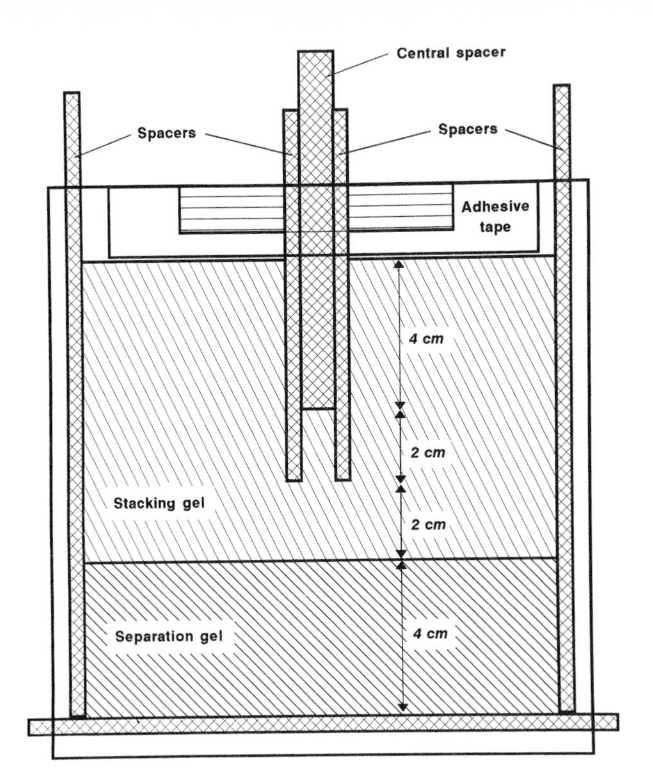

FIGURE 1 Protein elution–concentration gel system.

used. Wash the gel pieces extensively with distilled water to remove remaining acid (check with pH paper).

2. Remove the water and equilibrate the gel pieces in sample buffer for at least 2 hr at room temperature. Shake repeatedly. If the pH becomes too low, adjust to pH 6.8 by adding 1 *M* Tris base solution. Likewise, cut a number of gel pieces that do not contain protein and equilibrate similarly in sample buffer.

3. Prepare the elution–concentration gel system while the gel pieces are equilibrating. Assemble the glass plates with 2-mm-thick spacers as shown in Fig. 1. Note that the sample well is formed by a 1-cm broad spacer, placed between two parallel spacers (0.5-cm broad) that stay in the gel during the run. Attach the three slot-forming spacers to the top edge of the back gel plate with adhesive tape. Make sure to leave a few millimeters of space at the three outer edges for agarose sealing. Keep the plates together with fold-back clamps.

4. Seal the three outer edges with agarose using a Pasteur pipette. Hold the gel assembly angled and let the agarose run from the top. Keep the sealed side in a horizontal position until the agarose is solidified. Mark a line 4 cm from the bottom spacer.

5. Mix the separation gel solutions in a small beaker using the appropriate acrylamide concentrations (Table I) and pour the gel solution into the assembled glass plates to the marked line. Overlay the gel carefully with distilled water (at least 2 mm). Use a Pasteur pipette and let the water run slowly along the back glass plate. Allow the gel to polymerize.

6. Mix the stacking gel solution (Table II) in a beaker. Decant the water from the lower gel and fill up the space with the stacking gel solution. The level comes up to about 2 mm below the notch at the front plate. Remove any trapped air bubbles below the slot-forming spacers and allow the solution to polymerize.

7. Carefully remove the central of the three slot-forming spacers while leaving

TABLE I Composition of Separation Gel

Protein M_r range (kDa):	>70	25–70	<25
Acrylamide concentration:	10%	15%	20%
Solution 1 (acrylamide)	7.6 ml	11.3 ml	15.2 ml
Solution 2 (Tris–HCl, pH 8.8)	5.7 ml	5.7 ml	5.7 ml
Solution 5 (10% SDS)	225 μl	225 μl	225 μl
H_2O	9 ml	5.3 ml	1.4 ml
Solution 6 (10% APS)	75 μl	75 μl	75 μl
TEMED	10 μl	10 μl	10 μl

the two supporting spacers in the gel. This creates a well 1 × 4 × 2 mm (800 μl). Rinse the slot with distilled water and dry with strips of 3MM paper. Seal the edges of the two slot supporting spacers with a 1- to 2-mm layer of agarose (freshly boiled) using a Pasteur pipette. This prevents the sample to leak out in the gel during loading. Do not seal the bottom of the slot with agarose. If the agarose sealing fails, leave the agarose to solidify completely; it is then possible to draw out the agarose strip with a piece of dry 3MM paper.

8. Remove the bottom spacer and mount the slab gel in the electrophoresis apparatus.

9. Add the supernatant sample buffer (step 2) and transfer the equilibrated gel pieces one by one into the slot. Use pointed tweezers and a long needle to push down the gel pieces. Fill the sample well completely with "empty" gel pieces similarly equilibrated in sample buffer (step 2). Add eventually more sample buffer to completely overlay the gel pieces.

10. Fill the upper and lower chambers with electrophoresis buffer. The buffer level of the bottom chamber should be adjusted so not more than 0.5 cm of the gel is covered. Remove trapped air bubbles between the bottom glass plates with electrode buffer using a 10-ml syringe joined to a bent needle (see Fig. 1D in the article by Julio E. Celis and Eydfinnur Olsen in this volume). Start the run at 250 V. Cool the gel with an electrical fan during the run; the gel will become very warm at the top corners and the glass plates might break without cooling. Increase the voltage to 350 V when all the sample (bromophenol blue) has left the well and has entered the stacking gel. Maintain this voltage until the tracking dye starts to leave the bottom of the gel. For in-gel digestion the run can be stopped when the dye is halfway in the separation gel. See Fig. 2 for details of the run.

11. After the run, disassemble the plates and cut with the aid of a scalpel a 4 × 5-cm piece of the separation gel that contains the highly concentrated protein spot. Proceed for electroblotting or for staining followed by in-gel digestion (see below).

TABLE II Composition of Stacking Gel

Solution 4 (acrylamide)	16 ml
Solution 3 (1 *M* Tris–HCl, pH 7.1)	3.8 ml
Solution 5 (10% SDS)	320 μl
H_2O	11.6 ml
Solution 6 (10% APS)	140 μl
TEMED	10 μl

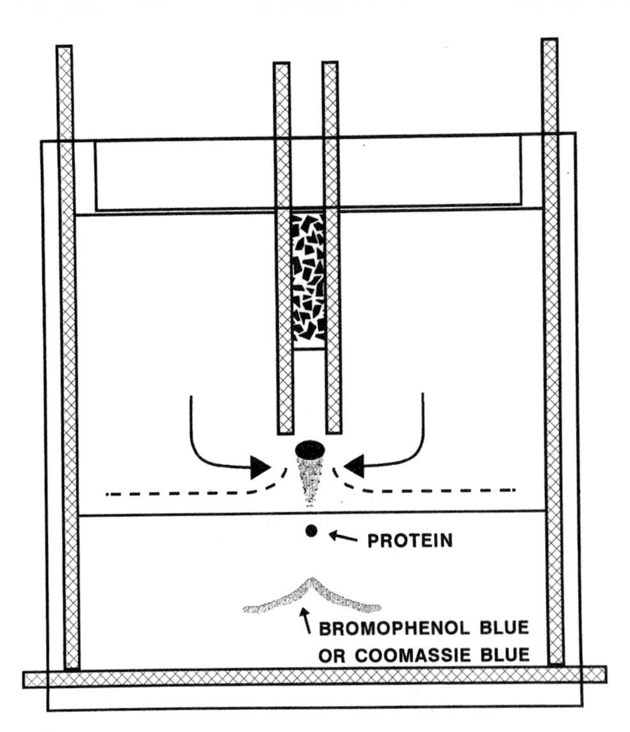

FIGURE 2 Gel pieces in the sample well and compression of the protein band arriving in the separation gel as a narrow spot.

Comments

This procedure is used for low-abundance 2D gel spots or faint 1D minigel protein bands. Protein is eluted from the multiple gel pieces with efficiencies that are generally higher than 80%. Coomassie-stained gels that are vacuum-dried onto 3MM paper (see the article by Julio Celis and Eyδfinnur Olsen) can be kept several years, mounted on a piece of cardboard and stored in boxes at room temperature. The protein from such long-term stored gels can be eluted with only negligible loss due to degradation or reaction of protein with the polyacrylamide gel matrix. Better recoveries may be obtained when the primary gel is not dried after staining or when the gel is immediately vacuum-dried. In this case protein detection may be performed by autoradiography of comigrating ^{35}S- or ^{14}C-labeled proteins. Proteins that are recovered by elution-concentration gel electrophoresis from multiple Coomassie-stained and dried gel spots generally become blocked at the NH_2 terminus.

Pitfalls

1. It is important not to crush the gel pieces but to use gel blocks. The crushed gel pieces are very difficult to load into the slot and they may swell during electrophoresis and trap small air bubbles, thereby interrupting the electrical current passing through the sample well.

2. Carefully adjust the pH of the sample to pH 6.8. To obtain the maximum compression effect, keep the pH of the stacking gel at 7.1.

3. It is important to completely fill up the slot with gel pieces.

4. If the protein is not compressed in a small volume, check for air bubble formation between the gel pieces and the pH or ion concentration of the sample buffer. Needle-shaped protein compression is mostly due to an excessive pH difference between sample and stacking gel; generally this occurs when the pH of the sample is too low.

5. Do not change significantly the dimensions of the elution–concentration gel system.

6. Do not use spacers that have been used previously with vaseline for sealing; otherwise the gel may leak.

B. IN-GEL DIGESTION

Solutions

1. *30% methanol:* To make 100 ml, mix 30 ml methanol with 70 ml distilled water and store at room temperature.

2. *50% acetonitrile, 0.2 M NH_4HCO_3, pH 8.9:* To make 100 ml, dissolve 1.58 g ammonium bicarbonate in 45 ml distilled water and add 50 ml of acetonitrile. Adjust pH with concentrated ammonia to pH 8.9 and add distilled water to a final volume of 100 ml. Store at 4°C.

3. *0.2 M NH_4HCO_3, 0.02% Tween 20, pH 8.9:* To make 100 ml, dissolve 1.58 g ammonium bicarbonate in 95 ml distilled water. Adjust the pH with concentrated ammonia to pH 8.9. Add 20 μl of Tween 20 and add distilled water to a final volume of 100 ml. Store at 4°C.

4. *Enzyme solutions:* These are made freshly before digestion. Trypsin is dissolved at a concentration of 1 mg/ml in digestion buffer (solution 3).

5. *60% acetonitrile, 0.1% trifluoroacetic acid:* To make 10 ml, mix 4 ml distilled water with 6 ml of acetonitrile and add 10 μl of TFA. Store at room temperature.

6. *60% acetonitrile, 0.1% trifluoroacetic acid, 0.02% Tween 20:* To make 10 ml, mix 4 ml distilled water with 6 ml of acetonitrile and add 10 μl of TFA and 2 μl of Tween 20. Store at room temperature.

Steps

1. Stain the gel with Coomassie brilliant blue to visualize the protein.

2. Cut the protein spot from the wet gel and submerge 3 × 2 hr at room temperature in 30% methanol. Wash twice for 20 min with 150 μl of 50% acetonitrile in 0.2 *M* ammonium bicarbonate, pH 8.9 (solution 2). Cut a gel piece of similar size as a blank.

3. Leave to semidry at room temperature on a piece of Parafilm for about 10 min.

4. Rehydrate the gel slice with 5 μl of 0.2 *M* ammonium bicarbonate, pH 8.9, containing 0.02% Tween 20.

5. Add 2 μl of the trypsin solution. After absorption of the protease solution, add 5-μl aliquots of solution 3 until the slice regains the original volume.

6. Place the gel slice in an Eppendorf tube and add sufficient rehydration buffer (solution 3) to immerse.

7. Carry out the digestion for 2 hr at 37°C. Stop by adding 1.5 μl TFA.

8. Extract the gel piece twice with 100 μl of 60% acetonitrile, 0.1% TFA for 20 min. For very hydrophobic peptides, a third extraction is done with 60% acetonitrile in 0.1% TFA and 0.02% Tween 20 (solution 6).

9. Combine supernatants and load on a reverse phase column.

10. Carry out steps 2–6 on a blank gel piece.

Comments

In-gel digestion is most successful when carried out on a single gel piece with a high protein-to-gel ratio, as is the case after reelution and concentration from combined spots (see above). In-gel digestion may yield a more general cleavage pattern, because the more hydrophobic peptides are not retained to the same extent as during on-membrane cleavage (see below). The method is a good alternative for proteins that blot poorly. For comments on HPLC separation see Section C.

Pitfalls

1. UV-absorbing compounds are eluted from the gel together with peptides and this may complicate consecutive HPLC peptide separation; therefore, it is advisable to use a blank sample too.

2. When large gel volumes are handled, large amounts of protease have to be added to reach the minimal concentration that keeps the protein active (for most proteases this is around 0.05 mg/ml digestion mixture). This may result in excessive autodigestion of the enzyme. Therefore, in-gel digestion should not be used when the protein concentration in the gel is low.

C. ON-MEMBRANE DIGESTION OF ELECTROBLOTTED PROTEINS

Solutions

1. *Transfer buffer:* 50 m*M* boric acid, 50 m*M* Trizma base. To make 1 liter, dissolve 3.1 g boric acid and 6.06 g Trizma base in 1 liter distilled water. Store at room temperature.

2. *Protein staining solutions: Solution 2A:* 0.1% Amido black or naphthol blue black, 40% methanol, 1% acetic acid. To make 100 ml, mix 59 ml distilled water with 40 ml methanol and 1 ml acetic acid. Dissolve 100 mg of amido black in this solution. *Solution 2B:* 0.2% Ponceau S, 1% acetic acid. To make 100 ml, add 1 ml acetic acid to 99 ml distilled water and dissolve 200 mg Ponceau S in this solution. The staining solutions are stored at room temperature and can be used for several months.

3. *Quenching solution:* 0.2% Polyvinylpyrrolidone ($PVP_0 30$). To make 100 ml, dissolve 200 mg of polyvinylpyrrolidone ($PVP_0 30$) in 100 ml distilled water. Aliquot in 10-mL portions and store at −20°C.

4. *Digestion buffer (4°C):* 0.1 *M* Tris–HCl, pH 8.5, 2 m*M* $CaCl_2$, 5% acetonitrile. To make 100 ml, dissolve 1.21 g Trizma base in approximately 90 ml distilled water. Add 2 ml of a 0.1 *M* $CaCl_2$ stock solution (1.47 g $CaCl_2 \cdot 2H_2O$ in 100 ml distilled water) and 5 ml acetonitrile. Adjust to pH 8.5 with 0.1 *M* HCl and make up to 100 ml with distilled water.

5. *Enzyme solutions:* These are made freshly before digestion. Trypsin is dissolved at a concentration of 1 mg/ml in digestion buffer.

Steps

1. Cut one or two pieces of PVDF membrane corresponding to the size of the gel. Soak the membrane for 5 min in methanol and rinse at least three times for 5 min with distilled water.

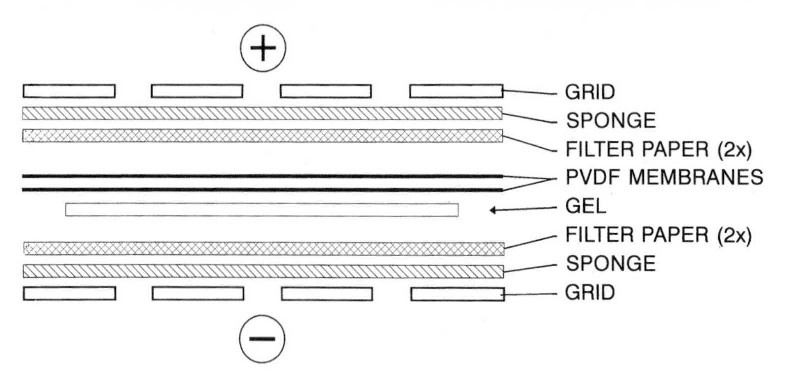

FIGURE 3 Blotting sandwich.

2. Mount the blotting sandwich as shown in Fig. 3: one sponge, two sheets of Whatman 3MM paper, the gel, the membrane(s), two sheets of Whatmann 3MM paper, and a second sponge. Use sponges that have been presoaked in transfer buffer for at least 10 min. Press gently to remove trapped air between the different layers. Place the blotting sandwich into the gel holder of an electroblotting cell with the gel oriented toward the negative electrode side of the gel holder (see step 3).

3. Fill the apparatus with transfer buffer and glide the gel holder in the cell with the gel side oriented toward the negative pole. Connect to the power supply and perform the transfer for at least 8 hr (or overnight) at 35 V. Alternatively, blotting can be done in a Mini-Trans Blot cell for at least 2–3 hr at 60 V, preferably at 4°C.

4. Disassemble the blotting sandwich and wash the PVDF membrane once for 5 min with distilled water. Immerse for 30 sec in staining solution 2A. Destain by washing several times for 2–4 min with distilled water until the proteins are visible as blue spots on a white background. Alternatively proteins can be detected by shaking the blot for 5 min in a solution of Ponceau S (solution 2B). Proteins are visible as red spots after destaining for 5 min in water.

5. Excise the protein spot from the membrane while the blot is still immersed in water and cut further into 3 × 3-mm pieces. Immerse the membrane piece(s) in an Eppendorf tube containing 500 μl of quenching solution. Incubate at room temperature for 30 min. Store further at −20°C if necessary.

6. Cut a piece of blank membrane and proceed as for the membrane pieces that contain protein.

7. Remove the quenching solution and wash the membrane pieces four times with 500 μl water. Perform a final wash with 500 μl of digestion buffer. Remove this buffer and replace with fresh digestion buffer. Use the minimal volume needed to submerge the membrane piece(s) (generally between 20 and 100 μl). Add 1 μl of the freshly prepared enzyme solution. The digestion proceeds for 4 to 6 hr at 37°C.

8. Add TFA to 10% (v/v) and incubate for 15 min at room temperature.

9. Transfer the digestion supernatant to a clean Eppendorf tube. Wash the membrane pieces twice with 100 μl of distilled water. Combine washing solutions with the original digestion mixture. The volumes used for washing may have to be reduced, depending on the size of the HPLC sample loop. The peptide solution is preferably separated immediately by reverse-phase HPLC or otherwise stored at −20°C until further HPLC analysis.

Comments

In general, on-membrane digestion is successful when more than 10 μg of protein is available (200 pmole of a 50-kDa protein).

It is advisable to stain the gel after blotting to monitor the blotting success. If a substantial amount of protein is left in the gel it will then be possible to perform in-gel digestion.

Some amido black stain may be released during quenching with the PVP_0 solution and during the enzymatic digestion. It elutes late in the HPLC chromatogram and does not interfere with the peptide separation. Although amido black or Ponceau S staining on blots is not as sensitive as Coomassie staining, the former procedures are still preferred because they produce fewer peaks interfering with subsequent HPLC separation.

Proteolytic degradation of membrane-bound proteins generally proceeds in an incomplete manner as compared with digestion in solution. Only the more hydrophilic peptides will be released from the membrane, but for larger proteins this is advantageous as the HPLC chromatograms will be simple.

Other proteases like Asp-N, V8 (Glu-C), Arg-C, and Lys-C are also suitable for on-membrane cleavage. Digestion buffers should be prepared according to the manufacturer's instructions.

Chemical cleavage can be carried out on PVDF membranes. This yields larger and more hydrophobic fragments which are less efficiently released from the membranes. This approach is therefore not of general use.

Peptides generated during on-membrane or in-gel digestion are separated by conventional reverse-phase HPLC methods. Peptides are monitored at 214–220 nm and collected manually. Columns 4.6 mm (normal-bore) and 2.1 mm (narrow-bore) in diameter are used. The former results in better peptide resolution, but the peptides are collected in larger volumes (200 μl instead of 40 μl) that have to be reduced by centrifugal vacuum evaporation before loading on the sequenator. Irreversible adsorption of short peptides to Eppendorf tubes is not a general problem, but the Eppendorf tubes may be precoated for 30 min with PVP_0 30. Peptides are either stored in the eluant at −20°C until further analysis or dried. Dried peptides can successfully be sequenced after several months of storage at −20°C.

Pitfalls

1. Exceptionally, proteins do not elute from the gel even after prolonged blotting periods. In these cases, 0.005% SDS may be added to the transfer buffer. Alternatively, in-gel digestion can be tried.

2. It is essential not to dry the PVDF membrane at any stage. The amount of peptides released can be reduced considerably, especially for low protein concentrations.

3. When nonmodified trypsin is used, autodigestion can be prominent, especially when the protein concentration is low. It is always advisable to make a blank sample and process it together with the protein sample.

REFERENCES

Aebersold, R. H., Leavitt, J., Saavedra, R. A., Hood, L. E., and Kent, S. B. H. (1987) Internal amino acid sequence analysis of proteins separated by one- or two-dimensional gel electrophoresis after *in situ* protease digestion on nitrocellulose. *Proc. Natl. Acad. Sci. USA* 84, 6970–6974.

Aebersold, R. H., Teplow, D. B., Hood, L. E., and Kent, S. B. H. (1986) Electroblotting onto activated glass. High efficiency preparation of proteins from analytical sodium dodecyl sulfate–polyacrylamide gels for direct sequence analysis. *J. Biol. Chem.* **261**, 4229–4238.

Bauw, G., De Loose, M., Inzé, D., Van Montagu, M., and Vandekerckhove, J. (1987) Alterations in the phenotype of plant cells studied by NH_2-terminal amino acid-sequence analysis of proteins electroblotted from two-dimensional gel-separated total extracts. *Proc. Natl. Acad. Sci. USA* **84**, 4806–4810.

Bauw, G., Van den Bulcke, M., Van Damme, J., Puype, M., Van Montagu, M., and Vandekerckhove, J. (1989) NH_2-terminal and internal microsequencing of proteins electroblotted on membranes. *In* "Methods in Protein Sequence Analysis" (B. Wittmann-Liebold, ed.), pp. 220–233. Springer-Verlag, Berlin.

Eckerskorn, C., Mewes, W., Goretzki, H., and Lottspeich, F. (1988) A new siliconized glass fiber as support for protein-chemical analysis of electroblotted proteins. *Eur. J. Biochem.* **176**, 509–519.

Matsudaira, P. (1987) Sequence from picomole quantities of proteins electroblotted onto polyvinylidene difluoride membranes. *J. Biol. Chem.* **262**, 10035–10038.

Patterson, S. D., Hess, D., Yungwirth, T., and Aebersold, R. (1992) High-yield recovery of electroblotted proteins and cleavage fragments from a cationic polyvinylidene fluoride based membrane. *Anal. Biochem.* **202**, 193–203.

Rasmussen, H.-H., Van Damme, J., Bauw, G., Puype, M., Gesser, B., Celis, J. E., and Vandekerckhove, J. (1991) Protein-electroblotting and microsequencing in establishing integrated human protein databases. *In* "Methods in Protein Sequence Analysis" (Jörnvall, Höög, and Gustavsson, eds.), pp. 103–114. Birkhäuser Verlag, Basel.

Rosenfeld, J., Capdevielle, J., Guillemot, J.-C., and Ferrara, P. (1992) In-gel digestion of proteins for internal sequence analysis after one- or two-dimensional gel electrophoresis. *Anal. Biochem.* **203**, 173–179.

Vandekerckhove, J., Bauw, G., Puype, M., Van Damme, J., and Van Montagu, M. (1985) Protein-blotting on polybrene-coated glass fiber sheets. A basis for acid hydrolysis and gas-phase sequencing of picomole quantities of protein previously separated on sodium dodecyl sulfate/polyacrylamide gels. *Eur. J. Biochem.* **152**, 9–19.

Amino-Terminal Protein Sequence Analysis

Heinz Nika and Ruedi Aebersold

I. Introduction

A. THE EDMAN DEGRADATION

The Edman degradation is an inherently simple process, consisting of two reaction steps: the coupling of phenylisothiocyanate (PITC) to the α-amino group of a polypeptide under basic conditions and a cyclization/cleavage reaction resulting in cleavage of the first peptide bond and release of the amino acid derivative from the protein chain under acidic conditions. The labile anilinothiazolinone that is released is converted in a secondary reaction to the more stable phenylthiohydantoin (PTH). PTHs are recovered from the protein sequencer by extraction, separated by reverse-phase (RP)-HPLC, and identified by their retention time. The essential steps of the Edman degradation are schematically illustrated in Fig. 1. The characteristics of the Edman degradation have the following practical implications: (1) N-terminal sequencing is a general method only for those proteins that contain a free α-amino group. A substantial fraction of all proteins, which has been estimated as high as 80% (Brown and Roberts, 1976), have modified α-amino groups (blocked proteins). Furthermore, any condition leading to chemical modification of the α-amino group has to be avoided during preparation of the sample for sequencing. Blocked proteins either need to be subjected to attempts to remove the chemical modification or to chemical or enzymatic fragmentation for the generation of internal peptide fragments (Aebersold *et al.,* 1987) (internal sequence analysis). (2) As PITC is reacting with primary and secondary amines, contaminants containing such groups will form reaction products with the reagent that are likely to interfere with PTH identification. It is essential that any such contaminant be avoided. (3) The Edman degradation consists of a series of chemical reactions, all of which are not quantitative. The size of PTH signals therefore progressively decreases during extended sequencing runs. Consequently, sequence information obtained by N-terminal sequencing is limited to the N-terminal part of the protein, and the length of the sequence obtained is, at least in part, a function of the amount of protein available for sequence analysis. Current state-of-the-art sequencers that evolved from the prototype gas–liquid-phase protein sequencer (Hewick *et al.,* 1981) allow routine operation at the 50- to 100-pmole level of polypeptide.

B. SAMPLE PREPARATION FOR N-TERMINAL SEQUENCE ANALYSIS

The preparation of protein and peptide samples in a form compatible with N-terminal sequencing is the most important and technically challenging aspect of

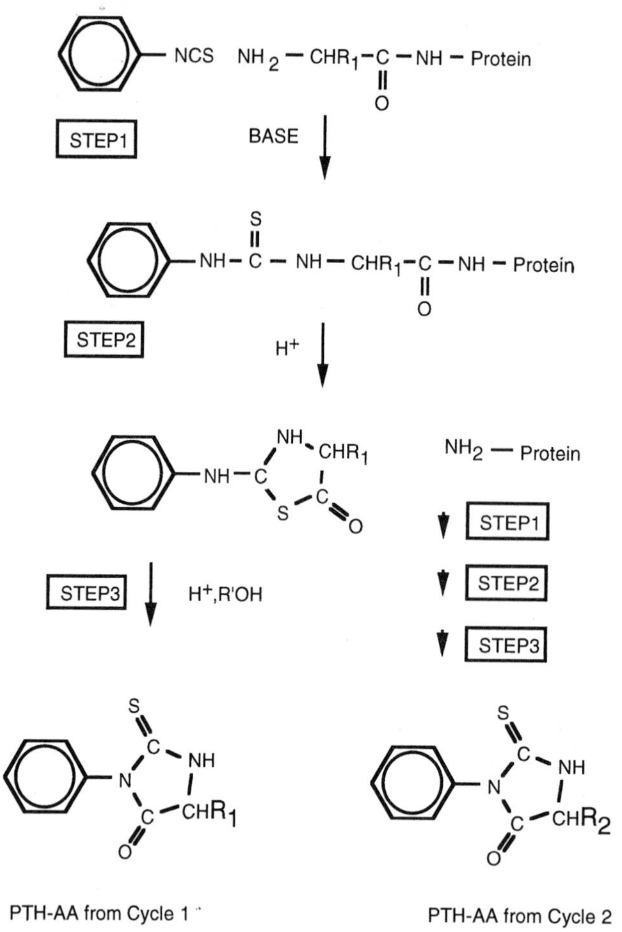

PTH-AA from Cycle 1

PTH-AA from Cycle 2

FIGURE 1 Chemistry of the PITC degradation of proteins from the N terminus. In step 1 of the degradation, the α-amino group of the protein reacts under basic conditions with the reagent (coupling). The resulting phenylthiocarbamyl peptide undergoes, in step 2, acid-catalyzed cyclization and concomitant cleavage of the anilinothiazolinone from the protein chain. In step 3, the derivatives are converted to the more stable PTH and analyzed by RP-HPLC to determine the identity of the amino acid.

the sequencing experiment. Conventional protein isolation techniques such as gel filtration, ion-exchange, affinity, and partition chromatography as well as preparative gel electrophoresis combined with electroelution produce protein samples in large solvent volumes containing salts, detergents, and other system-related contaminants. In addition, many of the classical protein purification techniques are of low resolution and suffer from systematic sample losses, in particular, in cases in which small amounts of protein are purified. Finally, the high solvent volume throughput during chromatographic purification increases the likelihood of artifactual modifications of the α-amino group. To avoid these pitfalls, mainly two high-resolution protein/peptide isolation techniques, HPLC (Regnier, 1983; Simpson *et al.*, 1989) and electrophoretic transfer of proteins from polyacrylamide gels to suitable supports (electroblotting), are used today for the preparation of protein samples for N-terminal sequencing (Laemmli, 1970; Vandekerckhove *et al.*, 1985; Aebersold *et al.*, 1986; Matsudaira, 1987, 1993). The procedures are schematically illustrated in Figs. 2 and 3, respectively, and are described step-by-step in Section III.

Consideration of critical parameters such as protein sample purity, sample volume, sample solvents, and sample amount frequently determines the choice of one of the purification strategies described below. To obtain unambiguous results, protein

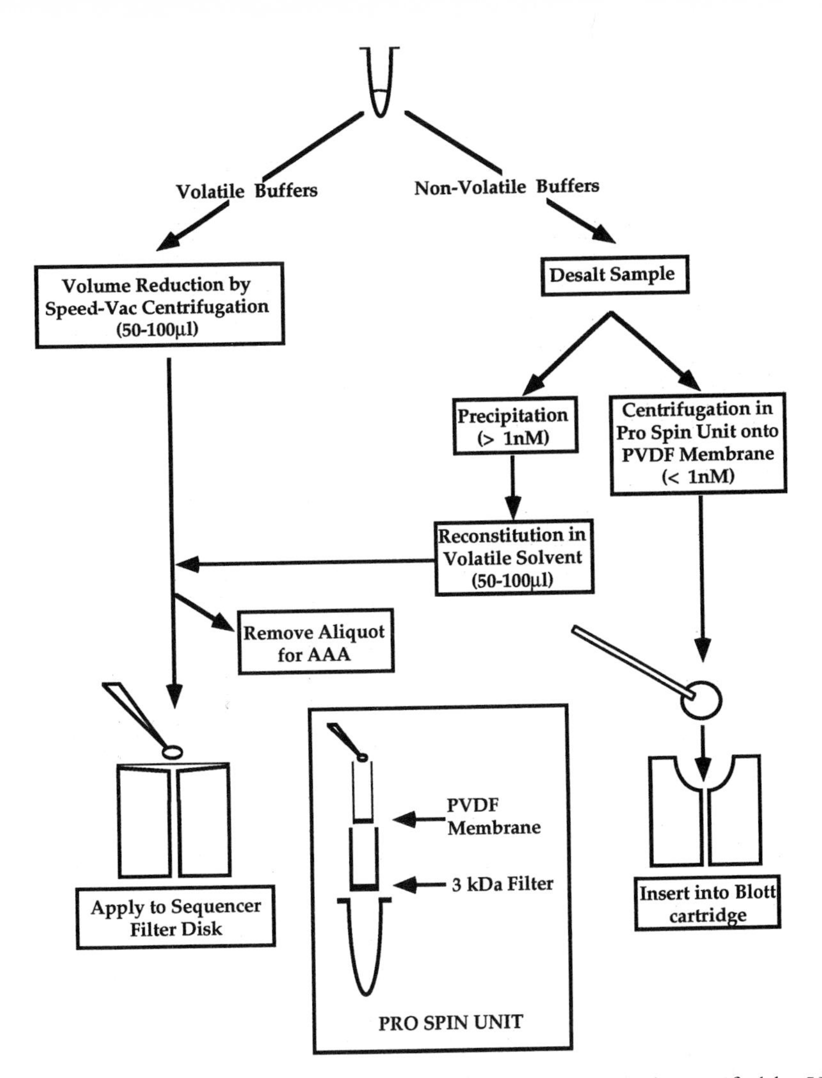

FIGURE 2 N-terminal sequence analysis of protein samples purified by HPLC. Samples recovered in volatile buffers are directly subjected to sequence analysis following application to the sequencer filter disk. Samples recovered in nonvolatile buffers are desalted by precipitation and applied on the sequencer filter disk after reconstitution in volatile solvents. Dilute sample solutions are desalted on ProSpin units by centrifugation and subsequent washing of the excised protein containing PVDF membrane disks. The disks are either sequenced in a standard or a specialized reaction cartridge (Blott cartridge). Insert shows the ProSpin Unit. AAA, amino acid analysis for protein quantitation.

samples are recommended to be at least 80% pure. Proteins recovered by HPLC as a single peak or by gel electrophoresis as a single band may be sufficiently pure to meet this requirement. However, chromatographic peaks or electrophoretic bands frequently contain more that one component. It is therefore advisable to assess the purity of a sample prior to committing the protein to sequence analysis using a high-sensitivity analytical separation system with different selectivity compared with the preparative technique used. In addition, samples need to be free of contaminants containing amines, compounds interfering with UV detection of PTHs, and depleted of amino-reactive functionalities.

For routine determination of unknown N-terminal protein sequences, at least 50–100 pmole of the purified protein should be available. The only method for the accurate quantitation of low picomole amounts of protein is quantitative amino acid composition analysis. Twenty to fifty picomoles of protein should be set aside

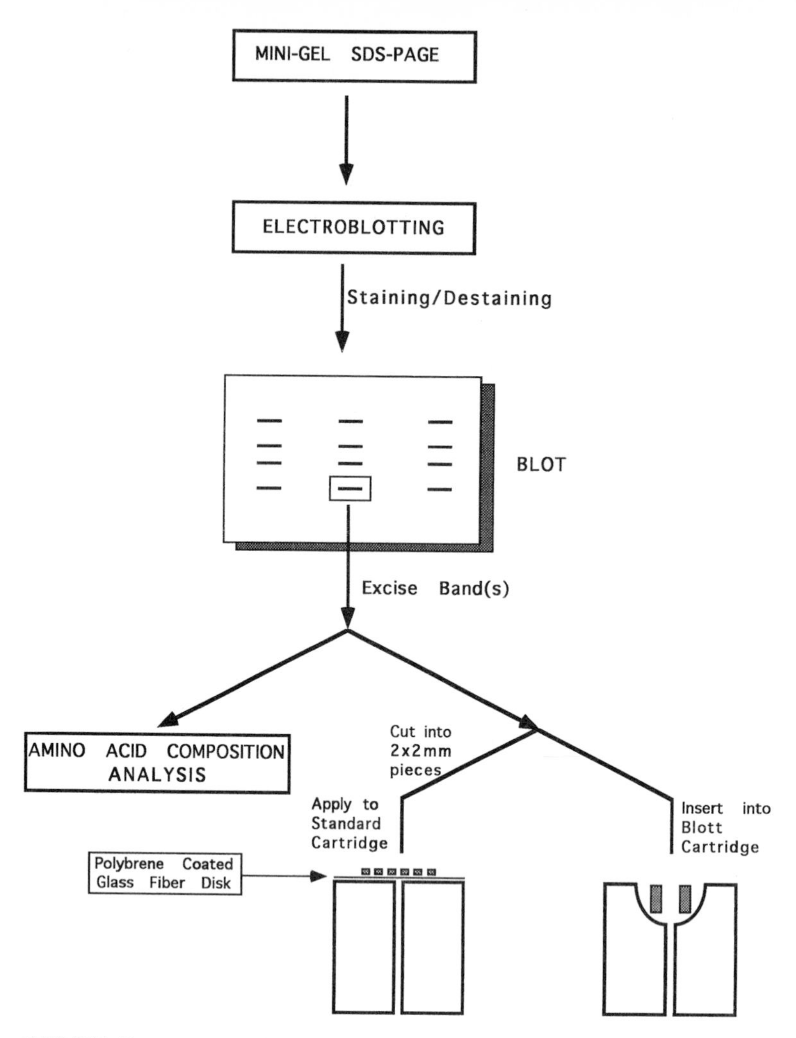

FIGURE 3 N-terminal sequence analysis of protein samples recovered by electroblotting from SDS–polyacrylamide gel. The proteins are separated by SDS–PAGE and isolated by electroblotting onto PVDF membranes. The proteins are visualized by staining and excised from the blot for subsequent sequence analysis on a standard or specialized reaction cartridge.

for amino acid analysis for samples that are applied to the sequencer in solution, e.g., samples purified by column chromatography. The amount of protein sample isolated by electroblotting can be estimated based on the staining intensity of the band on the blot. Although this method is less accurate than amino acid composition analysis, it has the advantage of being nondestructive.

II. Materials and Instrumentation

Any good-quality, commercially available HPLC system is suitable. To accommodate narrow-bore [2.1-mm inner diameter (i.d.)] columns, reproducible solvent gradient delivery at a flow rate of 200 μl/min is required. A variety of suppliers sell high-quality HPLC columns suitable for the isolation of polypeptides for sequencing. For high-sensitivity applications narrow-bore columns are essential. For gel electrophoresis/electroblotting, a commercially available minigel electrophoresis system (Mini-Protean Electrophoresis II Cell, Cat. No. 165-2940) and electroblotting system (Mini Trans-Blot Electrophoretic Transfer Cell, Cat. No. 170-3930) are provided by Bio-Rad.

The protocols described are compatible with any current commercial automated sequencer that can accommodate both electroblotted samples and polypeptides applied from solution. The Blott Cartridge (Cat. No. 401096) is available from Applied Biosystems. Additional instruments used include a vacuum concentrator (Speed-Vac concentrator Model SS1 or SS2, Savant Instruments, Inc.).

Reagents and solvents have to be of the highest purity possible. This is particularly true for solvents used in chromatography, as any trace contaminants are concentrated during application of the samples to the sequencer. For chromatography, HPLC-grade solvents which are offered by a variety of suppliers are suitable. All chromatography solvents are filtered through 0.2-μm Fluoropore filters (47-mm i.d., Cat. No. FSLW 04700) provided by Millipore Corporation and stored in a refrigerator at 4°C prior to use. For electrophoresis, high-quality chemicals and reagents from suppliers specialized in gel electrophoresis (e.g., Bio-Rad Laboratories) should be used. 3-(Cyclohexylamino-1-propanesulfonic acid) (CAPS) is provided by Aldrich Chemical Company. Coomassie brilliant blue R-250 is obtainable from Bio-Rad Laboratories. The Coomassie blue solution is filtered through 47-mm-i.d. Fluoropore membranes (Cat. No. FHLP 04700, Millipore Corporation) prior to use. For all applications water is doubly glass distilled and/or ultrafiltered to a resistance of greater than 17 MOhm using a Milli-Q Plus Water Purification System (Millipore Corporation) or a Nanopure Reagent Grade Water System (Barnstead/Thermolyne Corporation).

Commercially available polyvinylidene difluoride (PVDF) membranes with nominal pore sizes of 0.1 μm, such as Trans-Blot (Cat. No. 162 0185, Bio-Rad Laboratories) and Pro Blott (Cat. No. 400994, Applied Biosystems) and membranes with nominal pore sizes of 0.45 μm such as Immobilon-P (Cat. No. 1PVH 151 50., Millipore Corporation) and Westran (Cat. No. 71260, Schleicher & Schuell, Inc.) are suitable for N-terminal sequence analysis using the protocols described below. For protein sequencing, sequencing-grade reagents, solvents and other consumables provided by the supplier of the instrument have to be used. Bioglobin (Cat. No. 400979) and the ProSpin sample preparation cartridge (Cat. No. 401413) are provided by Applied Biosystems. *Caution:* Some chemicals used in protein sequence analysis are highly toxic. All sequencer chemicals have to be used with a high degree of caution.

III. Procedures

A. N-TERMINAL SEQUENCE ANALYSIS OF SAMPLES PURIFIED BY HPLC IN VOLATILE SOLVENTS

The procedure is schematically illustrated in Fig. 2.

Solutions

1. *Solvent A:* To make 1 liter of solvent A, add 1 ml of trifluoroacetic acid (TFA) to 999 ml of water.
2. *Solvent B:* To make 1 liter of solvent B, mix 1 ml of TFA with 900 ml of acetonitrile and 99 ml of water.

Solvents A and B are used for reverse-phase chromatography of proteins and peptides and as solvents for the final desalting step of proteins separated in nonvolatile buffers.

Steps

1. Collect polypeptide-containing fractions manually, based on UV absorbance detected by an on-line UV detector. UV absorbance is measured at 214 nm. Intact, unfragmented polypeptides can also be detected at 280 nm. Depending on the diameter of the column, samples are collected in fraction volumes between 100 and 1000 μl.

2. Collect fractions into plastic Eppendorf tubes, freeze immediately, and store at −20°C.

3. Reduce volume of the collected fraction in a Speed-Vac vacuum centrifuge to 50–100 μl prior to application of the sample to the sequencer cartridge.

4. Apply an aliquot of up to 30 μl of the sample onto a polybrene-treated glass fiber disk in the sequencer cartridge.

5. Dry the sample under a stream of inert gas.

6. Apply the next aliquot.

7. Repeat steps 4–6 until the total sample is applied.

Comments

With increasing sensitivity in the sequencing process there is a trend toward the use of narrow-bore (2.1-mm-i.d.) and microbore (1.0-mm-i.d.) columns. These columns provide for higher analyte detection sensitivity and considerably smaller peak elution volumes (Simpson *et al.*, 1989). With 1.0-mm-i.d. columns peptides can be recovered in as little as 30 μl of liquid and collected at the detector outlet directly onto the sequencing support, thus eliminating any sample losses due to sample absorption to the surface of the plastic tube. Quantitation of the collected polypeptide is provided by the signal size as detected by UV absorbance.

Pitfalls

1. To avoid irreversible sample loss, do not take samples to dryness.
2. Do not use glass tubes for sample collection or storage. Glass surfaces retain proteins stronger than polypropylene or polyethylene surfaces.
3. Avoid sample transfer between vials and prolonged storage at room temperature.
4. Strictly observe clean laboratory practices during sample application to the sequencer cartridge. This step is a common source of avoidable contamination.
5. Carefully calibrate the time required for the sample to flow from the UV detector to the collection outlet and consider this delay in collection of the sample.

B. N-TERMINAL SEQUENCE ANALYSIS OF SAMPLES IN NONVOLATILE SOLUTIONS

The procedure is schematically illustrated in Fig. 2. For optimal sequencer performance and minimal interference by UV-absorbing contaminants during PTH analysis samples must be free of salt- and/or amino group-containing additives. Below we describe two protocols for removal of contaminants by protein precipitation and sample centrifugation onto PVDF membranes.

1. Protein Precipitation by Trichloroacetic Acid

Solutions

1. *100% aqueous TCA solution:* To make 1 liter, add approximately 500 ml of water to 1000 g of TCA and stir in a boiling water bath. Add water to the still hot solution to a final volume of 1 liter. Make the final volume adjustment when the solution has assumed room temperature.

2. *1% aqueous TFA:* To make 10 ml, mix 0.1 ml of anhydrous TFA with 9.9 ml of water.

Steps

1. Collect protein solution in a transparent plastic tube with pointed tip.
2. Add a sufficient volume of the TCA stock solution to the protein solution to reach a final TCA concentration of 10%.
3. Keep sample on ice for a minimum of 1 hr.
4. Collect the precipitate by centrifugation in a microfuge for 2 min, and wash the pellet once with ice-cold acetone.
5. Dissolve the precipitate in less than 100 μl of a suitable volatile solvent, preferably 1% aqueous TFA.
6. From this solution remove a 5–10% aliquot for quantitation by amino acid composition analysis.
7. Apply an aliquot of up to 30 μl of the protein solution onto a polybrene-treated glass fiber disk in the sequencer cartridge.
8. Dry the sample thoroughly under a stream of inert gas.
9. Apply the next aliquot.
10. Repeat steps 7–9 until the total sample is applied.

Comments

For effective TCA precipitation a minimal sample concentration of 100 μg/ml is required. Other effective solvents for resolubilizing the precipitates are 0.1–1% aqueous SDS, hexafluoroacetone, and dilute (0.1–5%) acetic and formic acid.

Pitfalls

1. Proteins in dilute solutions do not effectively precipitate. Estimate the protein concentration from the chromatographic peak height.
2. Concentrate dilute protein samples by vacuum centrifugation to the minimum level of 100 μg/ml prior to precipitation.
3. If the protein fails to precipitate, use dialysis or desalting by size-exclusion chromatography as less preferred alternative methods.

2. Sample Centrifugation onto PVDF

Sample centrifugation onto PVDF membranes represents an alternative method to TCA precipitation and is particularly suited for very dilute protein samples. The following protocol is suitable for the adsorption of proteins onto PVDF disks prior to sequencing using the ProSpin sample preparation cartridge (Applied Biosystems).

Solution

20% aqueous methanol: To make 100 ml, add 20 ml of methanol to 80 ml of water.

Steps

1. Open the cap of the ProSpin cartridge unit and add 25 μl of methanol to wet the PVDF membrane.
2. Add the protein solution in a volume of up to 400 μl following removal of the methanol.
3. Close the cap of the unit and centrifuge the sample to dryness at up to 5600 *g*. This may take from 0.5 to 6 hr depending on sample volume and solution viscosity.
4. Open the cap and place the unit into a Speed-Vac for 5 min to dry the membrane.
5. Cut out the membrane from the unit insert and wash the membrane in an Eppendorf tube in 20% aqueous methanol to remove salts and detergent.
6. Cut the disk into pieces of the dimensions 2 $\times$ 2 mm and apply them to the sequencer cartridge.

Comments

The use of a horizontal rotor for centrifugation provides for the most even protein binding onto the membrane and is therefore recommended. Samples containing up to 2–3 *M* urea or guanidinium hydrochloride, 0.2% SDS, or 0.05% Triton X-100 are compatible with the use of the device. Samples containing higher concentrations of the named additives will interfere with protein binding to the membrane.

C. N-TERMINAL SEQUENCE ANALYSIS OF SAMPLES RECOVERED FROM SDS–POLYACRYLAMIDE GELS BY ELECTROBLOTTING

The procedure is schematically illustrated in Fig. 3. Isolation of proteins separated by one or two-dimensional SDS–PAGE followed by electrotransfer onto a support compatible with direct sequence analysis has become the method of choice for the isolation of proteins from complex protein mixtures for N-terminal sequencing. The following describes an optimized protocol.

Solutions

1. *100 mM CAPS stock solution:* Dissolve 22.13 g CAPS in 900 ml of water. Titrate with 2 *N* NaOH to pH 11, and add water to a final volume of 1 liter.

2. *Transfer buffer:* 10 m*M* CAPS in 10% methanol. Prepare 2 liters by mixing 200 ml of the CAPS stock solution with 200 ml of methanol and 1600 ml of water.

3. *0.1% Coomassie brilliant blue staining solution:* Dissolve 1.0 g of Coomassie blue in 400 ml of methanol and stir for 1 hr. Add 10 ml of glacial acetic acid and 590 ml of water. Stir for 30 min and filter through a Fluoropore membrane.

4. *Destaining solution:* To make 1 liter of destaining solution, mix 500 ml of methanol with 100 ml of glacial acetic acid and 400 ml of water.

Steps

1. Perform gel electrophoresis, preferably in a minigel electrophoresis system. Preferred gel thickness is 0.5 mm. As a system control, add 200 pmole of β-lactoglobulin A sequencing standard (Bioglobin).

2. Cut the PVDF membrane and two pieces of Whatman 3MM paper to the same size as the gel.

3. Wet the PVDF membrane in 50 ml of methanol in a plastic tray.

4. Immerse and equilibrate the membrane for 10–15 min in 50 ml of transfer buffer.

5. Equilibrate 0.5-mm-thick gels in 50 ml of the same buffer for 5 min. Thicker gels require proportionately longer equilibration times.

6. Wet the filter papers and the sponges in the same buffer and assemble the transfer stack in the blotting cassette starting from the anode (+) side in the following order: sponge, Whatman 3MM paper, PVDF membrane, gel Whatman 3MM paper, sponge.

7. Insert the blotting stack into the transblot cell filled with 1 liter of transfer buffer and electroblot at 50 V for 30 min.

8. After transfer, disassemble the stack and rinse the PVDF membrane several times with water prior to staining.

9. Stain and destain the gel with Coomassie blue staining solution to verify the success of the transfer.

10. Immerse the PVDF membrane in 30–50 ml of the staining solution and agitate using an orbital shaker for 1–2 min.

11. Decant the staining solution and destain the blot with several changes of destaining solution.

12. Rinse the membrane thoroughly with several changes of water and air-dry.

13. Excise the now sequencer-ready bands with a clean razor blade.

14. Cut the protein strips into small pieces with the dimensions 2 × 2 mm and place them into the standard sequencing reaction cartridge supported by a polybrene-coated glass fiber membrane.

15. Alternatively, use the Blott cartridge that is designed for sequencing electroblotted samples. This device accommodates up to four 3 × 7-mm membrane strips or one disk excised from the ProSpin centrifugation device.

Comments

Stained protein bands can be stored at −20°C for extended periods. Coomassie blue used on PVDF membranes can detect as little as 50 ng of protein. This corresponds to 1 pmole of a 50-kDa protein, which is well below the sensitivity level of the current generation sequencers.

Pitfalls

1. Irregular "swirl" patterns on the blots indicate air bubbles between the membrane and the gel during the electroblotting process. This can be avoided by carefully squeezing out trapped air during the assembly of the electroblotting stack using a clean glass test tube.

2. For optimal results use freshly prepared gel solutions. Always store gel solutions refrigerated.

3. Avoid excessive salt concentration in the sample solution. This leads to distorted protein bands. Desalt sample prior to electrophoresis.

4. Wrong polarity during the electroblotting process is a common experimental error which leads to total loss of the protein. It is therefore essential to check the assembly and orientation of the blotting stack as well as the polarity of the power supply.

5. To avoid high staining background use staining solution only once.

6. To avoid high amino acid background in the first few degradation cycles, extensively rinse the blot with water prior to sequence analysis and avoid use of contaminated laboratory equipment. In particular, tweezers, razor blades, and scalpels are a common source of contamination.

7. Low initial signal or absence of a signal from an intensely stained band indicates N-terminal blockage of the protein. Artifactual N-terminal blocking during the electrophoresis/electroblotting process can be detected by sequencing the β-lactoglobulin A control band (see point 1 above). Artifactual N-terminal blocking as detected by this assay can be minimized by keeping the protein-to-gel ratio high, by using gel chemicals of the highest purity available, and by using extensively (overnight) polymerized gels.

8. Low protein recovery on the blot can result from suboptimal transfer conditions, resulting in incomplete transfer or poor retention of the protein on the blot (overtransfer). The main reason for incomplete transfer is protein precipitation in the gel due to depletion of SDS. The problem can be minimized by inclusion of 0.005% of SDS in the transfer buffer. Overtransfer can be minimized by using a blotting membrane with high binding capacity and small nominal pore size and by reducing the transfer time.

IV. Conclusions

The success of a protein sequencing experiment depends on the choice and the competent application of a series of techniques. They concern purification of the protein, the actual sequencing process, and data interpretation. The protocols described above are compatible with modern high-sensitivity sequencing techniques. As choice of the right technique in a given situation is equally important to correct execution of the method, it is important that the general comments, which are intended to provide the understanding for the choice of the right technique, are seriously considered before precious protein samples are committed.

ACKNOWLEDGMENTS

The help of Hamish Morrison in preparing figures is gratefully acknowledged. R.A. is a Medical Research Council of Canada scholar.

REFERENCES

Aebersold, R. H., Leavitt, J., Saavedra, R. A., Hood, L. E., and Kent, S. B. (1987) Internal amino acid sequence analysis of proteins separated by one- or two-dimensional gel electrophoresis after in situ protease digestion on nitrocellulose. *Proc. Natl. Acad. Sci. USA* **84**, 6970.

Aebersold, R. H., Teplow, D. B., Hood, L. E., and Kent, S. B. (1986) Electroblotting onto activated glass: High efficiency preparation of proteins from analytical sodium dodecyl sulfate polyacrylamide gels for direct sequence analysis. *J. Biol. Chem.* **261**, 4229.

Brown, J. L., and Roberts, W. K. (1976) Evidence that approximately eighty percent of the soluble proteins from Ehrlich ascites cells are amino-terminally acetylated. *J. Biol. Chem.* **251**, 1009.

Hewick, R. M., Hunkapiller, M. W., Hood, L. E., and Dreyer, W. J. (1981) A gas–liquid solid phase peptide and protein sequenator. *J. Biol. Chem.* **256**, 7990.

Laemmli, U. K. (1970) Cleavage of structural proteins during the assembly of the head of bacteriophage T4. *Nature (London)* **227**, 680.

Matsudaira, P. (1987) Sequence from picomole quantities of proteins electroblotted onto polyvinylidene difluoride membranes. *J. Biol. Chem.* **262**, 10035.

Matsudaira, P. (1993) "A Practical Guide to Protein and Peptide Purification for Microsequencing," 2nd ed. Academic Press, San Diego.

Regnier, F. E. (1983) HPLC of proteins. *In* "Methods in Enzymology" (C. H. W. Hirs and S. N. Timasheff, eds.), Vol. 91, p. 137. Academic Press, San Diego.

Simpson, R. J., Moritz, R. L., Begg, G. S., Rubina, M. R., and Nice, E. C. (1989) Micropreparative procedures for high sensitivity sequencing of peptides and proteins. *Anal. Biochem.* **177**, 221.

Vandekerckhove, J., Bauw, G., Puype, M., Van Damme, J., and Van Montagu, M. (1985) Protein-blotting on polybrene-treated glass-fiber sheets. A basis of acid hydrolysis and gas phase sequencing of picomole quantities of protein previously separated on SDS–polyacrylamide gel. *Eur. J. Biochem.* **152**, 9.

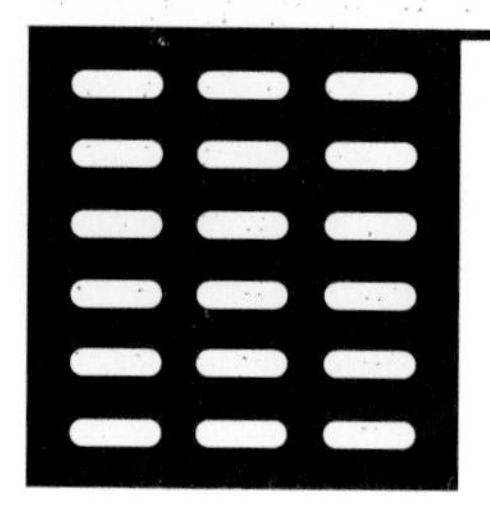

Sequencing Peptides Derived from the Class II Major Histocompatibility Complex by Tandem Mass Spectrometry

John R. Yates, III, Ashley L. McCormack, James B. Hayden, and Michael P. Davey

I. Introduction

Microcolumn reverse-phase HPLC electrospray ionization tandem mass spectrometry (ESI-MS/MS) is a rapid and sensitive technique for the analysis of complex mixtures of peptides. This technique is used to determine the amino acid sequence of unknown peptides, to verify the structure of proteins, and to determine posttranslational modifications (see also the article by Beth L. Gillece-Castro). In particular, the strength of this approach is the analysis of peptides in complicated mixtures, such as amino acid sequence analysis of peptides isolated from class I and II major histocompatibility T-cell receptor complexes (Hunt *et al.*, 1992a).

II. Materials and Instrumentation

Solvents were purchased from the following sources: 2-propanol (J. T. Baker, Cat. No. 9095-02), acetonitrile (Fischer Scientific, Cat. No. A996-4), and acetic acid (J. T. Baker, Cat. No. 6903-05). Fused silica capillaries were obtained from Polymicro Technologies: 375 μm o.d. × 198 μm i.d. (Cat. No. TSP375200) and 185 mm o.d. × 50 μm i.d. (Cat. No. TSP185050). Chromatographic supports were obtained from Yamamura Chemical Laboratories: YMC-GEL liquid chromatography support C_{18} BAQ-1010 ODS-AQ S-10 120A. The column packing device was homemade and is shown in Fig. 1A. Epoxy was obtained from Epoxy Technologies Inc. (Epo-tek 302). Material for the porous Teflon frits was purchased from Applied Biosystems (Cat. No. 400010). Materials for generation of major histocompatibility complex (MHC) peptides were obtained from the following sources—Gibco-BRL: Hepes buffer (Cat. No. 845-1334IL), L-glutamine (Cat. No. 810-1051IM), fetal bovine serum (Cat. No. 200-6140PK), RPMI-1640 medium (Cat. No. 430-1800EG) and protein A–agarose (Cat. No. 59185A); Amicon: Minicon B15 (Cat. No. 9031), Centricon 10 (Cat. No. 4205); Pharmacia LKB: CNBr-activated Sepharose (Cat. No. 17-0430-01); Sigma Chemical Company: Dulbecco's phosphate-buffered saline (PBS, Cat. No. D-1408), Nonidet P-40 (NP-40, Cat. No. N-6507), *n*-octyl-D-glucopyranoside (Cat. No. O-0630); ICN: PMSF (Cat. No. 195368), 1,10-phenan-

A

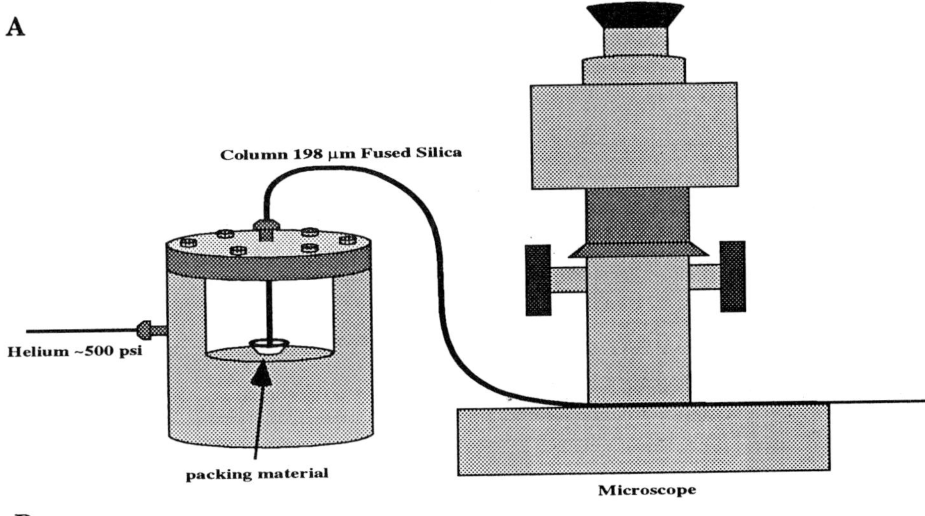

B

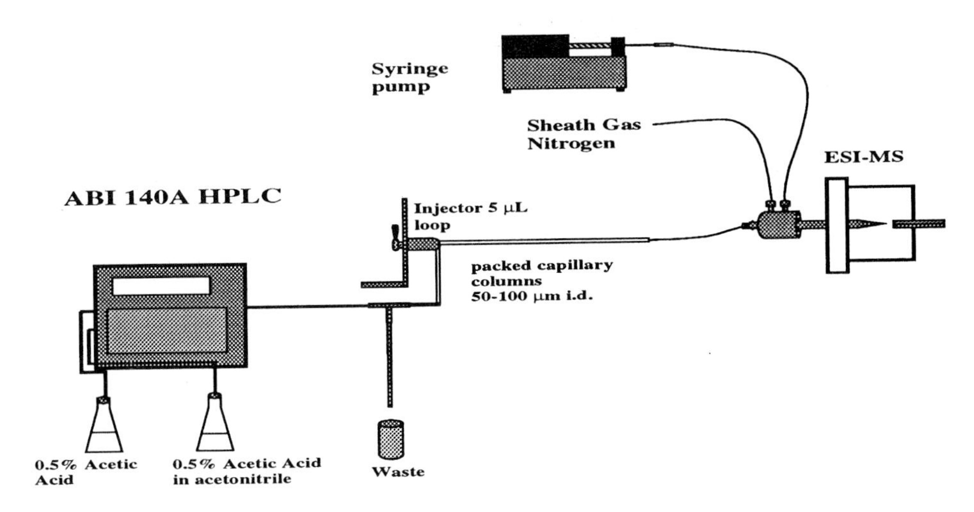

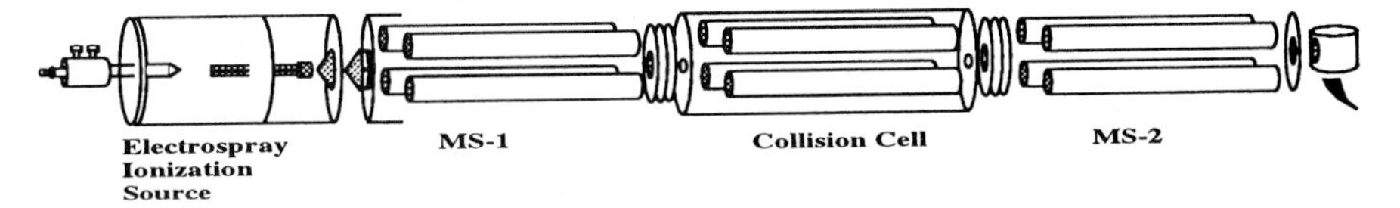

FIGURE 1 (A) Packing of the microcolumns for liquid chromatography. (B) Configuration of the HPLC for microcolumn liquid chromatography electrospray ionization mass spectrometry and the tandem mass spectrometer.

throline (Cat. No. 152553), pepstatin A (Cat. No. P4265), diethylamine (Cat. No. 150883).

The electrospray ionization tandem mass spectrometer was obtained from Finnigan MAT. Pumps for HPLC were purchased from Applied Biosystems (Cat. No. 140B, dual-syringe pump), and a sample injector was obtained from Rheodyne (Cat. No. 8125, 5-μl loop injector).

III. Procedures

A. ISOLATION OF PEPTIDES BOUND TO CLASS II MOLECULES

Solutions

1. *RPMI-1640 culture medium with 5% fetal calf serum:* To make 100 ml, add 5 ml of fetal calf serum to 95 ml of RPMI-1640. Store at 4°C.

2. *RPMI-1640 culture medium with 10% fetal calf serum:* To make 100 ml, add 10 ml of fetal calf serum to 90 ml of RPMI-1640. Store at 4°C.

3. *Cell lysis buffer:* To make 100 ml, add 200 mg of EDTA, 5 mg of pepstatin A, 26 mg of 1,10-phenanthroline, 17.4 mg of PMSF, and 1 ml of NP-40. Bring to a total volume of 100 ml with distilled water. Store at 4°C.

4. *1 M NaOH solution:* To make 1 liter, add 39.9 g of NaOH to 1 liter of distilled water.

5. *0.5 M NaCl solution and 0.58% acetic acid solution:* To make 1 liter, add 29.2 g of NaCl and 5.8 ml of glacial acetic acid to 1 liter of distilled water.

6. *Antibody coupling buffer:* To make 100 ml, add 0.87 g of NaCl and 0.84 g of $NaHCO_3$ to distilled water. Adjust pH to 8.4 and bring to a total volume of 100 ml.

7. *Phosphate-buffered saline solution with 1% NP-40:* To make 100 ml, add 1 ml of NP-40 to 10 ml of PBS 10×, and bring to a total volume of 100 ml. Store at 4°C.

8. *Phosphate-buffered saline:* To make 1 liter, add 100 ml of PBS 10× to 900 ml of distilled water.

9. *Phosphate-buffered saline solution with 0.5% NP-40 and 0.1% SDS:* To make 100 ml, add 0.5 ml of NP-40 and 0.1 g of SDS to 10 ml of PBS 10× and bring to total volume of 100 ml with distilled water. Store at 4°C.

10. *Phosphate-buffered saline solution with 1% n-octyl-β-D-glucopyranoside:* To make 100 ml, add 1 g of *n*-octyl-β-D-glucopyranoside to 10 ml of PBS 10× and bring to a volume of 100 ml with distilled water. Store at 4°C.

11. *Elution buffer:* To make 1 liter, add 15.2 ml of diethylamine, 29 g of NaCl, and 10 g of *n*-octyl-β-D-glucopyranoside to 750 ml of distilled water. Adjust the pH to 10.5 and bring to a volume of 1 liter.

12. *2.5 M Acetic acid solution:* To make 1 liter, add 142.9 ml of glacial acetic acid to 857 ml of distilled water.

13. *0.1 M Hydrochloric acid solution:* To make 1 liter, add 8.3 ml of concentrated HCl to 991.7 ml of distilled water.

14. *0.07% Trifluoroacetic acid solution:* To make 1 liter, add 0.7 ml to 999.3 ml of distilled water.

15. *0.06% Trifluoroacetic acid solution:* To make 1 liter, add 0.6 ml to 999.4 ml of distilled water.

Steps

1. An Epstein Barr-Virus-transformed B-cell line (HS-EBV) homozygous for HLA DRBI*0401 was used for this study. HLA DR typing was performed as previously described (Gao *et. al.,* 1990). Culture HS-EBV cells in RPMI-1640 culture medium with 5% fetal calf serum (Coligan *et al.,* 1992). Seed cells at 2×10^5 cells/ml in roller bottles and allow to grow until a density of 1×10^6 cells/ml

has been reached. Harvest cells by centrifugation, and resuspend in lysis buffer at a concentration of 1–2 $\times$ 10^8 cells/ml. Immediately freeze lysate at −20°C.

2. Prepare the antibodies, L243 (anti-DR, IgG_2a) and OKT3 (anti-CD3, IgG_2a), from hybridomas obtained from American Type Tissue Culture. Seed the hybridomas at 1 $\times$ 10^5 cells/ml in RPMI-1640 with 10% fetal bovine serum, and grow until 50% of the cells are dead. Harvest supernatant by centrifugation.

3. Filter supernatant through a 0.2-μm filter to remove any remaining debris, and add 1 *M* NaOH to correct the pH to approximately 8.0. Equilibrate a protein A column with PBS solution. After the supernatant is loaded, wash the column with at least 10 column volumes of PBS solution. Elute the antibody with a solution of 0.5 *M* NaCl and 0.58% acetic acid. Determine fractions containing the antibody by UV absorption at 280 nm. Pool and dialyze the fractions in antibody coupling buffer. Store antibody at −20°C.

4. Concentrate the antibodies to approximately 10 mg/ml in a Minicon B15 concentrator. Wash activated beads with 0.1 *M* HCl followed by coupling buffer. Mix 6 ml of beads with approximately 35 mg of each concentrated antibody and incubate at 4°C. Monitor the coupling reaction by UV absorption at 280 nm. When 90% coupling is reached, terminate the reaction by the addition of Tris. Make a third 6-ml column by coupling Tris to the CNBr-activated beads.

5. Place frozen lysate from approximately 1 $\times$ 10^{10} cells in a 37°C water bath until 50% thawed. Transfer the lysate to a small beaker and mix on a magnetic stir plate for 30 min at 4°C (Falk *et. al.*, 1991). Remove large debris by centrifugation at 2000 *g* for 10 min; further clarify lysate by ultracentrifugation at 150,000 *g* for 30 min (Falk *et al.*, 1991). Purify DR/peptide complexes as described by Buus *et al.* (1986) with modifications. Directly load the supernatant onto the antibody columns equilibrated with PBS, 1% NP-40. The columns are configured in series in the following order: Tris (general, nonspecific), OKT3 (isotype matched, nonspecific), L243 (DR specific). Wash the columns with a minimum of 10 vol of a PBS, 1% NP-40 solution, followed by at least 5 vol of a PBS, 0.5% NP-40, 0.1% SDS solution. Remove the L243 column from the series and wash with 5 or more vol of a PBS, 1% *n*-octyl-β-D-glucopyranoside solution. Remove the DR/peptide complexes with elution buffer into 2-ml fractions. The fractions containing DR/peptide are detected by BCA assay performed in a microtiter plate. Average total yield is 1.9 mg from 1 $\times$ 10^{10} cells. Check purity by SDS–PAGE.

6. Pool all fractions containing DR/peptide and concentrate in a Centricon 10 to a final volume of 200–300 μl. The large volume filtered through the Centricon 10 removes potential contaminants from the filter and limits sample losses. Discard the filtrate. Add 2.5 *M* acetic acid to the concentrated DR/peptide mixture in the Centricon 10 and mix thoroughly with a pipette. Separate the acid-eluted peptides from the α and β chains of the DR molecule by filtration through the original Centricon 10 (Demotz *et al.*, 1989; Hunt *et al.*, 1992b).

7. Fractionate the peptide filtrate by reverse-phase HPLC using a Vydac 2.1 $\times$ 250-mm C_{18} column. Solvent A is 0.07% TFA in water and solvent B is 0.06% TFA in 80:20 acetontrile to water. The gradient is 0–45 min, 2–40% B; 45–60 min, 40–75% B; and 60–65 min, 75–98% B. Monitor separation at 220 nm. Flow rate is 200 μL/min; collect 200-μl fractions. Concentrate HPLC fractions to a final volume of 20–30 μl. Freeze fractions at −20°C. Analyze each of the fractions by mass spectrometry.

B. PREPARATION OF MICROCOLUMNS FOR REVERSE-PHASE HPLC

Solutions

1. *HPLC solvent A:* To make 1 liter, add 5 ml of glacial acetic acid to 995 ml of distilled deionized water.
2. *HPLC solvent B:* To make 1 liter, add 5 ml of glacial acetic acid to a solution of 200 ml of distilled deionized water and 795 ml of acetonitrile.

Steps

1. Construct micro-capillary columns according to Shelley *et al.* (1984) with modifications. Rinse a 30-cm piece of fused silica capillary (375 μm o.d. × 198 μm i.d.) with 2-propanol and dry. Create a frit with a porous Teflon filter by pressing the end of the capillary up against a fingertip and twisting the capillary to cut out a piece of the Teflon corresponding to the outlet diameter of the capillary. Place the capillary with the frit inside a short piece of the Teflon tube (0.5 cm, 0.010 in. i.d.) and slide an exit column (30 cm, 185 μm o.d. × 50 μm i.d.) into the end of the tube directly into the other capillary. The Teflon tube acts as a guide for the exit column to drive the frit into the capillary ~10 mm. Withdraw the exit column ~5 mm, apply epoxy to the exit column at the joint, and push the epoxy back into the capillary, twisting the exit column to spread the epoxy around the inside of the capillary. After curing overnight, the frit and the epoxy joint should be stable to pressures of at least 2000 psi and solvents such as 0.1% trifluoroacetic acid, 0.5% acetic acid, 2-propanol, and acetonitrile.

2. The packing device is depicted in Fig. 1A. Wash the column with 2-propanol. Fill a polypropylene Eppendorf centrifuge tube (1.5 ml) with ~100 μg of packing material and 1 ml of 2-propanol, and sonicate briefly to suspend the material and minimize aggregation. Add a small magnetic stir bar to the solution. Place the solution in a high-pressure packing device (Fig. 1A), insert the column, and place the end of the column in the solution. To keep the packing material suspended in solution, place the packing device on a stirring plate and stir at medium speed. Helium gas at a pressure of ~500 psi is used to drive the packing material into the column while following progress of the packing under a microscope. Continue packing until the material fills a length of the capillary corresponding to 10–20 cm. Allow the pressure to slowly drop to zero. Pack the column bed by rinsing with 2-propanol at 1000 psi for a few minutes. Condition the column by rinsing with 100% solvent B and slowly reducing the percentage of solvent B until it reaches initial HPLC conditions (100% solvent A). Use a linear gradient of 100% solvent A to 20% solvent A over 30 min is to finish conditioning the column.

3. The configuration for microcolumn HPLC is shown in Fig. 1B.

Gradient	linear, 30 min, 0 to 100% (80:20 acetonitrile:0.5% acetic acid
Flow	100 μl/min, flow split at ~50/1, final flow rate 1–2 μl/min
Columns	198 μm i.d. × 30 cm, YMC-GEL C_{18}, 10 μm, 120-Å particles
Injector	5 μl, Rheodyne, 8125

C. ANALYSIS OF PEPTIDES BY ELECTROSPRAY IONIZATION MASS SPECTROMETRY

Steps

1. Insert the exit column of the micro-capillary HPLC column into the 26-gauge stainless-steel electrospray needle until the fused silica capillary exits the

A

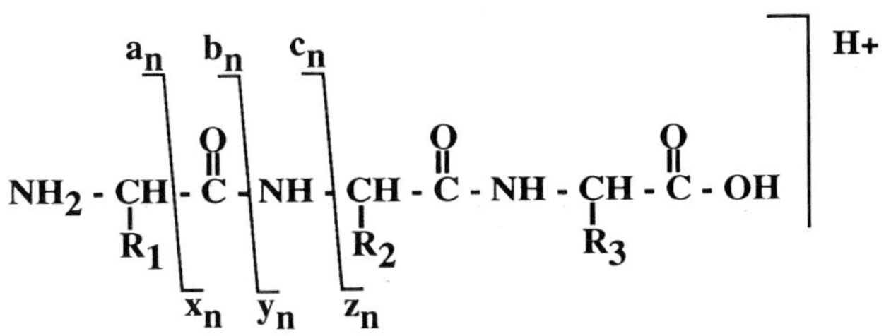

a_n b_n c_n H+

$$NH_2-CH(R_1)-C(=O)-NH-CH(R_2)-C(=O)-NH-CH(R_3)-C(=O)-OH$$

x_n y_n z_n

B

Amino acid	Single letter	Three-letter code	Mass
Glycine	G	gly	57
Alanine	A	ala	71
Serine	S	ser	87
Proline	P	pro	97
Valine	V	val	99
Threonine	T	thr	101
Cysteine	C	cys	103
Leucine	L	leu	113
Isoleucine	I	ile	113
Asparagine	N	asn	114
Aspartic Acid	D	asp	115
Glutamine	Q	gln	128
Lysine	K	lys	128
Glutamic Acid	E	glu	129
Methionine	M	met	131
Histidine	H	his	137
Phenylalanine	F	phs	147
Arginine	R	arg	156
Carboxymethyl Cystine	C	cmc	161
Tyrosine	Y	tyr	163
Tryptophan	W	trp	186

C

116 229 385 472 658 759 830 901 1016 1117 1188 1259 1387 1500 1601 1729

Asp Leu Arg Ser Trp Thr Ala Ala Asp Thr Ala Ala Gln Ile Thr Gln

1747 1632 1519 1363 1276 1090 989 918 847 732 631 560 489 361 248 147

FIGURE 2 (A) Fragmentation of peptides. (B) Single- and three-letter codes for amino acids and residue masses. (C) Amino acid sequence for the peptide analyzed by MS/MS. The spectrum is displayed in Fig. 3B.

tube. Draw the fused silica 1–2 mm back into the needle. The electrospray tandem mass spectrometer is depicted in Fig. 1B.

Sheath gas	Nitrogen at 0.2 l/min
Drying gas	Heated nitrogen (80–85°C, 15 psi), 4 l/min
Needle distance to capillary	2.5 cm
Capillary voltage	−3500–4100 V

2. Inject a 1-μl aliquot of sample to record the molecular weight of the peptides contained in one of the HPLC fractions.

Scan rate and mass range, Q_1	500 amu/sec, 400–1500 amu
Electron multiplier voltage	1200–1400 V

3. Perform sequence analysis of peptides during a second HPLC analysis by selecting the precursor ion with a 6-amu (FWHH)-wide window in Q_1 and passing the ions into the collision cell which is filled with argon to a pressure of 5 mtorr. Collision energies are on the order of 20 to 50 eV. The fragment ions produced in Q_2 are transmitted to Q_3, which is scanned at 500 amu/sec over a

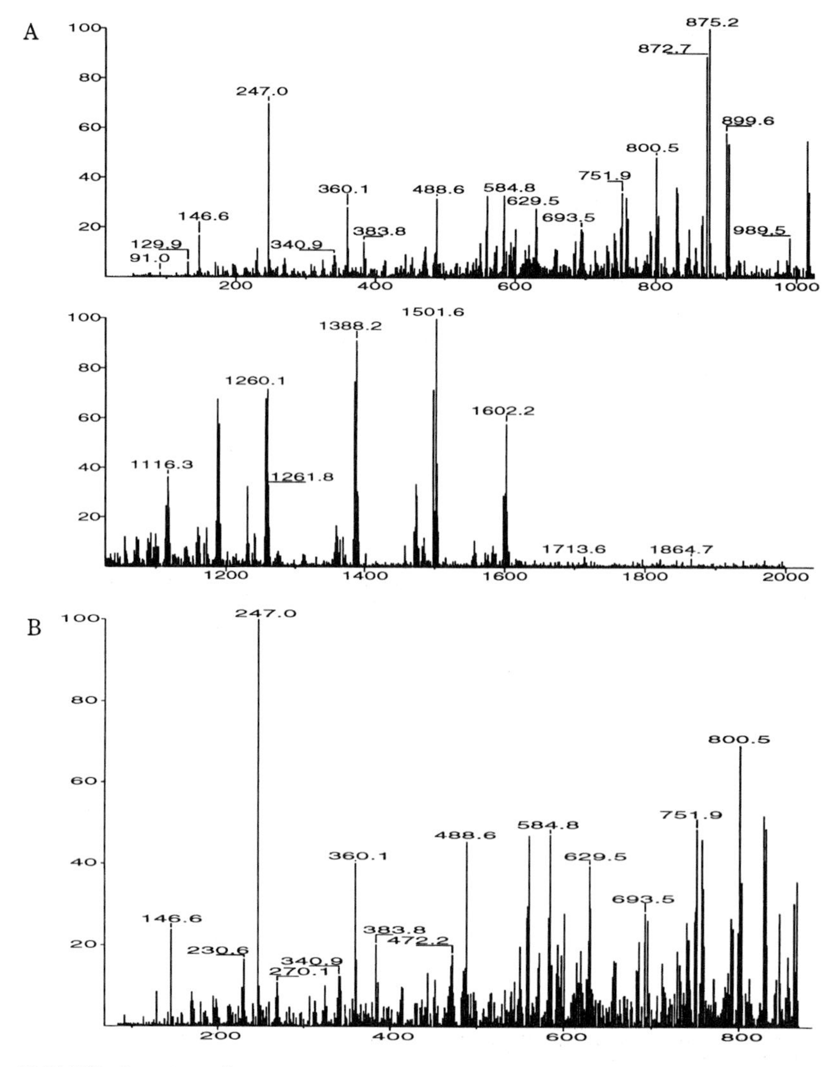

FIGURE 3 (A) Full MS/MS spectrum of *m/z* 875. (B) MS/MS spectrum displayed from *m/z* 50 to 850.

mass range from 50 amu to the molecular weight of the precursor ion to record the fragment ions. The electron multiplier setting is 400–600 V higher than that used to record the ions in the main beam. Q_3 is tuned to give peaks that are 1.5 amu wide.

IV. Comments

Under low-energy, multiple collision conditions, peptides fragment primarily at the amide bonds, producing sequence-specific fragmentation patterns. The types of fragment ions produced in these collisions are shown in Fig. 2A. Subtraction of the mass-to-charge ratios (*m/z*) for consecutive type b- or y-sequence ions gives a residue mass that corresponds to the amino acid in the larger fragment. Residue masses for the common amino acids are shown in Fig. 2B. To improve sensitivity the mass spectrometer is operated with less than unit mass resolution in Q_1 and Q_3. Thus, fragment ions have a cluster appearance created by selection of all the isotopes for the precursor ion and, in part, by the computer algorithm which defines peaks and assigns masses.

To demonstrate the sequencing process the MS/MS spectrum for the peptide shown in Fig. 2C will be interpreted. The mass spectrum is shown in Fig. 3A and

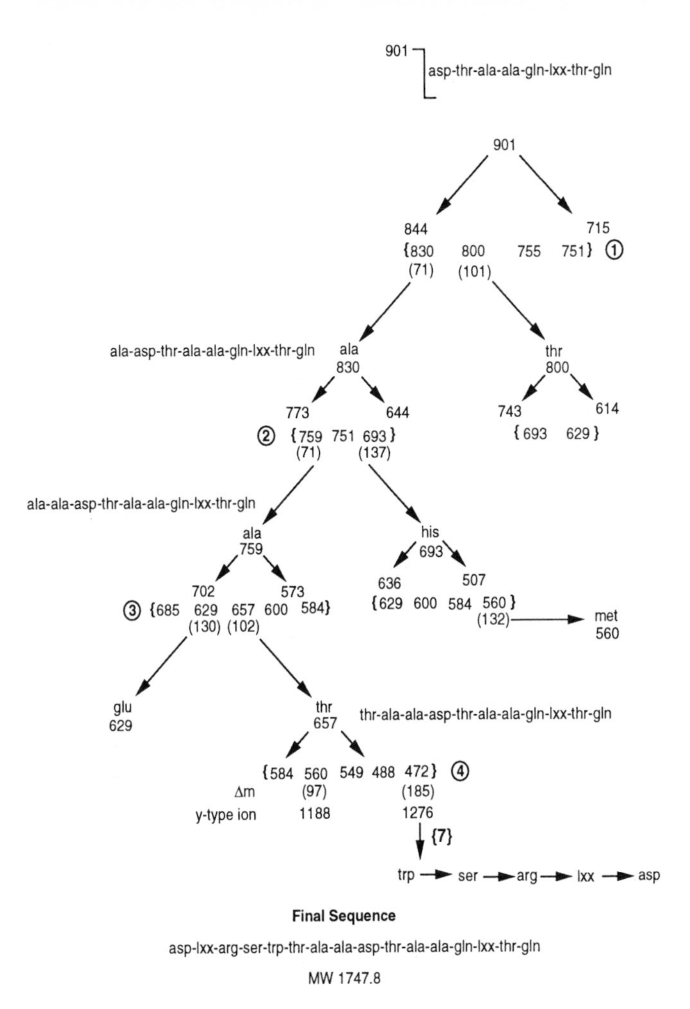

FIGURE 4 Schematic of the partial interpretation of the MS/MS spectrum derived from collisional activation of *m/z* 875.

a scheme of the process is presented in Fig. 4. The mass spectrum is produced by collisional activation of a doubly charged ion, $(M + 2H)^{2+}$, at *m/z* 875. The protonated molecular weight of this peptide is 1749 (average mass). Subtraction of the highest mass fragment ion, *m/z* 1602, yields a mass of 147. If this fragment ion is a type y ion, then the amino acid assignment is Phe and a corresponding type b ion would be observed at *m/z* 148. If *m/z* 1602 is a type b ion, the assignment is Gln. The evidence for a type b ion is the presence of a peak 28 Da (neutral loss of carbon monoxide from type b ion) below the major ion and an ion at *m/z* 146.6 which is a type y_1 ion for Gln. In general, the b_1 ions are absent from MS/MS spectra. Both type b and type y ions suffer losses of neutral molecules such as water (−18 amu) and ammonia (−17 amu). Losses of carbon monoxide are observed only from type b ions. The presence of these ions in the mass spectrum helps confirm assignment of ion type. The set of ions in the upper mass range appears to be a continuous type b ion series to *m/z* 901 which yields the following sequence: –Asp–Thr–Ala–Ala–Gln–Lxx–Thr–Gln. Lxx is either of the isomers Leu or Ile. After *m/z* 901 the sequence ion series becomes weaker, but the next fragment ion must lie between *m/z* 844 and 715 (901 − 57 and 901 − 186) (step 1). Four major ions exist in this region, *m/z* 830, 800, 755, and 751. Subtraction of each of these ions from *m/z* 901 yields masses of 71, 101, 146, and 150. A type y ion peak is present in the mass spectrum at *m/z* 918, so Ala is the correct assignment. The mass window for the next fragment ion is 773 and 644 (step 2). Fragment ions at 759, 751, and 693 are observed in this window. The ions at 759 and 693 produce mass differences of 71 and 137, which correspond to Ala and His, respectively. The potential sequences are now –Ala–Ala–Asp–Thr–Ala–Ala–Gln–Lxx–Thr–Gln and –His–Ala–Asp–Thr–Ala–Ala–Gln–Lxx–Thr–Gln. In pursuing the type b ion which corresponds to Ala, there are five potential sequence ions in the window between *m/z* 702 and 573: *m/z* 658, 657, 629, 600, and 584 (step 3). Two of the mass differences are within 1 amu of the mass of Thr and Glu. Again, it is important to look for the corresponding type y ions to decide which assignment is correct. The type y ion for the Thr is more intense than the ion for Glu, so Thr will be the tentative assignment. This process is continued to obtain a sequence of Asp–Lxx–Arg–Ser–Trp–Thr–Ala–Ala–Asp–Thr–Ala–Ala–Gln–Lxx–Thr–Gln. The sequence is verified by summing the masses for each of the amino acids, to ensure that the molecular weight of the peptide fits the observed molecular weight, and then determining if it corresponds to a known sequence.

V. Pitfalls

1. The Centricon filter must be prewashed prior to filtering the peptides from the DR complexes. A contaminant exists in the membrane that disrupts LC-MS analysis of the peptides.

2. Distilled and deionized water must be used in the HPLC solvents for LC-MS analysis to avoid the production of sodium or potassium adducts.

REFERENCES

Buus, S., Sette, A., Colon, S. M., Jenis, D. M., and Grey, H. (1986) Isolation and characterization of antigen–Ia complexes involved in T-cell recognition. *Cell* **47**, 1071–1077.

Coligan, J. E., Kruisbeck, A. M., Margulies, D. H., Shevach, E. M., and Strober, W. (eds.) (1992) "Current Protocols in Immunology." Greene Publishing and Wiley–Interscience, New York.

Demotz, S., Grey, H., Appella, E., and Sette, A. (1989) Characterization of a naturally processed MHC class II restricted T-cell determinant of hen egg lysozyme. *Nature* **342**, 682–684.

Falk, K., Rotzschke, O., Stevanovic, S., Gunther, J., and Rammensee, H.-G. (1991) Allele-specific motifs revealed by sequencing of self-peptides eluted from MHC molecules. *Nature* **351**, 290–296.

Gao, X., Fernandex-Via, M., Shumway, W., and Stastny, P. (1990) DNA typing for class II HLA antigens with allele-specific or group-specific amplification. I. Typing for subsets of HLA-DR4. *Hum. Immunol.* **27**, 40–50.

Hunt, D. F., Henderson, R. A., Shabanowitz, J., Sakaguchi, K., Michel, H., Sevilir, N., Cox, A. L., Apella, E., and Engelhard, V. N. (1992a) Characterization of peptides bound to the class I MHC molecule HLA-A2.1 by mass spectrometry. *Science* **255**, 1261–1263.

Hunt, D. F., Michel, H., Dickinson, T. A., Shabanowitz, J., Cox, A. L., Sakaguchi, K., Appella, E., Grey, H. M., and Sette, A. (1992b) Peptides presented to the immune system by the murine class II major histocompatibility complex molecule I-A^d. *Science* **256**, 1817–1820.

Shelley, D. C., Gluckman, J. C., and Novotny, M. V. (1984) Dead-volume free termination for packed capillary columns in microcapillary liquid chromatography. *Anal. Chem.* **56**, 2990–2992.

Mass Spectrometry: Detection and Characterization of Posttranslational Modifications

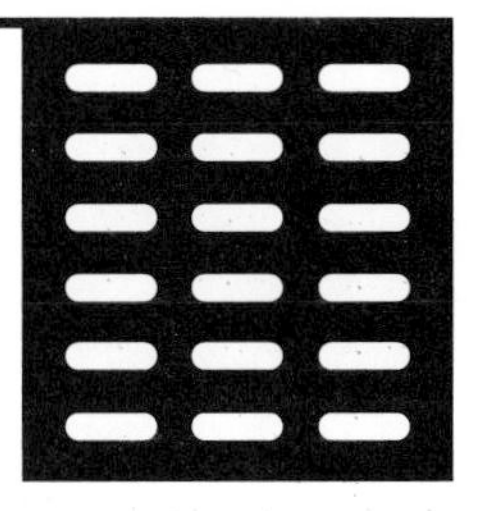

Beth L. Gillece-Castro

I. Introduction

The process of forming a mature protein begins with the translation of the mRNA sequence to an amino acid sequence. Many posttranslational modifications to the protein backbone or side chains may be required for activity (Krishna and Wold, 1993); each of these modifications changes the molecular weight of the protein. Important examples of modifications (Krishna and Wold, 1993) to secreted and membrane proteins are proteolysis of signal sequences; glycosylation of asparagine, serine, and threonine residues; formation of disulfide bridges; hydroxylation of amino acids; addition of fatty acid, isoprenyl, or glycosylphosphoinositol membrane anchors; and proteolysis of prohormones or proenzymes. Similarly, modifications of cytoplasmic proteins or cytoplasmic tails of membrane proteins include phosphorylation and glycosylation. Protein isolation procedures may induce the deamidation of asparagine or glutamine residues and the oxidation of methionine residues, or the inadvertent cleavage of the peptide sequence by contaminating proteins.

A difference in the observed molecular weight of the intact protein compared with the translated DNA or amino acid sequence suggests that one or more of these posttranslational modifications has occurred. Subsequent digestion of the protein to peptides allows the sites of modification to be identified by the mass shift of the relevant peptide or peptides (Carr *et al.*, 1991). In addition, labile bonds such as phosphoryl bonds (Huddleston *et al.*, 1993a) and glycosyl bonds (Conboy and Henion, 1992; Carr *et al.*, 1993; Huddleston *et al.*, 1993b) are broken by collisional activation to give diagnostic fragments associated with the peptide sites of modification. Matrix-assisted laser desorption ionization can be used to analyze intact proteins and peptide mixtures (Carr *et al.*, 1991). As the ability to analyze large biomolecules by electrospray ionization was developed (Fenn *et al.*, 1989), mass spectrometric techniques now allow complete characterization of mature proteins. The methods detailed here use electrospray ionization (ESI) mass spectrometry to characterize intact proteins and HPLC-ESI mass spectrometry to characterize peptides produced by trypsin digestion of proteins. Phosphorylated peptides are characterized after chromatography on metal ion chelating columns (Nuwaysir and Stults, 1993).

II. Materials and Instrumentation

HPLC-grade, Burdick and Jackson acetonitrile (Cat. No. 015-4DK) and water (Cat. No. 365-4DK) are purchased from Baxter Scientific Products; Milli-Q Plus

(Cat. No. ZD40) high-purity water (Millipore) can be substituted for Burdick and Jackson water. Acetic acid (Cat. No. 38012-1), iodoacetic acid (Cat. No. I-680-6), ammonium hydroxide (Cat. No. 22,122-8), ferric chloride hexahydrate (Cat. No. 23,648-9), 4-ethyl morpholine (Cat. No. 23,952-6), and polypropylene glycols (PPGs) 425, 1000, and 2000 (Cat. No. 20,230-4; 20,232-0; and 20,233-9) are obtained from Aldrich Chemical. Trifluoroacetic acid (Cat. No. 53102V) is obtained from Pierce. Ammonium bicarbonate (Cat. No. A-6141), ammonium acetate (Cat. No. A-7262), and guanidine hydrochloride (Cat. No. G-4505) are purchased from Sigma Chemical. Dithiothreitol (Cat. No. 708,984) is obtained from Boehringer-Mannheim. Sequencing-grade, modified Promega trypsin (Cat. No. PR-V5111) and hydrochloric acid are purchased from Fisher Scientific. NAP-5 gel filtration columns (Cat. No. 17-0853-01) and chelating Sepharose Fast Flow medium (Cat. No. 17-0575-02) are obtained from Pharmacia.

The HPLC system consists of a pump, flow splitter, injector, capillary column, detector, and a capillary transfer line to the mass spectrometer (Fig. 1). The gradient HPLC pump (Model 140A, Cat. No. 140A-00) and the UV programmable absorbance detector (Model 783A, Cat. No. 9003-7831) are both obtained from Applied Biosystems, Inc. An HPLC injection valve (Cat. No. C10W) with a 20-μl loop and a 5-μl loop are available from Valco Instruments Co., Inc. LC Packings International supplies a flow splitter (Acurate Microflow Processor) and capillary HPLC columns (Fusica II with 5-μm C_{18} particles in 380 μm $\times$ 15 cm columns). LC Packings also supplies a capillary flow cell (U-Z View) to modify the Applied Biosystems UV detector. Capillary tubing with 75-μm i.d. (Cat. No. TSP075150) is obtained from Polymicro Technologies, Inc.

Low-pressure flangeless fittings for immobilized metal-ion affinity chromatography are available from Upchurch Scientific, Inc. (Cat. Nos. P200x and P202x). These unions are fitted with pieces of 5-mm-diameter Durapore polyvinylidene difluoride hydrophilic low binding membrane (Cat. No. STSV 096S, Millipore).

An API-III triple-quadrupole mass spectrometer (or the single-quadrupole counterpart) with articulated, pneumatically assisted nebulizer atmospheric ionization is available from Perkin–Elmer Sciex Instruments. Any mass spectrometer equipped with an electrospray ionization source capable of LC/MS analysis can be substituted; however, some potentials and flows may need to be adjusted for another instrument. A Harvard Apparatus 22 syringe pump is used for sample infusion with 25-μl Hamilton blunt-tipped (SNR) syringes.

III. Procedures

A. INTACT MOLECULAR WEIGHT DETERMINATION

Solution

50% aqueous acetonitrile with 0.5% acetic acid (v/v): To make 500 ml, add 249 ml acetonitrile to 249 ml high-purity water, add 2.5 ml glacial acetic acid, and stir. Store at room temperature.

Steps

1. Dissolve intact desalted protein in 50% aqueous acetonitrile with 0.5% acetic acid (v/v) to a concentration of 1–10 μM.
2. Infuse 5–10 μl of the protein solution into the mass spectrometer using the Harvard syringe pump fitted with a 25-μl syringe at 2 μl/min.

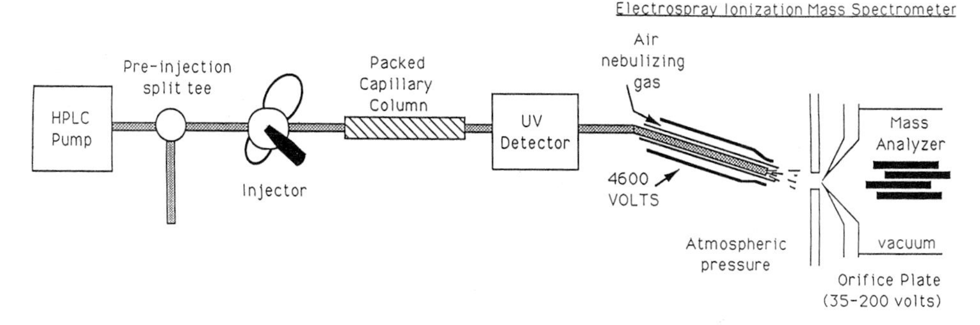

FIGURE 1 Diagram of the capillary HPLC configuration as attached to the electrospray ionization mass spectrometer. Flow through the 320-μm-i.d. packed capillary columns is adjusted to 4 μl per minute.

3. Scan the mass spectrometer from *m/z* 400 to 2400 with data points every 0.1–0.2 *m/z* (Fig. 2A).
4. Reconstruct the *m/z* data to molecular weight (Fig. 2B) to match against the calculated average molecular weight of the protein (Fig. 2C).

B. PEPTIDE MOLECULAR WEIGHT DETERMINATION

Solutions

1. *Reduction Buffer:* 10 m*M* dithiothreitol in 6 *M* guanidine, pH 8.5. To make 10 ml, dissolve 5.73 g guanidine–HCl in high-purity water. Add 424 mg Tris and 3.36 mg EDTA with stirring, and adjust the pH to 8.5 with HCl. Add 15.43 mg dithiothreitol to make a 10 m*M* solution, and adjust to 10 ml. Cover with nitrogen and store at 4°C.

2. *Alkylation Buffer:* 350 m*M* iodoacetic acid in 0.5 *M* NaOH. To make 1 ml, dissolve 20 mg sodium hydroxide in high-purity water, add 65.1 mg iodoacetic acid, and vortex. Store at 4°C in the dark.

3. *50 mM ammonium bicarbonate:* To make 10 ml, dissolve 39.5 mg ammonium bicarbonate in high-purity water, and vortex. Store at room temperature.

4. *HPLC solvents:* To make 1 liter of solvent A, add 20 ml of acetonitrile to 980 ml of high-purity water, add 1 ml of trifluoroacetic acid, and stir. To make 1 liter of solvent B, add 900 ml of acetonitrile to 100 ml of high-purity water, add 800 μl trifluoroacetic acid, and stir. Solvents should be degassed by sparging with helium or by sonication under vacuum.

Steps

1. Reduce and *S*-carboxymethylate disulfide bonds as follows. Dissolve protein in reduction buffer to a concentration of 0.2–0.5 mg/ml. A minimum volume of 10 μl or approximately 100 pmole is required. Incubate for 4 hr at 37°C. Add sufficient iodoacetic acid in 0.5 *M* NaOH to make the solution 35 m*M* in iodoacetic acid. Incubate for 45 min at room temperature in the dark. Quench the reaction using DTT, 3.5 times the amount of iodoacetic acid.

2. Desalt by gel filtration on a Pharmacia NAP-5 column into 50 m*M* ammonium bicarbonate buffer, pH 8.5. Load the protein solution in 500-μl volume using the ammonium bicarbonate to dilute the reduction/

A

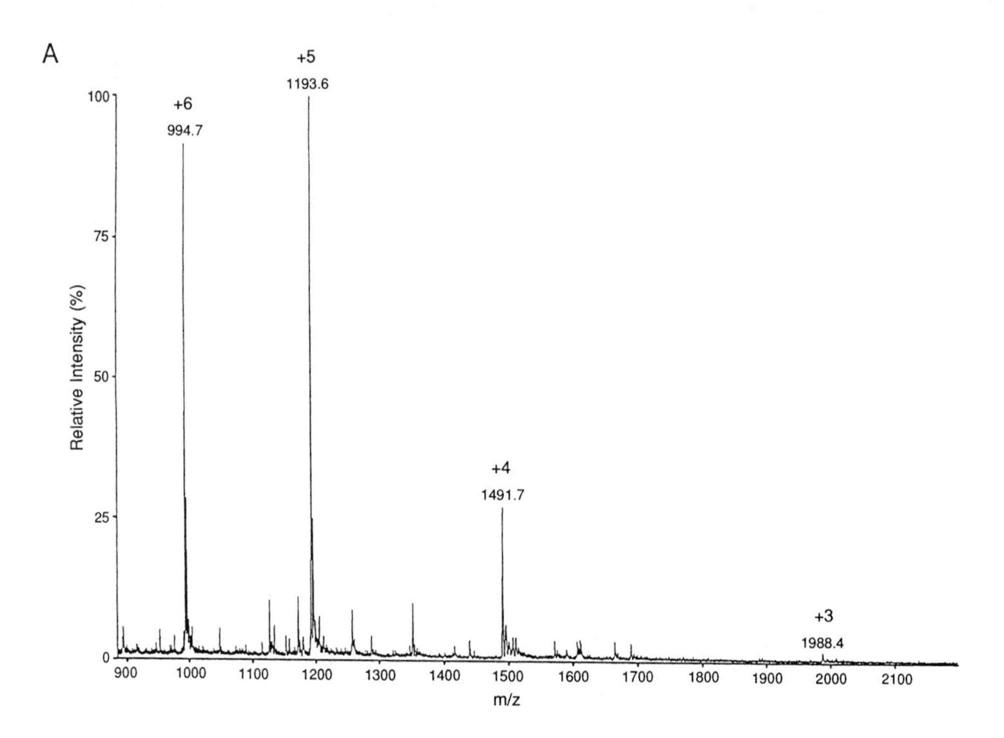

B

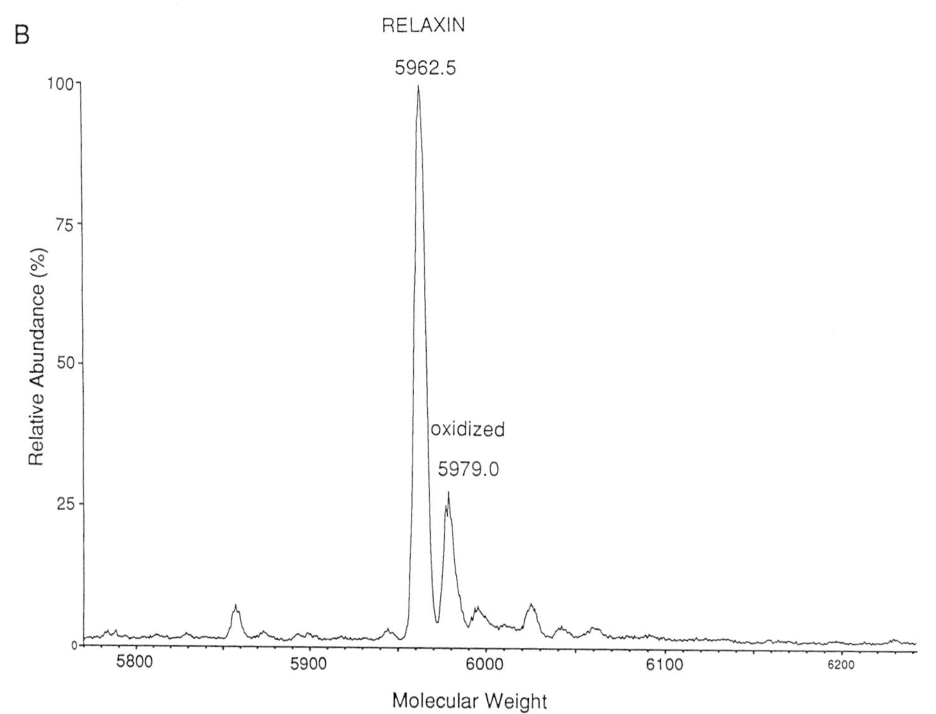

C

B-Chain

MPRLFFFHLLGVCLLLNQFSRAVA↓DSWMEEVIKLCGRELVRAQIAICGMS
TWSKR↓SLSQEDAPQTPRPVAEIVPSFINKDTETINMMSEFVANLPQELKLT
LSEMQPALPQLQQHVPVLKDSSLLFEEFKKLIRNRQSEAADSSPSELKYLGL
DTHSRKKR↓QLYSALANKCCHVGCTKRSLARFC A-Chain

carboxymethylation buffer as necessary. Collect the next 700 μl of eluate containing the desalted protein.

3. Digest with sequencing-grade trypsin at 1:50 enzyme:substrate ratio. Incubate at 37°C for 2 hr. Dry *in vacuo*.

4. Separate 50–100 pmole of proteolytic peptides with an LC Packings capillary C_{18} column (380 μm × 150 mm) using a flow rate of 4 μl/min. The aqueous acetonitrile gradient typically consists of 0–67% solvent B in 60 min.

5. Set the orifice potential or skimmer potential of the mass spectrometer to 80 V. Set the mass resolution to $m/\Delta m$ 1000. Acquire data to disk from 400 to 2000 u at 0.25 u/step and 1 msec/step. Set the mass defect to 50 mmu/100 u.

6. To interpret the LC/MS data file, eliminate background peaks and reduce broad peaks to a single spectrum by computer subtraction routines such as Enhance or Strip Scan (PE/SCIEX). Calculate expected molecular weights for tryptic peptides. Macintosh-based programs are available to do this such as MacBioSpec (formerly MacProMass) and PeptideMap (PE/SCIEX). Match the masses found to the expected molecular weights. To identify modifications, look for masses detected but unmatched; for example, see Fig. 3 and Table 1.

C. GLYCOSYLATION CHARACTERIZATION

See Conboy and Henion (1992), Carr *et al.* (1993), and Huddleston *et al.* (1993b).

Steps

1–4. See Section B for protein reduction, alkylation, digestion, and HPLC.

5. Set the mass resolution to $m/\Delta m$ 1000. Set mass spectrometer for multiple ion scans. Scan for three carbohydrate-fragment masses 204 ($HexNAc^+$), 292 ($NeuAc^+$), and 366 ($Hex\text{-}HexNAc^+$). Use a scan width of 6 u for each ion and set the orifice or skimmer potential for each ion at 160 V. Set the fourth mass window for m/z 1200 with a scan width of 1600 (to scan from 400 to 2000) at an orifice or skimmer potential of 80 V to detect molecular ion species. Set the mass defect to 50 mmu/100 u. Acquire data to disk at 0.25 u/step and 1 msec/step.

6. To interpret the mass spectral data (see step 6 in Section B), extract ion chromatograms for masses 204, 292, and 366. For each chromatographic peak with these fragment ions, identify glycopeptide molecular weights (Fig. 4). Correlate glycopeptide masses with peptides containing asparagine, threonine, or serine residues. For example the observed molecular weights of 3218.4 and 3874.8 were correlated to residues 130–138(Asn) of bovine fetuin (see Fig. 4) plus a biantennary or triantennary complex oligosaccharide.

FIGURE 2 (A) Electrospray ionization mass spectrum of intact relaxin showing multiple charge states in the mass/charge domain. (B) Reconstructed relaxin spectrum in the molecular weight domain. (C) Protein sequence of preprorelaxin showing sites of proteolysis at arrows and the mature sequence underlined. Three disulfide bonds are present in the final active form consisting of disulfide-linked A-chain and B-chain. In addition, the N-terminal glutamine on the B-chain is cyclized to pyroglutamic acid to give a predicted molecular weight of 5963.1. The observed mass of 5962.5 reflects all of these modifications, and the observed mass of 5979.0 shows that a fraction of the molecules contains an oxidized methionine residue. Reprinted, with permission, from Marriott *et al.* (1993).

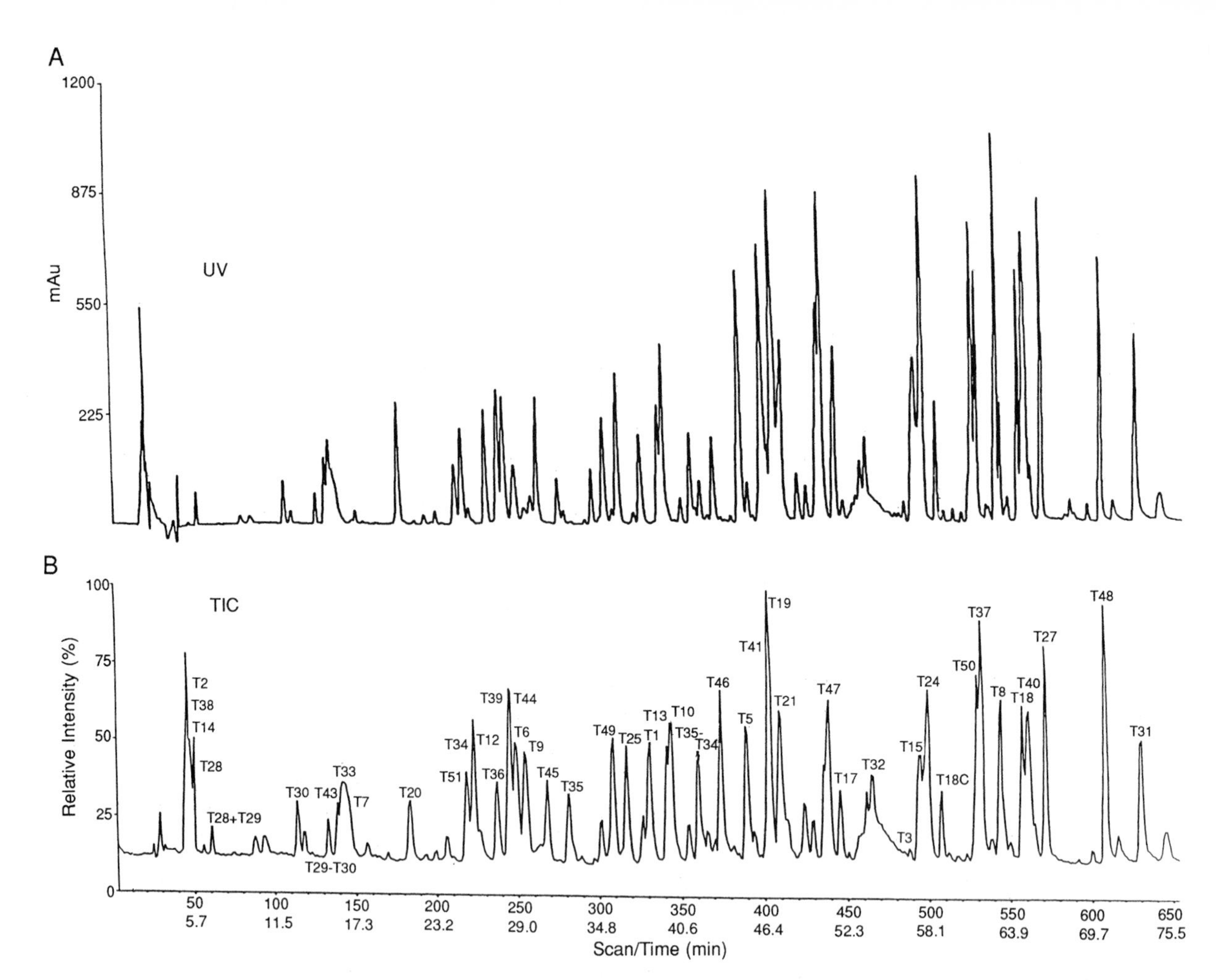

FIGURE 3 HPLC chromatogram of the tryptic peptides produced from recombinant human tissue plasminogen activator (M_r 60 kDa) with UV monitoring (A) or total ion current (TIC) as measured by the electrospray mass spectrometer (B). Reprinted, with permission, from Ling *et al.* (1991). Each tryptic peptide is identified by its order in the sequence from 1 to 51. Glycopeptide masses observed are listed in Table I.

TABLE I Glycopeptides Observed in a LC/MS Analysis

		Expected mass	Observed mass[a]
1	$Man_5GlcNAc_2$-(T11) (high mannose)	4233.46	4231.86
2	$Man_6GlcNAc_2$-(T11) (high mannose)	4395.60	4394.10
3	$Man_7GlcNAc_2$-(T11) (high mannose)	4557.75	4554.60
4	$NANAGal_2Man_3GlcNAc_4Fuc$-(T17) (diantennary)	5136.06	5133.01
5	$NANAGal_2Man_3GlcNAc_4Fuc$-(T45) (diantennary)	3189.49	3188.40
6	$NANA_2Gal_2Man_3GlcNAc_4Fuc$-(T45) (diantennary)	3480.75	3478.20
7	$NANA_2Gal_3Man_3GlcNAc_5Fuc$-(T45) (triantennary)	3846.11	3843.3
8	$NANA_3Gal_3Man_3GlcNAc_5Fuc$-(T45) (triantennary)	4137.37	4134.82

[a] Calculated from monoisotopic weights.

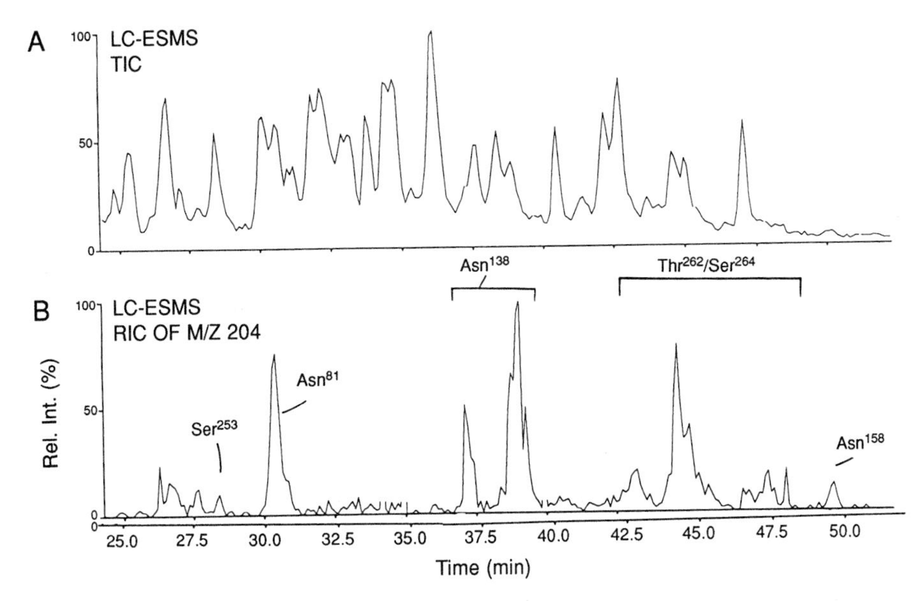

FIGURE 4 HPLC chromatograms of the peptides produced from bovine fetuin by trypsin and Asp-N as measured by the electrospray mass spectrometer: (A) Total ion current (TIC); (B) reconstructed ion chromatogram (RIC) for ion 204. Glycopeptides containing residues Asn 81, Asn 138, Asn 158, Ser 253, and Thr 262/Ser 264 were observed in the LC/MS analysis. Reprinted, with permission, from Carr *et al.* (1993).

D. PHOSPHORYLATION CHARACTERIZATION

See Huddleston *et al.* (1993a) and Nuwaysir and Stults (1993).

Solutions

1. *Reduction buffer:* 10 m*M* dithiothreitol in 6 *M* guanidine, pH 8.5. See Section B, solution 1. Eliminate the EDTA from this buffer.

2. *Alkylation buffer:* 350 m*M* iodoacetic acid in 0.5 *M* NaOH. See Section B, solution 2.

3. *100 mM N-ethylmorpholine:* To make 100 ml, add 1.27 ml N-ethylmorpholine to high-purity water. Adjust the pH to 8.0 with acetic acid.

4. *20% ethanol:* To make 100 ml, add 20 ml ethanol to high-purity water and adjust to 100 ml.

5. *30 mM $FeCl_3$:* To make 10 ml, dissolve 134 mg $FeCl_3$ in high-purity water, stir, and adjust to 10 ml.

6. *Immobilized metal-ion affinity chromatography solutions: Buffer A:* 0.1 *M* acetic acid. To make 10 ml, add 57.5 μl glacial acetic acid to high-purity water and adjust to 10 ml.
Buffer B: High-purity water.
Buffer C: pH 8.0, 0.1% (w/v) ammonium acetate. To make 10 ml, dissolve 10 mg ammonium acetate in high-purity water. Adjust to pH 8.0 with 10% aqueous ammonium hydroxide.
Buffer D: pH 9.5, 0.1% (w/v) ammonium acetate. To make 10 ml dissolve 10 mg ammonium acetate in high-purity water. Adjust to pH 9.5 with 10% aqueous ammonium hydroxide.

Steps

1. Follow reduction and *S*-carboxymethylation procedure as in Section B, step 1.

2. Desalt by gel filtration on Pharmacia NAP-5 columns into 0.1 *M* *N*-ethylmorpholine. Load the protein solution in 500-μl volume using the 0.1 *M* *N*-ethylmorpholine to dilute the reduction/carboxymethylation buffer as necessary. Collect the next 700 μl of eluate containing the desalted protein.

3. Digest with sequencing-grade trypsin at 1:50 enzyme:substrate ratio. Incubate at 37°C for 2 hr.

4. Load a 1-mm-i.d. × 1.6-mm-o.d. × 10-cm-long piece of Teflon tubing with a 20% ethanol slurry of chelating Sepharose Fast Flow. The packing material is compacted by flowing 500 μl of Milli-Q water at 200 μl/min through the column. Activate the column with metal ion by pumping 300 μl of 30 m*M* $FeCl_3$ solution through the column at a rate of 20 μl/min. Wash the excess metal from the column with 2 ml Milli-Q water. Perform a blank run using all buffers before initial use of the column by passing 300 μl each of buffers A, B, C, and D sequentially through the column at 50 μl/min. Reequilibrate with 1 ml of buffer A.

5. Acidify the sample with 50% acetic acid to a pH of 3.5. Load the sample onto the column at a rate of 5 μl/min. Wash the column with 300 μl buffer A at 20 μl/min. Wash column with 300 μl buffer B at 20 μl/min. Wash column with 300 μl buffer C at 20 μl/min. Elute phosphopeptides with 300 μl buffer D directly into the mass spectrometer at 3 μl/min (see step 6). Phosphopeptides will elute as a mixture in one peak.

6. Connect the end union of the column via a 50-cm length of 70-μm-i.d. × 150-μm-o.d. fused silica capillary line to the mass spectrometer ion source. Acquire spectra from 400 to 2200 *m/z* using a step size of 0.5 u, a dwell time of 1.5 msec/step, a mass defect of 50 mmu/100u, and an orifice potential of 80 V. All spectra from on-line metal-ion affinity chromatography are background subtracted to remove buffer and column ions (see Fig. 5).

IV. Pitfalls

1. Detergents and salts interfere with protein molecular weight determinations, so proteins should be isolated to homogeneity in a volatile buffer system. Ideally, proteins are desalted by reverse-phase HPLC in aqueous acetonitrile or methanol solutions. These solvents can be infused directly into the mass spectrometer. Alternatively, proteins can be lyophilized from ammonium bicarbonate, ammonium acetate, or N-ethyl morpholine solutions.

2. Remove any detergents used to solubilize protein before determining molecular weight or digesting for peptide analysis.

3. Disulfide bonding is determined by comparing peptide molecular weights with and without reduction and alkylation.

4. When analyzing the molecular weight of peptides from larger proteins (>30 kDa) a gradient of up to 100 min improves peptide separation.

5. Ammonium bicarbonate or Tris–HCl need to be removed from any digest solutions before metal-ion affinity chromatography is performed. Primary or secondary amines compete for the iron on sample loading. Ultrafiltration and gel filtration are appropriate techniques for exchanging these buffer components.

6. Mass spectrometer potentials were determined on a PE/SCIEX API-III triple

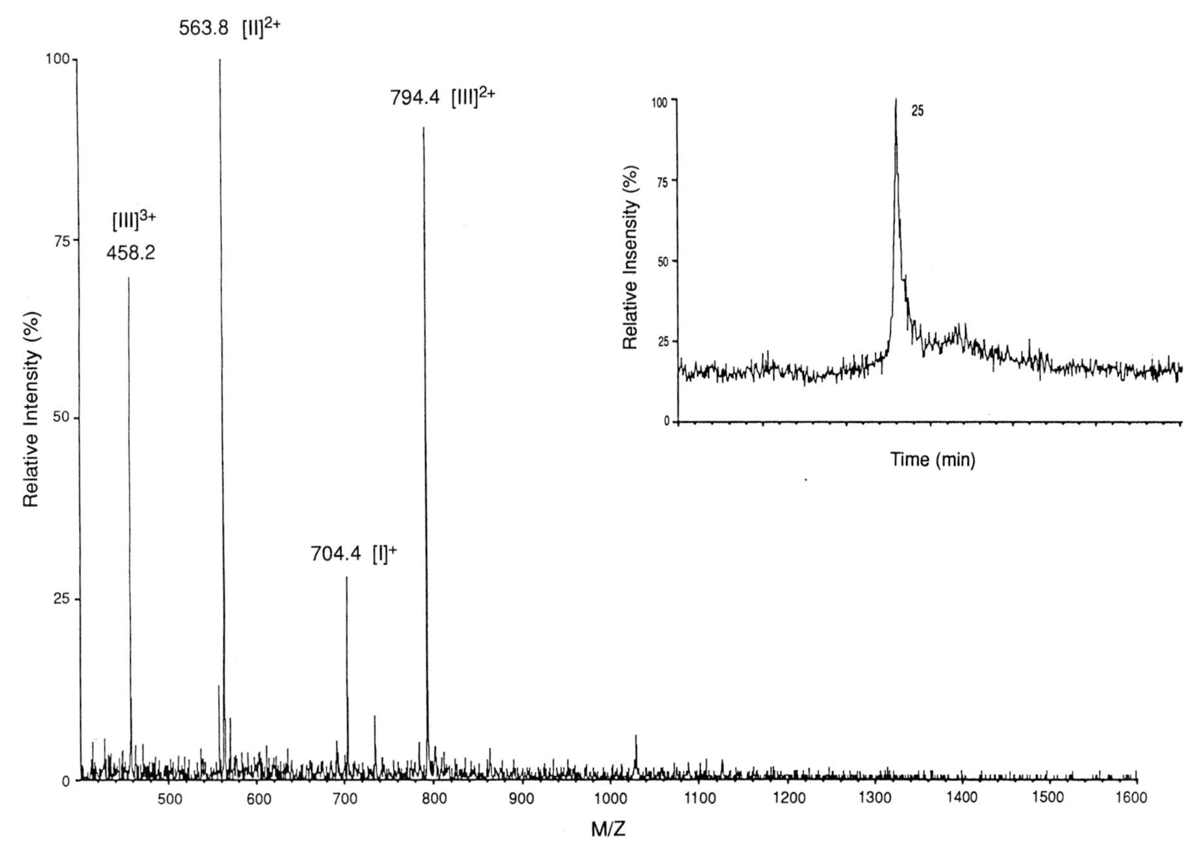

FIGURE 5 On-line immobilized metal-ion affinity chromatography electrospray ionization mass spectrometry of a mixture of three phosphotyrosine peptides. Inset shows the total ion chromatogram for their elution at pH 9.5 (buffer D). Peptide I (GVpYAASG) has a molecular weight of 703.65, peptide II (DRVpYIHPF) has a molecular weight of 1126.18, and peptide III (TFLPVPEpYINQSV) has a molecular weight of 1586.71. Protonated and multiply protonated peptides were observed. Reprinted, with permission, from Nuwaysir and Stults (1993).

quadrupole mass spectrometer with an atmospheric pressure nebulizer-assisted electrospray ionization source. Optimal potentials for other instruments should be experimentally determined using peptides, glycopeptides, or phosphopeptides.

REFERENCES

Carr, S. A., Hemling, M. E., Bean, M. F., and Roberts, G. D. (1991) Integration of mass spectrometry in analytical biotechnology. *Anal. Chem.* **63,** 2802–2824.

Carr, S. A., Huddleston, M. J., and Bean, M. F. (1993) Selective identification and differentiation of N- and O-linked oligosaccharides in glycoproteins by liquid chromatography–mass spectrometry. *Protein Sci.* **2,** 183–196.

Conboy, J. J., and Henion, J. D. (1992) The determination of glycopeptides by liquid chromatography/mass spectrometry with collision-induced dissociation. *J. Am. Soc. Mass Spectrom.* **3,** 804–814.

Fenn, J. B., Mann, M., Meng, C. K., Wong, S. F., and Whitehouse, C. M. (1989) Electrospray ionization for mass spectrometry of large biomolecules. *Science* **246,** 64–67.

Huddleston, M. J., Annan, R. S., Bean, M. F., and Carr, S. A. (1993a) Selective detection of phosphopeptides in complex Mixtures by electrospray liquid chromatography/mass spectrometry. *J. Am. Soc. Mass Spectrom.* **4,** 710–717.

Huddleston, M. J., Bean, M. F., and Carr, S. A. (1993) Collisional fragmentation of glycopeptides by electrospray ionization LC/MS and LC/MS/MS: Method for selective detection of glycopeptides in protein digests. *Anal. Chem.* **65**, 877–884.

Krishna, R. G., and Wold, F. (1993) Post-translational modifications of proteins. *In* "Methods in Protein Sequence Analysis" (K. Imahori and F. Sakiyama, eds.), pp. 167–171. Plenum Press, New York.

Ling, V., Guzetta, A. W., Canova-Davis, E., Stults, J. T., Hancock, W. S., Covey, T. R., and Shushan, B. I. (1991) Characterization of the tryptic map of recombinant DNA derived tissue plasminogen activator by high-performance liquid chromatography–electrospray ionization mass spectrometry. *Anal. Chem.* **63**, 2909–2915.

Marriott, D., Gillece-Castro, B., and Gorman, C. M. (1993) Prohormone convertase-1 will process prorelaxin, a member of the insulin family of hormones. *Mol. Endocrinol.* **6**, 1441–1450.

Nuwaysir, L. M., and Stults, J. T. (1993) Electrospray ionization mass spectrometry of phosphopeptides isolated by on-line immobilized metal-ion affinity chromatography. *J. Am. Soc. Mass Spectrom.* **4**, 662–669.

Plasma Desorption Mass Spectrometry of Peptides and Proteins

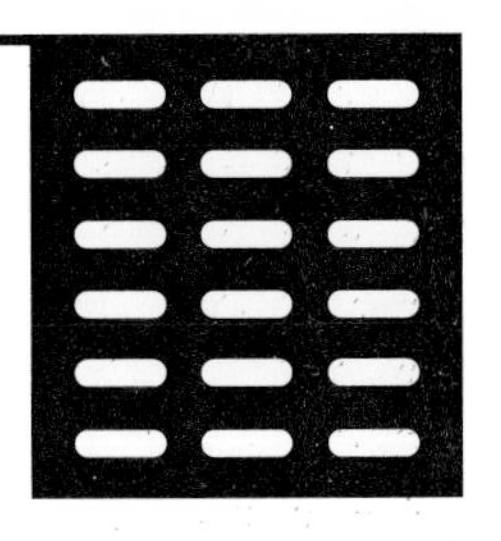

Peter Roepstorff

I. Introduction

Several mass spectrometric techniques including fast atom bombardment (FAB), plasma desorption (PD), matrix-assisted laser desorption/ionization (MALDI), and electrospray (ES) mass spectrometry (MS) are presently available for the analysis of peptides and proteins (Roepstorff and Richter, 1992). Of these techniques, mainly PDMS has gained footing in protein laboratories because the instrumentation is relatively cheap and simple to operate and because, taking advantage of a nitrocellulose matrix, it is compatible with most procedures in protein chemistry (Cotter, 1988; Roepstorff, 1989). Provided that the proper care is taken in the sample preparation procedure most peptides and small proteins (up to 10 kDa) are on a routine basis amenable to analysis by PDMS. Molecular mass information can be obtained with an accuracy of 0.1% or better. Structural information can be gained by application of successive biochemical or chemical procedures to the sample.

II. Materials and Instrumentation

Nitrocellulose membranes (Trans-Blot Transfer Medium, Cat. No. 162-0113) are obtained from Bio-Rad. Acetone, methanol, and acetic acid are analytical grade from Merck. 2-Propanol, acetonitrile, and trifluoroacetic acid are HPLC grade from Rathburn Chemicals Ltd. DTT and ammonium bicarbonate are from Sigma. All enzymes are sequencing grade from Boehringer-Mannheim. All water used is ultrahigh-quality water (UHQ water) purified on an Elgastat UHQ to a minimum of 18 MΩ resistance (Elga).

Plasma desorption mass spectrometer BioIon 20 and aluminized polyester targets are from BioIon. The spin apparatus was homemade (description available from the author). Gilson adjustable automat pipettes (2, 10, 20, 100, and 200 μl) are from Gilson Medical Electronics. The Heto Vac VR1 vacuum centrifuge equipped with a Heto CT110 cold trap is from Heto Lab).

III. Procedures

A. PREPARATION OF NITROCELLULOSE-COVERED TARGETS

Solution

Nitrocellulose solution: To make approximately 1 ml, cut a piece of nitrocellulose membrane (approximately 20 mg), weigh it in an Eppendorf tube,

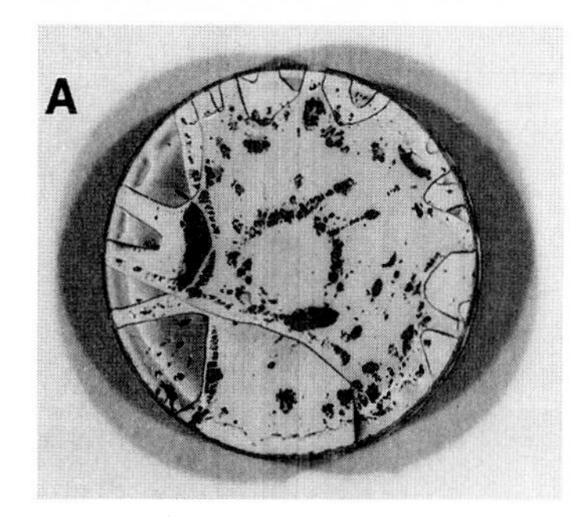

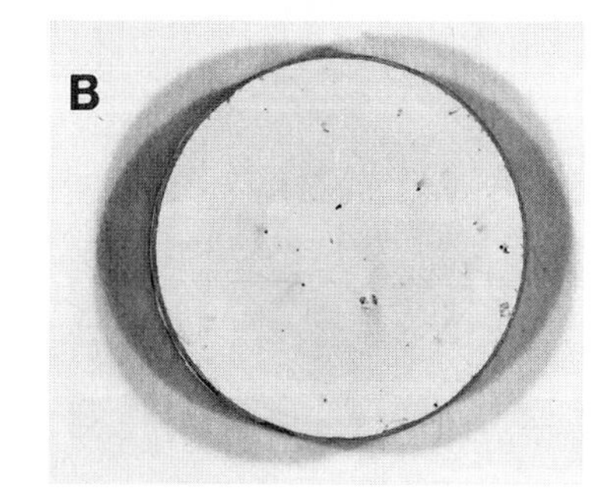

FIGURE 1 Poor (A) and good (B) nitrocellulose targets.

and add 1 ml of acetone per 20 mg of membrane. Solubilize by gently shaking for 10 min. Then dilute 1:1 (v/v) with 2-propanol. The solution must be used within the day of preparation.

Steps

1. Place the aluminized target in the target holder of the spin device and set the spin speed to that empirically determined (see step 5).
2. Add 10 μl nitrocellulose solution dropwise from a 20-μl Gilson automat pipette to the center of the spinning target.
3. Repeat step 2 one to two times until the central area of the target is covered with a reasonable layer of nitrocellulose.
4. Visually inspect the nitrocellulose targets for quality and sort into two categories: high quality for critical samples, i.e., high-molecular-mass M_r or small quantities; lower quality for other samples (Fig. 1).
5. Adjustment of the appropriate spin speed is done empirically by increasing the spin speed stepwise until a homogeneous layer of nitrocellulose is obtained without excessive loss of nitrocellulose solution.

B. APPLICATION OF SAMPLE TO THE NITROCELLULOSE TARGET

Solutions

1. *Sample solvent:* To make 10 ml, combine 100 μl trifluoroacetic acid plus 2.0 ml methanol and make up to a total volume of 10 ml with UHQ water. When appropriate, methanol may be replaced by ethanol or acetonitrile.

2. *Washing solvent:* To make 10 ml, take 100 μl trifluoroacetic acid and make up to a total volume of 10 ml with UHQ water.

Steps

1. To a lyophilized sample in an Eppendorf tube, add 20 to 1000 μl of sample solvent to a final sample concentration of 20 to 1000 pmol/μl.

2. Deposit 2–5 μl (depending on estimated sample concentration) of sample solution in the center of the nitrocellulose target with a 10-μl automat pipette. Increase the spin motor speed gradually to spread the sample solution on the surface. Dry the surface at full speed. Spreading of sample solution and drying propagates from the center and can easily be observed visually.

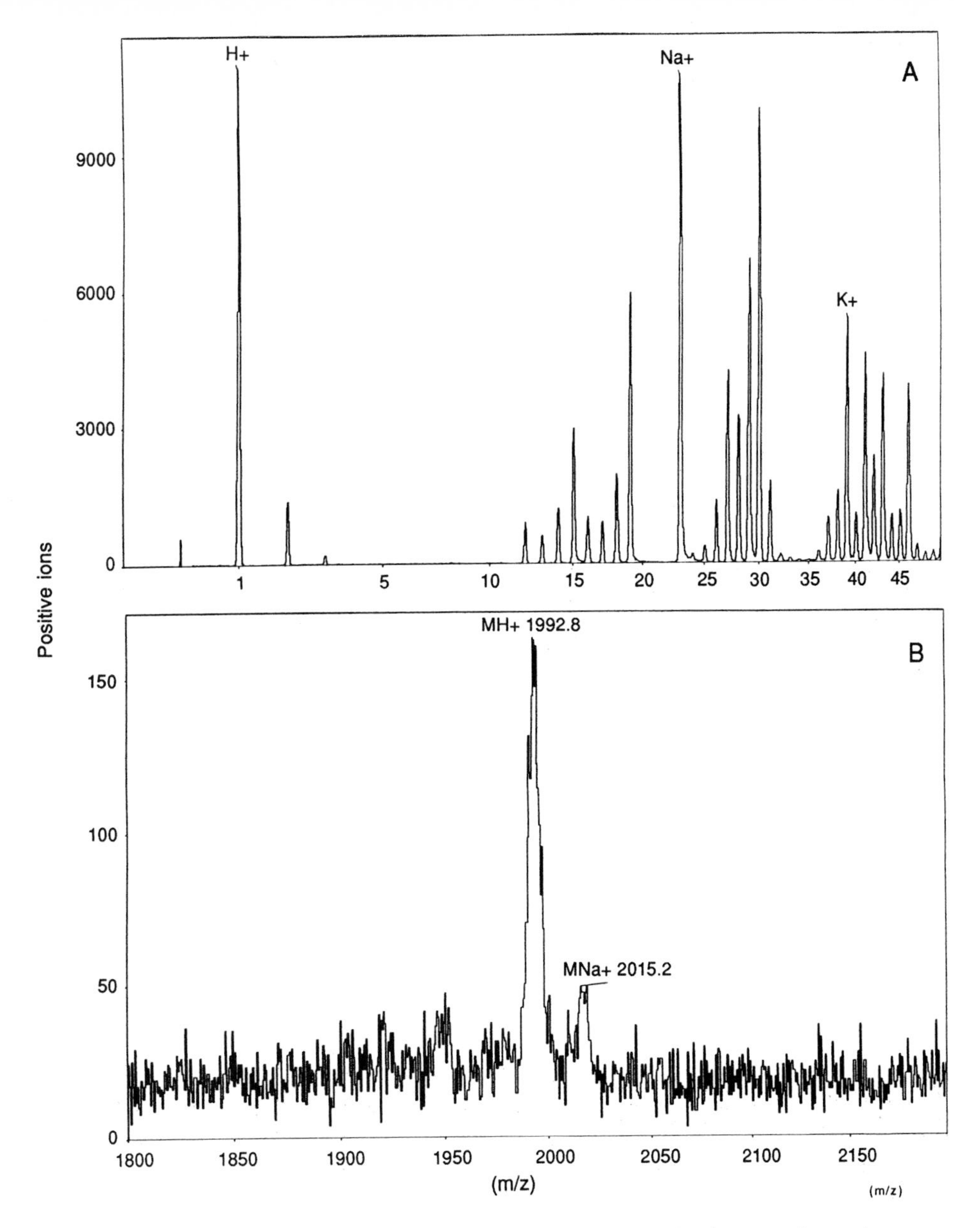

FIGURE 2 (A) Low *m/z* region of a PD spectrum of a peptide showing the peaks corresponding to H^+, Na^+, and K^+ (A). (B) Molecular ion region of the same spectrum. Both show that too large amounts of alkali metals are present in the sample.

3. Introduce the target into the mass spectrometer and record a spectrum for $0.5–1 \times 10^6$ start events.

4. Examine the spectrum for abundance of molecular ions and influence from alkali metal ions. Proceed to step 6 if too large amounts of alkali metal ions are indicated by the ratio between the relative abundances (RAs) of the ions at $m/z = 1$ (H^+), 23 (Na^+), and 39 (K^+) (RA Na^+ + RA K^+/RA H^+ must be less than 0.5) (Nielsen *et al.*, 1988) and/or the amount of Na and K adducts in the molecular ion region is high (Fig. 2). Proceed to step 5 if the signal-to-noise ratio of molecular ions is low in spite of low alkali metal content.

5. Record the spectrum once more for $5–10 \times 10^6$ start events or overnight.

6. Take the target out of the mass spectrometer and mount it on the spin

device. Apply 5 μl of washing solution to the center of the slowly spinning target with an automat pipette. Repeat the procedure one to three times depending on an estimate of the amount of alkali metals present. Dry at full speed and return to step 3.

C. *IN SITU* REACTIONS

Solutions

1. *0.1 M Ammonium bicarbonate:* To prepare 10 ml, dissolve 79 mg ammonium bicarbonate in 8 ml UHQ water. Adjust to the appropriate pH with 50% acetic acid (pH 7.8 and 4.2 are standard solutions in our laboratory). Adjust to 10 ml with UHQ water. Store at 4°C for a maximum of 14 days.

2. *Reduction buffer:* To prepare 200 μl reduction buffer (0.08 *M* DTT, 0.1 *M* ammonium bicarbonate, pH 7.8), dissolve 2.47 mg DTT in 200 μl 0.1 *M* ammonium bicarbonate, pH 7.8. Use the solution immediately.

3. *Enzyme stock preparations:* To make 1 ml trypsin, chymotrypsin, or endoproteinase Glu C stock solution, dissolve 1 mg enzyme in 1 ml UHQ water. Distribute the solution in 50-μl portions in 0.5-ml Eppendorf tubes, lyophilize in a vacuum centrifuge, and store at −20°C. To make 0.2 ml endoproteinase Asp-N stock solution, dissolve 10 μg enzyme in 200 μl UHQ water. Distribute in 10-μl portions, lyophilize, and store as above. To make 100 μl carboxypeptidase Y, A, or M stock solution, dissolve 100 μg enzyme in 100 μl UHQ water. Distribute in 10-μl portions, lyophilize, and store as above.

Steps

1. Remove the target from the mass spectrometer after step 3 in Section B.
2. Place the target on a moist filter paper in a small plastic box.
3. Distribute 5 μl of reduction buffer or enzyme solution on the surface with an automat pipette and place a microscope cover glass on top of the target. *To make the enzyme solution,* redissolve an aliquot of the lyophilized stock solution to a concentration of 1 μg/μl (for endoproteinase Asp-N 0.5 μg/μl) in 0.1 *M* ammonium bicarbonate solution adjusted to the desired pH (for digestion with endoproteinases, pH 7.8 and, for carboxypeptidases, pH 4.2 are generally used).
4. Put the lid on the plastic box and leave it 10 min at ambient temperature for reductions or 30 min at 37°C for enzymatic reactions.
5. Place the target on the spin device, spin-dry, and reanalyze the sample as in steps 2 and 3 of Section B.

D. SAMPLE RECOVERY

Solution

60% 2-Propanol recovery solution: To prepare 10 ml, mix 6 ml 2-propanol with 4 ml 0.1% trifluoroacetic acid solution.

Steps

1. Remove the target from the mass spectrometer after step 3 in Section B or C.

2. Cut the aluminum foil free of the brass ring of the target with a scalpel and place the foil in a 0.5-ml Eppendorf tube.
3. Add 100 μl recovery solution and leave it for 5 min.
4. Transfer the supernatant to another Eppendorf tube and lyophilize in a vacuum centrifuge. The sample can now be dissolved in an appropriate solvent for further studies.

E. TRANSFER OF SAMPLE TO A SEQUENCER

Steps

1. Remove the target from the mass spectrometer after step 3 in Section B.
2. Place the target in a plastic box with a moist filter paper as in step 2 of Section C, and add 10 ml of recovery solution (Section D) to the nitrocellulose surface.
3. Soak a piece of PVDF membrane for the sequencer in recovery solvent and place it on top of the nitrocellulose.
4. Close the lid of the plastic box, and leave it for 10 min. Then remove and dry the PVDF membrane and transfer it to the sequencer.

IV. Comments

The sample solvent described in Section IIIA dissolves most peptides and small proteins. More effective solvents compatible with the nitrocellulose target are up to 5% (v/v) trifluoroacetic acid and up to 50% (v/v) formic acid. Urea, guanidinium chloride, and reducing agents such as mercaptoethanol and dithiothreitol are acceptable if an extensive washing procedure is applied after sample application. Fractions collected from gradient RP-HPLC containing 0.1% trifluoroacetic acid and up to 50% acetonitrile, methanol, ethanol, or 2-propanol may be applied directly without prior lyophilization provided that the sample concentration is sufficient.

The peptide maps obtained on *in situ* reactions are often incomplete due to compound-specific suppression (Nielsen and Roepstorff, 1989). *In situ* reactions are especially valuable to confirm a tentative identification of a peptide based on the determined molecular mass. In such cases confirmation of one or more predicted cleavage sites is sufficient. *In situ* carboxypeptidase digestions are also less effective than digestions carried out in solution. Frequently only the C-terminal residue is identified or the sequence of a few residues can be determined (Klarskov *et al.*, 1989); however, this information is obtained without further sample use and often it is sufficient for confirmation of a peptide identity or a valuable supplement to N-terminal sequencing by Edman degradation.

Samples recovered from the nitrocellulose target have successfully been submitted to HPLC, reduction and alkylation, enzymatic digestion, cleavage with cyanogen bromide, and methyl esterification. Multiple analyses on the sample originally placed on the target, combining recovery, reactions on the recovered sample, HPLC and reapplication of the sample to nitrocellulose for further mass spectrometric analysis, followed by transfer to the sequencer, are possible (Jespersen *et al.*, 1993).

V. Pitfalls

1. Application of the washing procedure described in Section IIIB, step 6, may lead to removal of small and very hydrophilic peptides. If such are suspected to

be present, washing must be omitted or reduced to a single wash with a few microliters of washing solution.

2. The presence of most detergents, especially SDS, is devastating for PDMS of peptides. If detergents cannot be avoided, octyl glycoside has been found to be acceptable (Vorm *et al.,* 1993).

3. The most frequent reason for failure to obtain reasonable molecular ion abundance for peptides below 5 kDa is that the amount of peptide has been overestimated, with the result that too little sample has been applied.

REFERENCES

Cotter, R. J. (1988) Plasma desorption mass spectrometry: Comming of age. *Anal. Chem.* **60,** 781–793.

Jespersen, S., Talbo, G., and Roepstorff, P. (1993) Optimization of sample recovery from the nitrocellulose support used in plasma desorption mass spectrometry and its use for multiple analysis of insulin. *Biol. Mass Spectrom.* **22,** 77–83.

Klarskov, K., Breddam, K., and Roepstorff, P. (1989) C-terminal sequence determination of peptides degraded with carboxypeptidases of different specificity and analyzed by ^{252}Cf plasma desorption mass spectrometry. *Anal. Biochem.* **180,** 28–37.

Nielsen, P. F., Klarskov, K., Højrup, P., and Roepstorff, P. (1988) Optimization of sample preparation for plasma desorption mass spectrometry of peptides and proteins. *Biomed. Environm. Mass Spectrom.* **15,** 305–310.

Nielsen, P. F., and Roepstorff, P. (1989) Suppression effects in peptide mixture analysis by plasma desorption mass spectrometry. *Biomed. Environm. Mass Spectrom.* **18,** 131–137.

Roepstorff, P. (1989) Plasma desorption mass spectrometry of peptides and proteins. *Acc. Chem. Res.* **22,** 421–427.

Roepstorff, P., and Richter, W. J. (1992) Status and developments in mass spectrometry of peptides and proteins. *Int. J. Mass Spectrom. Ion Proc.* **118/119,** 789–809.

Vorm, O., Chait, B. T., and Roepstorff, P. (1993) Mass spectrometry of protein samples containing detergents. Presented at the 41st ASMS Conference on Mass Spectrometry and Allied Topics, San Francisco May 30–June 4, Poster WP 88.

Methods Optimization for the Analysis of Peptides Using Capillary Electrophoresis

Michael Albin and John E. Wiktorowicz

I. Introduction

Capillary electrophoresis (CE) is a relatively new analytical technique (for recent reviews, see Kuhr and Monnig, 1992; Weinberger, 1993) in which separations are performed in narrow inside diameter (i.d.) columns (25–100 μm) at high field strengths (hundreds of volts per centimeter). This results in a number of advantages that include very high resolution separations (to 10^6 plates/m) and rapid separation times (<30 min). The commercialization of automated instrumentation has enabled rapid, *automated* methods development to be performed, employing a number of different separation modes.

Separations in narrow, silica capillaries at high field strengths are defining features of the technique. The narrow diameters permit the use of high fields due to the efficient heat dissipation in the narrow columns. However, the upper operating field is limited to a value at which peak efficiency begins to decline as Joule heating becomes significant. This serves to define the maximum separation voltage, separation medium composition, and capillary diameter. The nature of the separation media and the structure of the analytes influence the observed mobility of the analytes under a given set of conditions. The observed mobility is a sum of the electroosmotic mobility (EOF) and the analyte mobility. The EOF is the bulk flow of liquid due to the surface charge on the capillary. The effect of a number of separation parameters on Joule heating, EOF, and analyte mobility are described below with respect to the optimization of separation conditions.

In any methods development strategy (Applied Biosystems, 1994) one attempts to maximize the separation properties of the technique while exploiting the unique chemical properties of the analytes to obtain the best separation possible. For the electrophoretic separation of peptides, the most critical factor that may affect the ability to achieve an adequate separation is the relationship of net charge and separation pH. The examples below illustrate this relationship for a small set of peptides and then elaborate on optimization parameters and pitfalls with a more complex system.

II. Materials and Instrumentation

All separations were performed on an Applied Biosystems Model 270A-HT automated capillary electrophoresis system. All separation media were prepared using Milli-Q water and filtered through 0.22-μm filters obtained from Gelman Sciences

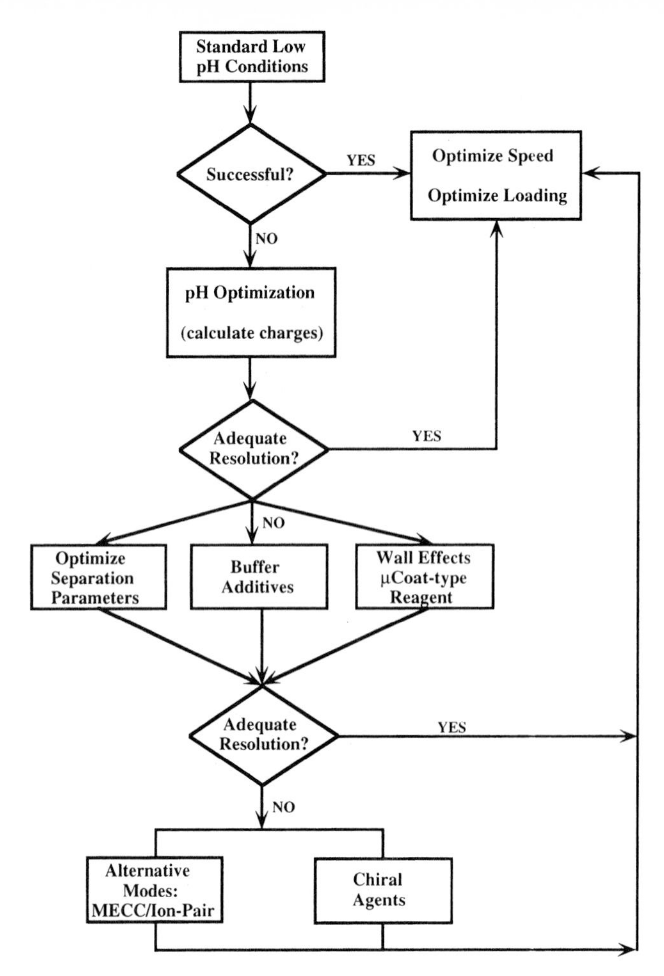

FIGURE 1 Flowchart of methods development strategy.

(Cat. No. 4192) prior to use. Capillaries [50-μm i.d., 365-μm outside diameter (o.d.), 72-cm total length, 50 cm to detector, Applied Biosystems, Cat. No. 0602-0014] were rinsed with 1 *N* NaOH (30 min.), water (5 min), and buffer (5 min) prior to initial use and with 0.1 *N* NaOH (1 min) followed by buffer (3 min) between analyses. Separations using MicroCoat (Applied Biosystems, Cat. No. 401488) followed the manufacturer's protocols. The endosmotic flow for each of the separations was measured by injection of a 1/400 dilution of mesityl oxide (Aldrich Chemical Co., Cat. No. M785-5) in water.

The peptides employed were synthesized on an Applied Biosystems Model 432 peptide synthesizer. Purified cytochrome c (Sigma Chemical Co., Cat. No. C-2506) and its tryptic digest were prepared as described previously (Chang *et al.*, 1993). Calculation of peptide charge as a function of pH was calculated using the program PIAA (Skoog and Wichman, 1986).

III. Procedures

The overall strategy for methods development is illustrated in the flowchart shown in Fig. 1. The individual steps are listed below, and recommended conditions are provided with a brief explanation and an illustrative example that highlights several key points.

A. EVALUATE pH DEPENDENCE OF SEPARATION

- Perform a set of free solution separations as a function of pH.

Points to Consider

1. If a good separation is obtained, narrower pH ranges can be explored to fine-tune the separation.
2. Moderate running conditions are selected and optimized in later steps to keep the running current low and minimize heating effects to prevent loss of resolution.
3. In general, the buffer chosen should have a low absorbance at the wavelength of interest and good buffering capacity at the pH of interest.

Steps

1. Prepare separation buffers at fairly low ionic strength (10–100 m*M*) and filter all reagents using ≤0.45-μm membranes.
2. Perform separations at intermediate field strengths (200–350 V/cm). Initial starting conditions employed for CE were as follows: buffer, 20 m*M* sodium phosphate, pH 2.5; separation, 25 kV, 30°C, 200 nm; injection, 1-sec vacuum; capillary, 72 cm (50 cm to detector), 50-μm i.d.
3. Perform separation using buffers at pH values of 4.0 (sodium acetate), 7.0 (sodium phosphate), and 9.0 (sodium tetraborate).

Figure 2 depicts the separation of three peptide fragments of cytochrome c (1 = CAQCHTVEK, 2 = TGPNLHGLFGR, 3 = IFVQK) at pH values ranging from 2.5 to 9.0 using 20 m*M* buffers and for the complete tryptic digest of horse heart cytochrome c (see Wheat *et al.*, 1991). Individual separation conditions are given in the figure captions. The following points are evident:

A change in the elution order is observed that is attributable to the change in individual peptide charge as a function of pH (see Table I). The relative charges of the peptides can be discerned from the elution order and position of a peak relative to a neutral species. Figure 2 reveals the more positive peptides appearing earliest.

An optimal pH region is directly discernible from the automated run and may be estimated from calculated charges if the sequences of individual peptides are known (a number of detailed studies on correlations between mobility and peptide physical properties have been performed, see Grossman *et al.*, 1988; Florance *et al.*, 1991; Issaq *et al.*, 1992; Rickard *et al.*, 1991).

At pH 4.0 there is considerable peak tailing due to analyte interaction with the bare silica capillary wall (p*I* of fragments > analysis pH).

B. OPTIMIZE KEY PARAMETERS

- Optimize resolution and analysis time for a given pH (chosen from step 1) as a function of buffer ionic strength, separation voltage, and temperature.

Points to Consider

1. An increase in ionic strength (at fixed voltage) will result in a decrease in peptide mobility at a given pH value. Additionally, a higher ionic strength may produce narrower peaks due to inhibition of analyte adsorption and sample

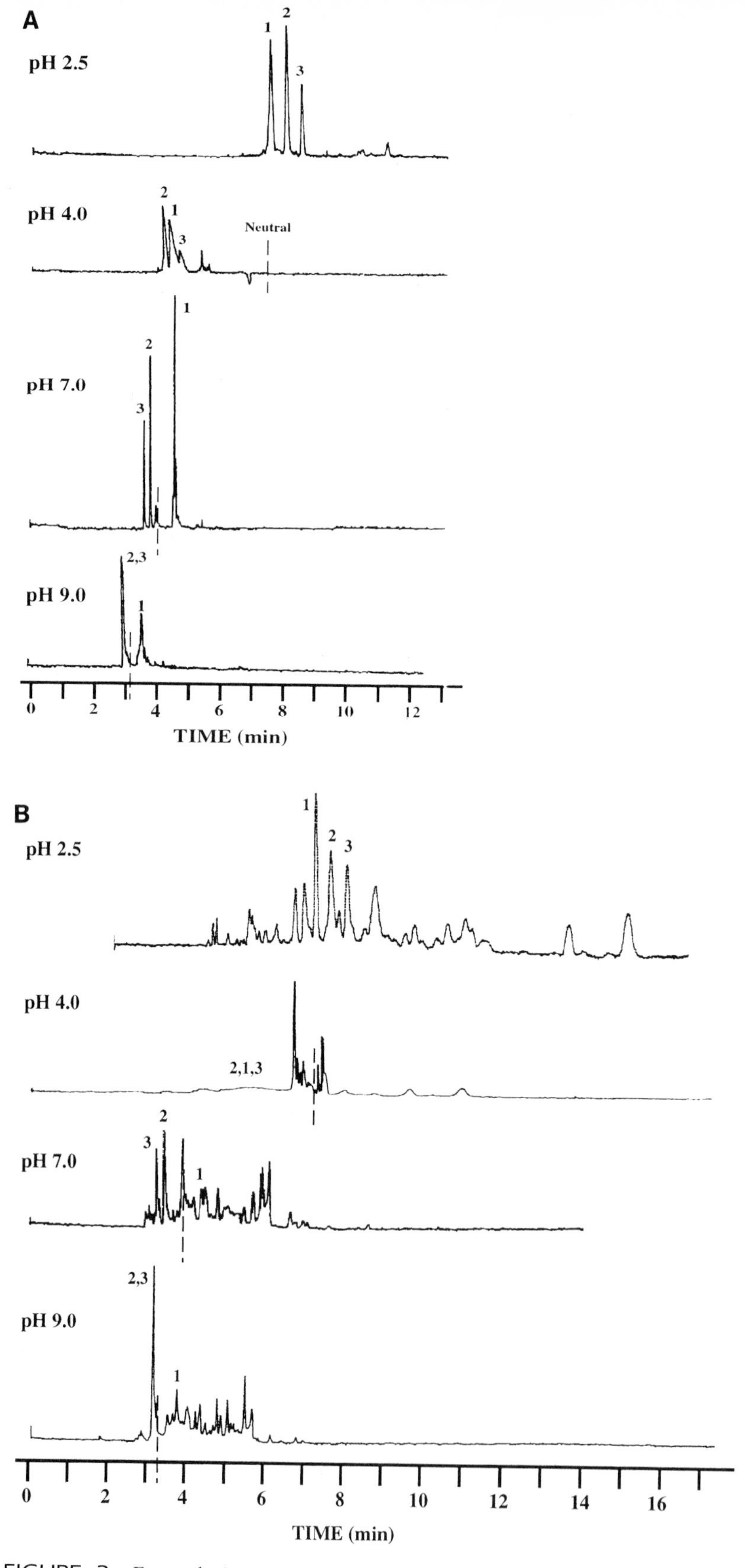

FIGURE 2 Free solution separation of model peptides and tryptic digest of cytochrome c. Capillary: 72 cm (50 cm to detector), 50-μm id; injection: 1-sec vacuum; analysis: 200 nm, 30°C; sample: ~100 μg/mL each peptide in water, ~100 μg/mL tryptic digest; buffer: sodium phosphate (pH 2.5, 7.0), sodium acetate (pH 4.0), sodium tetraborate (pH 9.0), 20 m*M* in all cases.

TABLE I Calculated Peptide Charges

	pH			
	2.5	4.0	7.0	9.0
CAQCHTVEK (1)	2.318	1.672	−0.003	−1.713
TGPNLHGLFGR (2)	2.323	2.005	1.083	0.569
IFVQK (3)	1.334	1.016	0.997	0.776

stacking (see step 3) effects until the point at which Joule heating becomes significant (see Vindevogel and Sandra, 1992).

2. An increase in voltage (field strength) will result in faster electrophoretic velocities and higher peak efficiencies until the system's ability to efficiently dissipate heat is exceeded. The simplest way to identify the maximum field strength tolerable is to monitor the current generated by the system at increasing voltages. As the system loses the ability to remove the generated heat, the relationship between applied voltage and generated current departs from linearity. The inflection point of the voltage: current relationship (Ohm's Law plot) defines the maximum field strength tolerable by the system.

3. An increase in temperature will result in faster ion mobilities as buffer viscosity decreases with increasing temperature. Care should be exercised as the buffer pH, and therefore the overall separation, can also be affected.

Steps

1. Optimize buffer ionic strength: For the chosen pH perform separations at increasing buffer concentrations until the current exceeds 150 μA.

2. Optimize field strength for optimal buffer formulation: Wash the capillary with base (0.1 *N* NaOH) for ~2 min, followed by the separation buffer for 5 min at the highest hydrodynamic flow available for the system. Apply increasing voltages (5 to 30 kV) for a few seconds and record the current generated. Construct an Ohm's law plot to select optimal field strength (see above).

3. Vary separation temperature at selected buffer conditions to slow down or speed up separation.

Figure 3 shows the effect of different separation parameters on the overall electropherogram for the more complicated separation of the tryptic digestion of cytochrome c. The starting point is the separation achieved at pH 7.0 in Fig. 2. Figure 3A demonstrates the importance of selecting an appropriate ionic strength for the separation. Figures 3B and 3C demonstrate the effects of separation parameters that can be readily adjusted in an automated fashion to modify separation speed and efficiency.

C. OPTIMIZING INJECTION/SENSITIVITY

• Inject sufficient material to ensure good quantitation while maintaining adequate resolution.

Points to Consider

In general, for samples with high UV absorptivity, sample concentrations greater than 10 μg/ml will yield reasonable signals using hydrodynamic injections, irrespec-

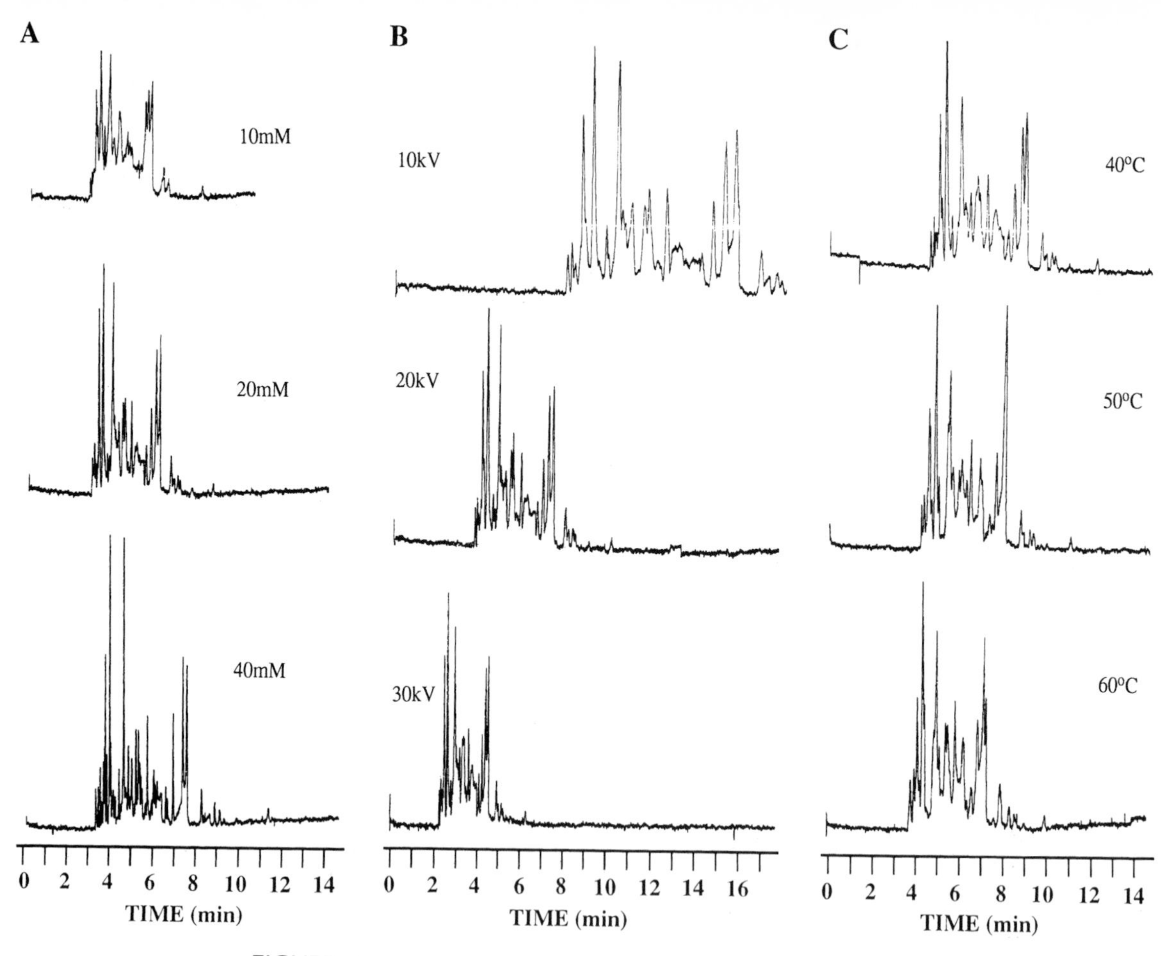

FIGURE 3 Separation of tryptic fragments of horse heart cytochrome c at pH 7.0. (A) Ionic strength dependence—30°C, 25 kV. (B) Field strength dependence—20 m*M* sodium phosphate, 30°C. (C) Temperature dependence—20 m*M* sodium phosphate, 15 kV.

tive of the sample matrix. The injection time can be increased to obtain better signal sensitivity; however, too large an injection will severely impact resolution. A number of methods are available to increase the injection volume while maintaining narrow sample zones and thereby improving sensitivity (Albin *et al.*, 1993). Significant enhancements are observed as the ionic strength of the separation buffer is increased with respect to the sample matrix, or the sample matrix conductivity is decreased ("stacking").

Step

Increase injection (hydrodynamic) time until analyte resolution for a given separation is impaired. If sensitivity is still inadequate the following may be tried:

Increase separation ionic strength relative to sample matrix and perform electrokinetic injection (injection at ~5 kV).

Increase capillary diameter and reoptimize separation. Note that the optimal field strength will be lower due to greater Joule heating in the larger-diameter capillary and may impact overall resolution.

It is clear from the above methodology that several of the parameters are coopera-

TABLE II Separation Parameters: Effects on Separation

Parameter	Result of Increase	Comments
pH	Increases EOF	Can effect analyte charge(s)
Ionic strength	Decreases EOF Increases sample stacking Can limit wall interactions	Must keep Joule heating under control
Field strength	Increases EOF	Can result in higher efficiences Must keep Joule heating under control
Temperature	Decreases buffer viscosity Increases mobilities	Can alter buffer pH, thereby affecting selectivity Peptides with higher-order structure may change behavior
Buffer additives		
Surfactants	Anionic: increases EOF Alternative separation mode	Can afford sample solubility
Organics	Typically decreases EOF	Can affect selectivity
Metal ions	Reduces wall interactions	Can affect selectivity
Urea	Solubilizes analytes	
Chiral reagents	Enhances selectivity for chiral analytes	
Capillary inside diameter	Increases Joule heating (higher running currents)	May yield greater sensitivity

tive in their effects. Table II indicates the effects of individual parameters on a separation. In general, once an initial separation has been achieved, the interplay of ionic strength, field strength, and stacking effects/sensitivity can be systematically investigated. For example, if lower buffer ionic strengths do not adversely affect resolution, then the lowest possible should be selected. Current will be proportionately decreased, as will the power, and higher held strengths are permitted. However, this will limit the effectiveness of sample stacking techniques.

Another factor is the internal diameter of the capillary. A decrease in capillary diameter will result in a decrease in the current flow as well as an increase in the thermal efficiency of the system. Higher field strengths can then be used. The penalty to be paid will be a shorter detection path length. Higher analyte concentrations will be necessary to exploit this alternative, or various injection chemistries that "stack" sample at the point of injection must be employed.

IV. Pitfalls

If the above procedures do not provide satisfactory results, several courses of action are available.

A. ALTERNATIVE SEPARATION MODES

A number of other separation mechanisms can be realized by simply altering the nature of the separation medium. Micellar electrokinetic capillary chromatography (MECC) involves the use of charged surfactants in the separation media where analytes partition between aqueous and micellar phases (Terabe *et al.*, 1984; Vindevogel and Sandra, 1992; Terabe, 1992). In this mode, highly polar analytes elute

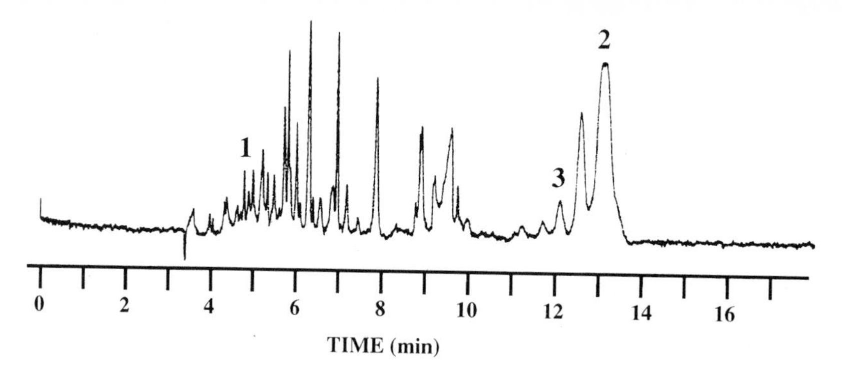

FIGURE 4 Alternative separation methods for model peptides/cytochrome c digest—MECC. Buffer: 20 m*M* sodium tetraborate, 100 m*M* SDS, pH 9.0. All other conditions as in Fig. 2.

earliest (remain in aqueous phase in the prevalent case where the charges of the micelle and analyte are the same) and more hydrophobic species (residing within the micelle) elute at later times. This mode allows for the analysis of neutral as well as charged analytes.

Figure 4 shows the separation of the cytochrome c digest employing an alternative separation mechanism (MECC) illustrating the quite different selectivity that can be obtained. The different separation mechanism can often provide additional structural clues as to the physical properties of the peptides (hydrophobicity).

Ion-pairing reagents such as hexanesulfonic acid can be added to the micellar separation media to modify the interaction between ionic analytes and micelles. A cationic ion-pairing agent will enhance the interaction between anionic analytes and anionic micelles.

Buffer additives may also be used in the separation media to adjust the electroendosmotic flow, modify analyte mobility, enhance the solubility of components, or reduce wall interactions (Terabe, 1992; Mosher, 1990). The relative effects of different agents are indicated in Table II.

B. CHIRAL RESOLUTION

Chiral peptides can be resolved by the addition of chiral reagents to the separation media. Cyclodextrins or bile salts have been employed for this purpose (Terabe, 1992).

C. WALL INTERACTION

In many cases broad, asymmetric peaks are observed that can be indicative of solute interactions with the capillary wall. If cationic analytes are involved, this behavior is to be expected, since at pH 4.0, silanols are deprotonated and will attract cationic species (e.g., basic residues of peptide side chains).

One approach to minimize these interactions is accomplished by the method of charge reversal (Wiktorowicz and Colburn, 1990). This approach reversibly coats the capillary surface with a polymeric cationic reagent. The reversal of capillary surface charge serves to repel the cationic peptides and minimize wall interactions. In addition, the polymeric character of the coating agent binds strongly enough to the capillary that its presence in the separation buffer is not required. Thus the unique chemical properties of the peptides can be exploited in the separations without the

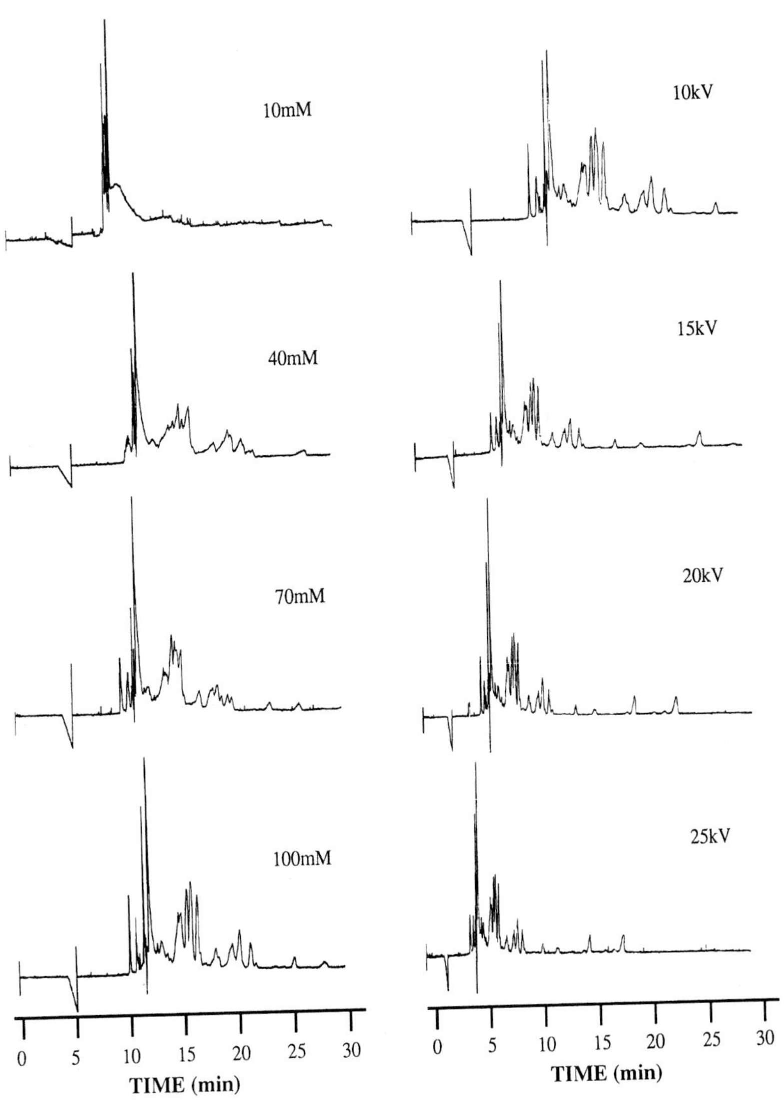

FIGURE 5 Separation of tryptic fragments of horse heart cytochrome c: Charge-reversed—pH 4.0, sodium acetate, 200 nm, 30°C; ionic strength dependence at −10 kV, field strength dependence at 100 m*M* buffer concentration.

potential for coating reagent:peptide interaction which may mask these chemical properties and complicate the analysis.

The ability to inhibit wall interaction is demonstrated in Fig. 5. The complete tryptic digest of cytochrome c is analyzed at pH 4.0, with optimization accomplished by modifying the ionic strength of the buffer and separation field strength. A dramatic improvement in the separation is achieved by increasing the ionic strength. From these data, the best separation conditions can easily be identified, and the complex mixture spiked with the isolated peptides to identify them within the mixture.

REFERENCES

Albin, M., Grossman, P. D., and Moring, S. E. (1993) Sensitivity enhancement for capillary electrophoresis. *Anal. Chem.* 65, 489A–498A.

Applied Biosystems (1994) "Methods Development Guide to Capillary Electrophoresis." Foster City, CA.

Chang, I-J., Gray, H. B., and Albin, M. (1993) Characterization of protein modification sites in metalloproteins using capillary electrophoresis. *Anal. Biochem.* **212**, 24–27.

Florance, J. R., Konteatis, Z. D., Macielag, M. J., Lessor, R. A., and Galdes, A. (1991) Capillary zone electrophoresis studies of motilin peptides. Effects of charge, hydrophobicity, secondary structure and length. *J. Chromatogr.* **559**, 391–399.

Grossman, P. D., Wilson, K. J., Petrie, G., and Lauer, H. H. (1988) Effect of buffer pH and peptide composition on the selectivity of peptide separations by capillary zone electrophoresis. *Anal. Biochem.* **173**, 265–270.

Issaq, H. J., Janini, G. M., Atamna, I. Z., Muschik, G. M., and Lukszo, J. (1992) Capillary electrophoresis separation of small peptides: Effect of pH, buffer additives, and temperature. *J. Liq. Chromatogr.* **15**, 1129–1142.

Kuhr, W. G., and Monnig, C. A. (1992) Capillary electrophoresis. *Anal. Chem.* **64**, 389R–407R.

Mosher, R. A. (1990) The use of metal ion-supplemented buffers to enhance the resolution of peptides in capillary zone electrophoresis. *Electrophoresis* **11**, 765–769.

Rickard, C., Strohl, M. M., and Nielsen, R. G. (1991) Correlation of electrophoretic mobilities from capillary electrophoresis with physiochemical properties of proteins and peptides. *Anal. Biochem.* **197**, 197–207.

Skoog, B., and Wichman, A. (1986) Calculation of the isoelectric points of polypeptides from the amino acid composition. *Trends Anal. Chem.* **5**, 82–83.

Terabe, S. (1992) Selectivity manipulation in micellar electrokinetic chromatography. *J. Pharm. Biomed. Anal.* **10**, 705–715.

Terabe, S., Otsuka, K., Ichikawa, A., and Ando, T. (1984) Electrokinetic separations with micellar solutions and open-tubular capillaries. *Anal. Chem.* **56**, 111–113.

Vindevogel, J., and Sandra, P. (1992) "Introduction to Micellar Electrokinetic Chromatography." Hüthig, Heidelberg.

Weinberger, R. (1993) "An Integrated Approach. Practical Capillary Electrophoresis." *Academic Press,* New York.

Wheat, T. E., Young, P. M., and Astephen, N. E. (1991) Use of capillary electrophoresis for the detection of single-residue substitutions in peptide mapping. *J. Liq. Chromatogr.* **14**, 987–998.

Wiktorowicz, J. E., and Colburn, J. C. (1990) Separation of cationic proteins via charge reversal in capillary electrophoresis. *Electrophoresis* **11**, 769–777.

SECTION G

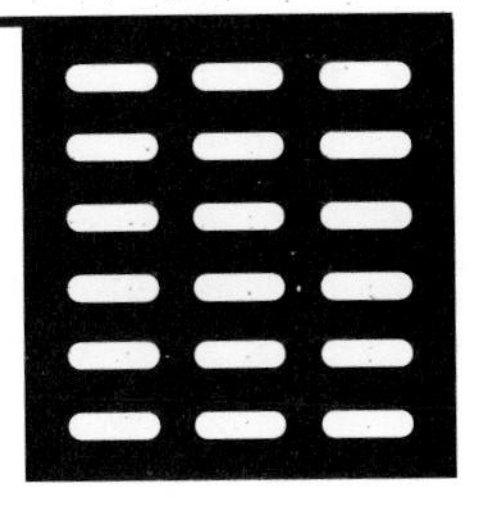

Amino Acid Analysis

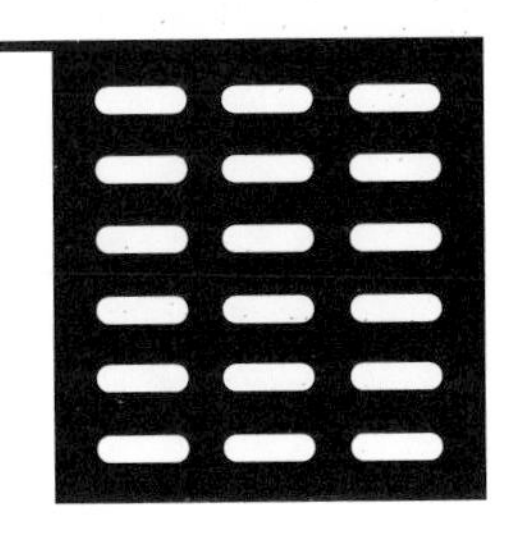

Amino Acid Analysis on Microscale from Electroblotted Proteins

Friedrich Lottspeich, Christoph Eckerskorn, and Rudolf Grimm

I. Introduction

Amino acid analysis is routinely used to determine the amount and the composition of proteins, peptides, and free amino acids. Proteins today often are isolated by SDS–PAGE and electroblotting onto a chemically inert membrane like polyvinylidenfluoride (PVDF) (Matsudaira, 1987) or modified glass fiber (Eckerskorn *et al.*, 1988a; Eckerskorn and Lottspeich, 1993). The only possibility of quantifying those membrane-bound proteins is amino acid analysis directly from the membrane (Eckerskorn *et al.*, 1988b; Ploug *et al.*, 1989; Tous *et al.*, 1989; Nakagawa and Fukuda, 1989).

Amino acid analysis involves two major steps: complete hydrolysis of proteins and peptides, followed by quantification of the amino acids liberated. Hydrolysis is the most crucial step, especially susceptible to contamination and to loss of sample. With submicrogram amounts of samples it has to be performed in gas phase, because of reduced contamination compared with liquid hydrolysis.

High-sensitivity amino acid analysis is usually done by precolumn derivatization (for a review, see Lottspeich and Henschen, 1982) followed by reverse-phase HPLC in an fully automated and dedicated instrument. The described combined *o*-phthaldialdehyde (OPA)/9-fluoromethoxycarbonyl (FMOC) derivatization of the amino acid has the advantage of being sensitive and, at the same time, reacting with all amino acids commonly present in proteins (Schuster, 1988).

In this protocol, amino acid analysis on the submicrogram level of proteins and peptides electroblotted onto PVDF as well as in solution is described.

II. Materials and Instrumentation

Amino acid standards (10, 25, and 100 pmole, Cat. Nos. 5061-3334, 5061-3333, and 5061-3332), OPA reagent (Cat. No. 5061-3335), FMOC reagent (Cat. No. 5061-3337), and 0.4 *N* borate buffer (Cat. No. 5061-3339) were obtained from Hewlett–Packard. Sodium acetate (Cat. No. 6267) and 37% hydrochloric acid (Cat. No. 13386) were from Merck, and methanol, acetonitrile, and tetrahydrofuran from Baker. Triethylamine (Cat. No. 90340) was obtained from Fluka.

Microvials (100 μl, Cat. No. 5180-0844), 2-ml vials (Cat. No. 5182-0538), 8-mm crimp caps (Cat. No. 5180-0842), 11-mm crimp caps (Cat. No. 5181-1210), and crimping tool (Cat. No. 8710-1643) were from Hewlett–Packard. Protein hydrolysis was carried using the Pico-Tag hydrolysis workstation and reaction vessels (Waters Millipore). All amino acid analyses were performed on the Hewlett–

Packard AminoQuant amino acid analysis system. The analyzer consists of the standard 1090 HPLC Series II system equipped with autosampler, autoinjector, temperature-controlled column compartment and built-in diode-array detector. The system is run with AminoQuant software. Separation of the amino acid derivatives was performed on Hewlett–Packard amino acid analysis column (Cat. No. 79916AA-572). The Speed-Vac concentrator (Savant) was preferentially equipped with a membrane vacuum pump (DIVAC 2.4L, Leybold).

III. Procedures

A. HYDROLYSIS OF ELECTROBLOTTED PROTEINS

Solutions

1. *Hydrolyzing acid:* Prepare 100 ml 6 *N* HCl containing 0.5% (w/v) by diluting 63 ml of a 37% (i.e., about 10 *N*) HCl with 37 ml double-distilled water. Dissolve 0.5 g phenol in the hydrolyzing acid by carefully stirring up to complete dissolution of the phenol crystals. Store at room temperature. Refresh the solution monthly.

2. *Wash solution:* 50% (v/v) acetonitrile in water with 0.1% trifluoroacetic acid (TFA). To prepare a 100-ml solution, dilute 50 ml acetonitrile in 50 ml double-distilled water. Add 100 μl TFA and stir carefully. Store at room temperature.

3. *Reconstitution solution:* 0.4 *N* borate buffer containing 50 pmole norvaline and 50 pmole sarcosine. Weigh 29.3 mg norvaline and 22.3 mg sarcosine and transfer them to a 50-ml graduated flask. Make up to 50 ml with 0.1 *N* HCl. Mark the flask 5 nmole ISTD (internal standard). To prepare 10 ml of the reconstitution solution, dilute 100 μl of the 5-nmole ISTD solution in 9.9 ml of 0.4 *N* borate buffer. Store in the refrigerator.

Steps

Ensure that immediately after the destaining procedure, the stained PVDF blot containing the protein bands is washed extensively with double-distilled water. In Fig. 1, steps 2, 3, and 5 are shown schematically.

1. Mark the glass microvials with a glass engraver.

2. Excise with a scalpel the Coomassie blue-stained protein bands carefully, so that only stained (protein containing) membrane slices are used for hydrolysis.

3. Place the excised protein bands with Teflon tweezers into the microvials.

4. Pipette 50 μl of the 10-, 25-, and 100-pmole amino acid standards into microvials and dry them down in a Speed-Vac.

5. Bring all microvials into the Pico-Tag reaction vessels and pipette 200 μl of the hydrolyzing acid at the bottom of the vessel. Evacuate the vessel up to 100 mbar on the Pico-Tag hydrolysis workstation. Purge the vessel for 15 sec with nitrogen. Repeat evacuation and nitrogen purging twice. Leave the vessel finally under vacuum and bring the evacuated vessel into the hydrolysis station which has been preheated to 155°C. Perform evacuation and nitrogen purging carefully to completely rid the vessel of oxygen. Otherwise, methionine, serine, threonine, and tyrosine residues will be oxidized!

6. Run the hydrolysis for 100 min to achieve complete protein hydrolysis.

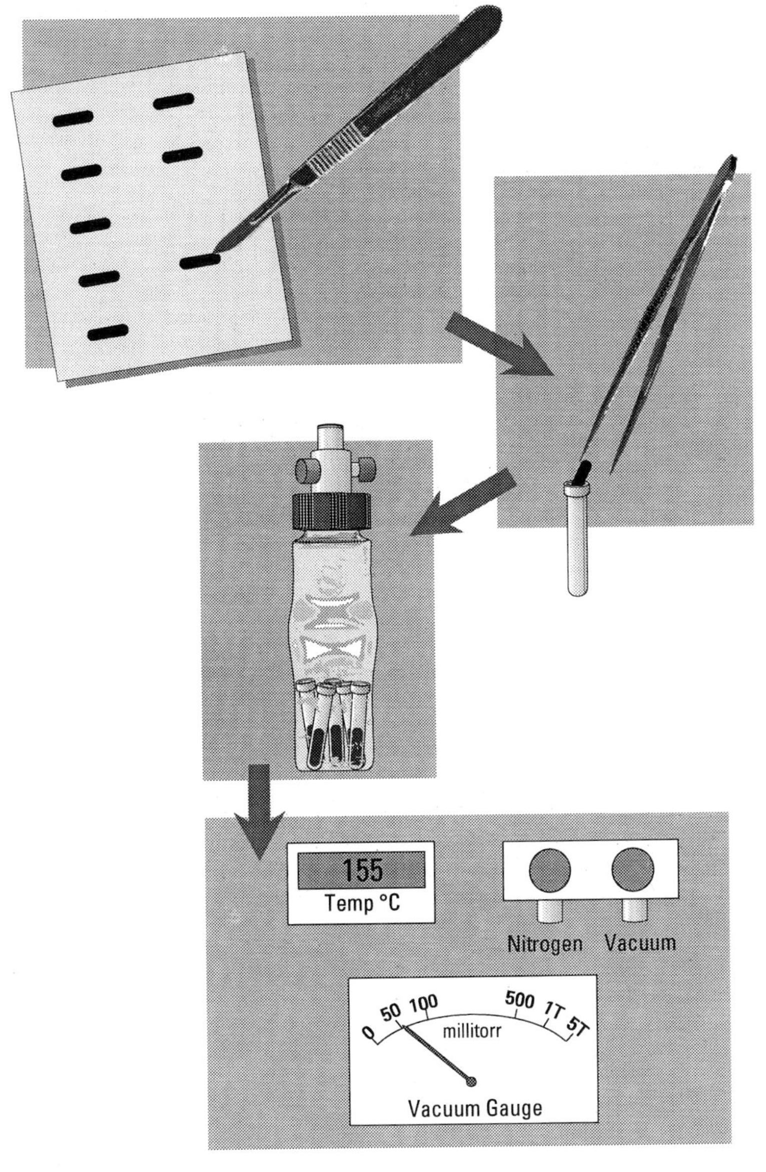

FIGURE 1 Schematic drawing of steps 2, 3, and 5 of the hydrolysis protocol for electroblotted proteins.

7. Take the reaction vessel out of the hydrolysis station and keep the vessel at room temperature to cool down. Open the reaction vessel carefully, and place the microvials with Teflon tweezers into a Speed-Vac.

8. Dry the microvials for 20 min in the Speed-Vac.

9. Place the microvials with Teflon tweezers in a microvial rack and add 100 μl of the wash solution (50% acetonitrile with 0.1% TFA).

10. Cap the vials and vortex the microvials for 15 sec.

11. Decap the microvials and place the microvials with Teflon tweezers into the Speed-Vac. Dry down to complete dryness (about 1–1.5 hr).

12. Remove the membrane slices from the microvials by turning them around and carefully hitting them with one finger.

13. Dissolve the dried down protein hydrolysate with 10 μl and the amino

TABLE I Amino Acid Composition of BSA Electroblotted onto PVDF

Amino acid	Retention time (time)	Found	Lit.
Asx	1.263	58.3	56
Glx	1.440	76.2	77
Ser	4.200	27.3	28
His	5.124	15.4	17
Gly	5.333	30.5	16
Thr	5.688	31.9	34
Ala[a]	7.022	46.0	46
Arg	7.244	22.2	23
Tyr	8.731	17.6	19
Val	10.750	35.1	36
Met	11.027	3.5	4
Phe	12.373	25.8	27
Ile	12.609	14.4	14
Leu	13.255	60.9	61
Lys	13.933	54.2	59
Pro	17.483	28.4	28

[a] Ala was taken as reference amino acid.

acid standards with 50 μl of 0.4 *N* borate buffer containing 50 pmole norvaline and 50 pmole sarcosine by vortexing for 15 sec each.

14. Proceed to the analysis of amino acids, i.e., Section C.

B. HYDROLYSIS OF PROTEINS AND PEPTIDE IN SOLUTION

Follow exactly the protocol given in Section A, except:

1. In step 2, put the dissolved salt-free sample in the bottom of the microvial.
2. In step 3, dry down completely the sample in a Speed-Vac.
3. Omit step 12.

C. SEPARATION OF THE AMINO ACIDS

Place the microvials into the autosampler of the amino acid analyzer system. Put 100-μl aliquots of OPA and FMOC reagents as well as 1 ml of 0.4 *N* borate buffer into the autosampler and start the fully automated amino acid analyzer system as described in the manufacturer's manual.

IV. Comments

A representative analysis of bovine serum albumin electroblotted onto PVDF is given in Table I. The corresponding chromatogram is shown in Fig. 2. Under the standard conditions given, asparagine and glutamine are completely converted to aspartic acid and glutamic acid, respectively. Destruction of serine (up to 50%) and threonine (up to 30%) is usually expected. Cysteine and tryptophan are destroyed

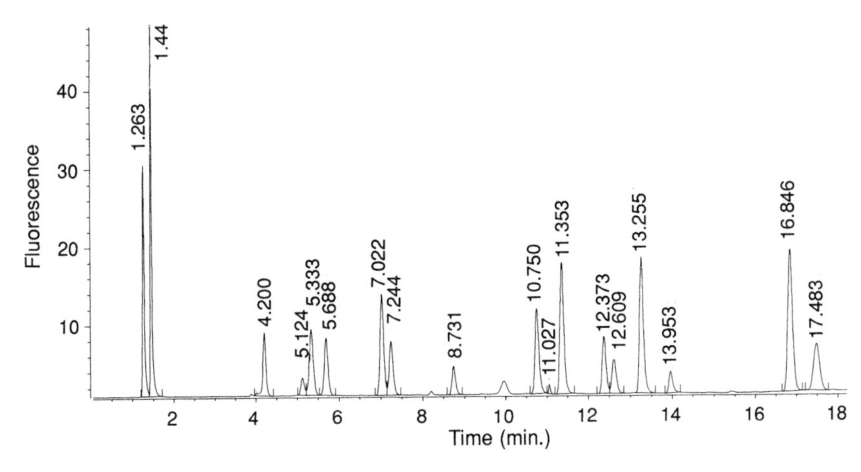

FIGURE 2 Amino acid analysis from 3 μg serum albumin electroblotted onto PVDF.

almost completely; special protocols have to be followed for their determination (Nakagawa and Manabe, 1992; Ploug *et al.*, 1992).

V. Pitfalls

1. Avoid any contamination (salts, detergents, free amino acids).
2. Work extremely cleanly and accurately.
3. When manipulating samples always wear gloves.
4. Use quality-controlled (not outdated!) buffers, reagents, and HPLC columns.
5. All reverse-phase HPLC systems used for amino acid analysis are very sensitive to minimal changes in buffer concentrations, gradient shape, and temperature.
6. Prove integrations: Are the baseline settings correct?

REFERENCES

Eckerskorn, C., Jungblut, P., Mewes, W., Klose, J., and Lottspeich, F. (1988b) *Electrophoresis* **9,** 830–838.

Eckerskorn, C., and Lottspeich, F. (1993) *Electrophoresis* **14,** 831–838.

Eckerskorn, C., Mewes, W., Goretzki, H., and Lottspeich, F. (1988a) *Eur. J. Biochem.* 509–519.

Lottspeich, F., and Henschen, A. (1982) Proteins, peptides and amino acids. *In* "HPLC in Biochemistry" (H. P. Hupe, A. Henschen, F. Lottspeich, and W. Völter, eds.). VCH-Verlag, Weinheim.

Matsudaira, P. (1987) *J. Biol. Chem.* **262,** 10035–10038.

Nakagawa, S., and Fukuda, T. (1989) *Anal. Biochem.* **181,** 75–78.

Nakazawa, S., and Manabe, K. (1992) *Anal. Biochem.* **206,** 105–108.

Ploug, M., Jensen, A. L., and Barkholt, V. (1989) *Anal. Biochem.* **181,** 33–39.

Ploug, M., Stoffer, B., and Jensen, A. L. (1992) *Electrophoresis* **13,** 148–153.

Schuster, R. (1988) *J. Chromatogr.* **431,** 271–284.

Tous, G. I., Fausnaugh, J. L., Akinyosoye, O., Lackland, H., Wintercash, P., Vitoria, F. J., and Stein, S. (1989) *Anal. Biochem.* **179,** 50–55.

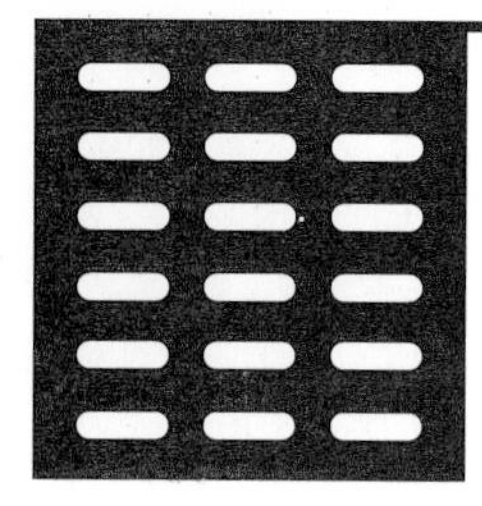

Phosphopeptide Mapping and Phosphoamino Acid Analysis on Cellulose Thin-Layer Plates

Peter van der Geer, Kunxin Luo, Bartholomew M. Sefton, and Tony Hunter

I. Introduction

Phosphopeptide mapping is an important technique in the study of protein phosphorylation. It is used to determine the number and precise identity of sites of phosphorylation, to estimate the stoichiometry of phosphorylation at particular sites, and to deduce the identity of protein kinases responsible for their phosphorylation. Additionally, comparative phosphopeptide mapping is an invaluable tool for determining the identity, or lack of identity, of phosphoproteins obtainable only in trace amounts. In two-dimensional phosphopeptide mapping the protein of interest is labeled with [^{32}P]orthophosphate either *in vivo* or *in vitro*, and digested to completion with site-specific proteases or chemicals. The resulting peptides are separated in two dimensions on thin-layer cellulose (TLC) plates by electrophoresis in the first dimension and chromatography in the second dimension. The radioactive phosphopeptides are then visualized by exposure to X-ray film or a phosphorimager screen. Phosphopeptide mapping has the advantage that it is extremely sensitive, requiring only a few hundred disintegrations per minute of ^{32}P-labeled protein. In addition, individual phosphopeptides can be isolated from the inert cellulose coating of the plate, and used for further characterization including phosphoamino acid determination, N-terminal sequencing, and secondary digestion with additional proteases and chemicals.

II. Materials and Instrumentation

Tissue grinder microcentrifuge tubes and pestles (Cat. No. 749520-0000) were obtained from Kontes. The Speed-Vac concentrator (Cat. No. SC-100) was supplied by Savant. The HTLE 7000 thin-layer electrophoresis apparatus and the LCT-100 large chromatography tank were supplied by CBS Scientific. The Bio-Rad Trans-Blot apparatus (Cat. No. 170-3910) was supplied by Bio-Rad. Immobilon-P membrane (Cat. No. IPVH 000 10) was obtained from Millipore. Whatman 3MM paper (Cat. No. 303 0917) was obtained from Whatman LabSales. Cellulose (100 μm) 20 × 20-cm glass-backed plates (Cat. No. 5716-7) were obtained from E. M. Science. Oxford ultramicropipettes and disposable capillary tips (Cat. No. 21-199-9) were obtained from Fisher Scientific. Disposable plastic microtransfer pipettes (Cat. No. 147500) were obtained from Research Products International. Porous poly-

Cell Biology: A Laboratory Handbook

ethylene disks (6.5 mm, Cat. No. 006651) were supplied by Omnifit. *N*-Tosyl-L-phenylalanine chloromethyl ketone (TPCK)-treated trypsin (Cat. No. LS03740) and α-chymotrypsin (Cat. No. LS01448) were obtained from Worthington; endoproteinase Asp-N (Cat. No. 1420 488) and endoproteinase Glu-C (V8, Cat. No. 791 156) were obtained from Boehringer-Mannheim; proline-specific endopeptidase (Cat. No. 32-082-1) was obtained from ICN Biomedicals; thermolysin (Cat. No. 58656) was obtained from Calbiochem; and carboxypeptidase B (Cat. No. C-7011) was obtained from Sigma. Polyvinylpyrrolidone (Cat. No. PVP-360), phosphoserine (Cat. No. P-0753), phosphothreonine (Cat. No. P-1003), phosphotyrosine (Cat. No. P-5024), cyanogen bromide (Cat. No. C-6388), *N*-chlorosuccinimde (Cat. No. C-0762), hydroxylamine (Cat. No. H-2391), ϵ-DNP-lysine (Cat. No. D-0380), and xylene cyanole FF (Cat. No. X-4126) were obtained from Sigma. Phenylisothiocyanate (Cat. No. 26922G) was obtained from Pierce. Other chemical reagents and solvents were obtained at the highest possible grade from various chemical supply houses.

III. Procedures

In general, proteins to be analyzed by two-dimensional phosphopeptide mapping will be isolated after SDS–PAGE. Two strategies can be used for recovering the protein of interest from the gel. The protein can be eluted from the gel, precipitated with trichloroacetic acid (TCA), or acetone, and oxidized before digestion (Sections A and B; see, for example, van der Geer and Hunter, 1990). Alternatively, the fractionated proteins can be transferred from the gel electrophoretically to a nitrocellulose, nylon or Immobilon membrane and then subjected to digestion while bound to the membrane (Sections D and E; see, for example, Luo *et al.*, 1990). The digestion of membrane-bound proteins is rapid and minimizes losses, but this procedure does have some potential drawbacks. It is not suitable for proteins that transfer inefficiently to membranes, and the recovery of hydrophobic peptides may be poor. The hydrophilicity of phosphopeptides provided by the phosphate moiety, however, may render them particularly suitable for analysis by this procedure. The usefulness of this technique should be evaluated in each case.

A. ELUTION OF PROTEINS FROM SDS–POLYACRYLAMIDE GELS

Solutions

1. *50 mM NH_4HCO_3:* Make this solution up fresh by dissolving 0.4 g NH_4HCO_3 in 100 ml deionized water. The final pH should be ~7.3. On storage the pH of this solution rises. It can subsequently be used for trypsin and chymotrypsin digestion when its pH is ~8.3.

2. *SDS:* Prepare 10% sodium dodecyl sulfate (SDS) by making up 10 g SDS to 100 ml in deionized water.

3. *Carrier protein:* Dissolve RNase A or bovine immunoglobulins in deionized water to give a final concentration of 1 mg/ml. Boil the RNase solution 5 min to inactivate any residual proteases. Store carrier protein solutions frozen at −20°C.

4. *Trichloroacetic acid:* Prepare 100% trichloroacetic acid (TCA) by dissolving solid TCA in enough deionized water to give a final volume in milliliters equal to the number of grams of TCA being dissolved.

Steps

1. Resolve ^{32}P-labeled protein samples by SDS–PAGE. Dry the gel onto paper or dialysis membrane, and mark around the edges of the dried gel with ^{35}S-labeled India ink (10 μCi/ml) or fluorescent ink.

2. Expose the gel to X-ray film or a phosphorimager plate. Line up the markers around the gel with their images on the film or copy of the phosphorimage, staple them together, and place this sandwich on a light box on a glass plate.

3. Identify, mark, and cut out the protein bands from individual lanes using a single-edged razor blade.

4. Peel the paper or membrane backing from the gel, and remove residual paper by scraping gently with a razor blade (do not be too enthusiastic and scrape away gel).

5. Place the pieces of gel in a 1.5-ml disposable tissue grinder microcentrifuge tube, and rehydrate in 400 μl freshly prepared 50 m*M* NH_4HCO_3, pH 7.3–7.6, for 5 min at room temperature.

6. Grind the swollen gel pieces using a tissue grinder pestle until they can be passed through a disposable tip for a 200-μl pipetman (the pestle can be rotated by hand or more conveniently by a variable speed electric drill). Transfer the gel bits to a 1.5-ml screw-cap microcentrifuge tube, and rinse the tissue grinder and tube twice with 200 μl 50 m*M* NH_4HCO_3. Add 40 μl β-mercaptoethanol and 8 μl 10% (w/v) SDS, boil for 2–3 min, and incubate for at least 90 min at room temperature or 37°C on a shaker.

7. Centrifuge for 2–3 min at 10,000 rpm in a microcentrifuge at room temperature, and transfer the supernatant, using a disposable transfer pipette, to a new 1.5-ml microcentrifuge tube. The transfer should be done immediately; otherwise the gel pellet reswells. Add 400 μl 50 m*M* NH_4HCO_3 containing 4 μl 10% SDS and 20 μl β-mercaptoethanol to the gel pellet, vortex, and shake again for at least 90 min.

8. Centrifuge for 2–3 min at 10,000 rpm in a microcentrifuge at room temperature, remove the supernatant, and combine with the first supernatant. Centrifuge the combined supernatants for 5–10 min at 10,000 rpm in a microcentrifuge at room temperature to remove any residual gel fragments, and transfer the supernatant to a new 1.5-ml microcentrifuge tube. (Before discarding the gel pellet, check by Cerenkov counting that the majority of the ^{32}P label is in the eluate; the recovery should be 60–80% of the starting radioactivity in the gel slice.)

9. Cool the cleared eluate on ice, add 20 μg carrier protein (20 μl of 1 mg/ml RNase A or immunoglobulins; RNase has the advantage of eliminating residual ^{32}P-labeled RNA contaminating the protein if it has been isolated from ^{32}P-labeled cells), mix well, add 250 μl ice-cold 100% TCA, mix well, and incubate 1 hr on ice (alternatively 4 vol of −20°C acetone can be used to precipitate the protein). Centrifuge for 15 min at 10,000 rpm in a microcentrifuge at 4°C, and then remove the supernatant using a disposable transfer pipette (before discarding the supernatant, check by Cerenkov counting that the majority of the ^{32}P label is in the pellet). A small white pellet should be visible. Centrifuge for 30 to 60 sec in a microcentrifuge to spin down residual liquid on the sides of the tube, and then remove the last traces of liquid with a pipette. Add 500 μl cold 96% ethanol, vortex, and centrifuge for 5 min at 10,000 rpm at 4°C. Remove the ethanol supernatant, and air-dry the pellet (do not lyophilize to complete dryness).

B. OXIDATION BY INCUBATION WITH PERFORMIC ACID

To avoid problems with partial oxidation of methionine and cysteine residues that can occur during SDS–PAGE, elution, and proteolytic digestion, which leads to spot doubling during chromatography, eluted proteins are generally treated with performic acid to oxidize the methionines and cysteines to methionine sulfone and cysteic acid, respectively. This step can be omitted, if the phosphopeptides of interest do not contain methionine or cysteine. No peptides are eluted from Immobilon-P by trypsin or chymotrypsin if the oxidation is carried out before proteolytic digestion; therefore, oxidation has to be done after the peptides are released from the membrane by proteolytic digestion in this protocol (see Section E).

Steps

1. Mix 9 parts 98–100% formic acid with 1 part 30% (w/v) hydrogen peroxide. Incubate 60 min at room temperature to allow performic acid to form.
2. Place the tube on ice and let the performic acid cool down to 0°C.
3. Add 50 μl ice-cold performic acid to the ethanol-washed TCA precipitate or dried peptide mix (see Section E) in a microcentrifuge tube. Vortex well to dissolve, and incubate 60 min on ice. Never let the sample warm up, as incubation with performic acid at higher temperatures may result in unwanted side reactions.
4. Add 400 μl deionized water, mix, and freeze on dry ice.
5. Evaporate the performic acid under vacuum in a Speed-Vac concentrator (this takes 3–4 hr). After evaporation the sample should appear as a small white cotton ball.

As the protein dissolves completely in performic acid, the sample can be split after step 4, if it is desired to carry out both proteolytic digestion (Section **C**) and phosphoamino acid analysis (Sections **H** and **I**) on the protein. As many fewer counts per minute are required for phosphoamino acid analysis, one-tenth to one-fifth of the sample should be enough for this purpose.

C. TRYPTIC AND CHYMOTRYPTIC DIGESTION OF TCA-PRECIPITATED PHOSPHOPROTEINS

Solutions

1. *Proteolytic enzymes: Trypsin:* Make up 1 mg/ml TPCK-treated trypsin in water or 1 m*M* HCl. Store frozen in small aliquots at −70°C or in liquid nitrogen.
2. *Proteolytic enzymes: Chymotrypsin:* Make up 1 mg/ml α-chymotrypsin in water or 1 m*M* HCl. Store frozen in small aliquots at −70°C or in liquid nitrogen.

Steps

1. Suspend the dried protein pellet in 50 μl 50 m*M* NH_4HCO_3, pH 8.0–8.3. Add 10 μg (10 μl of a 1 mg/ml stock) TPCK-treated trypsin (cleaves on the C-terminal side of arginine and lysine) or chymotrypsin (cleaves on the C-terminal side of phenylalanine, tyrosine, and tryptophan).

2. Incubate 3–4 hr at 37°C.

3. Add a further 10 μg of TPCK-treated trypsin or chymotrypsin and incubate another 3–4 hr at 37°C.

4. Add 400 μl deionized water, freeze, and lyophilize in a Speed-Vac (this takes 3–4 hr).

5. Dissolve the pellet in 400 μl deionized water and lyophilize.

6. Dissolve the pellet in 400 μl pH 1.9 or pH 4.72 electrophoresis buffer (Section G) for samples to be electrophoresed at those pH's, or in deionized water for electrophoresis at pH 8.9 or other pH's, and vortex vigorously. Centrifuge for 5 min at 10,000 rpm in a microcentrifuge at room temperature, transfer the supernatant, and lyophilize. It is very important that there is no particulate matter in this final supernatant.

7. At this stage the digest can be stored dry or −20°C dissolved in electrophoresis buffer or water prior to two-dimensional separation as described in Section G.

D. TRANSFER OF PROTEINS FROM POLYACRYLAMIDE GELS TO MEMBRANES

The alternative method for eluting a protein from an SDS gel involves transfer of the protein to a membrane. Nitrocellulose, nylon, and Immobilon-P membranes can all be used to carry out subsequent proteolytic digestion, but only nitrocellulose is suitable for CNBr digestion, and for acid hydrolysis only Immobilon-P can be used.

Solution

Transfer buffer: Dissolve 10.5 g Tris base and 50.4 g glycine in 2.8 liters deionized water and 0.7 liter methanol, and degas for 5–10 min. Add 17.5 ml 20% SDS.

Steps

1. Soak the gel for 5–10 min in transfer buffer.

2. Assemble the transfer sandwich: Scotch Brite pad (or equivalent scouring pad), three layers of Whatman 3MM paper, the gel, the membrane (nitrocellulose, nylon, or Immobilon-P—the latter has to be prewetted in methanol), three layers of 3MM paper, and another Scotch Brite pad. Transfer gel-fractionated proteins electrophoretically to a membrane under conditions that have been experimentally determined to be best for the protein of interest. With a Bio-Rad Trans-Blot apparatus, transfer of a 60-kDa protein can be accomplished using 60 V for 1 hr.

3. Disassemble the apparatus, rinse the blot with water several times to remove residual salt and detergent, wrap it in Saran wrap (or equivalent food wrap), apply alignment markers, and expose to X-ray film or a phosphorimager plate. Identify and cut out the protein of interest after aligning the membrane with the markers on the X-ray film or a copy of the phosphorimage. The membrane can be stained with India ink to detect proteins without affecting subsequent proteolytic digestion or acid hydrolysis.

Alternatively, proteins can be transferred to a membrane using a semidry blotter. This requires approximately 10 times less buffer than for a conventional transfer apparatus and reduces reagent costs, but transfer is not so efficient for high-molecular-weight proteins.

E. PROTEOLYTIC DIGESTION OF PROTEINS IMMOBILIZED ON MEMBRANES

Solutions

1. *Polyvinylpyrrolidone:* Make up 0.5% polyvinylpyrrolidone (PVP-360) by dissolving 0.5 g PVP-360 in 100 ml 100 m*M* acetic acid.
2. *Proteolytic enzymes:* 1 mg/ml stock solutions of TPCK-trypsin and chymotrypsin as described in Section C.
3. *NH_4HCO_3:* 50 m*M* NH_4HCO_3, pH 8.3 as described in Section A.

Steps

1. Soak the pieces of membrane containing the protein of interest (Section D) in 1 ml 0.5% PVP-360 in 100 m*M* acetic acid for 30 min at 37°C in a microcentrifuge tube. This blocks protein binding sites on the membrane and prevents the proteolytic enzyme from being adsorbed.

2. Aspirate the liquid. Wash the membrane with water extensively (5 × 1 ml) and then once or twice with freshly made 50 m*M* NH_4HCO_3.

3. Incubate the piece of membrane with 10 μg TPCK-treated trypsin or chymotrypsin for 2 hr in 200 μl 50 m*M* NH_4HCO_3, pH 8.3, at 37°C in a 1.5-ml microcentrifuge tube. The piece of membrane should be completely submerged (a 3 × 8-mm piece requires ~200 μl buffer).

4. Vortex, add a further 10 μg TPCK-treated trypsin or chymotrypsin to the sample, and incubate for another 2 hr at 37°C.

5. Add 300 μl water to the sample, and centrifuge at 10,000 rpm in a microcentrifuge for 5 min.

6. Transfer the liquid to a new microcentrifuge tube. Approximately 90% of the ^{32}P label should be present in the liquid.

7. Lyophilize in a Speed-Vac (this takes 3–4 hr).

8. If necessary, the dried peptides can now be oxidized by dissolving them in 50 μl ice-cold performic acid and proceeding as described in Section C.

9. At the end of oxidation, add 400 μl of water, freeze, and lyophilize in a Speed-Vac. Repeat this procedure once. Dissolve the sample in 6–10 μl electrophoresis buffer and spot the sample on a TLC plate as described in Section G1.

F. CNBr CLEAVAGE OF PROTEINS IMMOBILIZED ON NITROCELLULOSE MEMBRANE

In many cases it is informative to carry out phosphopeptide mapping using cyanogen bromide (CNBr) cleavage, which generates relatively large fragments by cleaving after every methionine. CNBr digestion can be done in a rehydrated gel piece or on eluted TCA-precipitated protein, but it is most convenient to carry out this digestion on proteins transferred to nitrocellulose (Luo *et al.,* 1991). (N. B. CNBr does not cleave oxidized methionine.)

Solution

CNBr: Weigh out 300 mg CNBr in a fume hood, dissolve in 1 ml 70% formic acid, and store at −70°C in small aliquots. Dilute to 50 mg/ml with 70% formic acid just before use.

Steps

1. Incubate the piece of nitrocellulose membrane, containing the protein of interest (Section D), with 50 mg/ml CNBr in 70% formic acid for 1–1.5 hr at room temperature in a capped 1.5-ml microcentrifuge tube, making sure that the piece of membrane is covered with liquid.
2. Centrifuge the samples for 5 min at 10,000 rpm in a microcentrifuge.
3. Transfer the liquid to a new microcentrifuge tube.
4. Lyophilize the sample in a Speed-Vac (a sample containing 200 μl 70% formic acid takes about 30 min to dry).
5. Redissolve the residue in 30–40 μl deionized water and lyophilize. Repeat this procedure once.
6. Dissolve the CNBr fragments in standard SDS sample buffer (if the bromphenol blue in the sample buffer turns yellow, this indicates the presence of residual formic acid in the sample and small amounts of concentrated Tris base, pH ~9, can be added to raise the pH). Analyze the peptides by SDS–PAGE on a 24% acrylamide, 0.054% bisacrylamide gel with a Tricine cathode buffer [0.1 *M* *N*-tris[hydroxymethyl]methylglycine (Tricine), 0.1% SDS, 0.1 *M* Tris base, pH 8.25].

G. SEPARATION OF PHOSPHOPEPTIDES IN TWO DIMENSIONS ON TLC PLATES

Proteolytic digests of phosphoproteins can be analyzed by reverse-phase high-performance liquid chromatography, by high-voltage capillary electrophoresis, or by two-dimensional separation on TLC plates. If digestion generates very large peptides, analysis can be carried out by SDS–PAGE using a high-percentage acrylamide gel (Section F). For samples with low levels of ^{32}P radioactivity, and to obtain maximum resolution, two-dimensional separation of phosphopeptides by electrophoresis and chromatography on cellulose thin-layer plates is recommended.

Solutions

1. *Electrophoresis buffers:*
   pH 1.9 buffer: 50 ml formic acid (88% w/v), 156 ml glacial acetic acid, 1794 ml water.
   pH 3.5 buffer: 100 ml glacial acetic acid, 10 ml pyridine, 1890 ml water.
   pH 4.72 buffer: 100 ml *n*-butanol, 50 ml pyridine, 50 ml glacial acetic acid, 1800 ml water.
   pH 6.5 buffer: 8 ml glacial acetic acid, 200 ml pyridine, 1792 ml water.
   pH 8.9 buffer: 20 g $(NH_4)_2CO_3$, 2000 ml deionized water.

Use reagent-grade solvents and deionized water. Pyridine is unstable and should be stored under nitrogen. Flush the bottle with nitrogen and seal the cap with Parafilm after use. Pyridine should not be used if it is very yellow. Buffers may be prepared well in advance of electrophoresis, but should be stored in glass bottles with airtight lids. After buffer preparation the pH should be checked. The pH value may vary by 0.2 pH unit depending on the quality or brand of the reagents or the type of deionized water used. Do not adjust the pH. If the pH of a buffer differs by more then 0.2 unit from the expected value, it is best to remake the buffer.

2. *Chromatography buffers:*

   Regular chromatography buffer: 785 ml *n*-butanol, 607 ml pyridine, 122 ml glacial acetic acid, 486 ml water.

   Phospho chromatography buffer: 750 ml *n*-butanol, 500 ml pyridine, 150 ml glacial acetic acid, 600 ml water.

   Isobutyric acid buffer: 1250 ml isobutyric acid, 38 ml *n*-butanol, 96 ml pyridine, 58 ml glacial acetic acid, 558 ml water.

Use reagent-quality solvents and deionized water. Buffers may be prepared well in advance of chromatography, but should be stored in glass bottles with airtight lids.

3. *Marker dye mixture:* Dissolve 5 mg ε-DNP-lysine (yellow) and 1 mg xylene cyanole FF (blue) in 1 ml of a 1:1 mixture of pH 4.72 electrophoresis buffer and deionized water.

The digestion products are separated in the first dimension by electrophoresis. The mobility in the electrophoresis dimension is determined by the ratio of the charge and the mass of a peptide and can be described by the formula $m_r = keM^{-2/3}$ in which m_r is the relative mobility, k is a constant, e is the electrical charge, and M is the mass of the molecule (Offord, 1966). The three buffers that are used most commonly for separation in the first dimension are pH 1.9 buffer, pH 4.72 buffer, and pH 8.9 buffer. These buffers are composed of volatile solvents that can be evaporated completely by air-drying the plates after electrophoresis. This allows chromatography or electrophoresis in a different buffer system in the second dimension. Optimal conditions for separation by electrophoresis are usually determined empirically, but in general phosphopeptides containing basic residues are resolved better at a lower pH. pH 1.9 buffer is usually the best starting point, especially because most peptides are soluble in pH 1.9 buffer, and streaked maps are obtained less often. Resolution can also be improved by increasing the electrophoresis time, which may require a change in the position of the origin to prevent peptides from migrating off the TLC plate.

Depending on the number of phosphorylation sites in the phosphoprotein to be analyzed, and the efficiency of proteolytic digestion as few as a 100 Cerenkov cpm of a phosphoprotein may suffice to give a satisfactory analytical peptide map. Ideally, a few hundred counts per minute should be used, and for most phosphoproteins this should be attainable by metabolic labeling of cells with ^{32}P, and easily achieved if *in vitro* phosphorylation with [γ-^{32}P]ATP is used to label the protein. If phosphoamino acid determination, secondary digestion, or Edman degradation are to be carried out on individual phosphopeptides (Sections I–L), then commensurately more starting radioactivity will be required.

1. Application of Proteolytic Digests to TLC Plates

Steps

1. Dissolve the lyophilized proteolytic digests in at least 6 μl pH 1.9 buffer or pH 4.72 buffer (for electrophoresis at pH 1.9 and pH 4.72, respectively) or deionized water (for electrophoresis at other pH's), using a vortex mixer (the final volume depends on the total number of counts per minute in the sample). Centrifuge the sample briefly in a microcentrifuge to ensure that any residual particulate matter is not applied to the plate.
2. Before spotting the samples, select and mark origins on a sufficient number

of 100-μm cellulose 20 × 20-cm glass-backed TLC plates (plastic-backed plates can also be used). Choose plates without gross irregularities in the cellulose coating that might affect the electrophoresis or chromatography. If the direction in which the plates were poured is obvious, then the samples should be electrophoresed in this direction (i.e., orient the plate so that the sides where there are gaps between the edges of the cellulose and the plate are parallel to the direction of electrophoresis). Mark the sample origin and dye origins with + marks on the cellulose surface of the plate, using a very soft blunt-ended pencil or on the back of the plate, using a permanent marker (Figs. 1.1 and 1.2). This can be done by placing the plate on top of a full-size marking template (reduced-size templates are shown in Fig. 2) on a light box (Fig. 1.2). The name of the sample should be written in the top left- or right-hand corner with a soft pencil.

3. Spot the digest with an ultramicropipette fitted with a disposable capillary tip (the tip is changed between each sample). Apply 0.2- to 0.5-μl drops, and dry between applications using a stream of cold air from an air line fitted with a filter to trap aerosols a particulate matter, and a 1-ml syringe or a Pasteur pipette to focus the flow (Figs. 1.3 and 1.4). Do not touch the plate with the air nozzle or the pipette tip, as gouges on the cellulose may affect the electrophoresis or the chromatography. Try to keep the area wetted with each application to a minimum as this results in better resolution. It is normal for a brown ring to form at the circumference of the wetted area.

4. After spotting the sample, apply 0.5 μl of marker dye mixture to the dye origin at the top of the plate (see Fig. 2). The marker dye is green, but separates into its blue and yellow constituents during electrophoresis. Migration of the marker dyes is used to ascertain that electrophoresis was carried out at the correct pH and for the right time. The blue marker is acidic at all pH's, and the yellow marker is neutral between pH's 3 and 8, and defines the position where electrically neutral peptides ran (phosphotyramine can be used as a neutral marker at pH 1.9). Due to endosmosis, which causes net buffer flow across the plate toward the cathode, neutral peptides migrate toward the cathode, with the distance depending on the pH.

2. Separation of Phosphopeptides in the First Dimension by Electrophoresis

The use of the HTLE 7000 thin-layer electrophoresis apparatus is recommended for the electrophoresis dimension, because it has several important features that may be missing in other systems. During electrophoresis the apparatus is closed using a clamping system. An airbag, which is connected to a pressure line delivering 10 lb/in.^{2}, is inflated and removes excess buffer from the plate as well as preventing buffer from siphoning up the wicks from the buffer tanks onto the TLC plate. Excess buffer on the plate may result in fuzzy maps. In addition, this system features a cooling system that prevents overheating during the run. The HTLE 7000 must be connected to a power supply that is capable of delivering at least 1.5 kV at 100 mA, running water at ~16°C, and an air line with a regulator valve capable of delivering a constant pressure. Figure 1 illustrates the use of the HTLE 7000.

Steps

1. Fill both buffer tanks with ~600 ml of the appropriate electrophoresis buffer.

2. Cut two 35 × 25-cm sheets of thin (0.1-mm or 0.004-in.) polyethylene sheeting. Set up the HTLE 7000 apparatus as is shown in Fig. 3. The polyethylene protector sheets should stick out ~4 cm at both sides and ~1 cm at

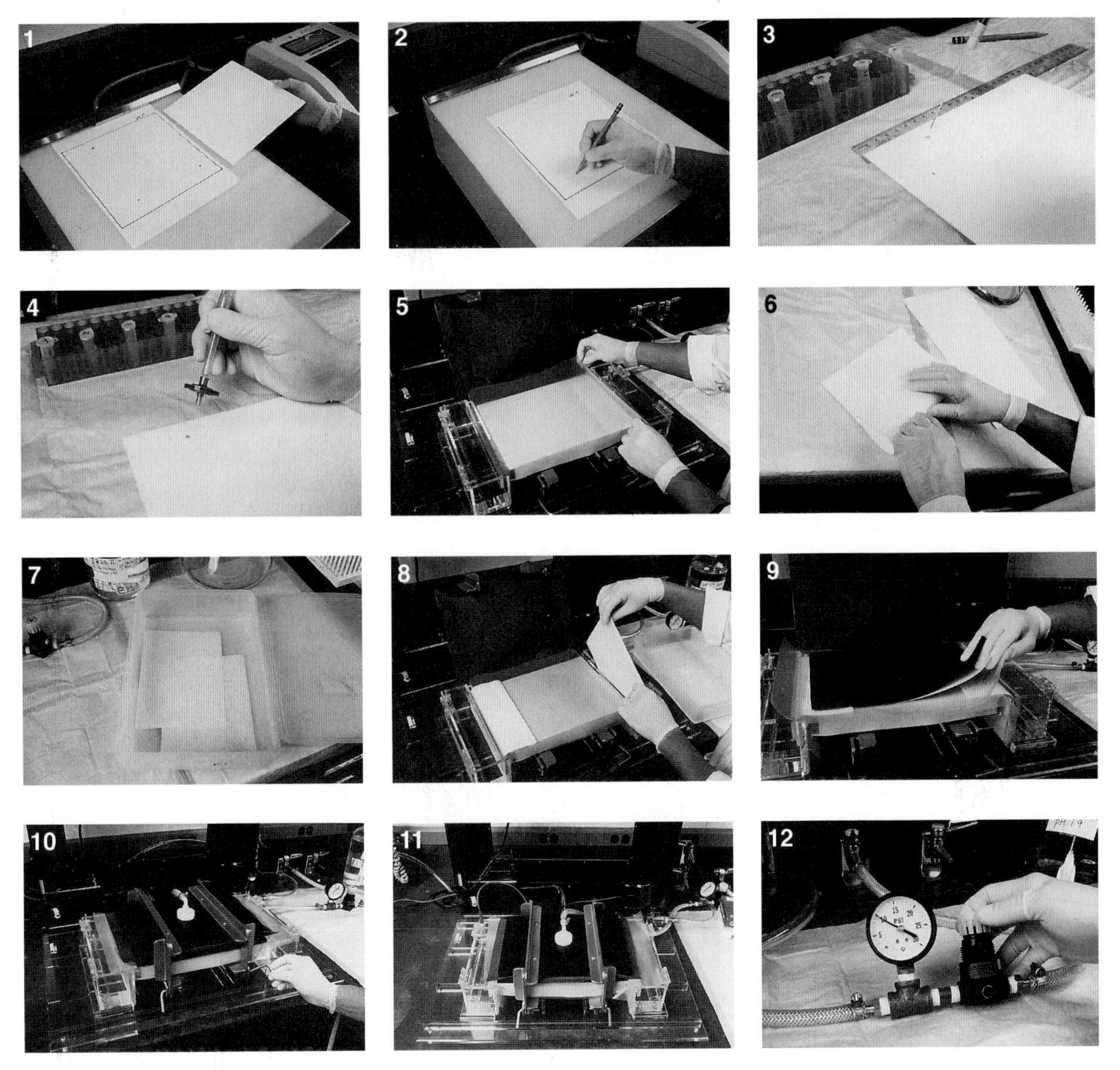

FIGURE 1 Illustration of preparation of TLC plates and use of the HTLE 7000 electrophoresis apparatus.

1. Template on lit light box; shows hand holding selected TLC plate about to be placed on an origin template.
2. Marking TLC plate with soft blunt pencil.
3. Spotting green marker dye: closeup view of end of pipette tip and size of spot.
4. Drying the green marker dye spot with the air filter.
5. Fitting the bottom polyethylene protector sheet: one end of the sheet up and one end being tucked down next to the buffer tank.
6. Folding the Whatman 3MM wicks: one flat on counter, one being folded.
7. Wetting the wicks: shows this being done in a plastic container.
8. Placing the wicks in buffer tanks: one wick installed in its slot and folded over, one being fitted into the slot of a buffer tank.
9. Shutting the apparatus: the installed top polyethylene protector sheet, white Teflon insulation sheet, and black neoprene cushion are held apart to show all three layers.
10. Putting the retaining pins into the apparatus.
11. The apparatus is closed and ready to have the airbag inflated.
12. Inflating the airbag: shows the air gauge at 10 lb/in.^{2}.

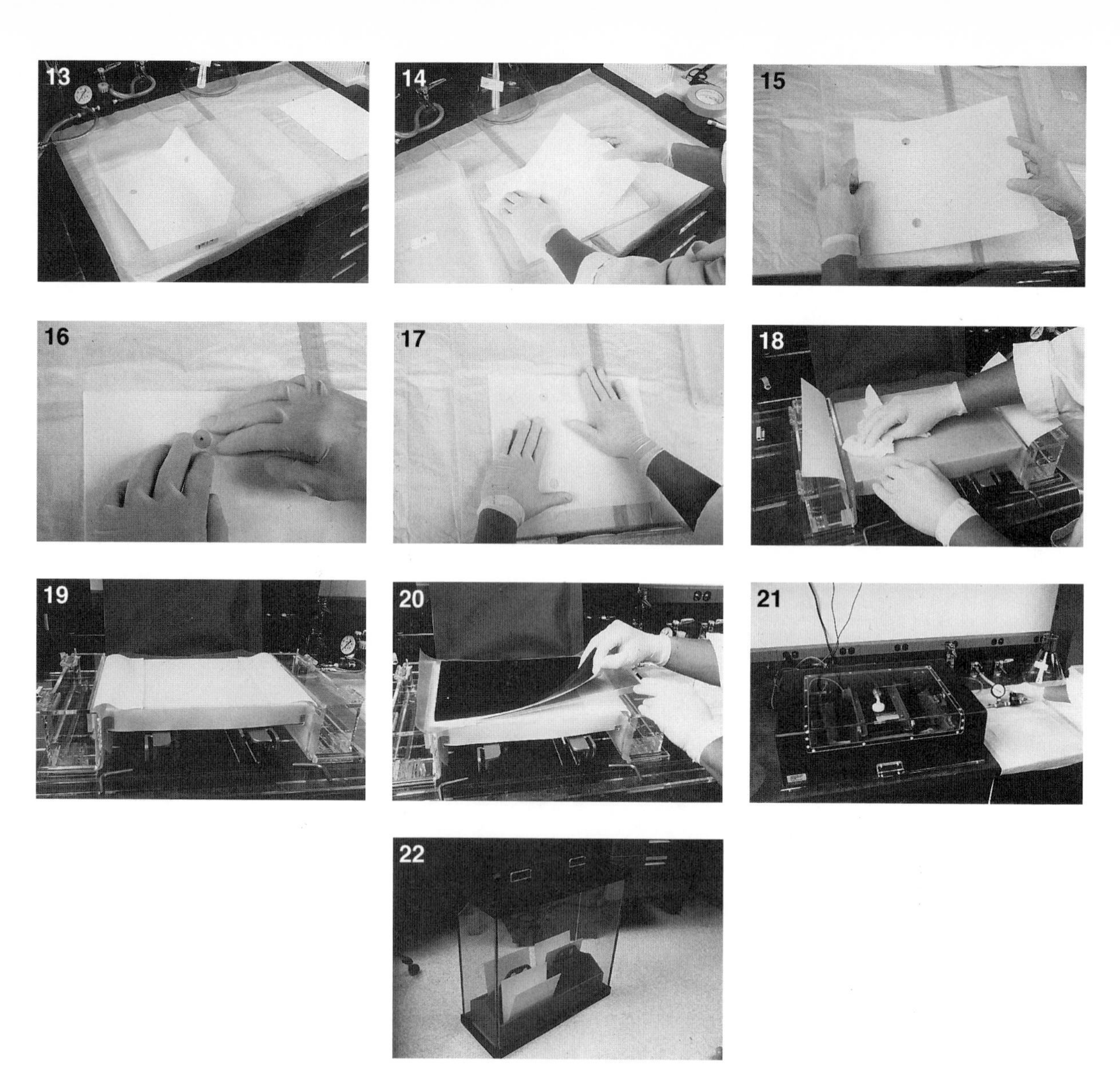

FIGURE 1 *Continued*

13. Wetting the blotter: shows the blotter soaking in buffer in a plastic container.
14. Adjusting the wetness of the blotter (before putting it on the TLC plate) by blotting it with filter paper.
15. Wetting the plate: shows the blotter being laid on the TLC plate, with the holes in the blotter aligned over the origin and green marker dye spots.
16. Concentrating the sample: shows closeup of fingers starting buffer in from edges of holes.
17. Wetting the rest of the TLC plate: shows use of flat of the hand (not fingertips) to wet the rest of the TLC plate.
18. Wiping off the protector sheets: apparatus open, hands wiping off sheets with tissues.
19. The plate on the open apparatus with the wicks folded onto the TLC plate.
20. Reassembling the apparatus: indicates three layers again with top open (this time with a plate in the apparatus).
21. The apparatus is ready: shows closed apparatus inside shut plexiglas cover, air gauge reading 10 $lb/in.^2$.
22. Ascending chromatography: shows plates in LCT-100 chromatography tank.

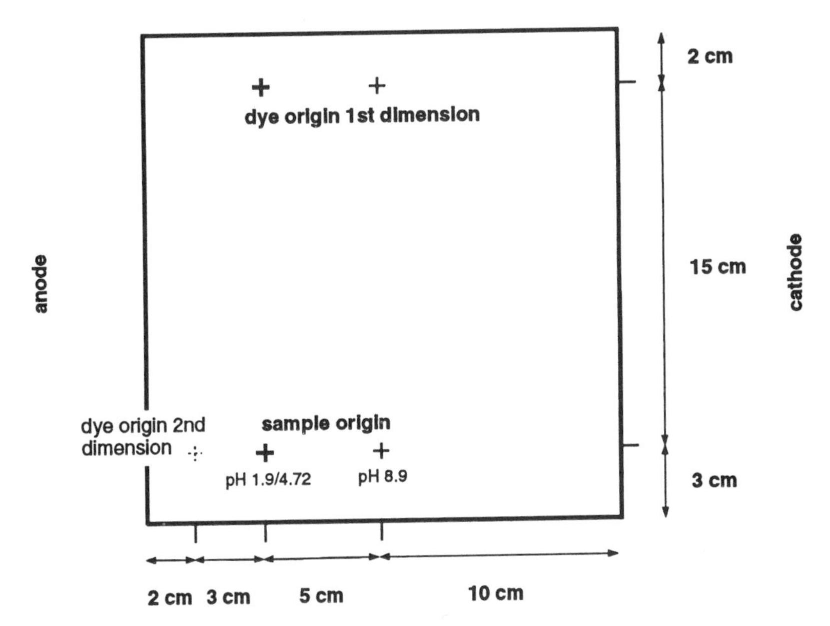

FIGURE 2 Marking TLC plates for separation of phosphopeptides by electrophoresis at pH 1.9 and 4.72 or pH 8.9. Sample and dye origins are usually marked on the plate with a blunt-ended, very soft pencil. The positions of the origins for different electrophoresis buffers are shown. For electrophoresis at pH 1.9 and 4.72, samples are spotted 5 cm from the left side of the plate and 3 cm from the bottom. For electrophoresis at pH 8.9, samples are spotted in the middle of the plate 3 cm from the bottom. Marker dye for electrophoresis is spotted above the sample origin 2 cm from the top of the plate. Marker dye for chromatography is spotted after electrophoresis in the position shown.

front and back. Tuck the lower protector sheet over the Teflon insulating sheet between the cooling plate and the buffer tanks (Fig. 1.5). Whenever samples with large amounts of radioactivity (>10,000 cpm) are run, the upper protector sheet should be discarded.

3. Cut two 20 × 28-cm sheets of Whatman 3MM paper. Fold the sheets of

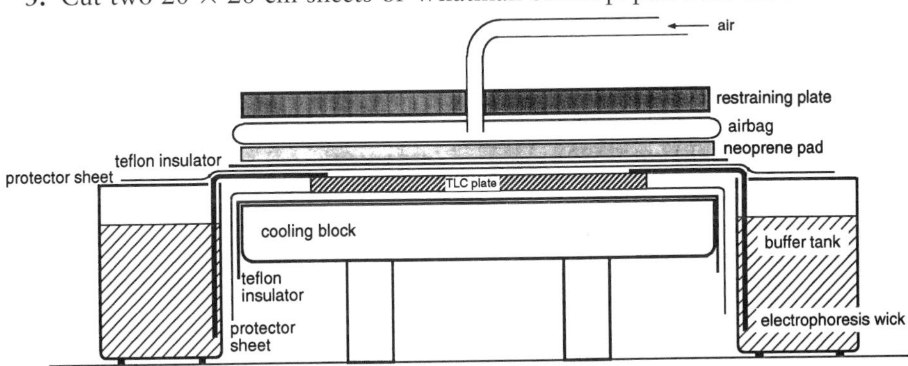

FIGURE 3 HTLE 7000 electrophoresis apparatus. This electrophoresis apparatus is equipped with an inflatable airbag and a cooling block. A cross section through the assembled apparatus is shown. To set up the apparatus cover the Teflon insulator on the cooling block with a polyethylene protector sheet; add buffer to the buffer tanks, place the double-layer Whatman 3MM electrophoresis wicks into the tanks, and fold them over the cooling plate; place a second protector sheet over the cooling plate, the wicks, and the buffer tank; place the Teflon insulator and the neoprene pad on top and close the apparatus; insert the securing pins (not shown) and inflate the airbag at 10 lb/in.^{2} to remove excess buffer from the wicks. Keep under pressure until ready for electrophoresis.

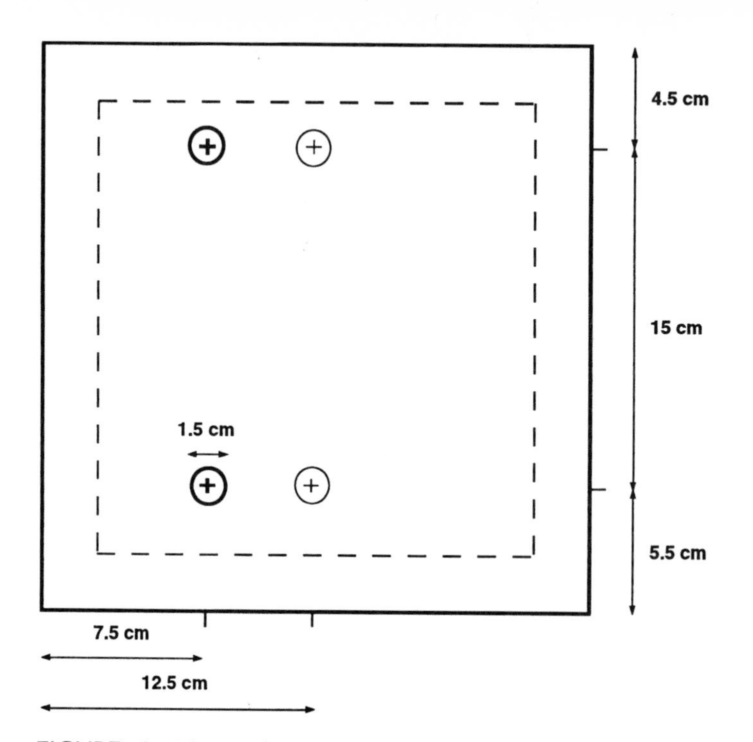

FIGURE 4 Blotters for wetting TLC plates before separation of phosphopeptides by electrophoresis in the first dimension. TLC plates are wetted with electrophoresis buffer using a blotter made from a double layer of Whatman 3MM paper sewn together around the edges with a zigzag stitch. The size of the blotter and the positions of the holes for the sample and dye origins are shown. The holes are made using a 1.5-cm-diameter cork borer (these are shown as circles with the marked origins from the plate showing through). Blotters can be reused many times but for one pH only.

paper lengthwise to give two 20 × 14-cm double-thickness electrophoresis wicks (Fig. 1.6). Wet the wicks in the appropriate electrophoresis buffer, and insert them into the tanks with the folded end up (Figs. 1.7 and 1.8). Fold the ends of the wicks over the cooling block. Place the upper polyethylene protector sheet over the wicks and then the upper Teflon insulating sheet and the neoprene pad on top (Fig. 9). Close the restraining plate with the attached airbag, and secure it with the two pins (Fig. 1.10). Turn the air pressure up to 10 lb/in.^{2}, which will inflate the airbag and squeeze out excess buffer from the wicks (Figs. 1.11 and 1.12). The wicks and buffers can be used for many consecutive runs at the same pH.

4. Make a blotter from two 25 × 25-cm squares of Whatman 3MM paper by stitching them together with a zigzag stitch around the edges and then cutting two circular 1.5-cm holes with a sharp cork borer in appropriate positions for the sample and marker dye origins (Fig. 4). Blotters can be reused many times, but a separate blotter should be used for each pH.

5. Wet the plate as follows. Soak the blotter briefly in electrophoresis buffer, and then remove excess buffer by blotting it momentarily with a sheet of Whatman 3MM paper (Figs. 1.13 and 1.14). Place the wet blotter on top of the plate, with the sample and marker origins in the center of the two holes. Next press the blotter onto the plate around the sample and marker origins with your fingertips to start the buffer flow uniformly round each circle, so that the sample is concentrated as the buffer front focuses on the origin (the brown material at the circumference of the dried sample should dissolve and move to the central origin mark) (Figs. 1.15 and 1.16). Then press gently on the other areas of the

plate to ensure that all the cellulose is wetted (Fig. 1.17). Once the origins are fully wetted and the sample has concentrated on the origin, remove the blotter. The plate should be dull gray after wetting. No shiny puddles of buffer should be present on the plate. If there are puddles, allow the excess buffer to evaporate or blot carefully with a tissue.

6. When ready to start, shut off the air pressure, and open the apparatus. Remove the pad, the Teflon sheet, and the upper polyethylene sheet, and wipe excess liquid from both polyethylene sheets with a tissue (Fig. 1.18).

7. Place the wetted plate, cellulose side up, on top of the lower polyethylene sheet, and fold the wicks over the plate so that they cover ~1 cm of the plate (Fig. 1.19). Place the upper polyethylene sheet over the plate, and carefully reassemble the apparatus (Fig. 1.20). Avoid moving the upper polyethylene sheeting laterally while it is in contact with the plate. Secure the lid with the pins, turn the air pressure up to 10 lb/in.^{2}, and turn on the cooling water flow (Fig. 1.21).

8. Switch on the high-voltage supply. Typically phosphopeptide maps are run for 20–30 min at 1.0 kV on the HTLE 7000. However, with other types of apparatus the voltage needed has to be determined empirically, and will depend on the distance between the electrodes.

9. Air-dry the plates for ~20 min in front of a fan (do not oven dry).

3. Separation of Phosphopeptides in the Second Dimension by Chromatography

The separation in the second dimension is done by ascending chromatography. The hydrophobicity of the different peptides determines their ability to partition between two phases. The chromatography buffer that migrates slowly to the top of the plate is the mobile phase; the cellulose on the plate forms the stationary phase. The hydrophobicity of a particular peptide determines the ratio of time spent in the mobile and stationary phases. A hydrophobic peptide that spends a greater part of the time during the separation in the mobile phase will migrate relatively fast toward the top of the plate. Conversely, a hydrophilic peptide that spends a greater part of the time bound to the stationary phase will move only slowly toward the top of the plate.

Shandon 500 (57 × 23 × 57 cm) tanks are particularly suitable for chromatography, but are no longer commercially available. With a row of water-filled glass bottles in the middle as a center support these tanks hold up to eight 20 × 20-cm plates. A similar-sized plastic tank with a tray to hold eight plates is now available from CBS Scientific. Alternatively, a smaller "glass-brick" tank can be used, which should be lined with Whatman 3MM paper to ensure equilibration of the vapor phase with the TLC plate during chromatography. For either type of chromatography tank, there should be 0.5–1.0 cm buffer in the tank, and the vapor phase in the tank should be allowed to equilibrate for several hours after adding new buffer before use.

Three different buffer systems are commonly used. "Regular chromatography buffer" is most often used for fingerprinting ^{35}S- or ^{125}I-labeled proteins. "Phospho chromatography buffer" is a more hydrophilic mixture, and is the buffer of choice for analyzing phosphopeptides. "Isobutyric acid buffer" is used to resolve extremely hydrophilic phosphopeptides, but this buffer is malodorous. There are no rules that predict which buffer will be best. Try all three buffer systems and select the buffer that gives the best resolution. Buffer tanks can be used for several months with replenishment as the buffer level falls, but it is essential that the lids form an airtight seal with the tank, to prevent evaporation of the buffer. This can be achieved with silicone vacuum grease. Some components in these buffers are more volatile than others and evaporation leads to a gradual change in buffer composition, thereby affecting the separation during chromatography. It is important therefore to minimize the time that buffer tanks are opened.

Steps

1. Before starting the chromatography, spot a drop (~0.5 μl) of green marker dye in the left- or right-hand margin of the plate at the same level as the sample origin (see Fig. 2). This will act as a marker for the chromatography dimension and can be used as a standard for calculating relative phosphopeptide mobilities (R_f's).

2. Place the dried plates in the tank in a nearly upright position so that the chromatography will occur in a direction at right angles to the direction of electrophoresis (Fig. 1.22). The top of the plates should rest against the wall of the tank or against the water-filled bottles forming the center support (when using a Shandon tank). Alternatively, a rack designed to hold several plates upright can be used. Replace the lid. Do not disturb or open a tank while chromatography is in progress.

3. Let the buffer run to within 1–2 cm of the top of the plate (this usually takes 8–16 hr depending on the batch of plates, the buffer system used, the quality of reagents used to make up the buffer, and the ambient temperature).

4. When chromatography is complete, remove all of the plates from the tank irrespective of exactly where the buffer front is on individual plates, and let them dry in a fume hood or a 65°C oven. Do not use the oven for drying if phosphopeptides are to be extracted from these plates afterward.

5. When dry, mark the plates with ^{35}S-labeled radioactive or fluorescent ink and expose the plates to X-ray film or to a phosphorimager plate. If autoradiography is to be used, presensitization of the X-ray film with a flash of orange light to an optical density of 0.2 and exposure with an intensifier screen at −70°C will greatly increase the sensitivity of detection of ^{32}P-labeled peptides.

H. ACID HYDROLYSIS OF PHOSPHOPROTEINS

Phosphoamino acid analysis is accomplished by partial hydrolysis of the purified ^{32}P-labeled protein either eluted from an SDS gel (Sections **A** and **B**) or when bound to Immobilon-P (Section **D**). Incubation of proteins or peptides in concentrated acid or base results in hydrolysis of peptide bonds and release of peptides and, eventually, individual amino acids. Phosphodiester bonds, however, are also unstable under these reaction conditions and dephosphorylation of the phosphoamino acids and release of free [^{32}P]phosphate also occur. As a consequence hydrolysis times are critical. Hydrolysis of membrane-bound phosphoproteins is recommended except in cases where the protein of interest transfers to Immobilon-P poorly.

1. Hydrolysis of Membrane-Bound Phosphoproteins

Steps

1. Place the strip of Immobilon-P membrane containing the ^{32}P-labeled protein of interest in a screw-cap microcentrifuge tube and rinse the membrane several times with deionized water.

2. Add 200 μl 5.7 *N* (constant boiling) or 6 *N* HCl, screw the cap on tightly, and incubate 60 min at 110°C.
3. Centrifuge for 5 min at 10,000 rpm in a microcentrifuge and transfer the supernatant to a new microcentrifuge tube.
4. Evaporate the HCl in a Speed-Vac. Now proceed as described in Section I.

2. Hydrolysis of Precipitated Phosphoproteins

Steps

1. Dissolve the TCA-precipitated protein, after the ethanol wash, in 50 μl 5.7 *N* (constant boiling) or 6 *N* HCl, and hydrolyze 1 hr at 110°C in a screw-cap 1.5-ml microcentrifuge tube.
2. Evaporate the HCl in a Speed-Vac. Now proceed as described in Section I.

I. DETERMINATION OF PHOSPHOAMINO ACID CONTENT IN PROTEIN AND PEPTIDE HYDROLYSATES

Phosphoamino acids can be separated from each other and from possible contaminating nucleotides by electrophoresis in two dimensions. Phosphothreonine (P.Thr) and phosphotyrosine P.Tyr comigrate during electrophoresis at pH 1.9, but separate well from phosphoserine (P.Ser). P.Thr separates well from P.Tyr during electrophoresis at pH 3.5. Phosphate, phosphopeptides, and the individual phosphoamino acids from relatively pure samples can be resolved adequately by electrophoresis in one dimension at pH 3.5. This method may be preferred when working with *in vitro* phosphorylated proteins or purified peptides, where phosphate, phosphopeptides, and phosphoamino acids are the only labeled compounds present in the hydrolysate. The principal advantage is that as many as 16 samples can be analyzed on a single plate. When working with *in vivo* labeled material, 3′-UMP and ribose 3′-phosphate generated from ^{32}P-labeled RNA, which are major contaminants, comigrate with P.Tyr during electrophoresis at pH 3.5. For further reading see Cooper *et al.* (1983) and Duclos *et al.* (1991). Phosphoamino acids can also be resolved by HPLC using anion-exchange columns.

Twenty to 100 ^{32}P cpm in a phosphoprotein or peptide sample is enough to obtain a reproducible phosphoamino acid analysis. Keep in mind that only ~20% of the radioactivity will actually be recovered as free phosphoamino acids.

Solutions

1. *Phosphoamino acid marker mixture:* Dissolve 1 mg phosphoserine, 1 mg phosphothreonine, and 1 mg phosphotyrosine in 1 ml deionized water. This solution is strongly acidic. It is stable for several years at 4°C.
2. *Ninhydrin staining solution:* Dissolve 0.25 g ninhydrin in 100 ml acetone.

Steps

1. Mix 15 parts pH 1.9 buffer with 1 part unlabeled phosphoamino acid marker mixture.

2. Dissolve the protein hydrolysates in at least 6 μl pH 1.9 buffer containing unlabeled phosphoamino acids, using a vortex mixer. Approximately 0.5 μg of each phosphoamino acid is needed for detection, and if only a small fraction of

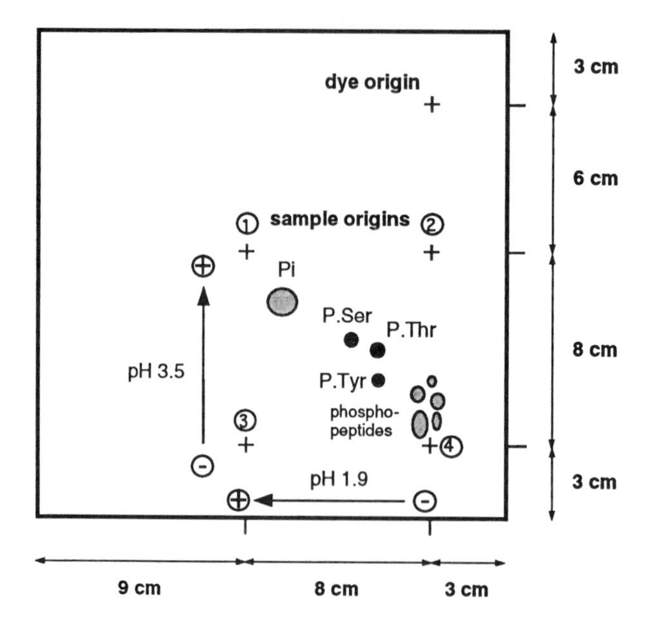

FIGURE 5 TLC plate marked for separation of phosphoamino acids in two dimensions. Four samples can be analyzed on one TLC plate. The positions of the sample origins, indicated as 1, 2, 3, and 4, are shown. Marker dye can be spotted on the fifth origin (upper right corner) before electrophoresis in the first dimension at pH 1.9 in the direction shown. The plate is rotated 90° for electrophoresis in the second dimension at pH 3.5 in the direction shown. The positions of phosphoserine (P.Ser), phosphothreonine (P.Thr), phosphotyrosine (P.Tyr), orthophosphate (P_i), and partial hydrolysis products (phosphopeptides) after two-dimensional separation are shown for a sample spotted on origin 4. Phosphoamino acids migrate from the cathode toward the anode during electrophoresis at pH 1.9 and 3.5.

the sample is going to be analyzed (e.g., if a large amount of radioactivity is available), then proportionately more marker mixture should be used.

3. Select 100-μm cellulose plates (Section G 1.2), and mark four origins and a dye origin with a blunt-ended extra soft pencil or on the back of the plate with a marker using the template shown (Fig. 5).

4. Centrifuge the dissolved hydrolysates for 30–60 sec in a microcentrifuge at room temperature to remove residual particulate matter. Spot the dissolved sample on a marked TLC plate (see Fig. 5; Section G 1.3). Apply 0.2 to 0.5 μl of the sample at a time with a micropipette fitted with a capillary tip and dry between each application, using an air line fitted with a filter and a 1-ml syringe to focus the flow. It is possible in some circumstances to spot the whole hydrolysate obtained from a membrane-bound protein. Up to four samples can be spotted on each plate. Apply marker dye on the indicated position on the plate (see Fig. 5).

5. Wet the plate with pH 1.9 buffer, using a blotter with five holes (Fig. 6A) as described in Section G 2.5.

6. Carry out electrophoresis for 20 min at 1.5 kV toward the positive electrode as described in Section G 2.

7. Remove the plate from the electrophoresis apparatus and dry the plate in front of a fan for ~30 min (the smell of acetic acid from the plate should be minimal at this stage).

8. Soak three strips of single-thickness Whatman 3MM paper, 3, 6.5, and 10 cm wide and 25 cm long, in pH 3.5 buffer containing ~0.1 m*M* EDTA (this prevents streaking in the second dimension). Wet the plate by placing the wetted

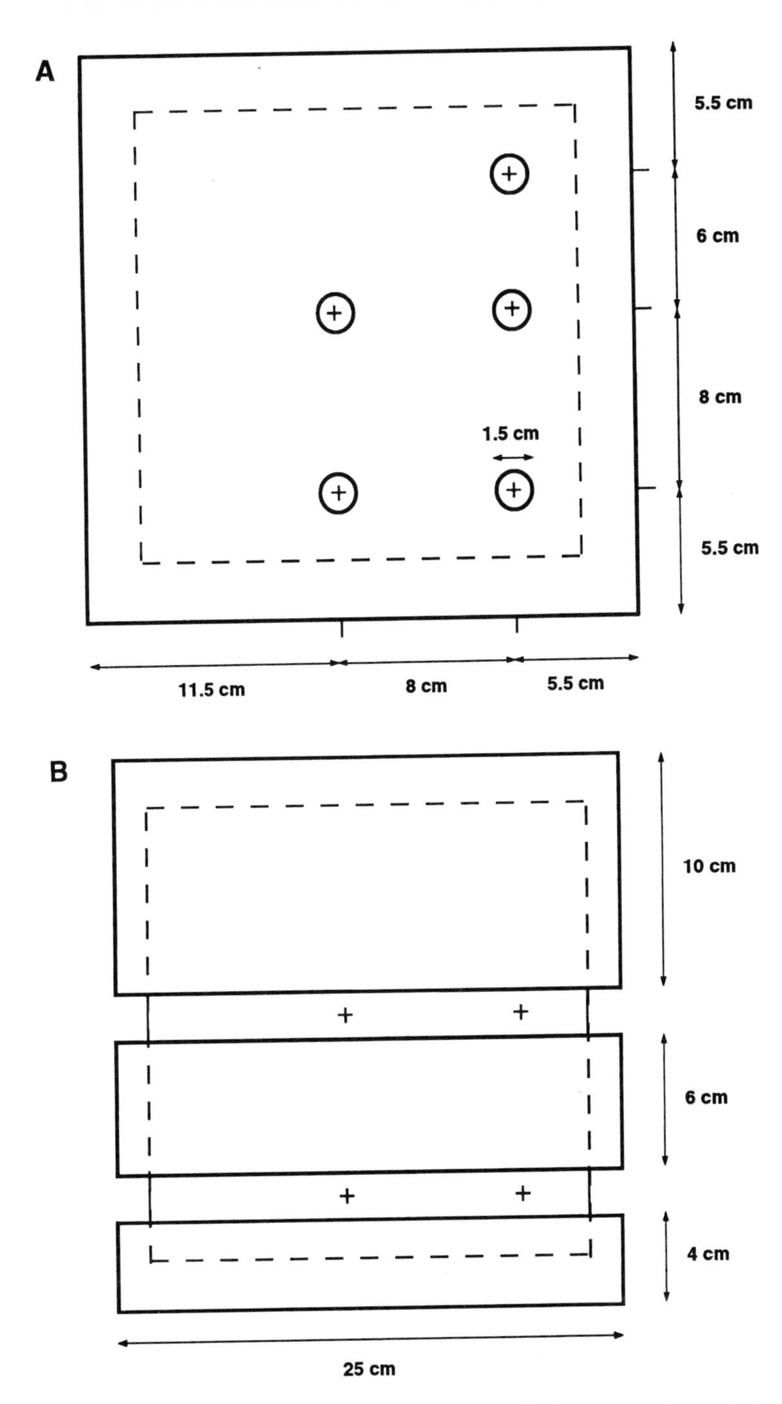

FIGURE 6 Blotters for wetting TLC plates before separation of phosphoamino acids in the first (A) and second (B) dimensions. The blotter for the first dimension is constructed from two sheets of Whatman 3MM paper as in Fig. 3. The blotters for the second dimension are single sheets of Whatman 3MM paper.

blotting strips on the plate and pressing gently with your fingertips on the edges of these strips so that the buffer moves toward the center between adjacent strips, thereby concentrating the sample on a line between the origins (Fig. 6B). It is normal for a sharp brown line to appear on this line. Make sure that the whole plate is wetted evenly, and that there are no puddles of buffer.

9. Rotate the plate 90° counterclockwise and place it on the electrophoresis

apparatus. Carry out electrophoresis for 16 min at 1.3 kV toward the positive electrode as described in Section G 2.

10. Remove the plate from the electrophoresis apparatus and dry the plate using a fan or in a 65°C oven.

11. Spray the plate with 0.25% ninhydrin in acetone and bake 15 min at 65°C to develop the stain of the three phosphoamino acid markers. Ninhydrin stains primary amino groups and the phosphoamino acid standards appear as purple spots (see Fig. 5 for key to the positions of the standards). The staining persists during autoradiography.

12. Mark the plate around the edges with ^{35}S-labeled radioactive ink and expose to presensitized X-ray film at −70°C with an intensifier screen or to a phosphorimager plate.

13. Identify the radioactive phosphoamino acids by aligning the stained standards with the X-ray film or a copy of the phosphorimage.

The times for electrophoresis given are for the HTLE 7000 system. They are chosen so that the migration of free phosphate is confined to the quadrant of the plate reserved for each sample (Fig. 5). Electrophoresis times should be optimized for other systems.

J. ISOLATION AND CHARACTERIZATION OF INDIVIDUAL PHOSPHOPEPTIDES FROM TLC PLATES

To characterize sites of phosphorylation, the susceptibility of phosphopeptides to digestion with different proteases or chemical cleavage agents can be tested. Phosphopeptides can also be subjected to manual Edman degradation. Individual phosphopeptides are purified after two-dimensional separation on TLC plates for further analysis as follows.

Steps

1. Align the TLC plate with the X-ray film or copy of the phosphorimage using the ^{35}S-labeled radioactive or fluorescent ink marks on the plate. Hold the sandwich over a light box and localize phosphopeptides of interest.

2. Slice the first 3–4 mm off the pointed end of a blue disposable pipette tip for a 1-ml pipetman and push a 6.5-mm-diameter porous polyethylene disk into the large end until it is firmly in place (Fig. 7).

3. Attach the large end of an elution tip to a vacuum line, turn on the vacuum, and scrape the cellulose from the area containing an individual phosphopeptide off the plate with the cut end of the tip (Fig. 7A). The dislodged cellulose will be sucked into the tip and caught against the porous polyethylene disk (Fig. 7A).

4. Remove the tip from the vacuum line, and place the tip, large end down, in a microcentrifuge tube (Fig. 7B). Add 100 μl pH 1.9 buffer through the small end of the tip, and let stand at room temperature for 5 min. Centrifuge for 5–10 sec at 2000 rpm in a microcentrifuge at room temperature. Be careful the tip does not hit the lid. Repeat this process twice using pH 1.9 buffer and twice using deionized water, collecting each eluate sequentially in the same tube.

5. Centrifuge the combined eluates for 5 min at 10,000 rpm in a microcentrifuge and transfer the supernatant to a new tube, being careful to leave all the residual cellulose particles behind. Lyophilize in a Speed-Vac.

6. Count the radioactivity in the cellulose and in the eluate by Cerenkov

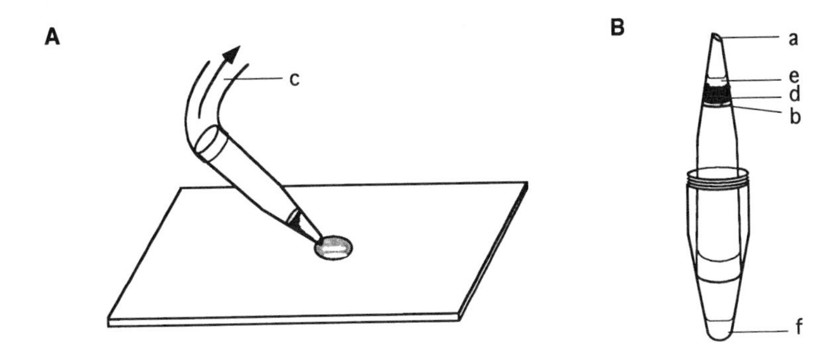

FIGURE 7 Isolation of phosphopeptides from TLC plates. The positions of individual phosphopeptides are marked on the TLC plates after aligning the plate with the X-ray film or a copy of the phosphorimage. To isolate peptides from the plates, cut the end off a blue (1-ml) pipette tip (a) with a razor blade and fit the tip with a 0.6-cm-diameter porous polyethylene disk (b) by pushing the disk in from the large end of the tip as far as it will go. Attach the large end of the tip to a vacuum line (c), turn on the vacuum, and scrape the cellulose particles off the plate so that they are sucked into the pipette tip and caught against the porous disk (A). After removing all the cellulose containing the phosphopeptide from the plate (stippled circle), detach the vacuum line and place the pipette tip, large end down, into a 1.5-ml microcentrifuge tube (B). Add 100 μl electrophoresis buffer (e) to the cellulose (d) through the top of the pipette tip, and leave for 5 min to elute the peptides from the cellulose. Centrifuge the buffer through the polyethylene filter to the bottom of the microcentrifuge tube (f) by a brief spin. To optimize the recovery repeat the elution procedure. Clear fine cellulose particles that pass through the porous disk from the eluate by centrifugation at 10,000 rpm.

counting. If elution was inefficient, reextract with another electrophoresis buffer, chromatography buffer, or 20% acetonitrile/0.1% trifluoroacetic acid in water.

7. The elution tips can be reused several times. To clean them, attach a vacuum line connected to a liquid trap to the small end of the tip and flush then sequentially with deionized water and 96% ethanol. Dry the tips under vacuum.

K. SECONDARY DIGESTION OF PHOSPHOPEPTIDES

Useful information about a phosphopeptide can be obtained by determining its susceptibility to cleavage by proteases other than that used for the primary digestion and to chemical cleavage agents. For example, for a tryptic peptide, chymotrypsin, endoproteinase Glu-C (V8), endoproteinase Asp-N, proline-specific endopeptidase, and thermolysin can be used for secondary digestion. Individual phosphopeptides are digested with proteases or chemical cleavage agents as follows.

Steps

1. Dissolve the dried purified peptide in 20 μl of appropriate digestion buffer (Table I), and split into two 10-μl aliquots.

2. For secondary digestion with a protease add 1 μg of proteolytic enzyme to one sample, and incubate both samples for 4 hr under the conditions given in Table I. For chemical cleavage the sample should be dissolved in water, split into two, dried and then taken up in equal volumes of buffer with or without added cleavage agent, and treated under the conditions given in Table I.

3. For samples digested with protease, at the end of the incubation add 1 μl

TABLE I Specificity of Different Protein Cleavage Reagents and Conditions for Cleavage

Reagent	Specificity	Conditions
Carboxypeptidase B	X-K_{CO_2H}, X-R_{CO_2H}	50 m*M* NH_4HCO_3, pH 8.0, 37°C
α-Chymotrypsin	F-X, W-X, Y-X	50 m*M* NH_4HCO_3, pH 8.3, 37°C
Endoproteinase Asp-N	X-CSO_3H, X-D	50 m*M* NH_4HCO_3, pH 7.6, 37°C
Endoproteinase Glu-C (V8)	E-X	50 m*M* NH_4HCO_3, pH 7.6, 37°C
Proline-specific endopeptidase	P-X	50 m*M* NH_4HCO_3, pH 7.6, 37°C
Thermolysin	X-L, X-I, X-V	50 m*M* NH_4HCO_3, pH 8.0, 1 m*M* $CaCl_2$, 55°C
TPCK-trypsin	K-X, R-X	50 m*M* NH_4HCO_3, pH 8.3, 37°C
Cyanogen bromide (CNBr)	M-X	50 mg/ml CNBr in 70% formic acid, 90 min, 21°C
Hydroxylamine[a]	N-G	2 *M* guanidine, 2 *M* NH_2OH, 0.2 *M* K_2CO_3 pH 9, 4 hr, 45°C
Formic acid	D-P	70% formic acid, 24–48 hr, 37°C
N-chlorosuccinimide[a] (NCS)	W-X	40 m*M* NCS in 5 *M* urea/50% acetic acid, 30 min, 21°C

[a] Proteins and peptides cleaved by NH_2OH and NCS under these conditions cannot be analyzed by two-dimensional TLC separation because of the high concentrations of nonvolatile salts, and have to be analyzed by SDS–PAGE or HPLC.

β-mercaptoethanol and boil for 2 min to inactivate the protease. Freeze and lyophilize to dryness.

4. Take up each sample in 6 μl water. Analyze half of each sample and a mixture of the other two halves on three separate TLC plates by electrophoresis and chromatography under the conditions used originally for purification of the peptide (Section G). Alternatively mark a TLC plate with three origins 5 cm apart, 3 cm from one edge. Spot half of each sample on the outside origins, and spot a mixture of the two samples on the center origin. Wet the plate using two pieces of Whatman 3MM paper so that the samples are sharpened onto a line running through the three origins. Electrophorese for one-half of the usual time at the normal voltage as described in Section G 2.

5. Dry the plate in front of a fan, and chromatograph in the same buffer as used originally as described in Section G 3.

6. Dry the plate in an oven at 65°C or in a fume hood, and expose to X-ray film with an intensifier screen at −70°C or to a phosphorimager plate.

7. If the digested sample has a peptide of different mobility from the starting peptide, and the mixed sample contains two peptides, this indicates that the phosphopeptide has a cleavage site for the protease or chemical used for digestion.

Partial digestion by proteases or multiple phosphorylations within a single peptide can each generate multiple related peptides on two-dimensional separation (see Boyle *et al.*, 1991a, for a discussion of how additional lysine or arginine residues or additional phosphates affect the mobility of a peptide). To determine whether two phosphopeptides are related, limited hydrolysis in HCl can be used to generate characteristic fingerprints for comparison.

Steps

1. Incubate the purified phosphopeptide for 30 min in 6 *N* HCl at 110°C.
2. Evaporate the HCl in a Speed-Vac.
3. Dissolve the hydrolysate in 5 μl deionized water, and analyze by separation in one or two dimensions on TLC plates. Good separation can be obtained by electrophoresis at pH 8.9 at 1 kV for 25 min followed by chromatography using Phospho Chromatography buffer in the second dimension. Alternatively, multiple samples can be spotted 1 cm apart on a line 5 cm from the edge of a TLC plate and resolved by electrophoresis at pH 3.5 for 30 min at 1.5 kV.
4. Phosphopeptides generating an overlapping pattern of subpeptides of identical mobility contain common sequences around one phosphorylation site (e.g., Meek and Eckhart, 1988).

L. EDMAN DEGRADATION OF PHOSPHOPEPTIDES

Provided the phosphoamino acid is close to the N terminus of the phosphopeptide one can identify the position of the phosphorylated residue by manual Edman degradation. Reliable analysis requires at least 50–100 cpm of purified phosphopeptide per cycle. It is technically difficult to run >5–6 cycles in colution, but Edman degradation of a phosphopeptide covalently attached to Sequelon membrane is possible, and allows more cycles to be carried out.

Solutions

1. *Phenylisothiocyanate:* Mix 5 vol of phenylisothiocyanate with 95 vol of pyridine.
2. *Heptane:ethyl acetate (10:1):* Mix 10 vol of heptane with 1 vol of ethyl acetate.
3. *Heptane:ethyl acetate (2:1):* Mix 2 vol of heptane with 1 vol of ethyl acetate.

Steps

1. Dissolve the purified peptide in 20 μl water in a 1.5-ml microcentrifuge tube using a vortex mixer.
2. Decide on the number of Edman steps to be taken. Remove a number of microliters equal to 20/(number of steps + 1) as a starting material sample, and store at 4°C. Restore the volume to 20 μl with water, and add 20 μl 5% phenylisothiocyanate in pyridine and mix.
3. Incubate the sample at 45°C for 30 min.
4. Add 200 μl of heptane:ethyl acetate (10:1 mix v/v) and vortex for 15 sec. Centrifuge briefly in a microcentrifuge to separate the phases, and remove the upper organic phase with a plastic disposable transfer micropipette, making sure

not to remove any aqueous phase. Repeat the extraction with 200 μl heptane:ethyl acetate (10:1) once.

5. Add 200 μl heptane:ethyl acetate (2:1) and extract the aqueous phase as described in step 4. Repeat this extraction once.

6. Freeze the final aqueous phase and lyophilize in a Speed-Vac (this takes about 30 min).

7. Take up the dried residue in 50 μl trifluoroacetic acid and incubate for 10 min at 45°C.

8. Evaporate the trifluoroacetic acid *in vacuo* in a Speed-Vac (this takes about 15 min).

9. Take up the dried residue in a volume of water equal to 20 μl minus the volume taken out as a sample of the starting material. Take out an aliquot the same size as the aliquot taken for the starting material (this is the product of cycle 1), and freeze. Restore the volume of the rest of the sample to 20 μl with water.

10. Repeat steps 3–9 until the requisite number of cycles have been completed.

11. Spot the starting material sample and the reaction products of each cycle onto a thin-layer 100-μm cellulose plate (1 cm apart), using an origin line in the center of the plate, and electrophorese for 25 min at 1 kV at pH 1.9 or 3.5 as described in Section G 2. Free [^{32}P]orthophosphate (50–200 cpm) should be used as a marker. If the peptide contains P.Tyr, PTH-P.Tyr should also be used as a marker (see below). After electrophoresis dry the plate and expose to X-ray film with an intensifier screen at −70°C or a phosphorimager plate. It is best to analyze the reaction products of all of the cycles on a single plate.

The release of free [^{32}P]phosphate at a particular cycle, which results from β elimination during cyclization, indicates the presence a P.Ser or P.Thr residue. P.Tyr is stable to cyclization and is released as the anilinothiazolinone derivative of P.Tyr. This can be converted to the phenylthiohydantoin (PTH) derivative of P.Tyr by incubation in 0.1 *N* HCl for 20 min at 80°C. Marker PTH-P.Tyr is readily synthesized by reacting P.Tyr with phenylisothiocyanate as described above in step 2, and can be detected as a dark spot when the TLC plate is examined under a hand-held UV light. In addition to the cycle at which free [^{32}P]phosphate or [^{32}P]PTH-P.Tyr is released, information on the sequence of the peptide may be obtained by the electrophoretic mobility shifts detected at each cycle. Thus, if a positive or negatively charged amino acid is removed at a cycle before the phosphoamino acid, there will be a corresponding shift in the mobility of the peptide. Remember that if the peptide contains a C-terminal lysine this will react with phenylisothiocyanate at cycle 1, which will cause the loss of a positive charge. It may be difficult to determine the position of a second, more C-terminal phosphorylated residue present in the same peptide.

M. STRATEGY FOR IDENTIFICATION OF PHOSPHORYLATION SITES

The most direct approach to the identification of a phosphorylation site is to sequence the purified phosphopeptide directly on an automated sequencer. This requires ~10–100 pmole of pure peptide. For this purpose, it is best to purify the phosphopeptide by HPLC, even if it is first separated by two-dimensional TLC separation, because peptides isolated from plates are usually not chemically pure. Sufficient amounts of phosphopeptide can often be obtained by ^{32}P labeling of recombinant protein, produced in bacteria or insect cells, with a purified protein kinase *in vitro*. Usually, however, sufficient chemical amounts are not available, and to identify the phosphorylation site in a phosphopeptide derived from a protein of known sequence the following strategy may be useful.

Steps

1. Based on the amino acid sequence of the protein derived from DNA sequencing, make a list of all the possible phosphopeptides that will be generated by digestion with the relevant proteases.

2. Make a table listing the properties of the individual candidate phosphopeptides (for example, see van der Geer and Hunter, 1990). List susceptibilities to digestion with proteases or chemicals, the position and the nature of the phosphate acceptor site(s), and the presence of cysteine and methionines within candidate peptides.

3. Determine the predicted mobilities of the primary and secondary peptides either using the parameters provided by Boyle *et al.* (1991a) or using the PeptidePlot program, which works in conjunction with the PeptideSort program as part of the GCG package of nucleic acid and protein sequence management software. As most endopeptidases do not work well as exopeptidases, they cleave peptide bonds adjacent to the N- or C-terminal residues very inefficiently. This applies both to the primary protease and to digestion with secondary proteases. In the case of trypsin, runs of two or more adjacent lysines or arginines will generate multiple partial digestion products including peptides that have an extra lysine or arginine at the N or C terminus in addition to the limit digest peptide. The mobilities of these peptides should also be calculated. In addition, the following specificities should be noted. Trypsin does not cleave Lys/Arg.Pro bonds, and cleaves Lys/Arg.Glu/Asp bonds and Lys/Arg.X.phosphoserine/phosphothreonine bonds inefficiently. Chymotrypsin does not cleave Trp/Tyr/Phe.Pro bonds or phosphotyrosine.X bonds.

4. Determine experimentally the susceptibility of the purified phosphopeptide (Section J) to secondary digestion with one or more proteases not used for the primary digestion and chemical cleavage agents such as CNBr (Section K).

5. Determine the position of the phosphorylated amino acid in the purified peptide by manual Edman degradation (Section L).

6. Provided the stoichiometry of phosphorylation is reasonably high the presence of methionine or cysteine residues in the phosphopeptide can be determined by mixing a digest of a sample metabolically labeled with [^{35}S]Met/Cys with a sample of the same protein labeled with ^{32}P prior to peptide mapping. Such doubly labeled maps are first exposed for ^{32}P, with an intensifier screen using aluminum foil between the film and the screen to shield the low-energy radiation emitted by the ^{35}S. After decay of the ^{32}P and treatment with an fluorographic enhancer, the maps can be exposed for ^{35}S. The two exposures can be lined up with the help of radioactive marks on the TLC plates.

7. Compare the actual properties of the phosphopeptide determined in steps 4–6 and the experimentally determined mobility with the theoretical properties and predicted mobilities of the peptides in the table. It should be possible to eliminate most of the peptides, leaving one or a few candidate peptides.

8. If an antipeptide antibody corresponding to the sequence around a candidate phosphorylation site is available, this antibody can be used for immunoprecipitation of proteolytic digests. To do this, preincubate the antibodies with protein A–Sepharose for 1 hr at 4°C. Collect the beads by centrifuging briefly in a microcentrifuge. Wash the beads several times with 50 m*M*

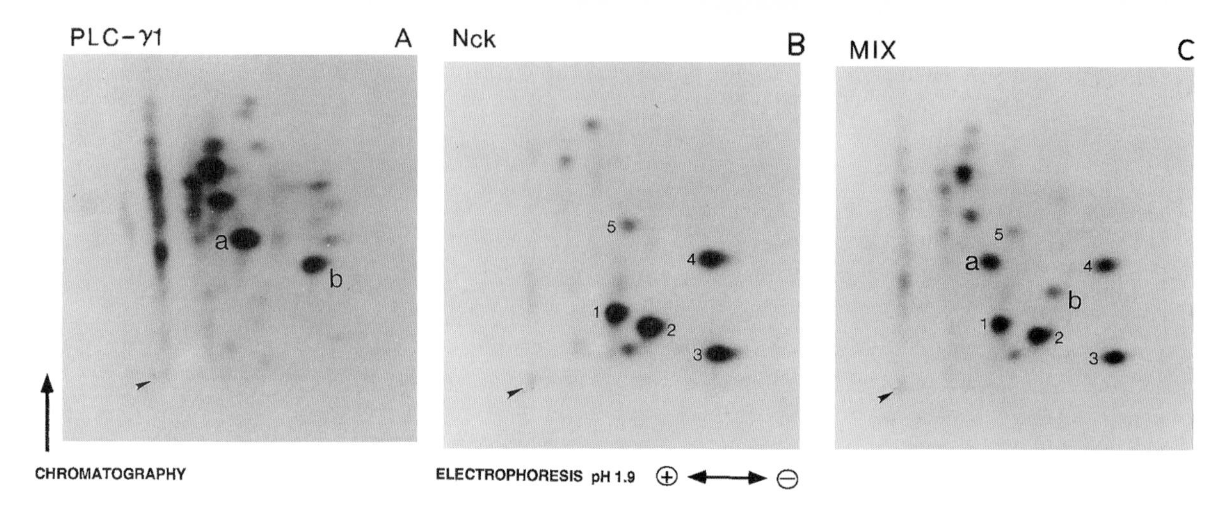

FIGURE 8 Representative two-dimensional phosphopeptide maps. ^{32}P-labeled phospholipase C γ1 (PLC-γ1) and Nck were isolated by immunoprecipitation from quiescent NIH 3T3 mouse fibroblasts, which had been labeled for 16 hr with 1 mCi/ml [^{32}P]orthophosphate and then treated for 5 min at 37°C with 50 ng/ml platelet-derived growth factor. Tryptic digests were generated as described in Sections A, B, and C and resolved by electrophoresis at pH 1.9 for 20 min at 1 kV (horizontal dimension with the origins indicated by arrowheads and the anode on the left), followed by chromatography in phospho chromatography buffer (vertical dimension) as described in Section G. (A) 700 cpm ^{32}P-labeled PLC-γ1 digest. (B) 500 cpm ^{32}P-labeled Nck digest. (C) Mix of ^{32}P-labeled PLC-γ1 and Nck digests, 300 cpm each. All plates were exposed for 3 days at −70°C with an intensifying screen to presensitized Kodak XAR film. The letters in A and numbers in B indicate phosphopeptides that can readily be resolved in the mix shown in C. This analysis was carried out by Jill Meisenhelder (Salk Institute, La Jolla, California). Further details can be found in Meisenhelder *et al.* (1989) and Meisenhelder and Hunter (1992).

NH_4HCO_3, pH 7.6. Incubate the beads with the proteolytic digest for 1 hr at 4°C on a shaker. Wash several times with 50 m*M* NH_4HCO_3, pH 7.6. Elute the bound peptides by adding 1 or 2 vol of pH 1.9 electrophoresis buffer. Centrifuge out the beads, remove the buffer, and lyophilize. Take up the dried residue in an appropriate electrophoresis buffer and analyze by two-dimensional separation on a TLC plate.

9. If purified recombinant protein is available (e.g., a glutathione-S-transferase (GST) fusion protein), then it may be possible to phosphorylate this protein with the relevant purified protein kinase in the presence of 1 m*M* ATP to achieve a high stoichiometry of phosphorylation. To this unlabeled sample one adds as a tracer ^{32}P-labeled protein generated with the same protein kinase and [γ^{32}P]-ATP. The mix is then subjected to proteolytic digestion, and the peptides are resolved by HPLC. Phosphopeptides are identified by monitoring for ^{32}P radioactivity, and peptides by UV monitoring. If necessary, radioactive peaks should by repurified by HPLC under a different condition until it is certain that the radioactivity corresponds to a single chemically pure peptide. This phosphopeptide can then be subjected to automated sequencing (at least 10 pmoles purified phosphopeptide will be needed). Remember that there will be no PTH-amino acid signal at the position of the phosphoamino acid, since phosphoserine and phosphothreonine are destroyed upon cyclization, and PTH-phosphotyrosine does not comigrate with PTH-tyrosine. The absence of a PTH-amino acid signal is a strong indication that this residue is phosphorylated, and this conclusion should be substantiated by comparing the peptide sequence with the predicted protein sequence to ensure that a hydroxyamino acid occurs at this position.

10. To establish the identity of a phosphorylation site a synthetic peptide

corresponding to the candidate phosphopeptide can be made and phosphorylated either chemically or enzymatically and tested for comigration in two dimensions with the purified phosphopeptide from the protein. If the synthesized peptide is not efficiently phosphorylated because it is too small, a longer peptide can be synthesized, phosphorylated, and then digested with the appropriate protease. The identity of a phosphorylation site can be confirmed by mutating the putative acceptor site and analyzing the phosphorylation of the mutant protein after transfection and expression in an appropriate cell line.

IV. Comments

The technical protocols for peptide mapping and subsequent analysis of phosphopeptides described in this article have been optimized over many years in the Molecular Biology and Virology Laboratory at the Salk Institute. More detailed descriptions of most of these protocols and discussions of the principles involved can be found in Cooper *et al.* (1983), Boyle *et al.* (1991a), and van der Geer *et al.* (1993). Representative papers from our group, where these methods have been used to analyze protein phosphorylation and identify phosphorylation sites, are Patschinsky *et al.* (1982), Cooper *et al.* (1984), Hunter *et al.* (1984), Gould *et al.* (1985), Cooper *et al.* (1986), Gould *et al.* (1986), Meek and Eckhart (1988), Weinmaster *et al.* (1988), Meisenhelder *et al.* (1989), van der Geer and Hunter (1990), Boyle *et al.* (1991b), Meisenhelder and Hunter (1992), and Krieg and Hunter (1992). A set of typical phosphopeptide maps carried out by these protocols is shown in Fig. 8.

V. Pitfalls

The major pitfalls are given within each protocol. Two main points are worth stressing again.

1. It is imperative at every step to avoid the presence of any foreign matter such as gel fragments, pieces of paper, and cellulose particles in samples digested with proteases or hydrolyzed with acid that are to be analyzed by two-dimensional thin-layer electrophoresis and chromatography.

2. The recovery of ^{32}P radioactivity should be monitored at every step by Cerenkov counting in a scintillation counter to ensure that the majority of the radioactivity ends up in the final sample.

REFERENCES

Boyle, W. J., Smeal, T., DeFize, L. H. K., Angel, P., Woodgett, J. R., Karin, M., and Hunter, T. (1991a) Activation of protein kinase C decreases phosphorylation of c-Jun at sites that negatively regulate its DNA-binding activity. *Cell* **64,** 573–584.

Boyle, W. J., van der Geer, P., and Hunter, T. (1991b) Phosphopeptide mapping and phosphoamino acid analysis by two-dimensional separation on cellulose thin-layer plates. *In* "Methods in Enzymology" (T. Hunter and B. M. Sefton, eds.), Vol. 201, pp. 110–149. Academic Press, San Diego.

Cooper, J. A., Esch, F. S., Taylor, S. S., and Hunter, T. (1984) Phosphorylation sites in enolase and lactate dehydrogenase utilized by tyrosine protein kinases in vivo and in vitro. *J. Biol. Chem.* **259,** 7835–7841.

Cooper, J. A., Gould, K. L., Cartwright, C. A., and Hunter, T. (1986) Tyr^{527} is phosphorylated in $pp60^{c-src}$: implications for regulation. *Science* **231,** 1431–1434.

Cooper, J. A., Sefton, B. M., and Hunter, T. (1983) Detection and quantification of phosphotyrosine in proteins. *In* "Methods in Enzymology" (J. D. Corbin and J. C. Hordman, eds.), Vol. 201, pp. 387–402. Academic Press, San Diego.

Duclos, B., Marcandier, and Cozzone, A. J. (1991) Chemical properties and separation of phosphoamino acids by thin-layer chromatography and/or electrophoresis. *In* "Methods in Enzymology" (T. Hunter and B. M. Sefton, eds.), Vol. 201, pp. 10–21. Academic Press, San Diego.

Gould, K. L., Woodgett, J. R., Cooper, J. A., Buss, J. E., Shalloway, D., and Hunter, T. (1985) Protein kinase C phosphorylates pp60^{src} at a novel site. *Cell* **42**, 849–857.

Gould, K. L., Woodgett, J. R., Isacke, C. M., and Hunter, T. (1986) The protein–tyrosine kinase substrate, p36, is also a substrate for protein kinase C in vitro and in vivo. *Mol. Cell. Biol.* **6**, 2738–2744.

Hunter, T., Ling, N., and Cooper, J. A. (1984) Protein kinase C phosphorylation of the EGF receptor at a threonine residue close to the cytoplasmic face of the plasma membrane. *Nature (London)* **311**, 480–483.

Krieg, J., and Hunter, T. (1992) Identification of the two major, EGF-induced tyrosine phosphorylation sites in the microvillar core protein ezrin. *J. Biol. Chem.* **267**, 19258–19265.

Luo, K., Hurley, T., and Sefton, B. M. (1990) Transfer of proteins to membranes facilitates both cyanogen bromide cleavage and two-dimensional proteolytic mapping. *Oncogene* **5**, 921–923.

Luo, K., Hurley, T., and Sefton, B. M. (1991) Cyanogen bromide cleavage and proteolytic peptide mapping of proteins immobilized to membranes. *In* "Methods in Enzymology" (T. Hunter and B. M. Sefton, eds.), Vol. 201, pp. 149–152. Academic Press, San Diego.

Meek, D. W., and Eckhart, W. (1988) Phosphorylation of p53 in normal and simian virus 40-transformed NIH 3T3 cells. *Mol. Cell. Biol.* **8**, 461–465.

Meisenhelder, J., and Hunter, T. (1992) The SH2/SH3 domain-containing protein Nck is recognized by certain anti-phospholipase C-γl monoclonal antibodies and its phosphorylation on tyrosine is stimulated by platelet-derived growth factor and epidermal growth factor treatment. *Mol. Cell. Biol.* **12**, 5843–5856.

Meisenhelder, J., Suh, P.-G., Rhee, S. G., and Hunter, T. (1989) Phospholipase C-γ is a substrate for the PDGF and EGF receptor protein–tyrosine kinases in vivo and in vitro. *Cell* **57**, 1109–1122.

Offord, R. E. (1966) Electrophoretic mobilities of peptides on paper and their use in the determination of amide groups. *Nature (London)* **211**, 591–593.

Patschinsky, T., Hunter, T., Esch, F. S., Cooper, J. A., and Sefton, B. M. (1982) Analysis of the sequence of amino acids surrounding sites of tyrosine phosphorylation. *Proc. Natl. Acad. Sci. USA* **79**, 973–977.

Van der Geer, P., and Hunter, T. (1990) Identification of tyrosine 706 in the kinase insert as the major CSF-1-stimulated autophosphorylation site in the CSF-1 receptor in a murine macrophage cell line. *Mol. Cell. Biol.* **10**, 2991–3002.

Van der Geer, P., Luo, K., Sefton, B. M., and Hunter, T. (1993) Phosphopeptide mapping and phosphoamino acid analysis on cellulose thin-layer plates. *In* "Protein Phosphorylation: A Practical Approach" (D. G. Hardie, ed.), pp. 31–59. IRL Press, Oxford.

Weinmaster, G. A., Middlemas, D. S., and Hunter, T. (1988) A major site of tyrosine phosphorylation within the SH2 domain of Fujinami sarcoma virus P130$^{gag-fps}$ is not required for protein–tyrosine kinase activity or transforming potential. *J. Virol.* **62**, 2016–2025.

PART 15

APPENDICES

Cell and Tissue Culture Media: History and Terminology

Dale F. Gruber and David W. Jayme

I. Introduction

It is not within the scope of this article to present a treatise on the inception and evolution of the science (or art) of cell (or tissue) culture. Any pretext of a historical review would undoubtedly preclude what some consider important contributors. The purpose of this article is to review a portion of the experimental advances and allow the reader to establish a relative time frame and assessment to the development of culture techniques as they exist today. It also summarizes the nutritional applications of various cell culture components and provides a glossary to attempt standardization of *in vitro* culture terminology.

II. History of Cell and Tissue Culture

A. TISSUE CULTURE

The roots of tissue culture developed as a natural progression from embryological techniques in place during the late 19th century. Initial reports of tissue culture activities began to appear in scientific literature in the mid-1880s. Most often cited as the initial culture report was that which described the maintenance of chick embryonic tissue in warm saline (Roux, 1885). That initial report was followed a few years later by a description of the survival and migratory capability of frog leukocytes in saline (Arnold, 1887). Sixteen years elapsed before the survival and division of salamander leukocytes was described in hanging-drop cultures (Jolly, 1903).

At this early point, culturists had already demonstrated important concepts; i.e., under "appropriate conditions" cultured cells could survive, move, and proliferate *in vitro*. These were significant findings in their own right but other equally important questions needed to be addressed before culture acquired credibility as a scientific technique. One of the most important questions was (and, in some cases, still is) whether *in vitro* conditions were representative of the *in vivo* environment? There persists today healthy concern, and controversy, as to whether *in vitro* data can be extrapolated to *in vivo* situations. An early positive position on the relationship issue came as a result of experimental observations on explanted frog tissue function(s) in frog lymph clots *in vitro* (Harrison, 1907).

Culture application possibilities expanded following demonstration that coagulated plasma (Burrows, 1910) or tissue extracts were also capable of promoting *in vitro* growth (Carrel and Burrows, 1911). The clot technique was a valuable early research tool that generated considerable interest. As was later recognized, the majority of cultured cells do not require the supporting matrix that was provided by clot techniques. The science of tissue culture had acquired a new critical dimension: analysis of basic constituents necessary to the propagation of cells *sans* matrix. It was now the responsibility of investigators to define the nutritional requirements for their individual *in vitro* culture application(s).

B. DEVELOPMENT OF MEDIA

Although considerable research time has elapsed (more than 100 years), the basic culture paradigm is still being unraveled as culturists attempt to define fully their cellular specific requirements. During the first 50 years, tissue culture met with occasional culture successes in supplemented, buffered saline solutions or plasma clots. Contamination issues were rampant and by necessity had to be addressed before any nutritional issues could be adequately examined. Culture contamination issues abated somewhat following a report that demonstrated a direct relationship between the application of surgical aseptic principles and successful culture technique (Carrel, 1912). Prior to this point, tissue culture was considered by many to be a luxury technique not easily indulged in because of the high propensity to failure. Once contamination issues were somewhat rectified, success rates took an upturn and investigators turned more diligently to the characterization of the nutrient medium.

Under "appropriate conditions," many plant and animal cell types have the capacity to survive, multiply, and differentiate *in vitro*. Seventy years after its inception, up until the 1950s (and later by some estimates), tissue culture was perceived as a blend of science and witchcraft. Nutrient media have undergone considerable evolution and change, primarily over the last 40 years as formulations have become more "defined" and "optimized" under the rigors of scientific scrutiny. The complexity of medium development has been complicated by the observation that nutrient requirements differ according to cell type and culture condition. Specific growth requirements of various cell types are reviewed in detail elsewhere in this volume.

In *in vitro* culture, the extracellular milieu must supply all essential nutrients. Today we generally understand what constitutes an essential nutrient, although 50 years ago these elements were unknown. Controlled component experiments began in the early 1900s with the examination of the effects of seawater, serum, embryo extracts, and peptones at varying concentrations (Lewis and Lewis, 1911). It was another 20 years before the importance of amino acids in growth medium was described (Willmer and Kendall, 1932). Attempts to develop synthetic medium continued into the 1940s when dialyzed plasma was used as a basal medium and supplemented with amino acids similar to those found in fibrin (Fischer, 1941). Those studies culminated in the report of a medium, V-605, which today is more of historical rather than practical value (Fischer *et al.*, 1948), followed in 1950 by publication of medium 199 (Morgan *et al.*, 1950). Eagle's basal medium formulation, characterized as an isosmotic, pH-balanced mixture of salts, amino acids, sugars, vitamins, and other necessary nutrients, was described in 1955 (Eagle, 1955a,b). Such media were considered complex by formulation but not complete without the addition of a protein source such as plasma, serum, bodily fluid, or tissue extract. The importance of these medium formulations may not have been based in their application successes, but more in the fact that they were models for the evolution and development of most common media as they exist today.

III. Nutrient Medium Composition

Most catalogs of commercial suppliers contain extensive appendices describing the various formulations of conventional media. Such tables typically list medium components from the perspective of a medium kitchen. By contrast, Table I compares active molar concentrations of six representative classical media in a format designed to highlight differences and to facilitate their correlation with *in vitro* culture observations.

The nutrient environment for "acceptable" cell growth is basically simple, yet specifically complex. The cellular milieu must address numerous physical and chemical factors, including temperature, osmotic pressure, hydrogen ion concentration (pH), and the presence of inorganic salts, essential (and nonessential) amino acids, vitamins, dissolved gasses, and other unidentified growth materials provided through supplementation(s). Each of these interdependent requirements had to be assessed, independently and jointly, to ascertain optimal nutrient levels.

Inorganic salts

Inorganic salts constitute a significant portion of any medium. Their primary functions are to maintain pH and osmolality and to provide adequate concentrations of essential inorganic ions. Although numerous physiological salt solutions have been developed from inorganic salts, most are basically derivations of a salt solution originally described before the 19th century (Ringer, 1895). The first salt solution specifically for mammalian cells was proposed in 1910 (Tyrode, 1910). There are two general types of balanced salt solutions: the first type equilibrates in air (Hanks') and the second equilibrates with CO_2 tensions of 5–8% (Earle's). Basic inorganic salts supply much of the sodium, potassium, calcium, magnesium, chloride, and phosphate ions required for cell replication and other physiological functions. The following list constitutes the inorganic salts common to balanced salt solutions and medium formulations: $CaCl_2$, KCl, NaCl, $MgCl_2$, $MgSO_4$, $NaHCO_3$, Na_2HPO_4, NaH_2PO_4.

Buffering

The pH range that optimally supports cellular viability and proliferation is cellular dependent over a relatively narrow span. Buffers have been incorporated into medium to modulate pH shifts and maintain cellular homeostasis. Bicarbonate buffers have been used extensively in culture because they offered the advantages of low cytotoxicity and cost and provided some nutritional benefit. The major drawback to bicarbonate buffer is its relatively weak physiological buffering capacity. To enhance the capacity of media to withstand pH stressors, it has become common to supplement medium with organic buffers. Organic buffers minimize pH shifts when cultures are removed from the artificially high (versus ambient) carbon dioxide tensions required by bicarbonate buffers (Freshney, 1983) to maintain physiological pH.

Trace elements

Inorganic trace elements are required by some cells for proliferation. By definition, identification of trace elements has been difficult. Although some elements are purposeful additives to medium formulations, frequently they are present as contaminants of the nominal formulation constituents. Trace elements identified for cell culture importance include iron, zinc, selenium, copper, manganese, molybdenum, and vanadium.

Sugars

All media contain a carbon source for the generation of cellular metabolic energy. Glucose is the most common carbon source due to its capability of being rapidly converted into energy. Alternate carbon sources, such as fructose, mannose, galactose or pyruvate and glycogenic amino acids, may be used by cultured cells for various metabolic purposes.

TABLE I Biochemical Comparison of the Compositions of Selected Classical Medium Formulations

MEDIA	BME	DMEM	M199	McCoy's 5A	MEM	RPMI 1640
Inorganic ions (mM unless otherwise indicated)						
Calcium	1.0	1.8	1.8	1.8	1.8	0.4
Magnesium	0.5	0.8	0.8	0.8	1.0	0.4
Potassium	5.0	5.4	5.4	5.4	5.4	5.4
Sodium	120	160	150	140	140	140
Chloride	110	120	130	120	130	110
Phosphate	1.0	0.91	1.0	1.0	0.97	5.6
Sulfate		0.81	0.86	0.81		0.42
Nitrate		0.75 nM	1.2 nM			0.84
Cobalt				550 pM		3.7 μM
Iron		0.25	0.41			
Bicarbonate	20	44	26	26	26	24
Carbohydrates (μM)						
Acetate			610			
Deoxyribose			3.7			
Glucose	5000	5600	5600	17,000	5600	11,000
Ribose			3.3			
Vitamins and coenzymes (μM)						
Ascorbic acid			0.28	2.8		
Biotin	1.00		0.04	0.82		0.82
Folic acid	1.00		0.02	0.45	2.30	2.30
p-Amino benzoic acid			0.36	7.30		7.30
Nicotinic acid			0.20	4.10		
Nicotinamide	1.00	33.0	0.20	4.10	8.20	8.20
Pantothenic acid	1.00	17.0	0.04	0.84	4.60	1.00
Pyridoxine			0.12	2.40		4.90
Pyridoxal	1.00	20.0	0.12	2.50	6.00	
Riboflavin	0.10	1.10	0.03	0.53	0.27	0.53
Thiamine	1.00	12.0	0.03	0.59	3.00	3.00
Vitamin A			0.35			
Vitamin B_{12}				0.55 nM		3.7 nM
Vitamin D			0.25			
Vitamin E			0.02			
Vitamin K			0.06			
Amino acids (μM)						
Alanine			560	150		
Arginine	100	400	330	200	600	1100
Asparagine				300		330
Aspartate			450	150		150
Cysteine			0.63	260		
Cystine	50	200	83		100	200
Glutamate			910	150		140
Glutamine	2000	4000	680	1500	2000	2100
Glycine		400	670	100		130
Histidine	50	200	100	100	200	97
Isoleucine	200	800	300	300	400	380
Leucine	200	800	910	300	400	380

continues

continued

MEDIA	BME	DMEM	M199	McCoy's 5A	MEM	RPMI
		Amino acids (μM) (continued)				
Lysine	200	800	380	200	400	220
Methionine	50	200	200	100	100	100
Phenylalanine	100	400	100	100	200	91
Proline			350	150		170
Serine		400	480	250		290
Threonine	200	800	500	150	400	170
Tryptophan	20	80	98	15	50	24
Tyrosine	100	400	220	100	200	110
Valine	200	800	430	150	400	170
		Other ions (μM)				
Phenol red	14	42	42	7.1	14	14

Amino acids

On the basis of whole-animal nutritional studies, 14 amino acids are conventionally considered as essential for cultured cells: arginine, cysteine, cystine, glutamine, histidine, isoleucine, leucine, lysine, methionine, phenylalanine, threonine, tryptophan, tyrosine, and valine. Conversely, the naturally occurring nonessential amino acids include alanine, serine, asparagine, proline, glycine, aspartic acid, and glutamic acid. Nutritional requirements for amino acids vary, both quantitatively and qualitatively, with cell type, culture condition, and genetic modification.

Vitamins

Most media contain water-soluble B vitamins. Common to many formulations are vitamins B_1 (thiamine), B_2 (riboflavin), B_3 (niacinamide), B_5 (pantothenic acid), B_6 (pyridoxine), and B_9 (folic acid). Biotin (vitamin H), cyanocobalamin (vitamin B_{12}), and ascorbic acid (vitamin C) are also common vitamin components. Although choline and inositol are classically grouped with vitamin components, in cell culture they function as metabolic substrates rather than as catalysts.

Serum

Most historical medium formulations were supplemented with serum, tissue extracts, or other humoral fluids. As these supplements were vital to the success of the technique they undoubtedly supplied nutritional factors that were absent from the nutrient media. Although serum fractions have been characterized, total biochemical definition is a complex challenge, as it has been reported that serum contains more than 1000 proteins (Lambert and Birch, 1985). Complete characterization must identify cytokines and transport and attachment factors, as well as address other serum functions, such as pH buffering capacity, toxin inactivation, and protease activity. Such unspecified growth promotional and nutritional serum properties are perceived by users as "quality." Other contributors to "quality," inherent to serum supplementation, include lot-to-lot variability, availability, cost, and absence of adventitious contaminants.

Defined medium

Over the past 40 years, there have been significant advances in synthetic nutrient medium formulations. Application-specific scientific and regulatory concerns have propelled investigators toward the development of defined media. There appears to be an inverse correlation between the extent of medium definition and its range of use. As media become more defined, they are by design optimized for a particular cell type and are less conducive to the growth of other cellular types.

IV. Glossary of Cell Culture Terminology

The thrust toward development of defined cellular environments has resulted in a proliferation of "serum-free medium" formulations. With the advent of specialized medium technology was vendor marketing pressure to develop innovative commercial terminology. Unfortunately, marketing terminology has often outpaced (or confused) meaningful descriptive scientific terminology. Thought leaders in cell culture have expressed concern that marketing competition for nonstandardized terminology could promote considerable confusion in an uninformed research community. Standards for medium terminology have been recommended to differentiate between medium terminologies (e.g., serum-free, reduced serum, defined, chemically defined, and low protein). The designation "serumless," for example, may not necessarily mean devoid of protein, as serum portions may be replaced with other "undefined" supplements (i.e., serum fractions, tissue extracts, or conditioned medium). The scientific ideal, even after more than 100 years of research and development, is to develop a medium that is chemically defined and equivalent to serum-containing medium formulations in promoting normal cell growth and other biological functions. Listed below are clarifying definitions for several basic terms associated with tissue and cell culture.

Cell Regarded by most as the smallest, self-replicating, living unit.

Tissue An aggregate of cells of the same type.

Organ A composite of tissues with defined structure and function.

Explant A fragment of tissue transplanted from its original *in vivo* location and maintained *in vitro* in an nutrient medium.

Adherent cultures Cultures of cells that are attached to a natural or artificial substrate. Often referred to as monolayer cultures, but may be expanded to include multilamellar cultures.

Suspension cultures Cultures of free-floating cells not attached to substrate. Suspension requires agitation provided by mixing, stirring, spinning, or sparging. Suspension cultures may be monodisperse (single cell) or aggregated (clusters).

Population doubling The interval required by a cell population to double in density (or concentration).

Medium A mixture of inorganic salts and nutrients capable of sustaining cell survival *in vitro* for a 24-hr period.

Growth medium A medium that supplies the nutrients necessary for sustained *in vitro* cellular proliferation.

Maintenance medium A medium that will support cell survival and limited biological function but not sustained proliferation.

Organ culture The maintenance or growth of organ tissues which supports differentiation and preservation of normal tissue architecture or function.

Tissue culture A generic phrase often incorrectly used to describe the growth both of small tissue pieces (i.e., organ or explant culture) and of individual cells *in vitro*; most appropriately characterizes the growth or maintenance of explanted tissue or organs, which characterized much of the early scientific period of culture techniques.

Cell culture Culture of single-cell suspension. Refinements in dissociation and dispersion technique(s) eventually led to supplantation of organ and tissue culture with cell culture.

Primary cell culture Removal of cells mechanically, enzymatically, or chemically from a host organism and their relocation to a culture vessel.

Passage Successful transposition of cells from an original culture container to another culture vessel; synonymous with subculture.

Primary cell line In general, most investigators agree that after successful *in vitro* inoculation, cultured cells may be designated as a primary cell line. Thereafter, controversy exists as to whether subsequent passages of cells qualify them as primary, secondary, or tertiary forms.

Basal medium A formulation of defined nutrient components. Sustained cellular proliferation requires medium supplementation by serum or other growth factor additives.

Reduced serum medium A basal medium that is supplemented by growth additives. The growth additives may partially substitute for nutritional aspects normally supplied by serum, so that the required level of serum supplementation may be significantly diminished.

Serum-free medium A complete nutrient formulation capable of supporting sustained cellular proliferation or biological production without serum addition. May contain growth factors, serum fractions, tissue, or organ extracts.

Protein-free medium A complete nutrient formulation capable of supporting sustained cellular proliferation or biological production that is devoid of polypeptide components.

Defined medium A medium made entirely from biochemically defined components of synthetic origin, with the target objective being the absence of macromolecular elements.

V. Summary

In this brief review, we have touched on some points of historical significance in the development of the science of cell culture. From an overall perspective, substantial progress has been achieved, especially over the last 40 to 50 years. Investigators have made significant progress in identifying the function of numerous serum and formulation components. Not all growth components have been identified and significant research remains to explain culture anomalies. Only at the point of total definition will cell culture truly advance from an art form to a science. Serum-supplemented nutrient medium is often not conducive to the gathering of empirical scientific data under well-controlled culture conditions. Greater definition of growth medium components will be of maximum utility to scientists, because with definition comes knowledge.

REFERENCES

Arnold, J. (1887) Uber Teilungsvorgange an den Wanderzellen, ihre progressiven und retrogressiven Metamorphosen. *Arch. Mikrosk. Anat.* **30,** 205.

Burrows, M. T. (1910) The cultivation of the tissues of the chick embryo outside the body. *J. Am. Med. Assoc.* **55,** 2057.

Carrel, A. (1912) The permanent life of tissue outside the organism. *J. Exp. Med.* **15,** 516–528.

Carrel, A., and Burrows, M. T. (1911) Cultivation of tissues *in vitro* and its technique. *J. Exp. Med.* **13,** 387.

Eagle, H. (1955a) The specific amino acid requirements of mammalian cells (strain L) in tissue culture. *J. Biol. Chem.* **214,** 839–852.

Eagle, H. (1955b) Nutrition needs of mammalian cells in tissue culture. *Science* **122,** 501–504.

Fischer, A. (1941) Die Bedeutung der Aminosauren fur die Gewebezellen *in vitro. Acta Physiol. Scand.* **2,** 143.

Fischer, A., Astrup, T., Ehrensvard, G., and Oehlenschlager, V. (1948) Growth of animal tissue cells in artificial media. *Proc. Soc. Exp. Biol. Med.* **67**, 40–46.
Freshney, R. I. (1983) The culture environment. I. Substrate, gas phase, and temperature. *In* "Culture of Animal Cells—A Manual of Basic Technique" (R. I. Freshney, ed.), pp. 63–65. Alan R. Liss, New York.
Harrison, R. B. (1907) Observations on the living developing nerve fiber. *Proc. Soc. Exp. Biol. Med.* **4**, 140–143.
Jolly, J. (1903) Sur la duree de la vie et de la multiplication des cellules animales en dehors de l'organisme. *C. R. Soc. Biol.* **55**, 1266.
Lambert, K. J., and Birch, J. R. (1985) "Growth Media in Animal Cell Biotechnology" (R. E. Spier and J. B. Griffiths, eds.), p. 85. Academic Press, New York.
Lewis, M. R., and Lewis, W. H. (1911) The growth of embryonic chicken tissues in artificial media, agar and bouillion. *Bull. Johns Hopkins Hosp.* **22**, 126.
Morgan, J. F., Morton, H. J., and Parker, R. C. (1950) Nutrition of animal cells in tissue culture. I. Initial studies on a synthetic medium. *Proc. Soc. Exp. Biol. Med.* **73**, 1–8.
Ringer, S. (1895) Further observations regarding the antagonism between calcium salts and sodium, potassium and ammonium salts. *J. Physiol.* **18**, 425–429.
Roux, W. (1885) Beitrage zur Entwicklungsmechanik des Embryo. *Z. Biol.* **21**, 411.
Tyrode, M. V. (1910) The mode of action of some purgative salts. *Arch. Int. Pharmacodyn.* **20**, 205–223.
Willmer, E. N., and Kendall, L. P. (1932) The utilisation of proteoses by chicken heart fibroblasts growing *in vitro*. *J. Exp. Biol.* **9**, 149.

Representative Cultured Cell Lines and Their Characteristics

Robert J. Hay

Virtually thousands of different cell lines have been derived from human and other metazoan tissues. Many of these originate from normal tissues and exhibit a definable, limited doubling potential. Other cell lines may be propagated continuously since they either have become immortalized from the normal by genetic changes or have been developed initially from tumor tissue. Finite lines of sufficient doubling potential and continuous lines can both be expanded to produce a large number of aliquots, frozen, and authenticated for widespread use in research.

Institutions such as The American Type Culture Collection (ATCC) have been established to acquire, preserve, authenticate and distribute reference cell lines and microorganisms for use by the academic and industrial, scientific community (Hay *et al.*, 1992). The Cell Culture Department of The ATCC performs these functions to include human and animal cell lines with over 3200 available in 1993.

The advantages of working with well-defined cell lines free from contaminating organisms may appear obvious. Unfortunately, however, the potential pitfalls associated with the use of cell lines casually obtained and processed require repeated emphasis. Numerous occasions where lines exchanged among cooperating laboratories have been contaminated with cells of other species have been detailed and documented elsewhere (Nelson-Rees *et al.*, 1977, 1981). For example, lines supposed to be human have been found to be monkey, mouse, or mongoose. Similarly, the problem of intraspecies cross-contamination among cultured human cell lines has been recognized for over 25 years (Nelson-Rees *et al.*, 1974, 1981). The loss of time and research funds as a result of these problems is very extensive but incalculable.

While bacterial and fungal contaminations represent an added concern, in most instances they are overt and easily detected, and therefore have less serious consequences than the more insidious contaminations by mycoplasma. That the presence of these microorganisms in cultured cell lines often negates research findings entirely has been stated repeatedly over the years (Barile *et al.*, 1973; Hay *et al.*, 1989). However, the difficulties of detection and prevalence of contaminated cultures in the research community suggest that the problem cannot be overemphasized. These and related difficulties associated with use of cell lines obtained from different sources can be avoided if one acquires stocks from a centralized cell banking agency which applies appropriate quality control (Hay, 1992).

Representative human cell lines from normal and tumor tissues available from The ATCC are listed in Table I with a selection of a few of the more important characteristics. Similar data on a variety of cell lines from other animals is included in Table II.

TABLE I Representative Human Cell Lines (January 1993)[a]

Tissue/tumor (number available)	Designation	ATCC No.	Age	Sex	Race
Adrenal (2)	SW-13	CCL 105	55	F	W
	NCI-H295	CRL 10296	48	F	B
Bladder (9)	RT4	HTB 2	63	M	W
	HT-1376	CRL 1472	58	F	W
	UM-UC-3	CRL 1749	?	M	?
Bone marrow (5)	IM-9	CCL 159	?	F	W
	KG-1	CCL 246	59	M	W
	R54;11	CRL 1873	32	F	W
Brain (7)	A-172	CRL 1620	53	M	?
	U-87MG	HTB 14	44	F	W
Breast (26)	BT-20	HTB 19	74	F	W
	MCF-7	HTB 22	69	F	W
	SK-BR-3	HTB 30	43	F	W
Bronchus (2)	ChaGo K-1	HTB 168	45	M	?
	CCD-14Br	CCL 203	34	F	W
Cervix (12)	HeLa	CCL 2	31	F	B
	CaSki	CRL 1550	40	F	W
	ME-180	HTB 33	66	F	W
Colon (30)	FHC	CRL 1831	Fetuses		
	HT-29	HTB 38	44	F	W
	Caco-2	HTB 37	72	M	W
	SW480	CCL 228	50	M	W
Duodenum (1)	HuTu80	HTB 40	53	M	W
Embryonal carcinoma (4)	Tera 1	HTB 105	47	M	W
	NTERA-2	CRL 1973	22	M	W
Endometrium (5)	AN3 CA	HTB 111	55	F	W
	KLE	CRL 1622	64	F	W
	RL95-2	CRL 1671	65	F	W

Diagnosis	Source	Medium[b]	Comments
SCC[c]	Cortex	L15/10	Grade IV adenocarcinoma; gap junctions produce steroids; tumorigenic
Invasive carcinoma	Cortex	R2+	
Transitional cell, papilloma	Primary	MC10	Tumorigenic; well-differentiated HLA-I and -II
Transitional cell, grade III, invasive	Primary	EM10	Tumorigenic, colonies in soft agar, not treated
Transitional cell	Primary	EM10	Tumorigenic
Multiple myeloma	Bone marrow	R10	B-lymphoblastic cell synthesizes IgG-κ receptors for hGH, insulin, and calcitonin
Acute myelogenous leukemia	Bone marrow	IDM20	Responds to colony-stimulating factor, forming colonies in soft agar; differentiates to macrophages; near diploid
Acute leukemia	Bone marrow	AMEM10	Has t(4;11)(q21;123) and isochromosome q7; lacks T/B-cell markers; strong TdT
Glioblastoma	Primary	DM10	Nontumorigenic; poor colony formation in soft agar; inversion (9)(p11q34); translocation (9:19)
Glioblastoma, grade III	Primary	EM10	Tumorigenic, hypodiploid
Typical grade II adenocarcinoma	Primary	EM10	Tumorigenic, hyperdiploid
Adenocarcinoma	Pleural effusion	EM10+I	Estrogen receptors, bcl-1 mRNA differentiated, hypertriploid
Adenocarcinoma	Pleural effusion	MC10	Tumorigenic, poorly differentiated microvilli, desmosomes
Undifferentiated carcinoma	Subcutaneous metastasis	R10	Secretes α-hCG, estradiol, and progesterone
Cerebral aneurysm	Primary	EM10	Euploid fibroblast line; limited doubling potential
Adenocarcinoma	Primary	EM10	First human line; widely studied; G6PD A; 4 marker chromosomes
Epidermoid carcinoma	Metastasis to mesentery	R10	Secretes β-hCG
Invasive SCC	Metastasis to omentum	MC10	Tumorigenic; desomomes hypotriploid, XXX
Normal	Colon	F12/DM10+	Epithelial-like; lacks keratin; limited doubling potential
Well-differentiated grade II adeno-carcinoma	Primary	MC10	Tumorigenic; hypertriploid; 17 marker chromosomes
Adenocarcinoma	Primary	EM20	Hypertetraploid; exhibits enterocyte differentiation; tumorigenic
Grade III–IV adenocarcinoma	Primary	L15/10	Tumorigenic; K-*ras* codon 12
Adenocarcinoma	Primary	EM10	Tumorigenic; forms well-differentiated papilloma; pseudodiploid
Seminoma	Metastasis to lung	MC10	Not tumorigenic; bcl-1 mRNA
Testicular carcinoma	Metastasis to lung	DM10	Clone of Tera-2; pluripotent; differentiates on exposure to RA
Adenocarcinoma	Metastasis to lymph node	EM10	Yields malignant, undifferentiated tumor
Poorly differentiated adenocarcinoma	Primary	DM/F12-10	Tumorigenic; forms microvilli and junctional complexes
Moderately differentiated adenosquamous	Primary	DM/F12-10	Estrogen receptors; α-keratin; microvilli

continues

continued

Tissue/tumor (number available)	Designation	ATCC No.	Age	Sex	Race
Kidney (9)	Caki-1	HTB 46	49	M	W
	ACHN	CRL 1611	22	M	W
	769 P	CRL 1933	65	F	W
Leukemia/lymphoma (47)	CCRF-CEM	CCL 119	4	F	W
	Hut 78	TIB 161	50	M	W
	MOLT 4	CRL 1582	19	M	?
	HL-60	CCL 240	36	F	W
Liver (3)	Hep-3B	HB-8064	8	M	B
	Hep-G2	HB-8065	15	M	W
	SK-HEP-1	HTB 52	52	?	W
Lung (73)	A-549	CCL 185	58	M	W
	NCI-H146	HTB 173	59	M	W
	NCI-H441	HTB 174	?	M	?
	NCI-H82	HTB 175	40	M	W
	NCI-H820	HTB 181	53	M	W
	SK-LU-1	HTB 57	60	F	W
	WI-38	CCL 75	Fetus	F	W
	MRC-5	CCL 171	Fetus	M	W
	HLF-a	CCL 199	54	F	B
	CCD-19Lu	CCL 210	20	F	W
Melanoma (21)	C32	CRL 1585	53	M	W
	Hs294T	HTB 140	56	M	W
	SK-MEL5	HTB 70	24	F	W
	COLO 829	CRL 1974	45	M	W

Diagnosis	Source	Medium[b]	Comments
Renal carcinoma	Metastasis to skin	MC10	Tumorigenic; hypertriploid
Adenocarcinoma	Pleural effusion	EM10	Tumorigenic; invasive
Clear cell adenocarcinoma	Primary	R10	Tumorigenic; colonies in soft agar; microvilli and desmosomes; hypodiploid
ALL	Peripheral blood	R20	T lymphoblast; malignant in newborn hamsters; modal chromosome number 45–47
Sézary syndrome	Peripheral blood	R10	Mature T-cell line with inducer/helper phenotype; yields and responds to interleukin-2
ALL	Peripheral blood	R10	Stable T cell; high TdT; modal chromosome number 95
ALL	Peripheral blood	L15/10	Neutrophilic promyelocytes differentiate when exposed to RA and others; surface receptors for Fc
Hepatocellular carcinoma	Primary	EM10	Tumorigenic; produces haptoglobin, α-fetoprotein, albumin, α_2-
Hepatocellular carcinoma	Primary	EM10	macroglobulin; transferrin, fibrinogen, and other liver-specific proteins
Adenocarcinoma	Ascites	EM10	Produces α-antitrypsin; has Weibel–Palade bodies and vimentin
Carcinoma	Primary	F12K/15	Enzymes related to surfactant synthesis studied; lamellar inclusions but sparse
SCLC	Pleural fluid	R10	Tumorigenic; near triploid; high c-*myc* mRNA but no gene amplification; elevated biochemical markers for SCLC; keratin and vimentin positive
Pap.AC	Pericardial fluid	R10	Hyperdiploid; grows in soft agar; SP-A+; Clara and lamellar inclusions
SCLC	Pleural fluid	R10	Tumorigenic; near triploid, no Y; high c-*myc*; DNA and RNA, reduced amount and abnormal p53 mRNA (3.7 kb)
PapAC	Lymph node	A4	Near triploid; produces lamellar bodies and surfactants SP-A, -B and -C
Adenocarcinoma	Primary	EM10	Tumorigenic in immunotolerant rats; hypotetraploid
Normal	Primary	EM10	Euploid line, widely used in cell biology, aging research, virology, and vaccine manufacture
Normal	Primary	EM10	Euploid line, widely used in cell biology, virology, and vaccine manufacture
Normal	Primary	EM10	Diploid and stable; patient had epidermoid carcinoma of lung; tissue used was from site remote from cancer
Normal	Primary	EM10	Euploid; patient died of accidental head trauma
Amelanotic melanoma	Primary	EM10	Tumorigenic; hypodiploid with mode of 45
Metastatic melanoma	Metastasis to lymph node	DM10	Nerve growth factor and interferon receptors; responsive to RA; tumorigenic and grows in soft agar
Metastatic melanoma	Metastasis to axillary node	EM10	Tumorigenic
Malignant melanoma	Subcutaneous metastasis	R10	Prior to therapy; some melanin produced; B-cell counterpart available

continues

continued

Tissue/tumor (number available)	Designation	ATCC No.	Age	Sex	Race
	COLOR 829BL	CRL 1980	45	M	W
Myeloma/plasmacytoma (10)	HS-Sultan	CRL 1484	56	M	W
	RPMI 8226	CCL 155	61	M	?
	U266B1	TIB 196	53	M	?
Nasal septum (1)	RPMI 2650	CCL 30	52	M	?
Neuroblastoma (3)	IMR-32	CCL 127	13 months	M	W
	SK-N-MC	HTB 10	14	F	W
	SK-N-SH	HTB 11	4	F	?
Ovary (6)	Caov-3	HTB 75	54	F	W
	NIH:OVCAR-3	HTB 161	60	F	W
	PA-1	CRL 1572	12	F	W
Pancreas (10)	AsPC-1	CRL 1682	62	F	W
	Capan-1	HTB 79	40	M	W
	PANC-1	CRL 1469	56	M	W
Pharynx (2)	Detroit 562	CCL 138	?	F	W
	FaDu	HTB 43	56	M	W
Placenta (3)	BeWo	CCL 98	Fetus	M	?
	JEG-3	HTB 36	Fetus	?	?
	JAR	HTB 144	Fetus	?	?
Prostate (3)	PC3	CRL 1435	60	M	W
	LNCap.FGC	CRL 1740	50	M	W
	DU145	HTB 81	69	M	W
Rectum (2)	SW-837	CCL 235	53	M	W
	SW-1463	CCL 234	66	F	W
Retinoblastoma (2)	WERI-Rb-1	HTB 169	1	F	W
	Y79	HTB 18	2.5	F	W
Rhabdomyosarcomas (4)	A204	HTB 82	1	F	?
	RD	CCL 136	7	F	W

Diagnosis	Source	Medium[b]	Comments
Malignant melanoma	Peripheral blood	R10	Control B-cell line to CRL 1974; DNA fingerprinting confirms identity
Plasmacytoma	Primary	R10	Produces IgG-κ; hyperdiploid
Multiple myeloma	Peripheral blood	R20	Produces π light chains; no mature plasma cells
Myeloma	Peripheral	R15	IgE-λ secreting
Anaplastic SCC	Pleural effusion	EM10	Pseudodiploid with mode 46; keratin positive
Neuroblastoma with organoid differentiation	Abdominal mass	EM10	Neuroblasts and large hyaline fibroblasts
Neuroblastoma	Metastasis to supraorbital area	EM10	Pseudodiploid; dopamine hydroxylase positive
Neuroblastoma	Metastasis to bone marrow	EM10	Hypderdiploid; dopamine hydroxylase positive
Adenocarcinoma	Primary	EM10	Extremely unusual chromosome morphology
Progressive adenocarcinoma	Ascites	R20+	Tumorigenic; grows in soft agar; androgen and estrogen receptors
Teratocarcinoma	Ascites	EM10	Pseudodiploid, t(15q20q); highly malignant in nude mice
Metastatic carcinoma	Ascites	R20	Tumorigenic; CEA, PAA, and PSA positive hyperdiploid
Metastatic carcinoma	Liver metastasis	R15	Tumorigenic; hypotriploid
Epitheloid ductal carcinoma	Primary	DM10	Hypertriploid
Metastatic carcinoma	Pleural fluid	EM10	Keratin positive
Squamous cell	Primary	EM10	Tumorigenic; desmosomes; 19 marker chromosomes
Malignant gestational choriocarcinoma	Hamster xenograft	F12-15	Secretes placental hormones, hCG, human placental lactogen, estrone, estradiol, estriol, progestrone
Choriocarcinoma, Edwin–Turner tumor	Hamster xenograft	EM10	Secretes hCG, human chorionic somatomammotropin, and progesterone; tumorigenic
Choriocarcinoma	Primary	R10	Secretes estrogen, progesterone, gonadotropin, and lactogen
Adenocarcinoma, grade IV	Primary	F12K-7	Tumorigenic and grows in soft agar; low acid phosphatase and steroid reductase
Metastatic adenocarcinoma	Metastasis to supraclavicular lymph node	R10	Produces PSA, prostatic acid phosphatase; androgen receptors; tumorigenic
Metastatic carcinoma	Metastasis to brain	EM10	Grows in soft agar; weak acid phosphatase; triploid; desmosomes
Adenocarcinoma, grade IV	Primary	L15-10	Tumorigenic; hypodiploid
Adenocarcinoma, grades II–III	Primary	L15-10	Tumorgenic; CEA positive; hypertriploid
Retinoblastoma	Primary	R10	Tumorigenic in rabbits; no colonies in soft agar; near diploid with 15 or 16 markers
Retinoblastoma	Primary	R15	Reportedly reverse transcriptase positive
Embryonal rhabdomyosarcoma	Primary	MC10	Tumorigenic; near diploid with abnormality on 22p
Malignant rhabdomyosarcoma	Pelvic tumor	DM10	No myofibrils but myoglobin and myosin ATPase activity; complex hyperdiploid karyology; also designated TE32 and 130T

continues

continued

Tissue/tumor (number available)	Designation	ATCC No.	Age	Sex	Race
Sarcoma (26)	HOS	CRL 1543	13	F	W
	MG-63	CRL 1427	14	M	W
	SK-LMS-1	HTB 88	4	F	W
	SW 1353	HTB 94	72	F	W
Skin (20)	A-431	CRL 1555	85	F	?
	182-PFSK	CRL 1532	20	M	W
	MeKam	CRL 1279	10	M	W
	CCD-27Sk	CRL 1475	Fetus	M	B
	CCD-977Sk	CRL 1900	20	F	W
	CCD-966SK	CRL 1881	78	F	B
Stomach (5)	AGS	CRL 1739	54	M	W
	KATO-III	HTB 103	55	M	Mongoloid
	RF-1	CRL 1864	62	M	Hispanic
	RF-48	CRL 1863	62	M	Hispanic
Submaxilla (1)	A-253	HTB 41	54	M	W
Testes (3)	Cates1B	HTB 104	34	M	W
Thyroid (2)	SW579	HTB 107	59	M	W
	TT	CRL 1803	77	F	W
Tongue (4)	SCC-4	CRL 1624	55	M	?
	SCC-25	CRL 1628	70	M	?
Umbilicus (2)	HUV-EC-C	CRL 1730	Fetal		
	ECV304	CRL 1998	Fetal		
Vulva (2)	SW954	HTB 117	86	F	W
	SW962	HTB 118	64	F	W

[a] See Hay *et al.* (1992) for originators, references, and more detail.

[b] Abbreviations for medium used (on the left-hand side) include (EM) Eagle's minimum essential medium; (R) RPMI-1640; (DM) Dulbecco's modification of Eagle's medium; (F12 and F12K) Ham's medium and Kaighn's modification, respectively; (IDM) Iscove's modification of Eagle's medium; (L15) Leibovitz medium; (MC) McCoy's 5A medium; (AMEM) alpha modification of Eagle's medium (see Hay *et al.*, 1992, for formulas). The number on the right-hand side indicates percentage of serum (usually fetal bovine) used. Additional recommended ingredients are indicated by the "+" sign.

[c] SCC, squamous cell carcinoma; hGH, human growth hormone; Tdt, terminal deoxynucleotidyl transferase; hCG, human chorionic gonadotropin; RA, retinoic acid; G6PD, glucose-6-phosphate dehydrogenase; ALL, acute lymphoblastic leukemia; SCLC, small cell lung cancer; CEA, carcinoembryonic antigen; PSA, pancreas-specific antigen; PAA, pancreas-associated antigen.

Diagnosis	Source	Medium[b]	Comments
Osteogenic sarcoma	Primary	EM10	Flat morphology; sensitive to viral and chemical morphological transformation
Osteogenic sarcoma	Primary	EM10	Yields interferon on induction; hypotriploid with 18 or 19 markers
Leiomyosarcoma, Grade II	Primary, vulva	EM10	Tumorigenic; hypertriploid with complex karyotype
Chondrosarcoma	Primary, right humerus	L15/10	Hyperdiploid with trisomic N7 only
Epidermoid carcinoma	Primary	DM10	Tumorigenic and grows in soft agar; hypertriploid
Normal	Skin	DM10	Apparently normal but carrying gene for hereditary adenomatosis of the colon
Xeroderma pigmentosum	Skin	DM10	Xeroderma pigmentosum line from NIH series
Apparently normal	Skin	EM10	Established using skin from the chest area
Apparently normal	Skin	EM10	Established from skin of the breast
Apparently normal	Skin	EM10	Established from skin of the breast
Adenocarcinoma	Primary	F12-10	No prior therapy; tumorigenic t(13q14q) hyperdiploid
Gastric carcinoma	Pleural effusion	IDM10	Tumorigenic; hypotetraploid
Metastatic carcinoma	Primary	L15/10	Stains for mucin; CEA positive
Metastatic carcinoma	Primary metastasis	L15/10	Metastasis from CRL 1864 (RF-1); mucin and CEA negative
Epidermoid carcinoma	Primary	MC10	Hypotriploid; 14 marker chromosomes
Embryomal carcinoma	Metastasis to lymph node	MC10	Reportedly hypodiploid to diploid
SCC	Primary	L15/10	Tumorigenic
Medullary thyroid carcinoma	Primary	F12K/10	Tumorigenic; neuropeptides produced
SCC	Primary	F12/DM/10	Tumorigenic; involucrin negative; hypopentaploid; positive for 40-kDa keratin
SCC	Primary	F12/DM/10	Tumorigenic synthesizes low levels of involucrin; epidermal keratin; hypertriploid
Apparently normal	Umbilical vein	F12K/10+ECGS +heparin	Endothelial line; produces factor VIII; near diploid; limited life span
Apparently normal	Umbilical vein	199/10	Endothelial line; "spontaneously transformed"; immortal; has Weibel–Palade bodies and angiotensin-converting enzyme; factor VIII negative; tumorigenic; triploid karyotype (mode 80)
SCC	Primary	L15/10	Pseudodiploid
SCC	Metastasis to lymph node	L15/10	Tumorigenic; hypertriploid with at least 15 marker chromosomes

TABLE II Representative Cell Lines from Other Species (September 1993)

ATCC No.[a] (total/category)	Designation	Species	Culture medium[b]	Comments
CCL 34	MDCK	Canine	EM10	Kidney epithelial line; model chromosome number 78; forms domes in monolayer; used extensively in transport studies
CCL 70	CV1	African green monkey	EM10	From male kidney; modal number 60; supports replication of SV40[c] and many other viruses
CCL 81	Vero	African green monkey	199-5	From adult kidney; hypodiploid (mode 58); used extensively in virus assay and production
CCL 92	3T3	Murine	DM-CS10	From Swiss mouse embryo; hypertriploid (mode 68); contact sensitive; used for studies in oncogenic and viral transformation
CCL 209 (249)	CPAE	Bovine	EM20	Endothelial line from pulmonary artery; stable diploid karyotype; positive for angiotensin-converting activity
CRL 1476	A10	Rat	DM20	Smooth muscle line from thoracic artery of a DB1X embryo; myokinase and creatine phosphokinase positive
CRL 1581	Sp2/0-Ag14	Murine	DM10	Myeloma used as fusion partner in hybridoma production; HAT sensitive; nonsecretor
CRL 1651	COS-7	African green monkey	DM10	Transformed with origin-defective SV40; T antigen positive; suitable host in transfection studies
CRL 1711	Sf9	Fall armyworm	G+10	Clonally derived from pupal ovarian tissue; susceptible to infection by baculovirus expression vectors
CRL 1721	PC12	Rat	R10HS-5	From pheochromocytoma; responsive to nerve growth factor; catecholamine, dopamine, and norepinephrine positive
Patented				
CRL 8002	OKT4	Murine	IDM20	One of a series of patented hybridmomas; produces monoclonal to human helper T subset
CRL 8305	FRTL-5	Rat	F12K-5+	Thyroid epithelial cell line; produces thyroglobulin; responsive to thyroid-stimulating hormone
CRL 8509	528	Murine	R10	One of a series of patented hybridomas; produces monoclonal to epidermal growth factor receptor
CRL 8873	FHCR	Murine	R12+	Hybridoma FHCR-1-2624/FH6/FH0T-1-3019; secretes monoclonal to Le[x] ganglioside
CRL 10968 (578)	S4B6-1	Murine	R10	Produces monoclonal to murine interleukin-2

continues

continued

ATCC No.[a] (total/category)	Designation	Species	Culture medium[b]	Comments
Special collections				
HB 55	L243	Murine	DM10	Secretes an IgG2a cytotoxic antibody to a nonpolymorphic determinant on human Ia
HB 95	W6/32	Murine	DM10	Secretes an IgG2a cytotoxic antibody that reacts with monomorphic determinants on HLA-A, -B, and -C
HB 170	R4-6A2	Murine/rat	DM10	Secretes IgG1 monoclonal to murine gamma interferon
HB 188	11B11	Murine/rat	R10	Secretes IgG1 monoclonal to murine B-cell stimulatory factor (BSF-1, interleukin-4)
HB 198 (215)	F4/80	Murine/rat	R5	Secretes rat IgG2b antibody to murine macrophages
TIB 63	$P388D_1$	Murine	R15	A phagocytic monocyte/macrophage line that produces interleukin-1 in response to PMA or LPS
TIB 68	WEHI-3	Murine	IDM10+	A myelomonocytic line sensitive to LPS; produces colony-stimulating activity
TIB 71	RAW 264.7	Murine	DM10	A phagocytic monocyte/macrophage line; capable of antibody-dependent lysis of target cells
TIB 207	GK1.5	Murine	DM20	Secretes monoclonal to T-cell surface antigen L3T4 on a helper/inducer T-cell subset
TIB 214 (193)	CTLL-2	Murine	R10+	Clone of cytotoxic T cells dependent on interleukin-2 for proliferation

[a] The prefixes assigned to ATCC cell lines reflect the historical source of support for their addition to the Collection and, to a certain extent, the degree of characterization applied. Representative Certified Cell Lines (CCL); Cell Repository Lines (CRL) in the general and patent collections; hybridomas in the collection supported by the National Institute for Allergy and Infectious Diseases (HB); and cells important for studies in tumor immunology (TIB) are listed in this table. The CRL total does not include some 1900 additional cell lines in special collections. See Hay *et al.* (1992) for names of originators, references, and more detail.

[b] Abbreviations for medium used (on the left-hand side) include (EM) Eagle's minimum essential medium; (R) RPMI-1640; (DM) Dulbecco's modification of Eagle's medium; (F12K) Kaighn's modification of Ham's F12; (IDM) Iscove's modification of Eagle's medium; (199) medium 199; (G) Grace's insect medium (see Hay, *et al.*, 1992, for formulas). The number on the right-hand side indicates percentage of serum used, usually fetal bovine, bovine calf (CS), or horse serum (HS). Additional recommended ingredients are indicated by the + sign.

[c] SV40, simian virus 40; HAT, hypoxanthine aminopterin thymidine; PMA, phorbol myristate acetate; LPS, lipopolysaccharide.

REFERENCES

Barile, M. F., Hopps, H. E., Grabowski, M. W., Riggs, D. B., and Del Giudice, R. A. (1973) The identification and sources of mycoplasmas isolated from contaminated cultures. *Ann. NY Acad. Sci.* **225**, 252–264.

Hay, R. J. (1992) Cell line preservation and characterization. *In* "Animal Cell Culture, A Practical Approach" (R. I. Freshney, ed.), 2nd ed., pp. 95–148. IRL Press, Washington, DC.

Hay, R. J., Caputo, J., Chen, T. R., Macy, M. L., McClintock, P., and Reid, Y. A. (1992)

"Catalogue of Cell Lines and Hybridomas," 7th ed. American Type Culture Collection, Rockville, MD.

Hay, R. J., Macy, M. L., and Chen, T. R. (1989) Mycoplasma infection of cultured cells. *Nature (London)* **339**, 487–488.

Nelson-Rees, W. A., Flandermeyer, R. R., and Hawthorne, P. K. (1974) Banded marker chromosomes as indicators of intraspecies cellular contamination. *Science* **184**, 1093–1096.

Nelson-Rees, W., Daniels, W. W., and Flandermeyer, R. R. (1981) Cross-contamination of cells in culture. *Science* **212**, 446–452.

Nelson-Rees, W. A., and Flandermeyer, R. R. (1977) Inter- and intraspecies contamination of human breast tumor cell lines HBC and BrCa5 and other cell cultures. *Science* **195**, 1343–1344.

Working Safely with Radioactivity

Richard W. Davies

I. Introduction

Radioactivity features in many of the more powerful techniques used in cell biology today; however, in common with exposure to many other substances met in the laboratory, exposure to the ionizing radiation associated with radioactive materials carries a small risk of causing harm. The International Commission on Radiological Protection (ICRP) has promulgated the basic aims of radiation protection in a number of publications (e.g., ICRP26, ICRP60). They are summarized as justification, optimization, and limitation of exposure. Assuming that the laboratory use of particular radioactive techniques is justified on the grounds of providing a net benefit, then the most important concept is that of optimization. This means keeping all exposures as low as reasonably achievable (ALARA). This article describes practical techniques for minimizing exposure to radiation when using radioactive materials.

II. Materials and Instrumentation

Radioactivity is the property of any element or substance that spontaneously emits ionizing radiation. Five main types of ionizing radiation may be encountered (alpha rays, beta rays, gamma rays, X rays, neutrons) but only three are encountered routinely in life sciences: beta, X, and gamma rays. Beta particles are positive or negative electrons. They can be stopped by thin layers of water, plastic, or metal. Gamma and X rays are electromagnetic radiations similar to light and radiowaves, but with shorter wavelength. They can be very penetrating, and a heavy material like lead is needed to reduce their intensity to a suitably low level. Some radioactive materials emit more than one type of radiation, so it is important to review the characteristics of the radioactive material to be used.

A. THE KEY CHARACTERISTICS OF RADIOACTIVE MATERIALS

The key characteristics that need to be known about *any* radioactive material to plan the appropriate radiation protection measures are principal emissions and their energies; half-life; annual limit on intake (ALI); shielding requirement [e.g., half-value layer (HVL)]; monitoring requirements; and special considerations (e.g., physi-

TABLE I Key Properties of Selected Radionuclides Used in Life Sciences

Radionuclide	Half-life	Maximum beta energy (MeV)	Principal X or gamma energy (MeV)	Annual limit on intake (Bq) by inhlalation
Carbon-14	5730 years	0.156	Pure beta	9×10^{7a} (labeled organic compounds)
Hydrogen-3 (tritium)	12.4 years	0.0186	Pure beta	3×10^{9a} (tritiated water)
Iodine-125	59.6 days	Electron capture	0.027–0.035	2×10^{6b}
Iodine-131	8.04 days	0.806	0.080–0.723 (mainly 0.364)	2×10^{6b}
Phosphorus-32	14.3 days	1.709	Pure beta	3×10^{7a}
Phosphorus-33	25.4 days	0.249	Pure beta	3×10^{8a}
Sulfur-35	87.4 days	0.167	Pure beta	4×10^{8a} (inorganic compounds)

[a] Based on occupational effective dose equivalent limit of 50 mSv for stochastic risks. ALI from ICRP30 may change with adoption of ICRP60 and ICRP61.
[b] Based on occupational dose-equivalent limit of 500 mSv for deterministic (nonstochastic) risks to thyroid.

cochemical properties, forms, volatility). Table I gives the key properties of selected radionuclides used in life sciences.

B. MONITORING

It is important to distinguish between *radiation,* the rays or particles being emitted from the radioactive material, and *contamination,* uncontained radioactive material that is free to contaminate air, surfaces, or people. The detection of radiation does not necessarily imply contamination. It may simply be a contained source that is inadequately shielded.

The use of the correct detector for contamination monitoring is vital. A thin end-window Geiger–Müller detector is suitable for carbon-14, phosphorus-32, and other medium- to high-energy beta emitters but not for tritium. Tritium contamination is extremely difficult to monitor directly. The best practical method is to take "wipes" over 100 cm^2 with paper disks. Assessment of activity on the wipes can then be carried out by liquid scintillation counting or gas flow proportional counting. Wipe monitoring may also be necessary where there is a significant count rate from radioactive material in the vicinity or contained within the vessel which makes direct monitoring impracticable. X-ray and gamma-ray emitters (e.g., iodine-125) are generally detected more efficiently using a scintillation detector (with sodium iodide crystal, for example) rather than a Geiger counter.

When using monitoring equipment it is important to be methodical. Before each session of use, battery checks and measurement and recording of background need to be made. The unit of measurement is usually counts per second. Beta probes should be held close enough to the relevant surfaces to detect beta radiation (approximately 2 cm) but not so close as to result in the probe touching the potentially contaminated surface and thus itself becoming contaminated. Measurements should be recorded remembering to deduct the background counts. If precise quantitative rather than qualitative information is required, then reference must be made to the calibration data supplied with the instrument for the specific nuclide of interest. The techniques used for checking for contamination of the skin and clothing are the same as those used for monitoring the working environment.

Where there is an external radiation hazard as well as potential for contamination, appropriate dose rate monitoring should also be performed at regular intervals with a suitable instrument that responds to the particular radiation emitted by the nuclide. In general, dose rates should be kept as low as reasonably achievable in the working environment by, for example, use of local shielding. Note that dose rate monitoring equipment is calibrated to give measurements in appropriate radiation protection units (e.g., μSv/hr). It is these instruments that should be used when assessing the effectiveness of external protective measures, such as shielding.

C. PREPLANNING FOR EMERGENCIES

It is essential to prepare a contingency plan for what to do in the event of a radioactive spill or other emergency. This should be documented and all persons working in the laboratory need to be familiar with its provisions, which should include verbally warning all people in the vicinity; restricting unnecessary movement into and through the area; reporting the spill to the person in charge of radiation protection; and treating contaminated persons first.

It is also sensible to have a "spill kit" available for use in such circumstances. Typically the contents should include the following:

- Protective clothing (gloves, overshoes, aprons, etc.)
- Warning signs and spirit marker pens
- Sodium thiosulfate solution[1] (for iodine)
- Decontamination solution
- Long-handled forceps (approx 30 cm)
- Absorbent paper
- Waste bags and containers
- Adhesive tape
- Scissors

The cleanup protocol for minor spills (hundreds of kilobecquerels) should include instructions to wear protective clothing; stabilization with excess alkaline thiosulfate solution, if iodine; swabbing up of spill with absorbent paper; washing of area (with decontamination solution if required); monitoring of area; monitoring of self; recording of counts before and after decontamination.

With iodine, emergency protective action may be taken in the event of a confirmed intake. Thyroid uptake of radioiodine can be blocked by the oral administration of an excess of stable iodine. A medical adviser should be consulted with a view to maintaining a supply of stable iodine for administration in the event of a radioiodine intake. A suitable blocking dose is 100 mg of iodine, which should be taken as soon as possible after the incident and under medical supervision. The iodine can be administered conveniently in the form of tablets of potassium iodate (170 mg) or potassium iodide (130 mg). As these materials may cause mild discomfort in some cases, they should not be given prophylactically but only after confirmed intakes.

III. Procedures

Because X and gamma rays can penetrate the whole body from outside and more energetic beta particles can affect the superficial layers of tissue, they represent an *external hazard*. In life sciences, the primary interest is with unsealed sources; this means that there is also potential for contamination and for radioactive materials

[1] A suitable solution is prepared from sodium thiosulfate (25 g) and sodium iodide (2 g) in 1 liter of 1 *M* sodium hydroxide. Care should be taken to prevent sodium hydroxide from splashing onto the body or into the eyes.

to get inside the body where they are able to irradiate cells and tissues directly and thus present an *internal hazard.*

A. METHODS OF PROTECTION FROM THE EXTERNAL HAZARD

There are three basic methods of protection against the external radiation hazard: time, distance, and shielding. A combination of these methods coupled with safe working practice can ensure that doses are kept as low as reasonably achievable (ALARA).

1. Time

Although it is obvious that the shorter the time a person is exposed to radiation, the smaller the dose, this is perhaps the most underrated method of protection. A procedure may quite often be made overcomplicated and lengthy when in fact the carrying out of the task in a careful but prompt manner may be all that is required.

All work involving exposure to ionizing radiation must be planned and prepared for carefully in advance. It is always worth doing a dummy run without radioactivity to check out the procedures, to eliminate any awkward or unnecessary tasks, and to optimize the arrangement of the workstation. A discussion relating to the work should not be held next to the radioactive material if it could just as easily take place away from the area. Similarly, radiation dose rates should be kept as low as practicable in areas of high occupancy.

2. Distance

The intensity of electromagnetic radiation from a radioactive point source decreases with increasing distance, following the *inverse square law.*

$$D_1 r_1^2 = D_2 r_2^2$$

where D_1 and D_2 are the dose rates at distances r_1 and r_2 from a point source of radiation, respectively. A simple way of remembering is that *doubling* the distance reduces the radiation level to *one-quarter.*

While moving away from a source is a good protective measure, moving toward a source is quite the reverse, as the intensity of radiation now increases with decreasing distance. It is therefore important to remember that the radiation dose rate close to even a low activity source can be very high. The direct handling of tubes or vials of phosphorus-32 should therefore be avoided by use of stands, holders, or remote handling devices.

3. Shielding

Beta rays and X and gamma radiation have different powers of penetration, but all can be stopped or attenuated by some form of shielding material.

Beta rays may have a range of up to a few meters in air, depending on the energy (e.g., 8 m for phosphorus-32, 25 cm for carbon-14). A thickness of 1 cm of Perspex (or Plexiglas) will stop all the beta rays, but there will be generated "Bremsstrahlung," a form of X rays, which becomes more significant for higher-energy beta emissions.

The fractional yield of this "braking radiation" is directly related to the energy of the incident beta particle and the atomic number of the material it strikes, hence the recommendation to use low-atomic-number shielding like aluminum or (better still) Perspex for high-energy beta rays. The energy of the Bremsstrahlung will be up to the maximum energy of the beta rays involved, so it will be possible to measure some very low levels of penetrating radiation after a 1-cm Perspex shield with suitably sensitive dose rate monitoring equipment. With the activities routinely handled in life sciences laboratories, however, this will be radiologically insignificant. Use of safety glasses with plastic lenses is recommended when handling beta emitters as this readily reduces eye dose.

X and gamma rays are more penetrating than beta rays and may have a range of hundreds of meters in air (depending on the energy). They follow an exponential law of attenuation. The thickness of shielding required depends on the energy of the X or gamma radiation and the material of the shielding.

The half-value layer (HVL) of shielding material is a useful concept and is the thickness of a specified material that will cut down the incident radiation by one-half. For iodine-125 with an energy of 0.033 MeV, the HVL is 0.002 cm of lead; for iodine-131 with an energy of 0.364 MeV, the HVL is 0.25 cm of lead.

B. METHODS OF PROTECTION FROM THE INTERNAL HAZARD

An internal radiation hazard may arise if radioactive material gets inside the body. This could occur if radioactive gases or particles are breathed into the lungs; if radioactive material in any form is transferred to the mouth; if it is injected or enters through a cut or graze; or if the material is in a particular form that is absorbed through the intact skin. Clearly, once the radioactive material is inside the body it is in direct contact with tissues and cells and will continue to irradiate them until the radioactivity decays or the material is excreted from the body.

The key actions in protecting against the internal hazard are aimed at preventing the radioactive material from contaminating the working environment and individuals and, thus, from entering the body.

The basic methods of protection against the internal hazard are containment, labeling, monitoring, and safe working practice.

1. Containment

The practical approach to containment should be "defense in depth," so a spill tray suitably lined with absorbent paper on a bench of suitable design and construction (raised edges/stainless steel or laminate) in a designated area would be suitable for very small quantities of nonvolatile material. As the activity and volatility of the material increase, the tray should be itself held within the partial containment provided by a ventilated fume cupboard or slit box. (The linear flow rate through any working aperture of a ventilated enclosure should be at least 0.5 m sec^{-1} for nonvolatile materials and at least 0.75 m sec^{-1} for volatiles such as iodine.) If there is an external radiation hazard as well as the potential for contamination, then appropriate shielding must be used but care should be taken not to disturb the enclosure air flows. (Checks should be made with a smoke generator if there is any doubt.)

The radiological designation of the area forms one level of containment by ensuring that work with radioactivity and any contamination is restricted to a particular location. Active and inactive work should always be kept separate, preferably by maintaining rooms to be used solely for radioactive work.

2. Labeling

The designation of areas should be clear by having appropriate signs on doors warning of the potential for hazard from ionizing radiation in these areas. There should also be an indication of any special rules that apply on entry and exit (e.g., who is authorized to enter, what monitoring actions are required for persons or equipment leaving the area, the requirement for washing).

The area designation will carry with it rules for the wearing of appropriate protective clothing, for example, laboratory overalls, safety glasses, and surgical gloves; however, care should be taken when handling fine powders to avoid static charge on gloves. Local rules will define what dosimeters should be worn, for example, body films or thermoluminescent (TL) badge, and extremity TL dosimeter for work with high-energy beta emitters.

Labeling also applies to the workstation; it is important to label all storage containers, clearly indicating nuclide, compound, specific activity, total activity, date, and name of user. Where other containers or apparatus are used to hold or manipulate radioactivity during experiments, use appropriate clear means to warn others that these tubes, etc., are potentially contaminated, or clean to decontaminate them before leaving the workstation.

3. Monitoring

Regular monitoring of working areas is essential. Any abnormal levels or spills should be dealt with immediately. Particular care must be taken when using high-energy beta emitters, such as phosphorus-32, as low levels of contamination can give high skin doses. If attention is paid to safe methods of working, the likelihood of contamination should be small. Frequent monitoring of the work area will reveal any problems; however, it is essential that personal monitoring is also undertaken at the end of a work session. Any contamination found should be reported to the local supervisor so that it can be dealt with promptly. Workers must wash hands before leaving the area and do a final monitoring check to confirm that the hands are contamination free.

4. Safe Working Practice

Good housekeeping and cleanliness are essential features in the control of radioactive contamination. Spillages of radioactive material are less likely to occur in a tidy, well-arranged laboratory. Cleanliness basically means methodical working and frequent monitoring of the working area and one's own hands, clothing, and shoes. Particular care and attention to good practice are needed when removing radioactive material from enclosures or during transfers between work areas.

There will be local rules that define things that must be done (e.g., wear dosimeters) and things that must not be done (e.g., do not eat, drink, smoke or apply cosmetics) in the working area. Personal handkerchiefs should never be used; instead, disposable tissues must always be used. Workers should never use mouth-operated equipment or put anything in their mouths. Cuts or abrasions of the skin should be covered with an impervious dressing before entry into the work area. Items should not be removed from the area until they have been properly monitored and cleaned.

The residues from work with radioactive materials constitute "radioactive waste" and may be solid, liquid, or gaseous. Disposal of all radioactive waste is subject to statutory control. It is vitally important that everyone involved in the practical use of radiation and radioactivity act responsibly in protecting the environment by being aware of the requirements and complying with them.

One key action is to minimize the production of radioactive waste in the first place. This can be done by using the minimum quantity of radioactivity needed for a successful investigation; keeping unnecessary inactive materials out of the laboratory; and keeping the amount of inactive materials that are put into the workstations or enclosures to a minimum.

Waste must be segregated and treated according to local arrangements, for example, monitoring to separate inactive from active waste and keeping short half-life material separate from longer half-life material to facilitate the decay of the former to lower disposal categories.

After a program of experiments has been completed or before moving to work in another laboratory, all the waste generated must be disposed of appropriately and not left for successors to deal with.

REFERENCES

ICRP26 (1977) Recommendations of the International Commission on Radiological Protection. *Ann. ICRP* **1**(3).

ICRP30 (1977) Limits for intakes of radionuclides by workers. *Ann. ICRP* **2**(3/4); **4**(3/4); **6**(2/3); **7**; **8**(1–3); **19**(4).

ICRP60 (1990) 1990 Recommendations of the International Commission on Radiological Protection. *Ann. ICRP* **21**(1–3).

ICRP61 (1990) Annual limits on intake of radionuclides by workers based on the 1990 Recommendations. *Ann. ICRP* **21**(4).

Note Added in Proof: This article is written for persons working with radioactivity in laboratory conditions. The information and views it contains are not intended to be comprehensive and should not be treated as a substitute for specific advice from radiation protection advisors. No responsibility for any errors or ommissions herein can be accepted by the author, his firm, or the publisher.

LIST OF SUPPLIERS

The following list contains the addresses and numbers of suppliers whose products were used in the various protocols described in this handbook. This does not mean, however, that one cannot use products or equipment from other sources. In a few cases addresses and numbers are given in individual articles.

Acufine, Inc.
5441 N. Kedzie Avenue
Chicago, Illinois 66025
USA

ACUFIRM
Ernst Kratz
Postfach 401167
D-63276 Dreieich
Germany
TEL 49 6103 85024
FAX 49 6103 81090

Advanced Magnetics Inc.
61 Mooney Street
Cambridge, Massachusetts 02138–1038
USA
TEL 800 343 1346
FAX 1 617 497 6927

Aerosols
Generatorvej 6
DK-2730 Herlev
Denmark
TEL 45 4291 3811
FAX 45 4453 0155

African Reptile Park
P.O. Box 30129
Tokay 7966
South Africa

Agar Scientific Limited
66A Cambridge Road
Stansted, Essex CM24 8DA
England
TEL 44 279 813519
FAX 44 279 815106

ALA
Rugvaenget 36
DK-2630 Taastrup
Denmark
TEL 45 4371 6688
FAX 45 4371 8188

Aldrich Chemical Company Inc.
1001 West Saint Paul Avenue
Milwaukee, Wisconsin 53233
USA
TEL 800 558 9160
TEL 1 414 273 3850
FAX 800 962 9591
FAX 1 414 273 4979

Aldrich Chemical Company Ltd.
The Old Brickyard
New Road
Gillingham, Dorset SP8 4TL
England
TEL 44 800 717181
FAX 44 800 378538

Althor Products
Division of American Hinge Co.
496 Danbury Road
Wilton, Connecticut 06897
USA
TEL 1 203 762 0796
FAX 1 203 762 3180

Altromin Tier Labor Service
Langestrasse 42
D 32791 Lage, Lippe
Germany
TEL 49 5232 60880
FAX 49 5232 608820

Ambion
2130 Woodward Street #200
Austin, Texas 78744–1832
USA
TEL 800 888 8804
TEL 1 512 445 6979
FAX 1 512 445 7139

Ambion
ITC Biotechnology GmbH
Postfach 103026
69020 Heidelberg
Germany
TEL 49 6221 303907
FAX 49 6211 303511

American National Can Co.
1275 King Street
Greenwich, Connecticut 06836
USA
TEL 1 203 863 8185

American Radiolabeled Chemicals Inc.
11612 Bowling Green Drive
St. Louis, Missouri 63146
USA
TEL 1 314 991 4545
FAX 800 331 6661

American Type Culture Collection (ATCC)
12301 Parklawn Drive
Rockville, Maryland 20852
USA
TEL 800 638 6597
TEL 1 301 881 2600
FAX 1 301 231 5826

Amersham International PLC
Northern Europe Region
Lincoln Place, Green End
Aylesbury
Buckinghamshire, HP20 2PT
United Kingdom
TEL 44 296 39522
FAX 44 296 85910

Amersham International PLC
Amersham Place
Little Chalfont
Buckinghamshire HP7 9NA
United Kingdom
TEL 44 494 544000
FAX 44 494 542266

Amersham Life Sciences, Inc.
2636 South Clearbrook Drive
Arlington Heights, Illinois 60005-4692
USA
TEL 800 323 9750
TEL 1 708 593 6300
FAX 800 228 8735
FAX 1 708 593 8010

Amicon Division
W.R. Grace & Co.
72 Cherry Hill Drive
Beverly, Massachusetts 01915
USA
TEL 800 426 4266
TEL 1 508 777 3622
FAX 1 508 777 6204

Amicon GmbH
Neuer Weg 2
D-58453 Witten
Germany
TEL 49 2303 960600
FAX 49 2302 800905

Amresco Inc.
30175 Solon Industrial Parkway
Solon, Ohio 44139
USA
TEL 1 216 349 2805
FAX 1 216 349 1182

Applied Biosystems
A Division of Perkin-Elmer Corporation
850 Lincoln Centre Drive
Foster City, California 94404
USA
TEL 800 874 9868
TEL 1 415 570 6667
FAX 1 415 572 2743

Applied Imaging Corp.
2340A Walsh Ave., Bldg. F
Santa Clara, California 95051
USA
TEL 1 408 562 0250
FAX 1 408 562 0244

Argus Science
Hatituka 2-5-26, Ikeda
Osaka 563
Japan
TEL 81 6 855 2190
FAX 81 727 24 0721

ASSAB
JPM Medicin Teknik AB
S-64137 Katrineholm
Sweden
TEL 46 15018770
FAX 46 15018798

Astec
Shimen-cho minamisato 136-2
Kasuya-gun
811-22 Fukuoka
Japan
TEL 81 92 935 5585
FAX 81 92 936 6613

Aubry
10-12 rue du Vieux Colombier
75006 Paris
France
TEL 33 1 45 48 4949
FAX 33 1 45 48 3556

Auer Bittmann Soulie AG
Handled by E. Merck (Schweiz AG)
Rüchligstrasse 20
8953 Dietikon
Switzerland
TEL 41 1 745 1414
FAX 41 1 745 1100

Austral Biologicals
125 Ryan Industrial Court
Suite 207
San Ramon, California 94583
USA
TEL 800 433 7105
TEL 1 510 820 8390
FAX 1 510 820 6843

Avanti Polar Lipids, Inc.
500-1 A Whitling Drive
Pelham, Alabama 35124
USA
TEL 1 205 663 2494
FAX 1 205 663 0756

Avery Denison
5 Prime—3 Prime, Inc.
117 Brandywine Parkway
West Chester, Pennsylvania 19380
USA
FAX 1 215 344 7579

Axon Instruments
1101 Chess Drive
Foster City, California 94404
USA
TEL 1 415 571 9400
FAX 1 415 571 9500

Bachofer GmbH
Carl-Zeiss-Strasse 35
D-72734 Reutlingen
Germany
TEL 49 7121 54008
FAX 49 7121 54000

Baker Company, Inc.
P.O. Box Drawer E
Sanford Airport
Sanford, Maine 04073
USA
TEL 800 992 2537
TEL 1 207 324 8773
FAX 1 207 324 3869

Balzers Union Aktiengesellschaft
Postfach 75
FL-9496 Balzers
Fürstentum Liechtenstein
TEL 41 75 41922
FAX 41 75 42332

Barnstead Thermolyne
Subsidiary of Sybron Corp.
2555 Kerper Blvd.
P.O. Box 797
Dubuque, Iowa 52001-1461
USA
TEL 1 319 556 0039
FAX 1 319 556 0695

Baxter Diagnostics, Inc.
Scientific Products Division
1430 Waukegan Road
McGaw Park, Illinois 60085-6787
USA
FAX 1 714 474 9589

Baxter Diagnostics, Inc.
Scientific Products Division
17111 Red Hill Avenue
Irvine, California 92714
USA
TEL 800 553 2413
TEL 1 714 474 9589

Baxter Scientific Products
1750 Stone Ridge Drive
Stone Mountain, Georgia 30083
USA
TEL 800 964 5227
FAX 1 404 270 9645

Baxter Scientific Products Division
100 Raritan Center Parkway
Edison, New Jersey 08818
USA
TEL 1 908 225 4700
FAX 1 908 417 4679

B. Braun Biotech
International GmbH
Postfach 120
D-34212 Melsungen
Germany
TEL 49 5661 713704
FAX 49 5661 713702

BDH Laboratory Supplies
Merck Limited
Poole, Dorset BH15 1TD
United Kingdom
TEL 44 202 664617
FAX 44 202 666856

Beckman Instruments, Inc.
8920 Route 108
Columbia, Maryland 21045
USA
TEL 800 742 2345
FAX 800 643 4366

Beckman Instruments, Inc.
Bioanalytical Systems Group
2500 Harbor Boulevard, E-26-C
Fullerton, California 92634–3100
USA
TEL 800 743 2345
FAX 800 643 4366

Beckman Instruments, Inc.
Spinco Division
P.O. Box 10200
Palo Alto, California 94304
USA
TEL 800 742 2345
TEL 1 415 857 1150
FAX 800 643 4366
FAX 1 415 859 1694

Beckman Instruments (Japan)
6–17 Sanbancho Chiyoda-ku
Tokyo 101
Japan
TEL 81 3221 5831

Becton Dickinson
Immunocytometry Systems
2350 Qume Drive
San Jose, California 95131–1807
USA
TEL 800 223 8226
TEL 1 408 954 2682
FAX 1 408 954 2156

Becton Dickinson & Co. Ltd.
Kill O'The Grange
Dun Laoire
Co Dublin
Ireland
TEL 353 128 54800
TEL 353 128 54332

Becton Dickinson Fabersanitas S.A.
Carreteras Mequinenza S/N
22520 Fraga, Huesca
Spain
TEL 34 744 709000
FAX 34 744 70546

Becton Dickinson Labware
1 Becton Drive
Franklin Lakes, New Jersey 07417-1880
USA
TEL 800 235 5953
TEL 1 201 235 6800
FAX 1 201 847 6475

Becton Dickinson Microbiology Systems (formerly Baltimore Biologicals Limited-BBL)
P.O. Box 243
Cockeysville, Maryland 21030–0243
USA
TEL 1 410 771 0100
FAX 1 410 584 7121

Behringwerke AG Diagnostica
P.O. Box 1140
D-35001 Marburg
Germany
TEL 49 6421390
FAX 49 642139 3138

Bellco Glass, Inc.
P.O. Box B
340 Edrudo Road
Vineland, New Jersey 8360
USA
TEL 800 257 7043
TEL 1 609 691 1075
FAX 1 609 691 3247

Bellingham and Stanley Limited
Longfield Road
North Farm Industrial Estate
Tunbridge Wells
Kent TN2 3EY
England
TEL 44 892 536444
FAX 44 892 543 115

Bender & Hobein GmbH
Beutenbergstrasse 11
D-07740 Jena
Germany
TEL 49 3641 852283
FAX 49 3641 22256

Bernstein
Untere Bult 2
D-32437 Porta Westfalia
Germany
TEL 49 571 793 0
FAX 49 571 7909

Bibby Sterilin Ltd.
Tilling Drive
Stone, Staffs ST15 0SA
United Kingdom
TEL 44 785 812121
FAX 44 785 813748

Bie & Bertsen A/S
Sandbaekvej 7
DK-2610 Roedovre
Denmark
TEL 45 4494 8822
FAX 45 4494 2709

BIO 101, Inc.
1070 Joshua Way
Vista, California 92083
USA
TEL 800 424 6101
TEL 1 619 598 7299
FAX 1 619 598 0116

Biochrom KG
Leonorenstrasse 2–6
D-12247 Berlin
Germany
TEL 49 30 779 9060
FAX 49 30 771 0012

BioComp Instruments Inc.
650 Churchill Row
Fredericton, New Brunswick
Canada
TEL 1 506 453 4812
FAX 1 506 453 3583

BioIon AB
PO Box 15045
S-75215 Uppsala
Sweden
TEL 46 18552315
FAX 46 18551114

Bio-Lab Ltd.
P.O. Box 16071
91 160 Jerusalem
Israel
TEL 972 2 524 447
FAX 972 2 522 103

Biological Industries
Kibbutz Beth Haemek
25115 Israel
TEL 972 4 960595
FAX 972 4 968896

Bio-Logic Science Instruments
1, Rue De L'Europe
38640 Claix
France
TEL 33 76 98 68 31
FAX 33 76 98 69 09

Biomedical Research Instruments, Inc.
12264 Wilkins Avenue
Rockville, Maryland 20852
USA
TEL 800 327 9498
TEL 1 301 881 7911
FAX 1 301 881 8762

Biophysica Technologies, Inc.
P.O. Box 387
Sparks, Maryland 21152
USA
TEL 800 296 3212
FAX 1 410 472 3218

Bioproducts for Science
P.O. Box 29176
Indianapolis, Indiana 46229
USA
TEL 1 317 894 7536
FAX 1 317 894 1840

Bio-Rad Laboratories
2000 Alfred Nobel Drive
Hercules, California 94547
USA
TEL 800 424 6723
TEL 1 510 741 1000
FAX 800 879 2289
FAX 1 510 741 1045

Bio-Rad Laboratories Inc.
European Headquarters
Dreve du Sénéchal 19
1180 Brussels
Belgium
TEL 32 2375 5970
FAX 32 2374 6162

Bio-Rad Micromeasurements Ltd.
Haxby Road
York Y03 7SD
England
TEL 44 904 631351
FAX 44 904 645624

Bio-Rad Microscience Division
19 Blackstone Street
Cambridge, Massachusetts 02139
USA
TEL 1 617 864 5820
FAX 1 617 864 9328

Bioseed Genetics
2010 South Ankeny Boulevard
Ankeny, Iowa 50021
USA
TEL 1 515 964 6729
FAX 1 515 964 6730

Biotech Instruments Ltd.
Iotech House
75A High Street
Kimpton, Herts SG4 8PU
United Kingdom

BioWhittaker, Inc.
8830 Biggs Ford Rd.
P.O. Box 127
Walkersville, Maryland 21793-0127
USA
TEL 800 638 8174
TEL 1 301 898 7025
FAX 1 301 845 8291

Blades Biological Ltd.
Cowden, Endenbridge, Kent
United Kingdom
TEL 44 3 1285 0242
FAX 44 3 4285 0924

Boehringer Mannheim Corporation
9115 Hague Road
P.O. Box 50414
Indianapolis, Indiana 46250–0414
USA
TEL 800 262 1640
FAX 1 317 576 2754

Boehringer Mannheim GmbH
Sandhoferstrasse 116
Postfach 310 120
D-68298 Mannheim 31
Germany
TEL 49 621 7590
FAX 49 621 759 8509

Bopp & Co.
Postfach
CH-8046 Zürich
Switzerland
TEL 41 1 371 08 80
FAX 41 1 371 18 80

Bright Instrument Co. Ltd.
Stukeley Meadows
Huntingdon, Cambridge PE18 6EB
England
TEL 44 480 454528
FAX 44 480 456031

British Drug House Ltd.
Broom Road
Poole, Dorset BH12 4NN
England
TEL 44 703 643702
FAX 44 455 558586

BTX Inc.
11199 Sorrento Valley Road
San Diego, California 92121
USA
TEL 1 619 595 6006

Burleigh Instruments, Inc.
Burleigh Park
Fishers, New York 14453
USA
TEL 1 716 924 9355
FAX 1 716 924 9072

Calbiochem Novabiochem International
P.O. Box 12087
La Jolla, California 92039–2087
USA
TEL 800 854 3417
TEL 800 228 9622
TEL 800 628 8470 (Technical Service)
TEL 1 619 450 9600
FAX 800 776 0999
FAX 1 619 453 3552

Calbiochem Novabiochem GmbH
Lisztweg 1
65812 Bad Soden/T.
Germany
TEL 44 6196 63955
FAX 44 6196 62361

Campden Instruments, Ltd.
King Street
Sileby, Loughborough LE12 7LZ
United Kingdom
TEL 44 5 09 81 47 90
FAX 44 5 09 81 60 97

Canberra Packard Limited
Brook House
14 Station Road
Pangbourne, Berkshire RG8 7DT
England
TEL 44 734 844981
FAX 44 734 844059

Cappel Organon Teknika
100 Akzo Avenue
Durham, North Carolina 27704
USA
TEL 800 523 7620
FAX 1 919 620 2600

Cappel Organon Teknika N.V.
International Headquarters
Veedjik 58
B-2300 Turnhout
Belgium
TEL 32 1440 4040
FAX 32 1442 1600

Carl Roth GmbH & Co.
Postfach 211162
D-76161 Karlsruhe
Germany
TEL 49 721 56060
FAX 49 721 560649

Carl Zeiss, Inc.
One Zeiss Drive
Thornwood, New York 10594
USA
TEL 800 233 2343
TEL 1 914 747 1800
FAX 1 914 681 7446

Carl Zeiss
Abt. MI-VLA
Postfach 1369–1380
D-73446 Oberkochen
Germany
TEL 49 7364 203780
FAX 49 7364 204258

CBS Scientific
P.O. Box 856
Del Mar, California 92014
USA
TEL 1 619 755 4959
FAX 1 619 755 0733

Chance Propper Ltd.
Smethwick
United Kingdom
TEL 44 41 8896100
FAX 44 41 8871167

Chemical Concentrates (RBS) Ltd.
United 9, Chapel Park
Church Rd.
Business Centre
Sittingbourne, Kent ME10 3RW
United Kingdom
TEL 44 795 42091
FAX 44 795 42092

Ciba Corning
Industriestrasse 11
D-35463 Fernwald
Germany
TEL 49 641 40030
FAX 49 641 400311

Clark Electromedical Instruments
P.O. Box 8
Pangbourne
Reading RG8 7HU
United Kingdom
TEL 44 734 843 888
FAX 44 734 845 374

Claus Damm A/S
Bakkegaardsvej 202
DK-3050 Humlebæk
Denmark
TEL 45 4916 3388
FAX 45 4916 3330

Clay Adams
Division of Becton Dickinson
Diagnostic Instrumental Systems
383 Hillen Road
Townson, Maryland 21204
USA
TEL 800 638 8656

Codman and Shurtleff, Inc.
41 Pacella Park Drive
Randolph, Massachusetts 02368
USA
TEL 800 343 5966
FAX 1 617 986 5285

Cole-Parmer Instrument Company
7425 North Park Avenue
Chicago, Illinois 60714
USA
TEL 800 323 4340
FAX 1 708 647 9660

Collaborative Biomedical Products
Becton Dickson Labware
2 Oak Park
Bedford, Massachusetts 01730
USA
TEL 1 617 275 0004
FAX 1 617 275 0043

Commonwealth Serum Laboratories
45 Poplar Road
Parkville Victoria 3052
Australia
TEL 61 3 389 1911
FAX 61 3 389 1434

Concept GmbH
Postfach 10 17 64
W-6900 Heidelberg 1
Germany

Confocal Technologies Ltd.
South Harrington Building
Sefton Street
Liverpool L3 4BQ
United Kingdom

Corning, Inc.
P.O. Box 5000
Corning, New York 14831
USA
TEL 800 222 7740
TEL 1 404 565 3456
FAX 1 404 565 0003

Corning, Inc.
400 Old Lincoln Highway
One Lincoln Crossing
Fairless Hills, Pennsylvania 19030
USA
TEL 1 215 949 0400

Corning, Inc.
Western Region
Science Products Division
39899 Balentine Drive #325
Newark, California 94560
USA
TEL 800 222 7740

Corning Consumer S.A.
44 Avenue Valvins
BP No 01
F-77211 Avon Cedex
France
TEL 33 1 64697500
FAX 33 1 64234334

Costar
7035 Commerce Circle
Pleasanton, California 4588–8008
USA
TEL 800 334 1677

Costar Corporation
One Alewife Center
Cambridge, Massachusetts 02140
USA
TEL 800 492 1110
FAX 1 617 868 2076

Costar Europe Ltd.
Sloterweg 305a
1171 VC Badhoevedorp
The Netherlands
TEL 31 206596051
FAX 31 206597673

Coulter Electronics Limited
Northwell Drive
Luton LU3 3RH
England
TEL 44 582 49 14 14
FAX 44 582 49 03 90

Cox-Nelson Seed Co.
Katy, Texas 77449
USA

CPG Inc.
3 Borinski Road
Lincoln Park, New Jersey 07035
USA
TEL 1 201 305 8181
FAX 1 201 305 0884

Curtin Matheson Scientific
9999 Veterans Memorial Drive
Houston, Texas 77038–2499
USA
TEL 800 392 3353
FAX 1 713 878 3598

CVI Laser Corp.
361 Lindbergh Avenue
Livermore, California 94550
USA
TEL 1 510 449 1064
FAX 1 510 294 7747

Dagan Corp.
2855 Park Avenue S.
Minneapolis, Minnesota 55407
USA
TEL 1 612 827 5959
FAX 1 612 827 6535

Dage-MTI
701 Roeske Avenue
Michigan City, Indiana 46360
USA
TEL 1 219 842 5559

DAKO A/S
Produktionsvej 42
DK-2600 Glostrup
Denmark
TEL 45 44 92 00 44
FAX 45 42 84 18 22

DAKO Corporation
6392 Via Real
Carpinteria, California 93013
USA
TEL 1 805 566 6655
FAX 1 805 566 6688

Dakopatts
16 Manor Courtyard
Hughenden Avenue
High Wycombe, Bucks HP13 5RE
United Kingdom
TEL 44 494 452016
FAX 44 495 441553

Data Translation, Inc.
100 Locke Drive
Marlboro, Massachusetts 01752–1192
USA
TEL 1 508 481 3700
FAX 1 508 481 8620

David Bull Laboratories
Harris Road
Warwick CV34 5GH
United Kingdom
TEL 44 926 402003
FAX 44 926 401637

David Kopf Instruments
P.O. Box 636
7324 Elmo Street
Tujunga, California 91042
USA
TEL 1 818 352 3274
FAX 1 818 352 3139

Denley Instruments Ltd.
Bilbate Division No. 9
Low March London Road
Daventry, Northants NN11 4SD
United Kingdom
TEL 44 327 71467/705113
FAX 44 327 300619

Denville Scientific, Inc.
P.O. Box 304
Denville, New Jersey 07834
USA
FAX 1 201 328 0822

Diagen GmbH
Max-Volmer-Strasse 4
D-40724 Hilden
Germany
TEL 49 2103 892230
FAX 49 2103 892222

Diatome SA
Box 557
2501 Bienne
Switzerland
TEL 41 32515813
FAX 41 32515257

Difco
P.O. Box 14B
Central Avenue
East Molesey, Surrey KT8 0SE
England
TEL 44 81 979 9951
FAX 44 81 979 2506

Difco Laboratories
P.O. Box 331058
Detroit, Michigan 48232–7058
USA
TEL 800 521 0851
TEL 1 313 462 8500
FAX 1 313 462 8517

Digene Diagnostic, Inc.
2301-B Broadbirch Drive
Silver Spring, Maryland 20904
USA
TEL 1 301 470 6504
FAX 1 301 680 0696

Diversey A/S
Smedelholm 3–5
DK-2730 Herlev
Denmark
TEL 45 4284 4111
FAX 45 4284 6377

Dupont Co.
Medical Products Department
P.O. Box 800222
Wilmington, Delaware 19880
USA
TEL 800 551 2121
FAX 800 892 0719
FAX 1 301 892 0719

Du Pont de Nemours & Co.
549 Albany Street
Boston, Massachusetts 02118
USA
TEL 1 617 350 9595
FAX 1 617 542 8468

Du Pont de Nemours (France) S.A.
NEN Products
Avenue du Pacifique
B.P. 85
91943 Les Ulis Cedex A
France
TEL 33 1 69 82 54 50
FAX 33 1 69 82 52 00

Dynal Inc.
475 Northern Boulevard
Great Neck, New York 11021
USA
TEL 1 516 829 0039
FAX 1 516 829 0045

Dynal A.S.
P.O. Box 158
Skøyen
N-0212 Oslo
Norway
TEL 47 2206 1000
FAX 47 2250 7015

Dynatech Laboratories
14340 Sullyfield Circle
Chantilly, Virginia 22021
USA
TEL 1 703 803 1243
FAX 1 703 631 7816

E.I. du Pont de Nemours
Medical Products Department
Wilmington, Delaware 19898
USA
TEL 800 441 7515
TEL 1 302 441 7515
FAX 1 302 774 7321

Eastman Chemical Corporation
Laboratory & Research Products
1001 Lee Road
Rochester, New York 14652–3512
USA
TEL 800 225 5352
FAX 800 879 4979

Eastman Kodak Company
343 State Street
Rochester, New York 14650
USA
TEL 800 225 5352
TEL 1 716 724 4000
FAX 800 879 4779
FAX 1 716 724 0663

EDITEK (formerly Granite Diagnostics)
1238 Anthony Road
Burlington, North Carolina 27215
USA
TEL 800 334 1116
TEL 1 910 226 6311
FAX 1 910 229 4471

Edmund Scientific
101 E. Gloucester Pike
Barrington, New Jersey 08007-1380
USA
TEL 1 609 573 6882
FAX 1 609 573 6295

Elastin Products Co., Inc.
P.O. Box 568
Owensville, Missouri 65066
USA
TEL 1 314 437 2193
FAX 1 314 437 4632

Elga Ltd.
High Street, Lane End
High Wycombe, Bucks HP14 3JH
England
TEL 44 494 881393
FAX 44 494 881007

EM Science
P.O. Box 70
480 Democrat Road
Gibbstown, New Jersey 08027
USA
TEL 800 222 0342
FAX 609 423 4389

EM Separations Technology
P.O. Box 70
480 Democrat Road
Gibbstown, New Jersey 08027
USA
TEL 800 922 1084
TEL 1 609 224 0742
FAX 1 609 423 4389

Endecotts Ltd
9 Lombard Road
London SW19 3TZ
England
TEL 44 81 542 8121
FAX 44 81 543 6629

Engineering Office M. Wohlwend
9466 Sennwald
Switzerland
TEL 41 85 75924
FAX 41 85 76243

Epoxy Technology, Inc.
14 Fortune Drive
Billerica, Massachusetts 01821
USA
TEL 1 508 667 3805
FAX 1 508 663 9782

Eppendorf-Netheler-Hinz GmbH
Barkhausenweg 1
D-22331 Hamburg
Germany
TEL 49 40 53801 0
FAX 49 40 53801 556

European Culture Collection
Division of Biologies
PHLS Centre for Applied Microbiology and Research
Porton Down
Salisbury SP4 0JG
United Kingdom
TEL 44 980 610391
FAX 44 980611315

Falcon
Becton Dickinson Labware
2 Bridgewater Lane
Lincoln Park, New Jersey 07035
USA
TEL 800 235 5953
FAX 1 201 847 4841

Farnell Electronic Components
Canal Road
Leeds LS 122 TU
United Kingdom
TEL 44 532 633411

Filtron Pty. Ltd.
A.C.N. 051 958 377
18–20 Export Drive
Brooklyn, Victoria 3025
Australia
TEL 61 3315 1644
FAX 61 3315 1656

Finnigan MAT
355 River Oaks Parkway
San Jose, California 95134
USA
TEL 1 408 433 4800
FAX 1 408 433 4823

Finpipette
Labsystems Oy
P.O. Box 8
FIN-00881 Helsinki
Finland
TEL 358 75 821
FAX 358 759 1479

Fisher Scientific
711 Forbes Avenue
Pittsburgh, Pennsylvania 15129–4785
USA
TEL 800 766 7000
TEL 1 201 467 6400
FAX 800 926 1166
FAX 1 201 370 7415

Fisher Scientific
50 Fadem Road
Springfield, New Jersey 07081–3193
USA
TEL 1 201 467 6400
FAX 1 201 379 7415

Fisons Scientific Equipment
Bishop Meadow Road
Loughborough
Leicestershire LE11 ORG
England
TEL 44 509 231166
FAX 44 509 231893

FJW Optical Systems, Inc.
629 S. Vermont Street
Palatine, Illinois 60067-6949
USA
TEL 1 708 358 2500
FAX 1 708 358 2533

Flow Products
See ICN Biomedicals

Fluka Chemical Corporation
980 South Second Street
Ronkonkoma, New York 11779–7238
USA
TEL 800 358 5287
TEL 1 516 467 0980
FAX 800 441 8841
TEL 1 516 467 0663

Fluka Chemie AG
Industriestrasse 25
Postfach 260
CH-9470 Buchs
Switzerland
TEL 41 81 755 2511
FAX 41 81 756 5449

FMC BioProducts
191 Thomaston Street
Rockland, Maine 04841
USA
TEL 800 341 1574
FAX 1 207 594 3491

FMC BioProducts Europe
Risingevej 1
DK-2665 Vallensbaek Strand
Denmark
TEL 45 43 73 1122
FAX 45 43 73 5692

Forma Scientific
P.O. Box 649
Marietta, Ohio 45750
USA
TEL 800 848 3080
TEL 1 614 373 4763
FAX 1 614 373 6770

Fort Dodge Laboratories
P.O. Box 518
Fort Dodge, Iowa 50501
USA
TEL 800 685 5656
FAX 800 846 8626

Foster Findlay Associates Ltd.
148 West Road
Newcastle upon Tyne NE4 9QB
United Kingdom

Franz Morat KG (GmbH & Co)
Framo® Gerätetechnik
Hoechst 7
P.O. Box 10
D-79869 Eisenbach
Hochschwarzwald
Germany
TEL 49 7657 88 0
FAX 49 7657 88 333/222

Friedrich and Dimmock, Inc.
P.O. Box 230
Millville, New Jersey 08332
USA
TEL 1 609 825 0305
FAX 1 609 327 4299

Frederick Haer & Co.
Brunswick, Maine 04011
USA
TEL 1 207 729 1601
FAX 1 207 729 1603

Gallard-Schlesinger Industries Inc.
584 Mineola Avenue
Carle Place, New York 11514
USA
TEL 800 645 3044
TEL 1 516 333 5600
FAX 1 516 333 5628

Garner Glass
177 S. Indian Hill Road
Claremont, California 91711
USA
TEL 1 909 624 5071
FAX 1 909 624 7212

Garrett Seed Co.
Danbury, Texas 77534
USA

Gatan Inc.
6678 Owens Drive
Pleasanton, California 94588
USA
TEL 1 510 463 0200
FAX 1 510 463 0204

Gatan Inc.
780 Commonwealth Drive
Warrendale, Pennsylvania 15086
USA

Gelman Sciences
600 South Wagner Road
Ann Arbor, Michigan 48103–9019
USA
TEL 800 521 1520, ext 435
TEL 1 313 665 0651
FAX 1 313 761 1208

Gemini BioProducts, Inc.
5115-N Douglas Fir Road
Calabasas, California 91302
USA
TEL 1 818 591 7084

Genentech Inc.
460 Point San Bruno Blvd.
South San Francisco, California 94080
USA
TEL 1 415 266 1000
FAX 1 415 266 2391

General Valve Corporation
19 Gloria Lane
P.O. Box 1333
Fairfield, New Jersey 07004
USA
TEL 1 201 575 4844
FAX 1 201 575 4011

Genosys Biotechnologies Inc.
162A Cambridge Science Park
Milton Road
Cambridge CB4 4G11
United Kingdom
TEL 44 223 425 622
FAX 44 223 425 966

Genosys Biotechnologies Inc.
8701A New Trails Drive
The Woodlands, Texas 77381–4241
USA
TEL 1 713 363 3693
FAX 1 713 363 2212

Gen Pack
Lejrvej 27
DK-3500 Vaerløse
Denmark
TEL 45 4248 6200
FAX 45 4248 6261

Genzyme
50 Gibson Drive
Kings Hill, West Malling
Kent ME19 6HG
United Kingdom
TEL 44 732 220 022
FAX 44 732 220 024

Genzyme Diagnostics
One Kendall Square
Cambridge, Massachusetts 02139
USA
TEL 1 617 252 7500
FAX 1 617 252 7600

George Tiemann & Co.
84 Newton Plaza
Plainview, New York 11803
USA
TEL 800 843 6266

GIBCO BRL
Life Technologies Ltd.
PO Box 35
Trident House, Renfrew Road
Paisley PA3 4EF
Scotland
TEL 44 41 814 6100
FAX 44 41 887 1167

GIBCO BRL, Life Technologies Inc.
3175 Stanley Drive
P.O. Box 68
Grand Island, New York 14072–0068
USA
TEL 800 828 6686
TEL 1 301 840 8000
FAX 800 331 2286
FAX 1 301 258 8238

GIC
Havkaersvej 81, Tilst
DK-8381 Mundelstrup
Denmark
TEL 45 86 244100
FAX 45 86 245353

Gilson Medical Electronics, Inc.
3000 W. Beltline Hwy.
P.O. Box 27
Middleton, Wisconsin 53562
USA
TEL 1 608 836 1551
FAX 1 608 831 4451

Gilson
72 rue Gambetta, BP 45
F-95400 Villiers-le-Bel
France
TEL 331 3429 5000
FAX 331 3429 5080

Glaswerk Wertheim GmbH
Postfach 1265
D-97862 Wertheim
Germany
TEL 49 9342 8020
FAX 49 9342 802110

Graticules Ltd.
Morle Road
Tonbridge, Kent TN9 1RN
United Kingdom
TEL 44 732 359061
FAX 44 732 770217

Greiner GmbH (Greiner Labortechnik)
Maybach Str.
P.O. Box 1162
72636 Frickenhausen
Germany
TEL 49 7022 5010
FAX 49 7022 501 514

Guy Cox Software
P.O. Box 366
Rozella NSW 2039
Australia

Haake Mess-Technik GmbH
Dieselstrasse 4
W-7500 Karlsruhe
Germany
TEL 49 721 40940
FAX 49 721 4094 300

Hamamatsu Photonics Deutschland GmbH
PF 1244
Arzbergerstrasse 10
82211 Hersching
Germany
TEL 49 8153 37 0
FAX 49 8152 2658

Hamamatsu Photonics KK
325–6, Sunayama-cho
Hamamatsu City
430 Japan
TEL 81 53 452 2141
FAX 81 53 456 7889

Hamilton
P.O. Box 10030
Reno, Nevada 89529
USA
TEL 800 648 5950
TEL 1 702 858 3000
FAX 1 702 323 7259

Harlan Olac Ltd.
Shaws Farm
Blackthorn, Bicester
Oxfordshire OX6 OTP
England
TEL 44 869 243241
FAX 44 869 246759

Harlan Sprague Dawley, Inc.
P.O. Box 29176
Indianapolis, Indiana 46229
USA
TEL 1 317 894 7521
FAX 1 317 894 1840

Harvard Apparatus
22 Pleasant St.
South Natick, Massachusetts 01760
USA
TEL 1 508 665 7000
FAX 1 508 665 6029

Hayashi Rikagaku Co. Ltd.
Tokyo
Japan

Heka Electronik GmbH
Wiesentrasse 71
D-67466 Lambrecht/Pfalz
Germany
TEL 49 63 25 80 36
FAX 49 63 25 80 39

Heraeus Instruments
P.O. Box 1563
Nordstr. 71–73
D-63405 Hanau
Germany
TEL 49 6181 35465
FAX 49 6181 35749

Heraeus Sepatech
P.O. Box 1220
Am Kalkberg
D-3360 Osterode
Germany
TEL 49 5522 3160
FAX 49 5522 316119

Hestbech F. & Co.
P.O. Box 80
Bøgildsmindevej 3
DK-9400 Nørresundby
Denmark
TEL 45 9817 4444
FAX 45 9817 8330

Heto Holten Lab Equipment A/S
Gydevang 17–19
DK-3450 Alleroed
Denmark
TEL 45 4814 2777
FAX 45 4227 4655

Heto Lab Equipment A/S
Klintebjerg Vænge 3
DK-3460 Birkerød
Denmark
TEL 45 42817777
FAX 45 42274655

Hettich AG
Gartenstrassen 100
D-78532 Tuttingen
Germany
TEL 49 7461 7050
FAX 49 7461 705125

Hirschmann Labogeräte
Hauptstrasse 7–15
Postfach 1153
D-74246 Eberstadt
Germany
TEL 49 71345110
FAX 49 71344036

Histolab Products AB
Hulda Lindgrens Gata 6
S-42131 Västra Frölunda
Sweden
TEL 46 63 1433530
FAX 46 31 478989

Hitachi Koki Inc.
5-8-10 Sendagaya Shibuya-ku
Tokyo 151
Japan
TEL 81 3 5379 2360
FAX 81 3 3341 6188

Hitachi Scientific Instruments
Nissei Sangyo Co. Ltd.
Hogwood Industrial Estate
Finchampstead, Wokingham
Berkshire, RG11 4QQ
United Kingdom
TEL 44 734 328632
FAX 44 734 328779

Hoechst AG
Akttiengesellschaft
D-65926 Frankfurt
Germany
TEL 49 693050
FAX 49 69408665

Hoefer Scientific Instruments
654 Minnesota Street, Box 77387
San Francisco, California 94107–2387
USA
TEL 800 227 4750
TEL 1 415 282 2307
FAX 1 415 821 1081

Hoefer Scientific Instruments Ltd.
Newcastle-under-Lyme
Staffordshire ST5 0TT
United Kingdom
TEL 44 782 617317
FAX 44 782 617346

Holm & Halby A/S
Gydevang 17–19
DK-3450 Alleroed
Denmark
TEL 45 4814 2666
FAX 45 4227 4655

Hotpack Corporation
10940 Dutton Road
Philadelphia, Pennsylvania 19154
USA
TEL 800 523 3608

HUB Surgical Co.
902 Arch Street
P.O. Box 3336
Williamsport, Pennsylvania 17701
USA
TEL 800 332 8532
FAX 1 717 322 6549

HyClone Europe, Ltd.
Nelson Industrial Estate
Cramlington
Northumberland NE23 9BL
United Kingdom
TEL 44 670 734093
FAX 44 670 732537

HyClone Laboratories Inc.
1725 South HyClone Road
Logan, Utah 84321–6212
USA
TEL 800 492 5663
TEL 1 801 753 4584
FAX 800 533 9450
FAX 1 801 753 4589

ICN Biomedicals, Inc., European Headquarters
Thame Park Business Centre
Wenman Road
Thame, Oxfordshire OX9 3XA
United Kingdom
TEL 44 844 215522
FAX 44 844 213399

ICN Biomedicals, Inc.
Radiochemicals Division
3300 Hyland Avenue
Costa Mesa, California 92626
USA
TEL 800 854 0530
TEL 1 714 545 0113
FAX 800 334 6999
FAX 1 714 641 7275

Imperial Laboratories
Andover, West Portway
Hampshire SP10 3LF
United Kingdom
TEL 44 264 333311
FAX 44 264 332412

Improvision
Barclays Venture Centre
Sir William Lyons Road
Coventry CV4 7EZ
United Kingdom
TEL 44 203 692229
FAX 44 203 690091

Infors AG
Rittergasse 27
CH-4103 Bottmingen
Switzerland
TEL 41 61 421 7700
FAX 41 61 421 3720

Insect Virus Research Group
Oxford Bookes University
School of Biological and Molecular Sciences
Gipsy Lane Campus
Oxford OX3 0BP
United Kingdom
TEL 44 865 483291
FAX 44 865 483490

Instrutech Corporation
475 Northern Blvd., Suite 31
Great Neck, New York 11021
USA
TEL 1 516 829 5942
FAX 1 516 829 0934

Integrated Separation Systems
21 Strathmore Road
Natick, Massachusetts 01760
USA
TEL 800 433 6433
FAX 1 508 655 8501

Intergen Co.
2 Manhattenville Road
The Center at Purchase
Purchase, New York 10577
USA
TEL 800 431 4505
FAX 1 914 694 1429

Intermountain Scientific Corporation
1610 South Main, Suite H
Bountiful, Utah 84010
USA
TEL 800 999 2901
FAX 1 801 298 7892

International Biotechnologies, Inc. (Now **Scientific Imaging Systems**)
Eastman Kodak Company
25 Science Park
New Haven, Connecticut 06511
USA
Customer Service and Technical Support in Rochester
TEL 1 716 588 2572
FAX 1 716 722 6054

International Biotechnology Inc.
Subsidiary of Eastman Kodak Co.
36 Clifton Road
Cambridge CB1 4ZR
England
TEL 44 800 581700
FAX 44 223 243036

International Equipment Company
300 Second Avenue
Needham Heights, Massachusetts 02194
USA
TEL 1 617 449 8060
FAX 1 617 444 6743

Intervet UK Ltd.
Science Park
Milton Road
Cambridge CB4 4FP
United Kingdom
TEL 44 223 42 0221
FAX 44 223 42 0751

Iomega Europe GmbH
Bötzinger Strasse 48
D-79110 Freiburg im Breslau
Germany
TEL 49 761 45040
FAX 49 761 450 4414

Irvine Scientific
2511 Daimler Street
Santa Ana, California 92705
USA
TEL 800 437 5706
FAX 1 714 261 7800

Iwai Chemicals Company
2–10, 3-chome, Nihonbasi-honcho
Chuo-ku
Tokyo 103
Japan
TEL 81 3 32 412572
FAX 81 3 32 70 2444

Iwaki Glass Co. Ltd.
3-2-3 Marunouchi Chiyoda-ku
Tokyo 101
Japan
TEL 81 3 241 6221
FAX 81 3 211 7002

J. Bibby Science Products Ltd.
Stone, Staffordshire ST15 0SA
United Kingdom
TEL 44 785 812121
FAX 44 785 813748

Jackson ImmunoResearch Laboratories
P.O. Box 9
West Grove, Pennsylvania 19390
USA
TEL 800 367 5296
FAX 1 215 869 0171

Jandel Scientific
65 Koch Road
Carle Madera, California 94925
USA

Janssen Pharmaceutica NV
Janssen Pharmaceuticalaan 3
B-2440 Geel
Belgium
TEL 32 1460 4200
FAX 32 1460 4220

Jenaer Glaswerke Schott
Hattensbergstr. 10
55122 Mainz
Germany
TEL 49 6131 6061

Jencons Scientific Ltd.
Leighton Buzzard
Bedfordshire LU7 8UA
United Kingdom
TEL 44 525 372010
FAX 44 525 379547

Johnson Matthey Materials Technology
Orchard Road
Roystock, Herts SG8 SHE
United Kingdom
FAX 44 763 25 3000

JRH Biosciences
P.O. Box 14848
Lenexa, Kansas
USA
TEL 800 255 6032
FAX 1 913 469 5584

J. R. Scientific (Sera-Lab) Ltd.
Crawley Down
Sussex RH10 4FF
United Kingdom
TEL 44 342 716366
FAX 44 342 717351

J. T. Baker
H.-S.-Richardson-Strasse 1
D-64506 Grob-Gerau
Germany
TEL 49 6152 710378
FAX 49 6152 710 399

J. T. Baker B. V.
P.O. Box 1
400 AA Deventer
The Netherlands
TEL 31 5700 87500
FAX 31 05700 11342

J. T. Baker Chemical Co.
222 Red School Lane
P.O. Box 492
Phillipsburgh, New Jersey 08865
USA
TEL 800 582 2537
FAX 1 908 859 9318

Kartell S.P.A.
via Delle Industrie 1
I-20082 Noviglio (MI)
Italy

Katayama Chemical Industries Co., Ltd
2-5-10 Dosho-machi, Chuo-ku
Osaka 541
Japan
FAX 81 6 222 3804

Kem en Tec A/S
Lerso Parkallé
DK-2100 Cobenhagen Ø
Denmark
TEL 45 3927 1777
FAX 45 3120 0178

Kinematica GmbH
Luzernerstrasse 147a
CH-6014 Littau-Luzern
Switzerland
TEL 41 41 571257
FAX 41 41 571460

Koch-Light/New Brunswick Scientific Co.
163 Dickson Hill Road
Norths Mimms
Hatfield, Herts AL9 7JE
United Kingdom
TEL 44 707 275733
FAX 44 707 267859

Kodak
Kodak House
P.O. Box 66
Station Road
Hemel, Hempstead HP1 1JU
England
TEL 44 494 431717
FAX 44 442 844578

Kodak Eastman Company
EAMER
245 Hammersmith Road
London W6 8PL
United Kingdom
TEL 44 819824621
FAX 44 817419568

Kodak Laboratory Chemicals
See Eastman Kodak Company

Kontes Glass Company
1022 Spruce Street
Vineland, New Jersey 08360
USA
TEL 800 223 7150
TEL 1 609 692 8500
FAX 1 609 692 4766

Kontron Instruments GmbH
Geschaftsbereich Analytik
Siemens Strasse 1
D-85375 Neufahrn
Germany
TEL 49 8165 9220
FAX 49 8165 526722

Kurabo Co. Ltd.
14–5 Shimo-kida cho Neyagawa City
Osaka 572
Japan
TEL 81 720 20 4504
FAX 81 720 21 9641

Lab-Line Instruments, Inc.
15th & Bloomingdale Avenue
Melrose Park, Illinois 60160
USA
TEL 800 522 5463
FAX 1 708 450 0943

Laboratoires Merck-Clévenot S.A.
Division Réactifs
5 à 9, rue Anquetil
94736 Nogent-sur-marne Cedex
France
TEL 33 1 43 94 54 00
FAX 33 1 48 76 58 14

Labsystems Oy
P.O. Box 8
SF-00881 Helsinki
Finland
TEL 358 0 75821
FAX 358 0 789732

Laser Laboratory Systems
P.O. Box 166
Sarisbury Green
Southampton SO3 6YZ
United Kingdom
TEL 44 703 406124
FAX 44 703 405039

Lasertec Corporation
Unit 4, Wendell Court
16/20 Wendell Road
London W12 9RT
United Kingdom
TEL 44 81 7492273
FAX 44 81 7495363

LC Packings International
80 Carolina Street
San Francisco, California 94103
USA
TEL 800 621 2625
FAX 1 415 552 1859

Leica Inc.
P.O. Box 123
Buffalo, New York 14240–0123
USA
TEL 1 716 686 3000
FAX 1 716 686 3085

Leica Lasertechnik GmbH
Im Neuenheimer Feld 518
D-69120 Heidelberg 1
Germany
TEL 49 62 21 41 480
FAX 49 62 21 41 48 33

Leica Mikroskopie und Systeme GmbH
Ernst Leitz-Strasse
35530 Wetzlar
Germany
TEL 49 6441 290
FAX 49 6441293399

Leitz GmbH
35578 Wetzlar
Germany
TEL 49 6441 2070
FAX 49 6441 20712

Leo Løvens Kemiske Fabrik
Industriparken 55
DK-2750 Ballerup
Denmark
TEL 45 44 94 58 88
FAX 45 44 94 30 40

Leybold Heraus
Leybold AG Vaccum Teknik
Bonner Strasse 498
D-50968 Köln
Germany
TEL 49 221 3470
FAX 49 221 3471250

Lipid Products
Nutfield Nurserie
Crab Hill Lane
South Nutfield, Nr. Redhill
Surrey RH1 5PG
United Kingdom
TEL 44 737823277
FAX 44 737822561

List Electronics
Pfungstaedter Strasse 18 - 20
D-6100 Darmstadt 13
Germany
TEL 496151 56000
FAX 496151 56060

LKB/Pharmacia Biotechnology
Davey Avenue
Knowl Hill
Milton Keynes MK5 8PH
England
FAX 44908 690091

3M
3M Center-General Offices
I-94 and McKnight Road
St. Paul, Minnesota 55144–1000
USA
TEL 1 612 737 5009
FAX 1 612 733 9596

Macherey-Nagel
Neumann-Neanderstrasse
Postfach 101352
D-5160 Düren
Germany
TEL 49 2421 698 0
FAX 49 2421 620 54

Magenta Plast
Industrileddet 17
Svogerslev, DK-4000 Roskilde
Denmark
TEL 45 46 384690
FAX 45 46 384737

Mallinckrodt Chemicals
16305 Swingley, Ridge Drive
Chesterfield, Missouri 63017
USA
TEL 1 3145302000
FAX 1 3145302328

Mallinckrodt, Inc.
2703 Wagner Place
St. Louis, Missouri 30620
USA
TEL 800 354 2050
FAX 1 606 987 3456

Mallinckrodt, Inc.
P.O. Box 800
Paris, Kentucky 40361–0800
USA
TEL 800 354 2050
TEL 1 314 530 2063
FAX 1 314 530 2527

Martin Medizin-Technik
Gebrüder Martin GmbH & Co.
Ludwigstaler Strasse 132
Postfach 60
D-78532 Tuttlingen
Germany
TEL 49 7461 7060
FAX 49 7461 706193

Matrox (UK) Ltd.
6 Cherry Orchard West
Kembrey Park
Swindon, Wilts SN2 6UP
United Kingdom
TEL 44 793 614 002
FAX 44 793 614 336

Matsushita Electric
5770 Ambler Drive
Mississauga, Ontario L4W 2T3
Canada
FAX 1 416 238 2362

Mediatech
P.O. Box 17734
Washington Dulles International Airport
Washington, D.C. 20041
USA
TEL 800 235 5476

Medical Systems Corp.
1 Plaza Road
Greenvale, New York 11548
USA
TEL 800 654 5406
FAX 1 516 621 8503

Medicell International Ltd.
239 Liverpool Road
London N1 1LX
United Kingdom
TEL 44 71 607 2295
FAX 44 71 700 4156

Medicon EG
Postfach 4455
D-78509 Tuttlingen
Germany
TEL 49 746 220090
FAX 49 746 2200950

Memmert GmbH
P.O. Box 1720
D-91126 Schwabach
Germany
TEL 49 91 22 9250
FAX 49 91 22 14585

Menzel Glasbearbeitungswek
Saarbrueckener Strasse 248
D-38116 Braunschweig
Germany
TEL 49 531 590080
FAX 49 531 509799

Merck
Postfach 4119
Frankfurter Strasse 250
D-64271 Darmstadt 1
Germany
TEL 49 6151 720
FAX 49 6151 722000

Metzoplast SB/HK
Metzeler Plastics GmbH
Im Reinfeld 2
Postfach 1760
D-52407 Jülich-Kirchberg
Germany
TEL 49 2461 64 0
FAX 49 2461 64 210

Michel Terrier
Postfach 264
CH-6834 Morbio-Inferiore
Switzerland
TEL 41 91 435 537
FAX 41 91 439 391

Microbiological Associates
5221 River Road
Bethesda, Maryland 20850
USA
TEL 1 301 738 1000
FAX 1 301 654 3400

Microfiltration Systems
6800 Sierra Court
Dublin, California 94568
USA
TEL 800 334 7132
FAX 1 510 828 1194

Miele & Cie GmbH & Co.
Carl-Miele Strasse 29
D-33332 Gütersloh
Germany
TEL 49 5241 890
FAX 49 5241 89 2090

Milan Hadravsky Medical and Technical Consultancy
Cechova 13
32000 Plzen
Czech Republic

Millipore Corporation
880 Ashby Road
Bedford, Massachusetts 01730–9125
USA
TEL 800 645 5476
TEL 1 617 275 9200
FAX 1 617 533 8873

Millipore GmbH
Hietzinger Hauptstrasse 145
A-1130 Wien
Austria
TEL 43 1 877 8926
FAX 43 1 877 1654

Mini-Instruments Ltd.
8 Station Industrial Estate
Burnham on Crouch
Essex CM0 8RN
United Kingdom
TEL 44 621 783282
FAX 44 621 783132

Mitlacher GmbH
Am Hemel 7
D-55124 Mainz
Germany
FAX 49 6131 46 0 24

Modulation Optics
100 Forest Drive at East Hills
Greenvale, New York 11548
USA
TEL 1 516 484 8882
FAX 1 516 621 4768

Molecular Devices Corp.
Menlo Oaks Corporation Center
4700 Bohannon Drive
Menlo Park, California 32247
USA
TEL 1 415 322 4700
FAX 1 415 322 2069

Molecular Devices Corp.
1311 Orleans Drive
Sunnyvale, California 94089
USA
TEL 800 400 9060
TEL 1 415 322 4700
FAX 1 415 326 5134

Molecular Devices Corp.
Bahnhofstrasse 110
D-82166 Gäfelfing, Munich
Germany
TEL 49 898 54 5050
FAX 49 898 54 2238

Molecular Probes, Inc.
4849 Pitchford Avenue
P.O. Box 22010
Eugene, Oregon 97402–9144
USA
TEL 800 438 2209
TEL 1 503 465 8300
FAX 800 438 0228
FAX 1 503 344 6504

Molecular Research Center Inc.
5645 Montgomery Road
Cincinnati, Ohio 45212
USA
TEL 1 513 841 0900
FAX 1 513 841 0080

Multi-Technology Inc.
6507 South 400 West
Salt Lake City, Utah 84107
USA
TEL 1 801 226 9334
FAX 1 801 561 4360

Murex Diagnostics Inc.
3075 Northwoods Circle
Norcross, Georgia 30071
USA
FAX 1 404 449 4018
TEL 1 404 662 0660

Nacalai Tesque (Nakarai Chemical Company)
Nijo-Karasuma Nakagyo-ku
Kyoto 601
Japan
TEL 81 75 231 5301
FAX 81 75 231 2455

Nalgene Company
Nalgene Brand Products
P.O. Box 20365
Rochester, New York 14602–0365
USA
TEL 1 716 586 8800
FAX 1 716 586 8431

Narishige Scientific Instruments
27–9 Minamikarasuyama
4-chome
Setagaya-ku, Tokyo 157
Japan
TEL 81 3 33 08 83 83
FAX 81 3 33 08 87 00

Narishige USA, Inc.
404 Glen Cove Avenue
Sea Cliff, New York 11579
USA
TEL 1 516 676 0044
FAX 1 516 676 1480

NASCO
901 Janesville Ave.
Fort Atkinson, Wisconsin 53538
USA
TEL 800 558 9595
TEL 1 414 563 2446
FAX 1 414 563 8206

National Diagnostics
305 Patton Drive
Atlanta, Georgia 30336
USA
TEL 800 526 3867
TEL 1 404 699 2121
FAX 1 404 699 2077

NeoLab GmbH
Rischerstrasse 7
D-69123 Heidelberg
Germany
TEL 49 6221 844219 22
FAX 49 6221 844233

Newark Electronics
101 West Burnsville Parkway
Burnsville, Minnesota 55337–2509
USA
TEL 1 612 890 0584
FAX 1 612 895 5504

New Brunswick Scientific Biological
Edison House
163 Dixons Hill Road
North Mymms, Hatfield
Herts AL9 7JE
United Kingdom
TEL 44 707 275733
FAX 44 707 267859

New Brunswick Scientific Co., Inc.
P.O. Box 4005
44 Talmadge Road
Edison, New Jersey 08818–4005
USA
TEL 800 631 5417
TEL 1 908 287 1200
FAX 1 908 287 4222

Newport-Klinger Corporation
1791 Deere Avenue
Irvine, California 92714
USA
TEL 800 222 6440
FAX 1 714 963 2015

Nikon Corporation
Fuji Bldg. 2–3 Marunouchi 3-chome
Chiyoda-ku, Tokyo 100
Japan
TEL 81 3 2161039
FAX 81 3 32152170

Nikon Europe B.V.
Schipholweg 321
P.O. Box 222
N 1170 AE Badhoevedorp
The Netherlands
TEL 31 20 449 6222
FAX 31 20 449 6299

Nikon Inc. Instrument Group
1300 Walt Whitman Road
Melville, New York 11747-3064
USA
TEL 1 516 547 4200
FAX 1 516 547 0299

Nippon Gene
See Wako Pure Chemical

Noran Instruments GmbH
2551 West Beltline Highway
Middleton, Wisconsin 53562–2697
USA
TEL 1 608 831 6511
FAX 1 608 836 7224

North American Biologicals, Inc.
16500 NW 15th Avenue
Miami, Florida 33169
USA
TEL 1 305 628 0080
FAX 1 305 625 0925

NOVEX
4202 Sorrento Valley Blvd.
San Diego, California 92121
USA
TEL 1 619 452 6634
FAX 1 619 452 6635

Nunc
P.O. Box 280
Kamstrupvej 90
DK-4000 Roskilde
Denmark
TEL 45 4235 9065
FAX 45 4235 0105

Nunc, Inc.
2000 North Aurora Road
Naperville, Illinois 60566
USA
TEL 800 238 6862
FAX 1 708 416 2519

Nycomed Pharma AS
Lillogt 3
N-0401 Oslo 4
Norway
TEL 47 2 296 3636
FAX 47 2 296 3746

Ohtake Works Co. Ltd.
Tokyo
Japan

Olympus America Inc.
4 Nevada Drive
Lake Success, New York 11042
USA
TEL 800 446 5967
TEL 1 516 488 3880
FAX 1 516 222 7920

Olympus Corporation
Precision Instrument Division
800 Airport Blvd.
Suite 304
Burlingame, California 94010
USA
TEL 1 909 695 1908
FAX 1 909 695 1908

Olympus Optical Co., (Europe) GmbH
Postfach 104908
D-20034 Hamburg
Germany
TEL 49 40237730
FAX 49 4023773647

Omega Optical
P.O. Box 573
3 Grove Street
Battlesboro, Vermont 05301
USA
TEL 1 802 254 2690
FAX 1 802 284 3937

Omnifit USA Corp.
P.O. Box 450
8 Executive Drive
Toms River, New Jersey 08754
USA
TEL 1 908 914 0615
FAX 1 908 244 8140

ONCOR Corporation
209 Perry Parkway
Gaithersburg, Maryland 20877
USA
TEL 1 301 963 3500
FAX 1 301 926 6129

Optivision (Yorkshire) Ltd.
Ahed House
Dewsbury Road
Ossett, West Yorkshire WF5 9ND
United Kingdom
TEL 44 924 277727
FAX 44 924 280016

ORBIS Ingenieurbüro
Horst Wiemers
Ennenfeldstrasse 5
D-51674 Wiehl
Germany
TEL 49 2262 9047
FAX 49 2262 97148

Orem Medical Co.
1800 Belair Rd.
Benson, Maryland 21018
USA
TEL 1 410 879 4707
FAX 1 410 879 1329

Oxoid, Unipath Ltd.
Basingstoke, Hampshire
United Kingdom
TEL 44 256 841144
FAX 44 256 463388

Packard Instrument Company
80 Research Parkway
Meriden, Connecticut 06450
USA
TEL 800 323 1891
TEL 1 203 238 2351
FAX 1 203 639 2172

Panasonic
Matsushita Electric Industrial Co., Ltd.
Central P.O. Box 288
Osaka 530-91
Japan

Paragon Razor Company
Sheffield S8 0UJ
United Kingdom
TEL 44 742 551063
FAX 44 742 586738

Perkin-Elmer Corporation
Applied Biosystems Division
850 Lincoln Centre Drive
Foster City, California 94404
USA
TEL 1 415 570 6667
FAX 1 415 572 2743

Perkin-Elmer Corporation
761 Main Avenue
Norwalk, Connecticut 06859-0001
USA
TEL 800 327 3002
TEL 1 203 762 1000
FAX 800 545 7547
FAX 1 203 762 6000

Perkin-Elmer
European Life Science Center
Paul-Ehrlich-Str. 17
D-63225 Langen
Germany
TEL 49 61 03 7080
FAX 49 61 03 708210

Perkin-Elmer Europe
Weiterstad
Germany
TEL 49 6150 1010
FAX 49 6150 101101

Pharmacia Biotech Europa
Procordia Eurocentre
Rue de la Fusée 62
Belgium
TEL 32 2727 4251
FAX 32 2727 4269

Pharmacia Biotech Norden AB
Djupdalsvägen 20-22
Box 776
191 27 Sollentuna
Sweden
TEL 46 86 238500
FAX 46 86 230069

Pharmacia LKB Biotech
800 Centennial Avenue
P.O. Box 1327
Piscataway, New Jersey 08855-1327
USA
TEL 800 526 3593
TEL 1 908 457 8000
FAX 800 329 3593
FAX 1 908 457 8100

PharMingen
11555 Sorrento Valley Road
San Diego, California 92121
USA
TEL 1 619 792 5730
FAX 1 619 792 5238

Phillips International
P.O. Box 218 NL
NL-5600 MD Eindhoven
The Netherlands
TEL 31 4079 1111
FAX 31 4075 7909

Philips Electron Optics
Building AAE
P.O. Box 218
5600 MD Eindhoven
The Netherlands
TEL 1 3140 766234
FAX 1 3140 766164

Phoenix Flow Systems
Phoenix, Arizona
USA

Photek
26 Castleham Road
St. Leonard's-on-Sea TN38 9NS
United Kingdom
TEL 44 424 850555
FAX 44 424 850051

Photometrics
3440 E. Britannia Drive
Tucson, Arizona 85706
USA
TEL 1 602 889 9933
FAX 1 602 573 1944

Photonic Science
Millham, Mountfield
Robertsbridge TN32 5LA
United Kingdom
TEL 44 580 881199
FAX 44 580 880910

Photonics Microscopy, Inc.
Butterfield Road, Suite 204A
Oak Brook, Illinois 60521
USA
TEL 1 312 325 1241
FAX 1 312 325 1245

Photon Technology International (PTI)
1 Deerpark Drive, Suite F
South Brunswick, New Jersey 08856
USA
FAX 1 908 329 9069
TEL 1 908 329 9010

Pierce and Warriner (UK) Ltd.
44 Upper Northgate Street
Chester CH1 4EF
United Kingdom
TEL 44 244382525
FAX 44 244373212

Pierce Chemical Company
3747 North Meridian Road
P.O. Box 117
Rockford, Illinois 61105
USA
TEL 800 874 3723
TEL 1 815 968 0747
FAX 800 842 5007
FAX 1 815 968 7316

Pierce Europe B.V.
P.O. Box 1512
3260 BA Oud Beijerland
The Netherlands
TEL 31 1860 19277
FAX 31 1860 19179

Pioneer Hi Bred Intl., Inc.
Johnston, Iowa 50131
USA

Polymicro Technologies, Inc.
3035 N. 33rd Drive
Tucson, Arizona 85017
USA
TEL 1 602 272 7437
FAX 1 602 278 1776

Polysciences Inc.
400 Valley Road
Warrington, Pennsylvania 18976–2590
USA
TEL 800 523 2575
FAX 1 215 343 0214

Poretics
111 Lindbergh Avenue
Livermore, California 94550–9520
USA
TEL 800 922 6090
TEL 1 510 373 0500
FAX 1 510 373 1725

Portex
Hythe, Kent CT21 6JL
United Kingdom
TEL 44 303 260551
FAX 44 303 266761

Princeton Instruments, Inc.
3660 Quakersbridge Road
Trenton, New Jersey 08619
USA
TEL 1 609 587 9797
FAX 1 609 587 1970

Prolabo
BP 369
75526 Paris Cedex 11
France
TEL 33 1 48 07 3800
FAX 33 49 23 17 50

Promega Corp.
2800 Woods Hollow Road
Madison, Wisconsin 53711–5399
USA
TEL 800 356 9526
TEL 1 608 274 4330
FAX 800 356 1970
FAX 1 608 277 2516

PROSEP b.v.b.a.
Lindenstraat 48
B-1930 Zaventem
Belgium
TEL 32 2720 8998
FAX 32 2725 1661

Protein Polymer Technologies
10655 Sorrento Valley Road
San Diego, California 92121
USA
TEL 1 619 558 6064
FAX 1 619 558 6477

Proxitronic
Robert-Bosch-Strasse 34
64625 Bensheim
Germany
TEL 49 6251 17030
FAX 49 6251 170390

Purina Mills Inc.
P.O. Box 66812
St. Louis, Missouri 63166–6812
USA
TEL 800 227 8941

Quantel SA
17, Avenue de l'Atlantique
Z.A. de Courtaboeuf
BP 23–91941 Les Ulis Cedex
France
TEL 33 1 69 29 17 00
FAX 33 1 69 29 17 29

Quantronix Corporation
45 Adams Avenue
Hauppauge, New York 11788
USA
TEL 1 516 273 6900
FAX 1 516 273 6958

Quantum Chemical Corporation
Gen. Lab Sup.
438 Pomton Road
Wayne, New Jersey 07470
USA

Queue System Inc.
275 Aikenroad
Asheville, North Carolina 28804
USA
TEL 1 704 658 2711
FAX 1 704 658 0363

Rainin Instrument Co.
Mack Road
Box 4026
Woburn, Massachusetts 01888–4026
USA
TEL 1 617 935 3050
FAX 1 617 938 1152

Rathburn Chemicals Ltd.
Walkerburn
Scotland
TEL 44 89 687 329
FAX 44 89 687 633

Reichert Division der Leica Aktiengesellschaft
Hernalser Haupstr. 219
Postfach 95
A-1171 Vienna
Austria
TEL 43 1 4616 410
FAX 43 1 46 0326

Reidel-de Häen AG
Postfach 100262
30926 Seelze
Germany
TEL 49 5137 9990
FAX 49 5137 999 123

Research Organics, Inc.
4353 East 49th Street
Cleveland, Ohio 44125
USA
TEL 800 321 0570

Research Products International Corp.
410 N. Business Center Drive
Mount Prospect, Illinois 60056
USA
TEL 800 323 9814
TEL 1 708 635 7330
FAX 1 708 635 1170

Rhône Poulenc
60470 Villiers Saint Paul
France
TEL 33 44 71 15 57

Roboz Surgical Instrument Co.
9210 Corporate Blvd., Suite 220
Rockville, Maryland 20850
USA
TEL 800 424 2984
FAX 1 301 590 1290

Roche Molecular Systems*
1145 Atlantic Avenue, Suite 100
Alameda, California 94501
USA
TEL 1 510 814 2849
FAX 1 510 814 2997

*Roche products are distributed through Perkin Elmer

Roth GmbH & Co.
Schoemperlenstrasse 1–5
76 185 Karlsruhe
Germany
TEL 49 721 56060
FAX 49 721 560649

RS Components
P.O. Box 99
Corby, Northhants NN17 9RS
United Kingdom
TEL 44 536 201201
FAX 44 536 201501

Sanyo/Gallenkamp (MSE)
Park House, Meridian East
Leicester LE3 2UZ
United Kingdom
TEL 44 5 33 63 0530
FAX 44 5 33 63 0353

Sarstedt
Romelsdorf
D-51581 Nümbrecht
Germany
TEL 49 2293 305 0
FAX 49 2293 305 122

Sarstedt
Newton, North Carolina 28658-0468
USA
TEL 800 257 5101
TEL 1 704 465 4000
FAX 1 704 465 0718

Sartorius GmbH
Weender Landstr. 94–108
37070 Göttingen
Germany
FAX 49 551 308 509
TEL 49 551 308 576

Saulas
16 bis, rue François Arago
F-93100 Montreuil
France
TEL 33 1 4858 7777
FAX 33 1 4858 8584

Savant Instruments, Inc.
110–103 Bi-County Boulevard
Farmingdale, New York 11735
USA
TEL 800 634 8886
TEL 1 516 249 4600
FAX 1 516 249 4639

Schleicher & Schuell GmbH
P.O. Box 4
D-37582 Dassel
Germany
TEL 49 5561 7910
FAX 49 5564 642309

Schleicher & Schuell Inc.
10 Optical Avenue
Keene, New Hampshire 03431
USA
TEL 800 245 4024
TEL 1 603 352 3810
FAX 1 603 357 3627

Schott Glaswerke
Postfach 2480
55014 Mainz 1
Germany
TEL 49 6131 660
FAX 49 6131 662003

Schwartz Mann Biotech
ICN Biomedicals
European Headquarters
Thame Park Business Centre
Wenman Road
Thame, Oxfordshire OX9 3XA
United Kingdom
TEL 44 844 215522
FAX 44 844 213399

Seikagaku America, Inc.
30 West Gude Drive, Suite 260
Rockville, Maryland 20850–1161
USA
TEL 800 237 4512
FAX 1 301 424 6961

Seikagaku Corporation
Tokyo Yakugyo Bldg.
1–5 Nihonbashi-honcho
2-chome Chuo-ku
Tokyo 103
Japan
TEL 813 3270 0536
FAX 813 3242 5335

Sepracor SA
35 Av. Jean Jaures
92395 Villeneuve la Garenne
France
TEL 33 1 46 85 92 00
FAX 33 1 47 92 26 55

Sera-Lab Limited
Crawley Down
Sussex RH10 4FF
England
TEL 44 342 71 63 66
FAX 44 342 71 73 51

Seromed
Polylabo
305 Route de Colmar
BP 36
France
TEL 33 88 65 80 20
FAX 33 88 39 74 41

Serva
Distributed through Cresent Chemical Company
1324 Motor Parkway
Hauppauge, New York 11788
USA
TEL 800 645 3412
TEL 1 516 348 0333
FAX 1 516 348 0913

Serva Biochemicals
50 A&S Drive
Paramus, New Jersey 07652
USA
TEL 800 645 3412
FAX 1 201 967 8858

Serva Feinbiochemica GmbH & Co.
P.O. Box 105260
Carl Benz Strasse 7
D-69115 Heidelberg
Germany
TEL 49 6221 5020
FAX 49 6221 502113

Shandon Lipshaw
Science Resp. Inc.
P.O. Box 162
Woxall, Pennsylvania 18979
USA
FAX 1 215 234 0983

Sharp Inc.
22–22 Nagaike-cho Abeno-ku
Osaka 545
Japan
TEL 816 621 1221

Shimadzu
7102 Riverwood Drive
Columbia, Maryland 21046
USA
TEL 800 477 1227
FAX 1 410 381 1222

Shimadzu Europa GmbH
Postfach 90260
D-47267 Duisburg
Germany
TEL 49 203 7687466
FAX 49 203 766625

Siegfried AG/SA
Verkauf Industrie
CH-4800 Zofingen
Switzerland
TEL 41 62 501 111
FAX 41 62 513 082

Sigma Chemical Company
P.O. Box 14508
3050 Spruce Street
St. Louis, Missouri 63178–9916
USA
TEL 800 325 3010
TEL 1 314 771 5750
FAX 800 325 5052
FAX 1 314 771 5757

Sigma Chemie GmBH
Grünwalder Weg 30
82041 Deisenhofen
Germany
TEL 49 89 613 01 122
FAX 49 89 613 51 35

Small Parts, Inc.
13980 NW 58th Court
P.O. Box 4650
Miami Lakes, Florida 33014
USA
TEL 1 305 557 8222
FAX 800 423 9009

Smith & Nephew
Nærum Hovedgade 2
P.O. Box 30
DK-2850 Nærum
Denmark
TEL 45 4180 6100
FAX 45 4280 6151

Sorvall
DuPont de Nemours GmbH
Biotechnology Systems Division
DuPont Strasse 1
61343 Bad Homburg
Germany
TEL 49 61 7287 2600
FAX 49 61 7287 2540

Sorvall Instruments
Du Pont de Nemours Co.
Medical Products Department
Wilmington, Delaware 19898
USA
TEL 800 551 2121

Spafas, Inc.
R.R. #2, Box 25
Rheinholds, Pennsylvania 17569
USA
TEL 1 215 267 7350
FAX 1 215 267 7869

Spectrum Medical Industries, Inc.
1100 Rankin Road
Houston, Texas 77073–4716
USA
TEL 800 634 3300
FAX 1 713 443 3100

SPI Supplies
Division of Structure Probe, Inc.
P.O. Box 342
West Chester, Pennsylvania 19380
USA
TEL 1 215 436 5400

Statens Serum Institute
Tuberculin Department
Artillerivej 5
DK-2300 Copenhagen S
Denmark
TEL 45 3268 3388
FAX 45 3268 3861

Stemmer PC-Systems GmbH
Gutenbergstrasse 11
D-82178 Puchheim
Germany
TEL 49 89 809020
FAX 49 89 8090216

Stephens Scientific
Division of Cornwell Corporation
Riverdale, New York 07457–1710
USA
TEL 201 831 9800
FAX 201 831 8009

Stratagene
11099 North Torrey Pines
La Jolla, California 92037
USA
TEL 800 424 5444
TEL 1 619 535 5400
FAX 1 619 535 0045

Sutter Instrument Company
40 Leveroni Court
Novato, California 94949
USA
TEL 1 415 883 0128
FAX 1 415 883 0572

Swann-Morton Ltd.
Owlerton Green
Sheffield S6 2BJ
United Kingdom
TEL 44 742 344 231
FAX 44 742 314 966

SYBRON/Barnstead
225 Rivermoor Street
Boston, Massachusetts 02132
USA
TEL 800 526 6934
FAX 1 319 556 0695

TAAB
J. Delville Technology
46 bis rue du Maréchal Joffre
78100 St. Germain en Laye
France
TEL 33 134 51 62 11
FAX 33 130 614957

TAAB Laboratories Equipment Ltd.
3 Minerva House
Calleva Industrial Park
Aldermaston, Reading
Berkshire RG7 4QW
England
TEL 44 734 81 7775
FAX 44 734 81 7881

TAGO, Inc.
P.O. Box 4463
887 Mitten Road
Burlingame, California 94011
USA
TEL 800 621 9013
FAX 1 415 692 9004

TAITEC Inc.
2693–1 Nishikata-Kamite Koshiya City
Saitama 343
Japan
TEL 81 489 88 8347
FAX 81 489 88 8350

Tandem Scanning Corporation
1705 Putter Lane
Reston, Virginia 22090
USA

Technical Instruments
348 Sixth Street
San Francisco, California 94103
USA

Technical Mfg. Corp.
15 Centennial Drive
Peabody, Massachusetts 01960
USA
TEL 800 542 9725
FAX 1 508 531 8682

Tecnomara
Industriestrasse 44
CH-8304 Walliselen-Zürich
Switzerland
TEL 41 1 8302277
FAX 41 1 8307852

Ted Pella, Inc.
P.O. Box 492477
Redding, California 96049–2477
USA
TEL 800 237 3526
FAX 1 916 243 3761

Tetko Inc.
333 South Highland Avenue
Briarcliff Manor, New York 10510
USA
TEL 1 914 941 7767
FAX 1 914 941 1017

Tekmar
P.O. Box 429576
Cincinnati, Ohio 45242
USA
TEL 1 513 247 7000
FAX 1 513 247 7043

Terumo Corporation
Interleuvenlaan 40
3001 Leuven
Belgium
TEL 32 16 38 12 11
FAX 32 16 22 91 04

Terumo Medical Corp.
P.O. Box 605
Elkton, Maryland 21921
USA
TEL 1 410 398 8500
FAX 1 410 392 7218

Tetenal Photowerk GmbH & Co.
P.O. Box 2029
D-22846 Norderstedt
Germany

The Microworks
P.O. Box 1110
Del Mar, California 92014
USA
TEL 1 619 942 2400

The National Collection of Yeast Cultures
AFRC
Colney Lane
Norwich
United Kingdom

Thomas Scientific
99 High Hill Road
Swedesboro, New Jersey 08085
USA
TEL 1 609 467 2000
FAX 1 609 467 3087

Tokyo Rikakikai Inc.
4–4-3 Nihonbashi-Muromachi Chou-ku
Tokyo 103
Japan
TEL 81 3 3245 0481
FAX 81 3 3241 0177

Tomy Seiko Co., Ltd
2–2-12 Asahi-cho, Nerima-ku
Tokyo 179
Japan
TEL 81 3 976 3111
FAX 81 3 930 7010

Tracor Europa
19 Cochran Close
Crownhill, Milton Keynes MK8 OAJ
United Kingdom
TEL 44 908 565626
FAX 44 908 566749

Tracor Europa BV
3821 BR Amersfoort
P.O. Box 1557
380 BN Amersfoort
The Netherlands
TEL 31 3353 6536
FAX 31 3356 3115

Triangle Biomedical Sciences, Inc.
2604-G Carver Street
Durham, North Carolina 27705
USA
TEL 1 919 477 9283
FAX 1 919 477 5883

UCB-Bioproducts S.A.
Chemin du Forest
B-1420 Braine-l'Alleud
Belgium
TEL 32 2386 2111
FAX 32 2384 5529

United States Biochemical Corp.*
26111 Miles Road
Cleveland, Ohio 44128
USA
TEL 800 321 9322
TEL 1 216 464 5075
FAX 800 535 0898
FAX 1 216 765 5000

*Products distributed by Amersham Life Science, Inc.

Uno Plast A/s
Unovej 1
DK-3390 Hundested
Denmark
TEL 45 4797 0101
FAX 45 4797 0202

Upchurch Scientific, Inc.
619 West Oak Street
P.O. Box 1529
Oak Harbor, Washington 98277–1529
USA
TEL 800 426 0191
FAX 800 359 3460

UpJohn
Simi Valley, California 93065
USA
TEL 800 821 7000

Upjohn Co.
7000 Portage Road
Kalamazoo, Michigan 49001-0199
USA
TEL 1 616 323 4000
FAX 800 852 6421

Upstate Biotechnology, Inc.
89 Saranac Avenue
Lake Placid, New York 12946
USA
TEL 1 617 890 8845
FAX 1 617 890 7738

Valco Instruments Co., Inc.
P.O. Box 55603
Houston, Texas 77255
USA
TEL 1 713 688 9345
FAX 1 713 688 8106

Vangard International
1111-A Green Grove Road
P.O. Box 308
Neptune, New Jersey 07754–0308
USA
TEL 800 922 0784
FAX 1 908 922 0557

Vector Laboratories
30 Ingold Road
Burlingame, California 94010
USA
TEL 800 227 6666
TEL 1 415 697 3600
FAX 1 415 697 0339

Vel N.V.
Geldenaaksebaan 464
B-3001 Leuven
Belgium
TEL 32 1639 1811
FAX 32 1639 1861

Verity Software House
Topsham, Maine 04086
USA
FAX 1 207 729 5443

VWR Scientific
P.O. Box 626
Bridgeport, New Jersey 08014
USA
TEL 800 234 9300
FAX 1 215 429 9340

VWR Scientific
P.O. 1002
600C Corporate Court
So. Plainfield, New Jersey 07080
USA
TEL 800 777 4972
FAX 508 485 0737

Vydac
The Separations Group
17434 Mojave Street
Hesperia, California 92345
USA
TEL 800 247 0924
TEL 1 619 244 6107
FAX 1 619 244 1984

Wako Bio Products
Wako Chemicals USA, Inc.
1600 Bellwood Road
Richmond, Virginia 23237
USA
TEL 800 992 9256
TEL 1 804 271 7677
FAX 1 804 271 7791

Wako Pure Chemical
Doshu-cho 3-1-2, Chuo-ku
Osaka 541
Japan
TEL 81 6 203 3741
FAX 81 6 210 5965

Warner Instrument Corporation
1125 Dixwell Avenue
Hamden, Connecticut 06514
USA
TEL 1 203 776 0664
FAX 1 203 776 1278

Waters
34 Maple Street
Milford, Massachusetts 01757
USA
TEL 800 252 4752
TEL 1 508 478 2000
FAX 1 508 624 8449

Waters Millipore
Hauptstrasse 87
65760 Eschborn
Germany
TEL 49 6196 4940
FAX 49 6196 43901

Weber Scientific International Ltd
40 Udney Park Road
Teddington, Middlesex TW11 9BG
United Kingdom
TEL 44 81 9776330
FAX 44 81 9434224

West Coast Scientific
1287 66th Street
Emeryville, California 94680
USA
TEL 800 367 8462
FAX 1 510 732 1131

Westfalia Separator
D-59302 Oelde
Germany
TEL 49 25 22 772839
FAX 49 25 22 772934

Whatman, Inc.
9 Bridgewell Place
Clifton, New Jersey 07014
USA
TEL 800 631 7290
TEL 1 201 773 5800
FAX 1 201 472 6949

Whatman LabSales
P.O. Box 1359
Hillsboro, Oregon 97123–9981
USA
TEL 800 942 8626
FAX 1 503 648 8118

Whatman Scientific Ltd.
Whatman House
St. Leonard's Road, 20/20 Maidstone
Kent ME16 OLS
United Kingdom
TEL 44 622 676670
FAX 44 622 677011

W. Möller, Glas end Elecktroden
Gubelstrasse 37
8050 Zurich
Switzerland
TEL 41 1 312 3435
FAX 41 1 312 4182

World Precision Instruments
375 Quinnipiac Avenue
New Haven, Connecticut 06510
USA
TEL 1 813 371 1003
FAX 1 813 377 5428

Worthington Biochemical Corp.
Halls Mill Road
Freehold, New Jersey 07728
USA
TEL 800 445 9603
TEL 1 908 462 3838
FAX 800 368 3108
FAX 1 908 308 4453

Wright Instruments
Unit 10, 26 Queensway
Enfield, Middlesex EN3 4SA
United Kingdom

Yakult Pharmaceutical Ind. Co. Ltd.
1–1-19 Higashi Shinbashi, Minato-ku
Tokyo 105
Japan
FAX 81 3 3575 1636

Yamamura Chemical Lab.
3233 Burnt Mill Drive
Wilmington, North Carolina 28403
USA
TEL 800 692 6311
FAX 1 919 343 0907

Zinsser
Howarth Road
Maidenhead, Berks SL6 1AP
United Kingdom
TEL 44 628 773202
FAX 44 628 721 99

Zymed Laboratories
52 South Linden Avenue, Suite 3
South San Francisco, California 94080
USA
FAX 1 415 871 499

INDEX

B

C

D

E

G

H

I

J

K

L

M

N

O

P

S

T

U

V